Custom Edition for Mt. San Antonio College

APPLIED BASIC
MATHEMATICS

William Clark · Robert Brechner

> **Note to students:** The material in this book has been specifically selected by your instructors. They have chosen to eliminate some material which is not critical to your course, and in doing so the price of the book has been adjusted to reflect the content removed.

Taken from:

Applied Basic Mathematics
by William Clark and Robert Brechner

Custom Publishing

New York   Boston   San Francisco
London   Toronto   Sydney   Tokyo   Singapore   Madrid
Mexico City   Munich   Paris   Cape Town   Hong Kong   Montreal

Cover Art: *Sunset over Charlestown,* by Erik Herman

Taken from:

Applied Basic Mathematics
by William Clark and Robert Brechner
Copyright © 2008 by Pearson Education, Inc.
Published by Addison-Wesley
Boston, Massachusetts 02116

This special edition published in cooperation with Pearson Custom Publishing.

Pearson
Custom Publishing
is a division of

www.pearsonhighered.com

ISBN 10: 0-558-08467-2
ISBN 13: 978-0-558-08467-7

Contents

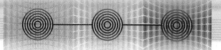

About the Authors

Bill Clark teaches at Harper College in the Chicago area. Prior to his current position, he was a professor at Miami Dade College. An engaging and dynamic teacher, he has initiated a number of programs to serve diverse student populations. He was instrumental in the implementation of Miami Dade's Title V Calculus program. He has also developed and implemented a multicultural infusion project and a number of learning communities. Clark holds

BS and MS degrees in mathematics from Northwestern University. In his leisure time, Bill enjoys travel and long walks with his dog, Toby.

Bob Brechner has taught at Miami Dade College for the past 41 years. He currently holds the position of Professor Emeritus. Over the years, he has been Adjunct Professor at Florida International University, Florida Atlantic University, and the International Fine Arts College. Brechner holds a BS in Industrial Management from the Georgia Institute of Technology in Atlanta, Georgia, and an MBA from Emory University in Atlanta. His other publications include *Contemporary Mathematics for Business and Consumers, A Little Math with Your Business,* and *Guidelines for the New Manager.*

Bob lives in Coconut Grove, Florida, with his wife, Shari Joy. His passions include travel, photography, tennis, running, and boating.

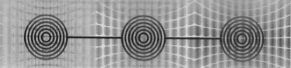

Whole Numbers

Mathematics is an important tool in everyday activities and whole numbers provide the basic foundation. In this chapter, we begin our study of basic mathematics with addition, subtraction, multiplication, and division of whole numbers. Once we have mastered these basic operations, we will learn about order of operations, which tells us how to simplify expressions that contain more than one operation. Then we will learn how to solve application problems involving whole numbers.

ACCOUNTING

Accounting is a profession that uses mathematics extensively. Accountants track companies' expenses as well as prepare, analyze, and verify financial statements. They keep public records, make sure taxes are paid properly, and look for ways to run businesses more efficiently.

A bachelor's degree is the minimum requirement. To advance in the accounting profession, you'll need additional certification or graduate-level education.

Those in the accounting field can earn the certified public accountant designation by meeting experience and educational requirements and by passing an exam.

One important financial statement used frequently by accountants is the balance sheet. See Numerical Facts of Life on page 93 for an explanation and an application problem involving a balance sheet.

1.1   UNDERSTANDING THE BASICS OF WHOLE NUMBERS

LEARNING OBJECTIVES

A. Identify the place value of a digit in a whole number

B. Write a whole number in standard notation and word form

C. Write a whole number in expanded notation

D. Round a whole number to a specified place value

E. Apply your knowledge

digits
The numbers 0, 1, 2, 3, 4, 5, 6, 7, 8, and 9.

Hindu-Arabic or **decimal number system**
A system that uses the digits to represent numbers.

natural or **counting numbers**
Any of the numbers 1, 2, 3, 4, 5, 6, 7, 8, 9, 10, 11, 12, 13, 14, 15 ....

whole numbers
Any of the numbers 0, 1, 2, 3, 4, 5, 6, 7, 8, 9, 10, 11, 12, 13, 14, 15 ....

The ability to read, write, comprehend, and manipulate numbers is an integral part of our lives. Therefore, we begin our study of mathematics with a look at numbers and the basic operations we can perform on them.

| Objective 1.1A | Identify the place value of a digit in a whole number |

The numbers 0, 1, 2, 3, 4, 5, 6, 7, 8, and 9 are called **digits**. The **Hindu-Arabic** or **decimal number system** is a system that uses the digits to represent numbers. The **natural** or **counting numbers** are any of the numbers 1, 2, 3, 4, 5, 6, 7, 8, 9, 10, 11, 12, 13, 14, 15 .... The three dots (...) indicate that the list goes on indefinitely. The whole numbers include zero together with the natural numbers. That is, the **whole numbers** are any of the numbers 0, 1, 2, 3, 4, 5, 6, 7, 8, 9, 10, 11, 12, 13, 14, 15 .... There is no largest natural number or whole number.

The position of a digit in a whole number tells us the value of that digit. For example, at the time of this writing, the national debt was $8,387,058,376,174. The three 8s in this very large whole number represent different values because of their placements. Below is the place value chart.

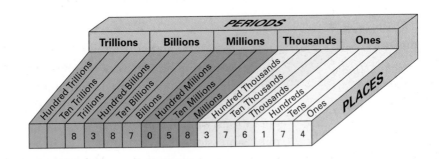

Note that the place value chart breaks up a whole number into different groups or periods: *ones, thousands, millions, billions, trillions*. Moreover, each period contains three places. Looking at this chart, we note that the first 8 is in the trillions place, the second 8 is in the ten billions place, and the third 8 is in the millions place.

EXAMPLE 1   **Identify the place value of a digit in whole number**

Identify the place value of the indicated digit.

a. 488   **b.** 1,370,128   **c.** 369,395   **d.** 18,000,000   **e.** 12,386

SOLUTION STRATEGY

a. 4<u>8</u>8   hundreds

b. 1,3<u>7</u>0,128   ten thousands

c. <u>3</u>69,395   hundred thousands

d. <u>1</u>8,000,000   ten millions

e. 12,38<u>6</u>   ones

TRY-IT EXERCISE 1

Identify the place value of the indicated digit.

a. <u>8</u>,395,470

b. 57,67<u>5</u>

c. 214,<u>3</u>55

d. <u>1</u>9

e. 1<u>3</u>4,221

Check your answers with the solutions in Appendix A. ■

Objective 1.1B	**Write a whole number in standard notation and word form**

In each of the examples above, note the use of commas. A representation for a number in which each period is separated by a comma is called **standard notation** or **standard form**. For example, the number 32158 is commonly written in standard notation as follows.

standard notation or **standard form**
A representation for a number in which each period is separated by a comma.

32,158

It is sometimes necessary to write numbers in word form. You have undoubtedly done so if you have ever written a check. The following rule tells us how to properly write a number in word form.

> ### Rule for Writing a Whole Number in Word Form
>
> To write a whole number in word form, write the numbers in each period followed by the name of the period and a comma. Hyphenate the numbers 21 through 99 except 30, 40, 50, 60, 70, 80, and 90 whenever these numbers appear in any period.

The number 8,387,058,376,174, has five periods. In word form, we write this number as follows.

8,387,058,376,174

eight trillion,

three hundred eighty-seven billion,

fifty-eight million,

three hundred seventy-six thousand,

one hundred seventy-four

Note that the word *and* is not used in writing whole numbers. When we read or write a whole number, we never use the word *and*.

EXAMPLE 2   Write a whole number in standard notation and word form

Write each number in standard notation and word form.

a. 591190   **b.** 43245   **c.** 958   **d.** 215648430   **e.** 1690

SOLUTION STRATEGY

NUMBER	STANDARD NOTATION	WORD FORM
a. 591190	591,190	five hundred ninety-one thousand, one hundred ninety
b. 43245	43,245	forty-three thousand, two hundred forty-five
c. 958	958	nine hundred fifty-eight
d. 215648430	215,648,430	two hundred fifteen million, six hundred forty-eight thousand, four hundred thirty
e. 1690	1690	one thousand, six hundred ninety

TRY-IT EXERCISE 2

Write each whole number in standard notation and word form.

a. 1146

b. 9038124

c. 773618

d. 27009

e. 583408992

Check your answers with the solutions in Appendix A. ∎

| Objective 1.1C | Write a whole number in expanded notation |

Expanded notation or **expanded form** is a representation of a number as a sum of its ones place, tens place, hundreds place, and so on, beginning with the highest place value.

As an example, consider the number 42,359. There are 4 ten thousands, 2 thousands, 3 hundreds, 5 tens, and 9 ones. In expanded notation, we write one of the following.

$$40,000 + 2000 + 300 + 50 + 9$$

or

4 ten thousands + 2 thousands + 3 hundreds + 5 tens + 9 ones

expanded notation or **expanded form**
A representation of a number as a sum of its ones place, tens place, hundreds place, and so on, beginning with the highest place value.

EXAMPLE 3　Write a whole number in expanded notation

Write each whole number in expanded notation.

a. 582　　**b.** 15,307　　**c.** 647,590

SOLUTION STRATEGY

a. 582

　　500 + 80 + 2

　　5 hundreds + 8 tens + 2 ones

582 has 5 hundreds, 8 tens, and 2 ones.

b. 15,307

　　10,000 + 5000 + 300 + 7

　　1 ten thousand + 5 thousands
　　　+ 3 hundreds + 7 ones

15,307 has 1 ten thousand, 5 thousands, 3 hundreds, and 7 ones. Note that there are no tens to include in the expanded form.

c. 647,590

　　600,000 + 40,000 + 7000 + 500 + 90

　　6 hundred thousands + 4 ten thousands
　　　+ 7 thousands + 5 hundreds + 9 tens

647,590 has 6 hundred thousands, 4 ten thousands, 7 thousands, 5 hundreds, and 9 tens. Note that there are no ones to include in the expanded form.

TRY-IT EXERCISE 3

Write each whole number in expanded notation.

a. 8290　　　　**b.** 75,041　　　　**c.** 709,385

Check your answers with the solutions in Appendix A. ■

| Objective 1.1D | Round a whole number to a specified place value |

Sometimes an approximation to a number may be more desirable to use than the number itself. A **rounded number** is an approximation of an exact number.

rounded number
An approximation of an exact number.

For example, if a trip you are planning totals 2489 miles, you could express the distance as 2500 miles. A state might list its population of 6,998,991 as 7,000,000. An annual salary of $54,230 could be referred to as $54,000.

Steps for Rounding Numbers to a Specified Place Value

Step 1. Identify the place value to which the number is to be rounded.

Step 2. If the digit to the right of the specified place value is 4 or less, the digit in the specified place value remains the same.
If the digit to the right of the specified place value is 5 or more, increase the digit in the specified place value by one.

Step 3. Change the digit in each place after the specified place value to zero.

EXAMPLE 4   Round a whole number to a specified place value

Round each number to the specified place value.

a. 416,286 to the nearest hundred

b. 9212 to the nearest thousand

c. 334,576,086 to the nearest million

d. 38,216 to the leftmost place value

e. 2,903,872 to the leftmost place value

SOLUTION STRATEGY

a. 416,286

416,300

The digit in the hundreds place is 2. Since the digit to the right of the 2 is 8, round 2 up to 3 and change each digit thereafter to 0.

b. 9212

9000

The digit in the thousands place is 9. Since the digit to the right of the 9 is 2, keep the 9 and change each digit thereafter to 0.

c. 334,576,086

335,000,000

The digit in the millions place is 4. Since the digit to the right of the 4 is 5, round 4 up to 5 and change each digit thereafter to 0.

d. 38,216

40,000

The digit in the leftmost place is 3. Since the digit to the right of the 3 is 8, round 3 up to 4 and change each digit thereafter to 0.

e. 2,903,872

3,000,000

The digit in the leftmost place is 2. Since the digit to the right of the 2 is 9, round 2 up to 3 and change each digit thereafter to 0.

TRY-IT EXERCISE 4

Round each number to the specified place value.

a. 67,499 to the nearest thousand

b. 453 to the nearest hundred

c. 6,383,440,004 to the nearest ten million

d. 381,598 to the leftmost place value

e. 1,119,632 to the leftmost place value

Check your answers with the solutions in Appendix A. ■

<table>
<tr><td>**Objective 1.1E**</td><td>**Apply your knowledge**</td></tr>
</table>

READ AND INTERPRET A TABLE

Now that we know about whole numbers, we introduce a way in which numbers may be presented. A **table** is a collection of data arranged in rows and columns for ease of reference. Tables will be further explored in Chapter 8, Data Presentation and Statistics.

table
A collection of data arranged in rows and columns for ease of reference.

Rule for Reading a Table

Scan the titles of the columns to find the category in question. Then, scan down the column to find the row containing the information being sought.

EXAMPLE 5   Read and interpret data from a table

Use the table *Average Annual Salaries—Selected Occupations* to answer each question.

AVERAGE ANNUAL SALARIES—SELECTED OCCUPATIONS

YEAR	TEACHER	ACCOUNTANT	ATTORNEY	ENGINEER
1970	$ 8,635	$10,686	$16,884	$14,695
1976	$12,592	$15,428	$24,205	$20,749
1982	$18,945	$25,673	$39,649	$34,443
1988	$28,071	$33,028	$55,407	$45,680
1994	$35,764	$39,884	$64,532	$56,368
1998	$39,360	$45,919	$71,530	$64,489
2001	$43,250	$52,664	$82,712	$74,920
2003	$45,085	$63,103	$91,722	$76,311
2006	$56,700	$68,120	$95,309	$82,215

Sources: American Federation of Teachers; http://www.salaries.com.

a. Which occupation had the highest average salary in 2006?

b. What was the average annual salary for an accountant in 1998?

c. What was the average annual salary for an engineer in 1982? Write your answer in word form.

d. Round the average salary for a teacher in 2006 to the nearest thousand.

SOLUTION STRATEGY

a. attorney

b. $45,919

c. thirty-four thousand, four hundred forty-three dollars

d. $57,000

Scan the last row to find the information being sought.

Scan the titles of the columns to find the category in question. Then, scan down the column to find the row containing the information being sought.

TRY-IT EXERCISE 5

Use the table *Average Annual Salary—Selected Occupations* on page 7 to answer each question.

a. Which occupation had the lowest average salary in 2006?

b. What was the average annual salary for an accountant in 2006?

c. What was the average annual salary for a teacher in 1982? Write your answer in word form.

d. Round the average salary for an engineer in 2003 to the nearest thousand.

Check your answers with the solutions in Appendix A. ■

SECTION 1.1 REVIEW EXERCISES

Concept Check

1. The numbers 0, 1, 2, 3, 4, 5, 6, 7, 8, and 9 are called _____.

2. A system that uses the digits to represent numbers is called the Hindu-Arabic or _____ number system.

3. Any of the numbers 1, 2, 3, 4, 5, 6, 7, 8, 9, 10, 11, 12, 13, 14, 15 . . . are called _____ or _____ numbers.

4. Any of the numbers 0, 1, 2, 3, 4, 5, 6, 7, 8, 9, 10, 11, 12, 13, 14, 15 . . . are called _____ numbers.

5. A representation for a number in which each period is separated by a comma is known as _____ notation.

6. When a number such as 385 is written as 300 + 80 + 5, we say that the number is written in _____ notation.

7. A _____ number is an approximation of an exact number.

8. In rounding, if the digit to the right of the specified place value is 5 or more, _____ the digit in the specified place value by one. Otherwise, the digit remains the same.

9. In rounding, each digit to the right of the place value to which a number is to be rounded is changed to a _____ .

10. A _____ is a collection of data arranged in rows and columns for ease of reference.

Objective 1.1A   Identify the place value of a digit in a whole number

GUIDE PROBLEMS

11. For the number 128, identify the digit in each place.

    a. ones place _____

    b. tens place _____

    c. hundreds place _____

12. For the number 8360, identify the name of each place value.

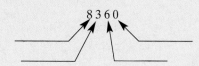

Identify the place value of the indicated digit.

13. 67<u>5</u>

14. 4<u>7</u>8

15. <u>4</u>899

16. 1<u>6</u>30

17. 56,2<u>3</u>7

18. 63,4<u>1</u>0

19. 1<u>5</u>1,436

20. 195,0<u>3</u>9

21. 780,<u>9</u>84

22. 225,<u>5</u>38

23. <u>4</u>01,804

24. 175,4<u>4</u>5

25. <u>4</u>,938,286

26. 2,5<u>6</u>2,785

27. 8,4<u>7</u>2,711,337

28. <u>7</u>,962,881,954

Objective 1.1B   Write a whole number in standard notation and word form

GUIDE PROBLEMS

29. In word form, 729 is " _____ _____ twenty-nine."

30. In word form, 1202 is "one thousand, _____ _____ two."

31. In standard form, 32809 is written _____ . In word form, this number is "thirty-two thousand, eight hundred _____ ."

32. In standard form, 5349201 is written _____ . In word form, this number is "five _____ , three hundred _____ _____ , two hundred _____ ."

Write each number in standard notation and in word form.

33. 26   **34.** 751

35. 812   **36.** 1479

37. 9533   **38.** 45000

39. 81184   **40.** 23606

41. 58245   **42.** 6555347

43. 498545   **44.** 7228145017

| Objective 1.1C | Write a whole number in expanded notation |

GUIDE PROBLEMS

45. Write number 271 in expanded form.

200 + _____ + 1

46. Write 9813 in expanded form.

_____ + 800 + 10 + 3

Write each number in expanded notation.

47. 73   **48.** 695   **49.** 2746   **50.** 9689

51. 25,370   **52.** 46,273   **53.** 896,905   **54.** 703,300

Objective 1.1D   **Round a whole number to a specified place value**

GUIDE PROBLEMS

55. Round 853 to the nearest hundred.

   a. What digit is in the hundreds place?

   b. Which place determines what we must do in the hundreds place?

   c. What digit is in that place?

   d. Explain what to do next.

   e. Write the rounded number.

56. Round 132,449 to the nearest ten thousand.

   a. What digit is in the ten thousands place?

   b. Which place determines what we must do in the ten thousands place?

   c. Which digit is in that place?

   d. Explain what to do next.

   e. Write the rounded number.

Round each number to the specified place value.

57. 4548 to the nearest ten

58. 12,819 to the nearest hundred

59. 590,341 to the nearest thousand

60. 591,680 to the nearest hundred thousand

61. 434,530 to the nearest ten thousand

62. 125,516 to the nearest ten

63. 4,970,001 to the nearest million

64. 2,258,932 to the nearest hundred

65. 94,141,952 to the nearest ten million

66. 76,002,009 to the nearest thousand

67. 3,939,413 to the leftmost place value

68. 1,943,477 to the leftmost place value

Objective 1.1E   **Apply your knowledge**

69. In 2005, the U.S. Postal Service had seven hundred fifty-two thousand, one hundred twenty-eight employees. Write this number in standard notation.

70. In 2003, Ford Motor Company had three hundred fifty thousand, three hundred twenty-one employees. Write this number in standard notation.

71. In 2008, the budget for the U.S. federal government was two trillion, nine hundred two billion dollars. Write this number in standard notation.

72. In 2006, Wal-Mart had revenue of three hundred twelve billion, four hundred twenty-seven million dollars. Write this number in standard notation.

73. How would you write the word portion of a check in the amount of $3497?

KELLY STEVENS 37 Jackson Avenue #4A Pimsler, OH 03178	210
DATE *March 1, 2007*	
PAY TO THE ORDER OF *Pimsler University*	$ 3497.00
DOLLARS	
BANKCO™	
MEMO *tuition*	*Kelly Stevens*
I:012200159I: 71135 59229II 1299	

74. How would you write the word portion of a check in the amount of $852?

BARRY PARKER 4815 First Street Burketown, OR 62342	437
DATE *7/21/07*	
PAY TO THE ORDER OF *GADGET TOWN*	$ 852.00
DOLLARS	
BANKCO™	
MEMO *HDTV*	
I:513929803I: 39012 77639II 0925	

75. In 2003, the federal government's Bureau of Engraving and Printing spent $30,000,000 on a publicity and advertising campaign to announce the introduction of the new $20 bill. Write the amount spent in word form.

76. The Eiffel Tower has 2,500,000 rivets. Write this number in word form.

77. The cruise ship *Summit Star* is 965 feet long and 106 feet wide. The ship weighs 91,000 tons. Write these three numbers in word form.

78. The number of possible ways of playing just the first four moves on both sides in a game of chess is 318,979,564,000. Write this number in word form.

79. On a recent shopping trip, Ignacio spent $1237. Round this number to the nearest ten.

80. MacArthur Dairy Farms has 13,229 cows. Round this number to the nearest hundred.

81. Federal individual income tax began in 1913 with 400 pages of tax rules and regulations. In 2005, these rules and regulations, published by CCH, Inc., were 46,847 pages in length. Round this number to the nearest thousand.

82. According to the president's Office of Management and Budget, the U.S. deficit in 2010 is estimated to be $182,708,000,000. Round this number to the nearest billion.

Use the chart *Earnings Increase with More Education* for exercises 83–88.

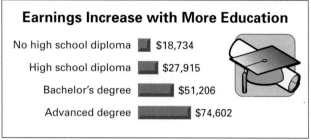

Earnings Increase with More Education

No high school diploma $18,734

High school diploma $27,915

Bachelor's degree $51,206

Advanced degree $74,602

Source: Census Bureau, 2004 statistics

83. Write in word form the average yearly salary of workers with a bachelor's degree.

84. Write in word form the average yearly salary of workers with a high school diploma.

85. Round to the nearest hundred the average salary of workers with no high school diploma.

86. Round to the nearest ten thousand the average salary of workers with an advanced degree.

87. Round to the nearest thousand the average salary of workers with a bachelor's degree.

88. Round to the nearest ten the average salary of workers with a high school diploma.

1.2 ADDING WHOLE NUMBERS

Addition is the mathematical process of combining two or more numbers to find the total. Let's say that a particular Apple Store sold 2 iPods in the morning and 3 iPods in the afternoon. We use addition to find the total number of iPods sold that day.

LEARNING OBJECTIVES

A. Use the addition properties

B. Add whole numbers

C. Apply your knowledge

In an addition problem, the $+$ symbol is called the plus sign. It is placed between the numbers being added. Numbers that are added together are called **addends**. The result of adding numbers is called a **sum**.

$$2 \quad + \quad 3 \quad = \quad 5$$

addend   addend   sum

To add, we often vertically format the addends so that their place values are aligned.

```
   2    addend
 + 3    addend
 ───
   5    sum
```

addition
The mathematical process of combining two or more numbers to find the total.

addends
Numbers that are added together.

sum
The result of adding numbers.

Objective 1.2A   Use the addition properties

We use three special properties or rules of addition regularly. The first property tells us that 0 added to any number equals the original number. For example, $3 + 0 = 3$ and $0 + 3 = 3$.

Addition Property of Zero

Adding 0 to any number results in a sum equal to the original number. That is, for any number a, we have the following.

$$a + 0 = a \text{ and } 0 + a = a$$

The next property tells us that the order in which we add two numbers does not matter. As an example, consider the sums $2 + 3$ and $3 + 2$. Both equal 5.

Commutative Property of Addition

Changing the order of the addends does not change the sum. That is, for any numbers a and b, we have the following.

$$a + b = b + a$$

The final property tells us that the way in which we group numbers in an addition problem does not change the sum. We generally group numbers using parentheses, and we always add the numbers within the parentheses first. As an example, consider the following.

$$(2 + 3) + 4$$
$$5 + 4$$
$$9$$

Also,

$$2 + (3 + 4)$$
$$2 + 7$$
$$9$$

Note that no matter how we group the numbers in the addition problem, we get the same result.

Associative Property of Addition

Changing the grouping of addends does not change the sum. That is, for any numbers a, b, and c, we have the following.

$$(a + b) + c = a + (b + c)$$

EXAMPLE 1   Demonstrate the various properties of addition

a. Add $0 + 7$.

b. Show that $5 + 3 = 3 + 5$.

c. Show that $(2 + 4) + 6 = 2 + (4 + 6)$.

SOLUTION STRATEGY

a. $0 + 7 = 7$ Addition property of zero.

b. $5 + 3 = 3 + 5$

$\quad\quad 8 = 8$ Add $5 + 3$. Add $3 + 5$.

Thus, $5 + 3 = 3 + 5$.   Commutative property of addition.

c. $(2 + 4) + 6 = 2 + (4 + 6)$

$\quad\quad 6 + 6 = 2 + 10$ Add $(2 + 4)$. Add $(4 + 6)$.

$\quad\quad\quad 12 = 12$ Add $6 + 6$. Add $2 + 10$.

Thus, $(2 + 4) + 6 = 2 + (4 + 6)$.   Associative property of addition.

TRY-IT EXERCISE 1

a. Add $34 + 0$.

b. Show $81 + 15 = 15 + 81$.

c. Show $(5 + 2) + 8 = 5 + (2 + 8)$.

Check your answers with the solutions in Appendix A. ■

Objective 1.2B	**Add whole numbers**

To add whole numbers, write the digits of the addends in columns with the place values (ones, tens, hundreds, etc.) vertically aligned. Then, add the digits in each column beginning with those in the ones column.

EXAMPLE 2   **Add whole numbers**

Add.

a. $42 + 31$ **b.** $201 + 416 + 152$

SOLUTION STRATEGY

a.
$$
\begin{array}{r}
42 \\
+\,31 \\
\end{array}
$$
Write the digits of the addends in columns with the place values vertically aligned.

$$
\begin{array}{r}
42 \\
+\,31 \\
\hline
3 \\
\end{array}
$$
Add the digits in the ones column.

$$
\begin{array}{r}
42 \\
+\,31 \\
\hline
73 \\
\end{array}
$$
Add the digits in the tens column.

The sum is 73.

b. 201
416
+ 152   Write the digits of the addends in columns with the place values vertically aligned.

201
416
+ 152
    9   Add the digits in the ones column.

201
416
+ 152
   69   Add the digits in the tens column.

201
416
+ 152
  769   Add the digits in the hundreds column.

The sum is 769.

TRY-IT EXERCISE 2

Add.

a. 325 + 504   **b.** 16 + 11 + 151

Check your answers with the solutions in Appendix A. ∎

Consider the following problem.

$$878$$
$$+ 245$$

To begin, we add the digits in the ones column: $8 + 5 = 13$. Certainly, we cannot write a two-digit number in the ones column. Rather, we write 3 in the ones column and write 1 at the top of the tens column. We refer to this process as *carrying*. We write this as follows.

$$\overset{1}{8}78$$
$$+ 245$$
$$\overline{3}$$

We can do this because $13 = 1$ ten $+ 3$ ones.

Continuing the problem, we add the digits in the tens column: $1 + 7 + 4 = 12$. Again, we cannot write a two-digit number in the tens column. Rather, we write 2 in the tens column and carry the 1 to the top of the hundreds column.

$$\overset{1\,1}{8}78$$
$$+ 245$$
$$\overline{23}$$

Again, this works because 1 ten $+ 7$ tens $+ 4$ tens $= 12$ tens $= 1$ hundred $+ 2$ tens.

Learning Tip

When performing addition, if the sum in a column is greater than nine, write the ones digit in that column and carry the tens digit to the top of the column to the left.

Finally, we add the digits in the hundreds column: $1 + 8 + 2 = 11$. Since this is the leftmost column, we don't have to carry. Rather, we just write this result below the horizontal bar. Our final answer is written as follows.

$$
\begin{array}{r}
\overset{11}{878} \\
+\ 245 \\
\hline
1123
\end{array}
$$

EXAMPLE 3   Add whole numbers when carrying is necessary

Add.

a. $45 + 89$

b. $4817 + 6785$

SOLUTION STRATEGY

a.
$$
\begin{array}{r}
\overset{1}{} \\
45 \\
+\ 89 \\
\hline
4
\end{array}
$$
Add the digits in the ones column. Since the sum, 14, is a two-digit number, write the 4 in the ones column and carry the 1 to the top of the tens column.

$$
\begin{array}{r}
\overset{1}{} \\
45 \\
+\ 89 \\
\hline
134
\end{array}
$$
Add the digits in the tens column. Since this is the leftmost column, write the sum, 13, under the horizontal bar.

The sum is 134.

b.
$$
\begin{array}{r}
\overset{1}{} \\
4817 \\
+\ 6785 \\
\hline
2
\end{array}
$$
Add the digits in the ones column. Since the sum, 12, is a two-digit number, write the 2 in the ones column and carry the 1 to the top of the tens column.

$$
\begin{array}{r}
\overset{11}{} \\
4817 \\
+\ 6785 \\
\hline
02
\end{array}
$$
Add the digits in the tens column. Since the sum, 10, is a two-digit number, write the 0 in the tens column and carry the 1 to the top of the hundreds column.

$$
\begin{array}{r}
\overset{111}{} \\
4817 \\
+\ 6785 \\
\hline
602
\end{array}
$$
Add the digits in the hundreds column. Since the sum, 16, is a two-digit number, write the 6 in the hundreds column and carry the 1 to the top of the thousands column.

$$
\begin{array}{r}
\overset{111}{} \\
4817 \\
+\ 6785 \\
\hline
11,602
\end{array}
$$
Add the digits in the thousands column. Since this is the leftmost column, write the sum, 11, under the horizontal bar.

The sum is 11,602.

TRY-IT EXERCISE 3

Add.

a. 78 + 49

b. 492 + 1538

c. 4510 + 8393 + 190

Check your answers with the solutions in Appendix A. ■

The following steps summarize addition of whole numbers.

Steps for Adding Whole Numbers

Step 1. Write the digits of the addends in columns with the place values (ones, tens, hundreds, etc.) vertically aligned.

Step 2. Beginning with the ones column, add the digits in each column. If the sum of any column is a two-digit number, write the rightmost digit under the horizontal bar and carry the leftmost digit to the top of the next column to the left.

Step 3. Repeat this process until you reach the leftmost column. For that column, write the sum under the horizontal bar.

Objective 1.2C   **Apply your knowledge**

Addition of whole numbers is one of the most basic mathematical operations. It is used in everyday activities such as totaling a supermarket purchase. Addition is also necessary in tackling complicated scientific and engineering problems.

When we encounter application problems involving addition, we will not simply be given a column of numbers to add. We will more than likely be required to analyze a situation and understand which facts are given, which are missing, and which need to be determined. Complete coverage of application problems is found in Section 1.7.

For now, be aware of some key words and phrases that can indicate addition.

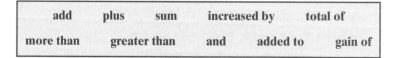

add	plus	sum	increased by	total of
more than	greater than	and	added to	gain of

EXAMPLE 4   **Solve an application problem using addition**

On Tuesday, you write a check for $62 at the supermarket. On Wednesday, you write a check in the amount of $325 for auto repairs, and on Thursday, you write a check for $14 for dry cleaning. What is the total amount of your three purchases?

SOLUTION STRATEGY

```
  1 1
   62
  325      To determine the total amount of your three purchases, add the numbers.
+  14
$401
```

TRY-IT EXERCISE 4

A driver for Package Express drove 44 miles to his first delivery and 78 miles to the next. After lunch he drove 26 miles to his third delivery and then 110 miles back to the warehouse. What is his total mileage for the day?

Check your answer with the solution in Appendix A. ■

FIND THE PERIMETER OF A POLYGON

A **polygon** is a closed, flat geometric figure in which all sides are line segments. An example of a polygon is a rectangle. By definition, a **rectangle** is a polygon with four right angles in which opposite sides are parallel and of equal length.

Other examples of polygons include squares, triangles, or irregularly shaped objects. We shall learn more about geometric figures in Chapter 7, Geometry.

| rectangle | square | triangle | irregular polygons |

One common application of addition is to find the perimeter of a polygon. The **perimeter of a polygon** is the sum of the lengths of its sides.

polygon
A closed, flat geometric figure in which all sides are line segments.

rectangle
A polygon with four right angles in which opposite sides are parallel and of equal length.

perimeter of a polygon
The sum of the lengths of its sides.

EXAMPLE 5   Find the perimeter of a polygon

You have a rectangular-shaped garden. As illustrated, it has a length of 21 feet and a width of 12 feet. What is the perimeter of your garden?

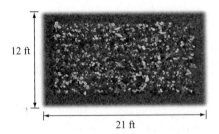

12 ft

21 ft

SOLUTION STRATEGY

```
  21      To determine the perimeter of the garden, add the lengths of its sides.
  21
  12
+ 12
  66
```

The perimeter of the garden is 66 feet.

TRY-IT EXERCISE 5

Find the perimeter of each polygon.

a.

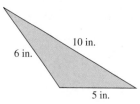

b.

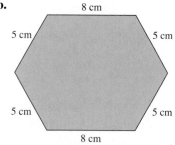

c.

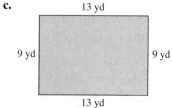

Check your answer with the solution in Appendix A. ■

SECTION 1.2 REVIEW EXERCISES

Concept Check

1. The mathematical process of combining two or more numbers to find the total is called _____.

2. Numbers that are added together are known as _____.

3. When performing addition, we often format addends vertically so that their _____ _____ are aligned.

4. The identity property of addition states that adding _____ to a number results in a sum equal to the original number.

5. The commutative property of addition states that changing the _____ of the addends does not change the sum.

6. The associative property of addition states that changing the _____ of addends does not change the sum.

7. When performing addition, if the sum of any column is a two-digit number, write the rightmost digit under the horizontal bar and _____ the leftmost digit to the top of the next column to the left.

8. A closed, flat geometric figure in which all sides are line segments is called a _____.

Objective 1.2A   **Use the addition properties**

GUIDE PROBLEMS

9. 12 + 0 = _____

This example demonstrates the addition property of
_____.

11. Show that 13 + 21 = 21 + 13.

13 + 21 = 21 + 13

34 = _____

This example demonstrates the _____
property of addition.

10. 0 + _____ = 41

This example demonstrates the addition property of
_____.

12. Show that (4 + 9) + 12 = 4 + (9 + 12).

(4 + 9) + 12 = 4 + (9 + 12)

13 + 12 = 4 + _____

_____ = _____

This example demonstrates the _____ property of
addition.

13. Add 0 + 128.

14. Add 0 + 2000.

15. Show that 35 + 20 = 20 + 35.

16. Show that 42 + 6 = 6 + 42.

17. Show that (3 + 10) + 8 = 3 + (10 + 8).

18. Show that 40 + (15 + 5) = (40 + 15) + 5.

Objective 1.2B   **Add whole numbers**

GUIDE PROBLEMS

19. $\begin{array}{r} 79 \\ + 20 \\ \hline 9\_ \end{array}$

20. $\begin{array}{r} 522 \\ + 21 \\ \hline 5\_3 \end{array}$

21. $\begin{array}{r} {}^{1}782 \\ + 55 \\ \hline \_37 \end{array}$

22. $\begin{array}{r} \overline{3}19 \\ + 59 \\ \hline 378 \end{array}$

Add.

23. $\begin{array}{r} 80 \\ + 12 \\ \hline \end{array}$

24. $\begin{array}{r} 33 \\ + 64 \\ \hline \end{array}$

25. $\begin{array}{r} 10 \\ + 61 \\ \hline \end{array}$

26. $\begin{array}{r} 50 \\ + 35 \\ \hline \end{array}$

27. $\begin{array}{r} 66 \\ + 22 \\ \hline \end{array}$

28. $\begin{array}{r} 57 \\ + 40 \\ \hline \end{array}$

29. $\begin{array}{r} 42 \\ + 70 \\ \hline \end{array}$

30. $\begin{array}{r} 31 \\ + 86 \\ \hline \end{array}$

31. $\begin{array}{r} 371 \\ + 38 \\ \hline \end{array}$

32. $\begin{array}{r} 275 \\ + 31 \\ \hline \end{array}$

33. $\begin{array}{r} 427 \\ + 858 \\ \hline \end{array}$

34. $\begin{array}{r} 975 \\ + 129 \\ \hline \end{array}$

35. $\begin{array}{r} 1256 \\ + 1001 \\ \hline \end{array}$

36. $\begin{array}{r} 4210 \\ + 2088 \\ \hline \end{array}$

37. $\begin{array}{r} 5735 \\ + 8996 \\ \hline \end{array}$

38. $\begin{array}{r} 3387 \\ + 8807 \\ \hline \end{array}$

39.   831
     523
 + 364

40.   332
     285
 + 699

41.   379
     232
 + 536

42.   757
     621
 + 881

43.   2778
     663
     114
     72
 + 398

44.   1419
     280
     467
     41
 + 500

45.   5472
     4126
     850
     58
 + 799

46.   901
     8226
     434
     82
 + 1610

47. 143 + 89

48. 668 + 71

49. 2656 + 9519

50. 2378 + 6977

51. 598 + 1248 + 1871

52. 692 + 1713 + 3336

53. 239 + 1268 + 1590

54. 713 + 1919 + 8223

Objective 1.2C   Apply your knowledge

55. What is 548 plus 556?

56. How much is 354 increased by 281?

57. What is 259 more than 991?

58. How much is 125 added to 299?

59. Find the sum of 608, 248, and 96.

60. What is the total of 663, 518, and 613?

61. An airplane flying at 23,400 feet climbed 3500 feet to avoid a thunderstorm. What is the new altitude of the plane?

62. Contempo Design Lighting manufactured 3430 desk lamps in April, 2779 in May, and 3124 in June. How many lamps did the company manufacture in this three-month period?

63. Elton Technologies sold $46,700 in circuit breakers last month. If this month they are projecting sales to be $12,300 higher, how much are the projected sales for this month?

64. Jessy paid $13,589 plus her old car trade-in for a new car. If the trade-in was worth $3650, how much did she pay for the new car?

65. Last semester, Morley paid school tuition of $1433. He also bought books for $231, a calculator for $32, and other supplies for $78. What was the total amount of his school expenses?

66. Last year, 4432 people ran the Metro Corporate Marathon. This year, 6590 ran the race. What was the total number of runners for these two years?

You are the manager of Murrieta's Restaurant. Use the chart of meals served per day for exercises 67–69.

MURRIETA'S RESTAURANT—MEALS SERVED

	MONDAY	TUESDAY	WEDNESDAY	THURSDAY	FRIDAY	TOTAL MEALS
Breakfast	215	238	197	184	258	
Lunch	326	310	349	308	280	
Dinner	429	432	375	381	402	
Late night	124	129	98	103	183	
Daily totals						

67. Calculate the total number of meals served each day.

68. Calculate the total number of breakfasts, lunches, dinners, and late night meals served during the five-day period.

69. Calculate the total number of meals served for the five-day period.

Use the chart *Sources of Vitamin C* for exercises 70–72.

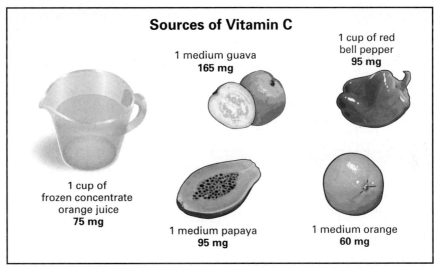

Source: American Dietetic Association

70. How many milligrams of vitamin C are there in 1 medium guava and 1 medium orange?

71. How many milligrams of vitamin C are there in 1 medium papaya and 2 cups of red bell pepper?

72. How many milligrams of vitamin C are there in 3 cups of frozen concentrate orange juice and 2 medium guavas?

Find the perimeter of each polygon.

73.

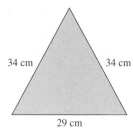

34 cm   34 cm

29 cm

74.

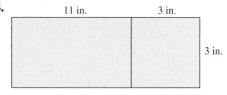

11 in.   3 in.

3 in.

75. Samantha is installing a fence around her yard. The illustration shows the length of each side of her yard. How many feet of fencing does Samantha need to complete the project?

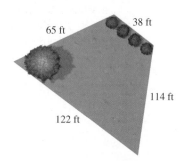

65 ft   38 ft

114 ft

122 ft

76. Jason is measuring an irregularly shaped ceiling for crown molding. The illustration shows the length of each side of the ceiling. What is the total number of feet of molding needed for the project?

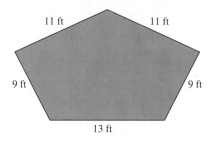

11 ft   11 ft

9 ft   9 ft

13 ft

CUMULATIVE SKILLS REVIEW

1. Write two hundred sixty-one thousand, eight hundred nine in standard notation. (1.1B)

2. Identify the place value of the 5 in 675,482. (1.1A)

3. Write 14,739 in expanded notation. (1.1C)

4. Round 34,506 to the nearest hundred. (1.1D)

5. Write 6114 in word form. (1.1B)

6. Write 653 in expanded notation. (1.1C)

7. Identify the place value of the 8 in 32,825. (1.1A)

8. Round 7,559,239 to the nearest ten thousand. (1.1D)

9. Johnson Enterprises sold three hundred sixty-five thousand, five hundred twenty-nine units last year.

    a. Write this number in standard notation. (1.1B)

    b. Round to the nearest thousand. (1.1D)

10. In 2005, Sony had revenue of $73,272,210,000.

    a. Round this number to the nearest million. (1.1D)

    b. Write the rounded number in word form. (1.1B)

1.3 SUBTRACTING WHOLE NUMBERS

Subtraction is the mathematical process of taking away or deducting an amount from a given number. For example, suppose that a mobile phone vendor begins the day with 7 mobile phones in inventory. If 3 phones are sold during the day, how many are left?

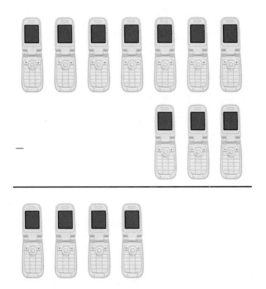

LEARNING OBJECTIVES

A. Subtract whole numbers

B. Apply your knowledge

subtraction
The mathematical process of taking away or deducting an amount from a given number.

In a subtraction problem, the − symbol is called the minus sign. The number from which another number is to be subtracted is called the **minuend**, and the number that is subtracted from a given number is called the **subtrahend**. The minuend always comes before the minus sign while the subtrahend always comes after it. The result of subtracting numbers is called the **difference**.

$$7 \quad - \quad 3 \quad = \quad 4$$
    minuend   subtrahend   difference

minuend
The number from which another number is subtracted.

We often format the minuend and subtrahend vertically so that the place values are aligned.

$$\begin{array}{r} 7 \\ -\ 3 \\ \hline 4 \end{array}$$
   minuend
   subtrahend
   difference

subtrahend
The number that is subtracted from a given number.

difference
The result of subtracting numbers.

Note that subtraction is the opposite of addition. In particular, if we add the difference, 4, to the subtrahend, 3, we get 7.

$$4 + 3 = 7$$

Objective 1.3A	Subtract whole numbers

To subtract whole numbers, write the digits of the minuend and subtrahend in columns with the place values vertically aligned. Then, subtract the digits in each column beginning with those in the ones column.

EXAMPLE 1   **Subtract whole numbers**

Subtract.

a. $39 - 25$ **b.** $347 - 122$

SOLUTION STRATEGY

a.
$$\begin{array}{r} 39 \\ -\ 25 \end{array}$$
Write the digits of the minuend and subtrahend in columns with the place values vertically aligned.

$$\begin{array}{r} 39 \\ -\ 25 \\ \hline 4 \end{array}$$
Subtract the digits in the ones column.

$$\begin{array}{r} 39 \\ -\ 25 \\ \hline 14 \end{array}$$
Subtract the digits in the tens column.

The difference is 14.

b.
$$\begin{array}{r} 347 \\ -\ 122 \end{array}$$
Write the digits of the minuend and subtrahend in columns with the place values vertically aligned.

$$\begin{array}{r} 347 \\ -\ 122 \\ \hline 5 \end{array}$$
Subtract the digits in the ones column.

$$\begin{array}{r} 347 \\ -\ 122 \\ \hline 25 \end{array}$$
Subtract the digits in the tens column.

$$\begin{array}{r} 347 \\ -\ 122 \\ \hline 225 \end{array}$$
Subtract the digits in the hundreds column.

The difference is 225.

TRY-IT EXERCISE 1

Subtract.

a. $355 - 242$

b. $767 - 303$

c. $4578 - 2144$

Check your answers with the solutions in Appendix A. ■

Consider the following problem.

$$724$$
$$- 562$$

When we subtract the numbers in the ones column, we get 2. But, when we try to subtract the digits in the tens column, we do not get a whole number. Indeed, $2 - 6$ is not a whole number! In order to do this problem and others like it, we apply the concept of *borrowing*. To understand how this works, let's first rewrite the minuend and subtrahend in expanded notation.

$$7 \text{ hundreds} + 2 \text{ tens} + 4 \text{ ones}$$
$$- 5 \text{ hundreds} - 6 \text{ tens} - 2 \text{ ones}$$

To subtract the numbers in the tens column, we manipulate the minuend by borrowing 1 hundred from the 7 hundreds. We then regroup the 1 hundred that we borrowed with the 2 tens.

7 hundreds + 2 tens + 4 ones
  = 6 hundreds + 1 hundred + 2 tens + 4 ones   Note: 7 hundred = 6 hundreds + 1 hundred
  = 6 hundreds + 10 tens + 2 tens + 4 ones   Note: 1 hundred = 10 tens
  = 6 hundreds + 12 tens + 4 ones

We can now subtract.

$$6 \text{ hundreds} + 12 \text{ tens} + 4 \text{ ones}$$
$$- 5 \text{ hundreds} - 6 \text{ tens} - 2 \text{ ones}$$
$$1 \text{ hundred} + 6 \text{ tens} + 2 \text{ ones} = 162$$

Rather than write out the expanded forms of the minuend and subtrahend, we prefer to use the following shorter form.

$$\begin{array}{r} 7\,2\,4 \\ -\,5\,6\,2 \\ \hline 2 \end{array}$$ Subtract the digits in the ones column.

$$\begin{array}{r} {}^{6\ \ 12} \\ 7\!\!\!/\,2\,4 \\ -\,5\,6\,2 \\ \hline 6\,2 \end{array}$$ Borrow 1 hundred from the 7 hundreds. Note: 1 hundred = 10 tens, and 10 tens + 2 tens = 12 tens. Cross out the 7 and write a 6 above it. Cross out the 2 and write 12 above it. Subtract the numbers in the tens column.

$$\begin{array}{r} {}^{6\ \ 12} \\ 7\!\!\!/\,2\,4 \\ -\,5\,6\,2 \\ \hline 1\,6\,2 \end{array}$$ Subtract the digits in the hundreds column.

The difference is 162.

EXAMPLE 2   Subtract whole numbers when borrowing is necessary

Subtract.

a. $1752 - 872$ **b.** $500 - 374$

SOLUTION STRATEGY

a.
$$
\begin{array}{r}
175\,\boxed{2} \\
-\ 87\,\boxed{2} \\
\hline
0
\end{array}
$$
Subtract the digits in the ones column.

$$
\begin{array}{r}
{}^{6\ 15} \\
1\,7\,\cancel{5}\,2 \\
-\ 8\,7\,2 \\
\hline
8\,0
\end{array}
$$
We cannot subtract 7 tens from 5 tens and get a whole number. To subtract in the tens column, borrow 1 hundred (10 tens) from the 7 hundreds. Cross out the 7 and write 6 above it. Cross out the 5 in the tens column and write 15 above it. Subtract the numbers in the tens column.

$$
\begin{array}{r}
{}^{16} \\
{}^{0\ \cancel{6}\ 15} \\
\cancel{1}\,\cancel{7}\,\cancel{5}\,2 \\
-\ 8\,7\,2 \\
\hline
8\,8\,0
\end{array}
$$
We cannot subtract 8 hundreds from 6 hundreds and get a whole number. To subtract in the hundreds column, borrow 1 thousand (10 hundreds) from the 1 thousand. Cross out the 1 in the thousands column and write 0 above it. Cross out the 6 in the hundreds column and write 16 above it. Subtract the numbers in the hundreds column.

The difference is 880.

b.
$$
\begin{array}{r}
500 \\
-\ 374 \\
\hline
\end{array}
$$
We cannot subtract 4 ones from 0 ones and get a whole number. To subtract in the ones column, we must borrow 1 ten. But, there are 0 tens from which to borrow. Therefore, we must first borrow 1 hundred.

$$
\begin{array}{r}
{}^{4\ 10} \\
\cancel{5}\,\cancel{0}\,0 \\
-\ 3\,7\,4 \\
\hline
\end{array}
$$
Borrow 1 hundred from the 5 hundreds. Cross out the 5 in the hundreds column and write 4 above it. Cross out 0 in the tens column and write 10 above it.

$$
\begin{array}{r}
{}^{9\ 10} \\
{}^{4\ \cancel{10}} \\
\cancel{5}\,\cancel{0}\,\cancel{0} \\
-\ 3\,7\,4 \\
\hline
6
\end{array}
$$
Now, borrow 1 ten from the 10 tens. Cross out the 10 in the tens column and write 9 above it. Cross out 0 in the ones column and write 10 above it. Subtract the numbers in the ones column.

$$
\begin{array}{r}
{}^{9\ 10} \\
{}^{4\ \cancel{10}} \\
\cancel{5}\,\cancel{0}\,\cancel{0} \\
-\ 3\,7\,4 \\
\hline
2\,6
\end{array}
$$
Subtract the numbers in the tens column.

$$
\begin{array}{r}
{}^{9\ 10} \\
{}^{4\ \cancel{10}} \\
\cancel{5}\,\cancel{0}\,\cancel{0} \\
-\ 3\,7\,4 \\
\hline
1\,2\,6
\end{array}
$$
Subtract the numbers in the hundreds column.

The difference is 126.

TRY-IT EXERCISE 2

Subtract.

a. $84 - 57$ **b.** $704 - 566$ **c.** $3000 - 1455$

Check your answers with the solutions in Appendix A. ■

The following steps summarize subtraction of whole numbers.

Steps for Subtracting Whole Numbers

Step 1. Write the digits of the minuend and subtrahend in columns with the place values vertically aligned.

Step 2. Beginning with the ones column, subtract the digits in each column. If the digits in a column cannot be subtracted to produce a whole number, borrow from the column to the left.

Step 3. Continue until you reach the last column on the left. For that column, write the difference under the horizontal bar.

Objective 1.3B   Apply your knowledge

Subtraction of whole numbers is one of the basic mathematical operations we encounter on an everyday basis. It is used to find the amount of something after it has been reduced in quantity. Complete coverage of solving application problems can be found in Section 1.7.

For now, be aware of some key words and phrases that can indicate subtraction.

subtract	minus	difference	decreased by	take away
reduced by	deducted from	less than	fewer than	subtracted from

As some examples, consider the following statements. Each is equivalent to the mathematical statement "$5 - 3$."

5 subtract 3   5 minus 3   the difference of 5 and 3

5 decreased by 3   5 take away 3   5 reduced by 3

3 deducted from 5   3 less than 5   3 fewer than 5   3 subtracted from 5

Note that the last four examples may be a bit unexpected. Read these statements carefully and be sure you understand them.

EXAMPLE 3   Solve an application problem using subtraction

An advertisement for Circuit City reads, "Sony 50-Inch Widescreen TV reduced by $475." If the original retail price of the TV was $4000, what is the new sale price?

SOLUTION STRATEGY

$$\begin{array}{r} \$4000 \\ -\ 475 \\ \hline \$3525 \end{array}$$

The key phrase *reduced by* indicates subtraction. Subtract the amount of the reduction, $475, from the original retail price, $4000.

$3525 new sale price

TRY-IT EXERCISE 3

Nifty Auto Sales advertised a Pontiac Grand Am on sale for $26,559. If the original price was $29,334, what is the amount of the price reduction?

Check your answer with the solution in Appendix A. ■

READ AND INTERPRET DATA FROM A BAR GRAPH

bar graph
A graphical representation of quantities using horizontal or vertical bars.

A **bar graph** is a graphical representation of quantities using horizontal or vertical bars. Bar graphs are used extensively to summarize and display data in a clear and concise manner. We will learn more about graphs in Chapter 8, Data Presentation and Statistics.

EXAMPLE 4   Solve an application problem using subtraction

Use the bar graph *Army Officer Monthly Pay* to answer each question.

Army Officer Monthly Pay

Major — $5,528
Lieutenant colonel — $6,329
Colonel — $7,233
Brigadier general (1 star) — $9,051
Major general (2 stars) — $10,009
Lieutenant general (3 stars) — $10,564
General (4 stars) — $11,875

Source: Defense Department

a. For which ranks is the monthly pay less than $7000 per month?

b. What is the monthly pay for colonel?

c. What is the difference in monthly pay between lieutenant general and major general?

d. What is the difference in monthly pay between colonel and major?

e. What is the difference in monthly pay between a general and a major general?

SOLUTION STRATEGY

a. Major and lieutenant colonel

b. $7233

c. $10,564   To find the difference, subtract $10,009 from $10,564.
     − 10,009
     ————
       $555

d. $7233   To find the difference, subtract $5528 from $7233.
     − 5528
     ————
     $1705

e. $11,875   To find the difference, subtract $10,009 from $11,875.
$\underline{-10,009}$
$1,866

TRY-IT EXERCISE 4

Use the bar graph *Army Officer Monthly Pay* on page 30 to answer each question.

a. For which ranks is the monthly pay more than $10,000?

b. What is the monthly pay for brigadier general?

c. What is the difference in monthly pay between colonel and lieutenant colonel?

d. What is the difference in monthly pay between general and brigadier general?

e. What is the difference in monthly pay between major general and lieutenant colonel?

Check your answers with the solutions in Appendix A. ∎

SECTION 1.3 REVIEW EXERCISES

Concept Check

1. The mathematical process of taking away or deducting an amount from a given number is known as _____.

2. In subtraction, the number from which another number is subtracted is called the _____.

3. In subtraction, the number that is subtracted is called the _____.

4. The result of subtracting numbers is known as the _____.

5. In subtraction, we often format the digits of the whole numbers vertically so that the _____ _____ are aligned.

6. If the digits in a column cannot be subtracted to produce a whole number, _____ from the column to the left.

Objective 1.3A   Subtract whole numbers

GUIDE PROBLEMS

7. 43
   $\underline{-\ 3}$
    4_

8. 85
   $\underline{-\ 4}$
    _1

9. 67
   $\underline{-\quad}$
    62

10. 7_
   $\underline{-52}$
    27

11. ^{12}
    82
   $\underline{-17}$
    65

12. ^{3}_
    4 1̸
   $\underline{-\ 6}$
    35

13. $^{0\ \overset{\_}{3}\ 15}$
    1̸ 4 5̸
   $\underline{-58}$
    87

14. $^{4\ \cancel{0}\ 12}$
    5̸ 1̸ 2
   $\underline{-454}$
    58

Subtract.

15.   55
       − 3

16.   49
       − 7

17.   39
       − 0

18.   42
       − 2

19.   57
       − 35

20.   71
       − 11

21.   85
       − 25

22.   49
       − 28

23.   88
       − 62

24.   97
       − 55

25.   54
       − 54

26.   29
       − 24

27.   65
       − 9

28.   31
       − 3

29.   53
       − 6

30.   73
       − 7

31.   90
       − 39

32.   80
       − 36

33.   35
       − 29

34.   62
       − 47

35.   517
       − 13

36.   458
       − 84

37.   658
       − 32

38.   748
       − 30

39.   835
       − 127

40.   849
       − 355

41.   716
       − 330

42.   479
       − 184

43.   8359
       − 4482

44.   5380
       − 1392

45.   76,947
       − 15,850

46.   12,563
       − 10,963

47. 415 − 18

48. 121 − 53

49. 758 − 654

50. 761 − 706

51. 1935 − 885

52. 7083 − 134

53. 6893 − 4887

54. 1560 − 1057

Objective 1.3B   **Apply your knowledge**

55. Subtract 17 from 36.

56. What is 85 minus 62?

57. Find 61 less 27.

58. How much is 349 decreased by 97?

59. What is 164 reduced by 48?

60. What is 243 less than 959?

61. How much is 2195 if you take away 1556?

62. Find the difference of 45,988 and 12,808.

63. In a three-hour period, the temperature dropped from 86 degrees to 69 degrees. By how many degrees did the temperature drop?

64. According to the 2000 U.S. Census, the U.S. population was 281,421,906. It is estimated that the U.S. population hit 300,000,000 on October 17, 2006. How many people were added to the population between 2000 and 2006?

65. A gasoline station begins the day with 3400 gallons of premium fuel. If 1360 gallons remain at the end of the day, how much fuel did the station sell?

66. Coastal Bend College had 5440 students last year and 6120 students this year. How many more students are there this year?

67. The Royal Peacock men's clothing shop had 1260 ties in inventory at the beginning of the Fall Fashion Sale. At the end of the sale 380 ties were left in stock. How many ties were sold?

Photo by Robert Brechner

68. Branford, Inc. projected profits for the year to be $3,250,000. If actual profits were $2,850,000, by how much more was the projection than the actual profits?

69. A Broadway musical was estimated to cost $2,370,000 to produce.

   a. If the actual cost was $2,560,000, by how much was the play over budget?

   b. If ticket sales totaled $7,450,000, how much was the profit?

   c. Write your answer for part b in words.

70. The population of Melville increased from 541,500 people in 2005 to 556,000 people in 2006.

   a. By how many people did the population increase?

   b. If the population decreased to 548,400 in 2007, how many people left Melville?

   c. Write your answer for part b in words.

71. Mike purchased a stereo at Circuit City for $580. He made a down payment of $88 and financed the balance.

   a. How much did he finance?

   b. If after the first year he still owed $212, how much did he pay off during the first year?

72. Marlena had $150 in her purse this morning. During the day she spent $6 for breakfast, $44 on a pair of shoes, and $30 on a belt. How much did Marlena have left?

73. The Gordon family spends $950 for rent and $350 for food each month. They have budgeted $1800 for total expenses each month. How much does the Gordon family have to spend on other things after paying rent and buying food?

74. At the Fashion Institute 92 students are majoring in design, 105 are majoring in retailing, and the remainder are majoring in fashion modeling. If the school has a total of 310 students with majors, how many fashion modeling students are there?

Use the bar graph *Superstar Video DVDs* for exercises 75–77.

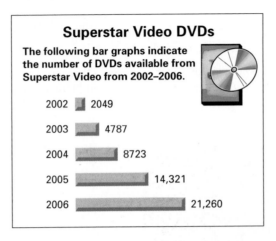

75. How many more DVDs were available in 2005 than in 2004?

76. How many fewer DVDs were available in 2002 than in 2003?

77. If 34,500 DVDs were available in 2007, what is the amount of the increase since 2006?

CUMULATIVE SKILLS REVIEW

1. Write 2510 in expanded notation. (1.1B)

2. Add 693 + 41 + 10,110. (1.2B)

$$\begin{array}{r} 693 \\ 41 \\ + 10{,}110 \\ \hline \end{array}$$

3. Name the place value of 6 in 1,463,440. (1.1A)

4. Show that (2 + 3) + 7 = 2 + (3 + 7). (1.2A)

5. Write two hundred nineteen thousand, eight hundred twelve in standard notation. (1.1B)

6. What is the total of the three numbers 225, 708, and 52? (1.2C)

7. Add 232 + 819. (1.2B)

8. Round 243,559 to the leftmost place value. (1.1D)

9. Write 35,429 in words. (1.1B)

10. Add 348 + 3909. (1.2B)

1.4   MULTIPLYING WHOLE NUMBERS

Suppose that a CompUSA store sold 6 computers each day for 4 days. How many computers did CompUSA sell in the four-day period?

To find the total number of computers sold during the four-day period, we can repeatedly add 6 a total of 4 times.

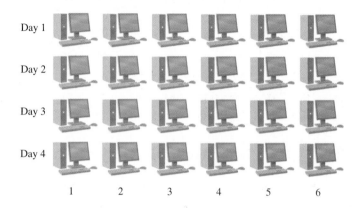

Note that $6 + 6 + 6 + 6 = 24$. Thus the store sold 24 computers in the four-day period.

Another way of determining the total number of computers sold is by using multiplication. **Multiplication** is the mathematical process of repeated addition of a value a specified number of times. In this example, we multiply 4 by 6 to determine that 24 computers were sold during the four-day period.

In a multiplication problem, the $\times$ symbol is called the multiplication sign. The numbers that are multiplied together are known as **factors**. The result of multiplying numbers is called the **product**.

$$4 \quad \times \quad 6 \quad = \quad 24$$
$$\text{factor} \qquad \text{factor} \qquad \text{product}$$

Symbolically, multiplication can also be expressed using a raised dot or parentheses.

$$4 \cdot 6 = 24 \qquad 4(6) = 24 \qquad (4)(6) = 24$$

To multiply, we often format factors vertically so that the place values are aligned.

$$\begin{array}{rl} 4 & \text{factor} \\ \times\ 6 & \text{factor} \\ \hline 24 & \text{product} \end{array}$$

Recall the following basic facts for multiplying the numbers 0 through 10. These are important because multiplication of larger numbers requires their repeated use.

multiplication
The mathematical process of repeated addition of a value a specified number of times.

factors
Numbers that are multiplied together.

product
The result of multiplying numbers.

BASIC MULTIPLICATION FACTS

x	0	1	2	3	4	5	6	7	8	9	10
0	0	0	0	0	0	0	0	0	0	0	0
1	0	1	2	3	4	5	6	7	8	9	10
2	0	2	4	6	8	10	12	14	16	18	20
3	0	3	6	9	12	15	18	21	24	27	30
4	0	4	8	12	16	20	24	28	32	36	40
5	0	5	10	15	20	25	30	35	40	45	50
6	0	6	12	18	24	30	36	42	48	54	60
7	0	7	14	21	28	35	42	49	56	63	70
8	0	8	16	24	32	40	48	56	64	72	80
9	0	9	18	27	36	45	54	63	72	81	90
10	0	10	20	30	40	50	60	70	80	90	100

Objective 1.4A   Use the multiplication properties

There are some properties associated with multiplying whole numbers that you should know. Two of these properties pertain to factors of 0 and 1, respectively. Notice that the product of any number and 0 is 0. For example, $3 \cdot 0 = 0$ and $0 \cdot 3 = 0$.

Multiplication Property of Zero

The product of any number and 0 is 0. That is, for any real number a, we have the following.

$$a \cdot 0 = 0 \cdot a = 0$$

Also, note that the product of any number and 1 is the number itself. For example, $3 \cdot 1 = 3$ and $1 \cdot 3 = 3$.

Multiplication Property of One

The product of any number and 1 is the number itself. That is, for any real number a, we have the following.

$$a \cdot 1 = 1 \cdot a = a$$

EXAMPLE 1   Use the multiplication properties of zero and one

Multiply.

a. $6 \cdot 0$ **b.** $0 \cdot 34$ **c.** $8 \cdot 1$ **d.** $1 \cdot 47$

SOLUTION STRATEGY

a. $6 \cdot 0 = 0$ Multiplication property of zero.

b. $0 \cdot 34 = 0$ Multiplication property of zero.

c. $8 \cdot 1 = 8$ Multiplication property of one.

d. $1 \cdot 47 = 47$ Multiplication property of one.

TRY-IT EXERCISE 1

Multiply.

a. $0 \cdot 84$

b. $219 \cdot 0$

c. $16 \cdot 1$

d. $1 \cdot 500$

Check your answers with the solutions in Appendix A. ◼

In Section 1.2, Adding Whole Numbers, we learned that addition is commutative, that is, the order in which we add numbers does not change the sum. We also learned that addition is associative, or, in other words, the way in which we group the addends does not change the sum. We now see that multiplication is commutative and associative as well.

Commutative Property of Multiplication

Changing the order of the factors does not change the product. That is, for any numbers a and b, we have the following.

$$a \cdot b = b \cdot a$$

Associative Property of Multiplication

Changing the grouping of the factors does not change the product. That is, for any numbers a, b, and c, we have the following.

$$(a \cdot b) \cdot c = a \cdot (b \cdot c)$$

EXAMPLE 2   Demonstrate the commutative and associative properties of multiplication

a. Show that $9 \cdot 7 = 7 \cdot 9$.

b. Show that $1(2 \cdot 3) = (1 \cdot 2)3$.

SOLUTION STRATEGY

a. $9 \cdot 7 = 7 \cdot 9$

    $63 = 63$ Multiply $9 \cdot 7$. Multiply $7 \cdot 9$.

    Thus, $9 \cdot 7 = 7 \cdot 9$ Commutative property of multiplication.

b. $1(2 \cdot 3) = (1 \cdot 2) \, 3$

      $1(6) = (2)3$ Multiply $2 \cdot 3$. Multiply $1 \cdot 2$.

        $6 = 6$ Multiply $1(6)$. Multiply $(2)3$.

Thus, $1(2 \cdot 3) = (1 \cdot 2)3$.   Associative property of multiplication.

TRY-IT EXERCISE 2

a. Show that $5 \cdot 8 = 8 \cdot 5$.

b. Show that $1(4 \cdot 2) = (1 \cdot 4)2$.

Check your answers with the solutions in Appendix A. ∎

The last multiplication property says that multiplication is *distributive*. To understand what this means, consider $6(5 + 3)$. First, note that we can simplify this expression in the following way.

$$6(5 + 3) = 6(8) = 48$$

But also note that $6(5 + 3)$ simplifies to the same number as $6 \cdot 5 + 6 \cdot 3$.

$$6 \cdot 5 + 6 \cdot 3 = 30 + 18 = 48$$

Since both $6(5 + 3)$ and $6 \cdot 5 + 6 \cdot 3$ simplify to 48, we conclude that $6(5 + 3) = 6 \cdot 5 + 6 \cdot 3$. In particular, note how the 6 distributes to the 5 and the 3 in the sum contained within parentheses.

$$6(5 + 3) = 6 \cdot 5 + 6 \cdot 3$$

This is known as the distributive property of multiplication over addition. We also have the distributive property of multiplication over subtraction. We state these properties formally as follows.

> **Distributive Property of Multiplication over Addition or Subtraction**
>
> Multiplication distributes over addition and subtraction. That is, for any numbers a, b, and c, we have the following:
>
> $$a(b + c) = ab + ac \quad \text{and} \quad a(b - c) = ab - ac$$
>
> $$(b + c)a = ba + ca \quad \text{and} \quad (b - c)a = ba - ca$$

EXAMPLE 3   **Demonstrate the distributive property of multiplication**

a. Show that $3(4 + 2) = 3 \cdot 4 + 3 \cdot 2$.

b. Show that $(5 - 2)7 = 5 \cdot 7 - 2 \cdot 7$.

SOLUTION STRATEGY

a. $3(4 + 2) = 3 \cdot 4 + 3 \cdot 2$

$\qquad 3(6) = 12 + 6$ Add $4 + 2$. Multiply $3 \cdot 4$. Multiply $3 \cdot 2$.

$\qquad\quad 18 = 18$ Multiply $3(6)$. Add $12 + 6$.

Thus, $3(4 + 2) = 3 \cdot 4 + 3 \cdot 2$.   Distributive property of multiplication over addition.

b. $(5 - 2)7 = 5 \cdot 7 - 2 \cdot 7$

$\qquad (3)7 = 35 - 14$ Subtract $5 - 2$. Multiply $5 \cdot 7$. Multiply $2 \cdot 7$.

$\qquad\quad 21 = 21$ Multiply $(3)7$. Subtract $35 - 14$.

Thus, $(5 - 2)7 = 5 \cdot 7 - 2 \cdot 7$.   Distributive property of multiplication over subtraction.

TRY-IT EXERCISE 3

a. Show that $5(9 - 6) = 5 \cdot 9 - 5 \cdot 6$.

b. Show that $(3 + 4)2 = 3 \cdot 2 + 2 \cdot 4$.

Check your answers with the solutions in Appendix A. ■

Objective 1.4B   Multiply whole numbers

Now that we have reviewed products involving single-digit whole numbers, we can consider problems involving any two whole numbers. Let's begin by considering $12(4)$, the product of a two-digit number and a single-digit number. We can calculate this product as follows.

$$12(4) = (10 + 2)4 \qquad \text{Write 12 in expanded form.}$$
$$= 10 \cdot 4 + 2 \cdot 4 \qquad \text{Apply the distributive property over addition.}$$
$$= 40 + 8 \qquad\qquad \text{Multiply.}$$
$$= 48 \qquad\qquad\quad \text{Add.}$$

Rather than writing out all of the details above, we commonly work this problem in the following way.

$$\begin{array}{r} 12 \\ \times\ 4 \\ \hline 8 \end{array}$$

Multiply 4 by 2 ones. $4 \cdot 2$ ones $= 8$ ones. Write 8 in the ones column.

$$\begin{array}{r} 12 \\ \times\ 4 \\ \hline 48 \end{array}$$

Multiply 4 by 1 ten. $4 \cdot 1$ ten $= 4$ tens. Write 4 in the tens column.

EXAMPLE 4   Multiply whole numbers

Multiply 32 · 4.

SOLUTION STRATEGY

$$
\begin{array}{r}
32 \\
\times\,4 \\
\hline
128
\end{array}
$$
      Multiply 4 · 2. Multiply 4 · 3.

TRY-IT EXERCISE 4

Multiply 72 · 3.

Check your answers with the solutions in Appendix A. ■

Sometimes it is necessary to *carry* just as we do in some addition problems. As an example involving carrying, let's consider 439 · 8.

$$
\begin{array}{r}
^{7} \\
439 \\
\times\,8 \\
\hline
2
\end{array}
$$
Note that 439 = 4 hundreds + 3 tens + 9 ones.
Multiply 8 by 9 ones. 8 · 9 ones = 72 ones = 7 tens + 2 ones.
Write 2 in the ones column and carry 7 to the top of the tens column.

$$
\begin{array}{r}
^{37} \\
439 \\
\times\,8 \\
\hline
12
\end{array}
$$
Multiply 8 by 3 tens and add 7 tens.
8 · 3 tens + 7 tens = 24 tens + 7 tens = 31 tens.
31 tens = 3 hundreds + 1 tens. Write 1 in the tens column and carry 3 to the top of the hundreds column.

$$
\begin{array}{r}
^{37} \\
439 \\
\times\,8 \\
\hline
3512
\end{array}
$$
Multiply 8 by 4 hundreds and add 3 hundreds.
8 · 4 hundreds + 3 hundreds = 32 hundreds + 3 hundreds = 35 hundreds.
35 hundreds = 3 thousands + 5 hundreds. Because this is the leftmost column, we are done.

EXAMPLE 5   Multiply whole numbers when carrying is necessary

Multiply 564 · 9.

SOLUTION STRATEGY

$$
\begin{array}{r}
^{3} \\
564 \\
\times\,9 \\
\hline
6
\end{array}
$$
Multiply 9 by 4.
9 · 4 = 36. Write 6 in the ones column and carry 3 to the top of the tens column.

$$
\begin{array}{r}
^{53} \\
564 \\
\times\,9 \\
\hline
76
\end{array}
$$
Multiply 9 by 6 and add 3.
9 · 6 + 3 = 54 + 3 = 57. Write 7 in the tens column and carry 5 to the top of the hundreds column.

$$
\begin{array}{r}
^{53} \\
564 \\
\times\,9 \\
\hline
5076
\end{array}
$$
Multiply 9 by 5 and add 5.
9 · 5 + 5 = 45 + 5 = 50. Because this is the leftmost column, we are done.

TRY-IT EXERCISE 5

Multiply $832 \cdot 7$.

Check your answer with the solution in Appendix A. ■

We now consider multiplication of larger whole numbers. As an example, consider $32 \cdot 14$.

$$32 \cdot 14 = 32(10 + 4) \qquad \text{Write 14 in expanded form.}$$
$$= 32(4 + 10) \qquad \text{Apply the commutative property of addition.}$$
$$= 32 \cdot 4 + 32 \cdot 10 \qquad \text{Apply the distributive property.}$$
$$= 128 + 320 \qquad \text{Multiply.}$$
$$= 448$$

We commonly perform such a multiplication problem in the following way.

$$\begin{array}{r} 32 \\ \times\ 14 \\ \hline 128 \end{array}$$
Multiply 4 by 32.
The product 128 is called a *partial product*.

$$\begin{array}{r} 32 \\ \times\ 14 \\ \hline 128 \\ 0 \end{array}$$
Below the partial product, write 0 in the ones column. We refer to this 0 as a *placeholder*.

$$\begin{array}{r} 32 \\ \times\ 14 \\ \hline 128 \\ 320 \end{array}$$
Multiply 1 by 32. Write 32 to the left of the placeholder.

$$\begin{array}{r} 32 \\ \times\ 14 \\ \hline 128 \\ +\ 320 \\ \hline 448 \end{array}$$
Add the partial products.

> **Learning Tip**
>
> A power of 10 is a natural number whose first digit is 1 and whose remaining digits are 0. The first four powers of 10 are 10, 100, 1000, and 10,000. The product of a nonzero whole number and a power of ten is the original whole number with as many zeros appended to it as there are in the power of ten. As an example, consider 32 multiplied by some powers of 10.
>
> $$32 \cdot 10 = 320$$
> $$32 \cdot 100 = 3200$$
> $$32 \cdot 1000 = 32,000$$
> $$32 \cdot 10,000 = 320,000$$

EXAMPLE 6   Multiply larger whole numbers

Multiply.

a. $89 \cdot 64$ **b.** $438 \cdot 251$

SOLUTION STRATEGY

a.
$$\begin{array}{r} \overset{3}{8}9 \\ \times\ 64 \\ \hline 356 \end{array}$$
Multiply $89 \cdot 4$.

$$\begin{array}{r} \overset{5}{8}9 \\ \times\ 64 \\ \hline 356 \\ 5340 \end{array}$$
Below the partial product, write 0 in the ones column as a placeholder.
Multiply $89 \cdot 6$. Write the product, 534, to the left of the placeholder.

$$\begin{array}{r} \overset{5}{89} \\ \times\ 64 \\ \hline 356 \\ +\ 5340 \\ \hline 5696 \end{array}$$

Add the partial products.

b.
$$\begin{array}{r} 438 \\ \times\ 251 \\ \hline 438 \end{array}$$

Multiply 438 · 1.

$$\begin{array}{r} \overset{1\ 4}{438} \\ \times\ 251 \\ \hline 438 \\ 21900 \end{array}$$

Below the partial product, write 0 in the ones column as a placeholder.

Multiply 438 · 5. Write the product, 2190, to the left of the placeholder.

$$\begin{array}{r} \overset{1}{438} \\ \times\ 251 \\ \hline 438 \\ 21900 \\ 87600 \end{array}$$

Below the second partial product, write 0 in the ones column and 0 in the tens column as placeholders.

Multiply 438 · 2. Write the product, 876, to the left of the placeholders.

$$\begin{array}{r} \overset{1}{438} \\ \times\ 251 \\ \hline 438 \\ 21900 \\ +\ 87600 \\ \hline 109{,}938 \end{array}$$

Add the partial products.

TRY-IT EXERCISE 6

Multiply.

a. 93 · 58

b. 256 · 321

Check your answers with the solutions in Appendix A. ■

The next example demonstrates what to do when 0 appears in the second factor.

EXAMPLE 7   Multiply larger whole numbers with zeros

Multiply 654 · 509.

SOLUTION STRATEGY

$$\begin{array}{r} \overset{4\ 3}{654} \\ \times\ 509 \\ \hline 5886 \end{array}$$

Multiply 654 · 9.

654
× 509
———
5886
00

Below the partial product, write 0 in the ones column as a placeholder.

Multiply 654 · 0. Because the product is zero, write another zero to the left of the placeholder.

  2 2
654
× 509
———
5886
327000

Multiply 654 · 5. Write the product, 3270, to the left of the placeholders.

654
× 509
———
5886
+ 327000
————
332,886

Add the partial products.

TRY-IT EXERCISE 7

Multiply 721 · 207.

Check your answer with the solution in Appendix A. ■

| Objective 1.4C | **Apply your knowledge** |

Multiplication is commonly used in application problems. Be aware that sometimes application problems require more than one mathematical operation. Complete coverage of how to solve application problems can be found in Section 1.7.

As with addition and subtraction, key words and phrases indicate when multiplication is to be used.

multiply	**times**	**product**	**product of**	**multiplied by**
of	**at**	**twice**	**double**	**triple**

EXAMPLE 8   Use multiplication to solve an application problem

The Actor's Playhouse sold 233 tickets at $29 each for a Saturday matinee of the production *Cats*. What was the total revenue for the performance?

SOLUTION STRATEGY

233
× 29
———
2097
4660
———
6757

The key word *at* indicates multiplication.

Multiply the number of tickets, 233, by the price per ticket, $29.

The total revenue for the performance was $6757.

TRY-IT EXERCISE 8

The local college sold 4397 boxes of donuts for their year-end charity event. Each box of donuts cost $12. What were the total proceeds of the fund-raiser?

Check your answer with the solution in Appendix A. ■

FIND THE AREA OF A RECTANGLE

area

The measure associated with the interior of a closed, flat geometric figure.

As a preview to Chapter 7, Geometry, we shall take a look at a common application of multiplication. Namely, we will find the area of a rectangle. **Area** is the measure associated with the interior of a closed, flat geometric figure. Area is measured in square units, such as square feet or square inches.

Consider a rectangle 4 inches long and 2 inches wide. Each small square measures 1 square inch. Together, the small squares form a rectangle with 2 rows of 4 squares each. Because there are 2 · 4 or 8 squares, the area of the rectangle is 8 square inches.

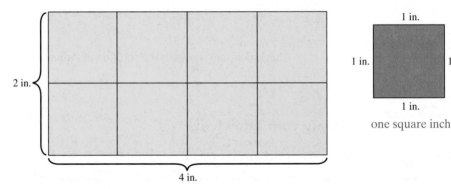

one square inch

The area of a rectangle can be expressed as the product of its length and its width. We use the following formula to calculate the area of a rectangle.

$$A = l \cdot w$$

From our example above, with $l = 4$ inches and $w = 2$ inches, we have the following.

$$A = 4 \text{ inches} \cdot 2 \text{ inches}$$
$$= 8 \text{ square inches}$$

EXAMPLE 9　　**Solve an application problem involving area**

The balcony of a condominium that is to be carpeted measures 22 feet long and 9 feet wide.

a. What is the area of the balcony?

b. If indoor/outdoor carpeting costs $6 per square foot, what is the cost of the carpet?

SOLUTION STRATEGY

a.　22　　　Use formula $A = l \cdot w$.
　　×9
　　────
　　198

The area is 198 square feet.

b. 198   Multiply the number of square feet, 198, by the cost per square foot, $6.
$\times$ 6
1188

The cost to install carpeting is $1188.

TRY-IT EXERCISE 9

The showroom of an automobile dealership measures 97 feet long and 38 feet wide.

a. What is the area of the showroom floor?

b. If tile costs $7 per square foot, and installation costs $2 per square foot, what is the total cost to tile the showroom?

Check your answers with the solutions in Appendix A. ■

SECTION 1.4 REVIEW EXERCISES

Concept Check

1. The mathematical process of repeated addition of a value a specified number of times is called _____.

2. Numbers that are multiplied together are known as _____.

3. The result of multiplying numbers is known as a _____.

4. The multiplication property of zero states that the product of any number and _____ is 0.

5. The multiplication property of one states that the product of any number and _____ is the number itself.

6. According to the commutative property of multiplication, $5 \cdot 7 =$ _____.

7. The associative property of multiplication states that the _____ of factors does not change the product.

8. According to the distributive property of multiplication over subtraction, $2(8 - 3) = 2 \cdot 8 -$ _____.

Objective 1.4A   Use the multiplication properties

GUIDE PROBLEMS

9. $4 \cdot 0 =$ ____

This example demonstrates the multiplication property of _____.

10. $13 \cdot 1 =$ ____

This example demonstrates the multiplication property of _____.

11. Show that $7 \cdot 3 = 3 \cdot 7$.

$$7 \cdot 3 = 3 \cdot 7$$
$$21 = \underline{\quad}$$

This example demonstrates the _____ property of multiplication.

12. Show that $2(1 \cdot 4) = (2 \cdot 1)4$.

$$2(1 \cdot 4) = (2 \cdot 1)4$$
$$2(\underline{\quad}) = (\underline{\quad})4$$
$$\underline{\quad} = \underline{\quad}$$

This example demonstrates the _____ property of multiplication.

13. Show that $2(3 + 4) = 2 \cdot 3 + 2 \cdot 4$.

$$2(3 + 4) = 2 \cdot 3 + 2 \cdot 4$$
$$2(\underline{\quad}) = \underline{\quad} + 8$$
$$\underline{\quad} = \underline{\quad}$$

This example demonstrates the _____ property of multiplication over _____.

14. Show that $3(5 - 2) = 3 \cdot 5 - 3 \cdot 2$.

$$3(5 - 2) = 3 \cdot 5 - 3 \cdot 2$$
$$3(\underline{\quad}) = 15 - \underline{\quad}$$
$$\underline{\quad} = \underline{\quad}$$

This example demonstrates the _____ property of multiplication over _____.

15. Multiply $0 \cdot 215$.

16. Multiply $92 \cdot 0$.

17. Multiply $82 \cdot 1$.

18. Multiply $1 \cdot 439$.

19. Show that $4 \cdot 8 = 8 \cdot 4$.

20. Show that $9 \cdot 3 = 3 \cdot 9$.

21. Show that $3(2 \cdot 4) = (3 \cdot 2)4$.

22. Show that $1(9 \cdot 7) = (1 \cdot 9)7$.

23. Show that $7(2 + 5) = 7 \cdot 2 + 7 \cdot 5$.

24. Show that $4(9 - 3) = 4 \cdot 9 - 4 \cdot 3$.

Objective 1.4B	**Multiply whole numbers**

GUIDE PROBLEMS

25.
$$\overset{2}{}28$$
$$\underline{\times\ 3}$$
$$\underline{}4$$

26.
$$\overset{4}{}56$$
$$\underline{\times\ 7}$$
$$\underline{}92$$

27.
$$\overset{\overline{}}{53}$$
$$\underline{\times\ 9}$$
$$477$$

28.
$$\overset{\overline{}}{36}$$
$$\underline{\times\ 9}$$
$$324$$

29.
$$16$$
$$\underline{\times\ 32}$$
$$32$$
$$\underline{80}$$
$$\overline{512}$$

30.
$$86$$
$$\underline{\times\ 13}$$
$$258$$
$$\underline{860}$$
$$\overline{1\underline{}18}$$

31.
$$326$$
$$\underline{\times\ 75}$$
$$1\ 630$$
$$\underline{22\ 820}$$
$$\overline{2\underline{},450}$$

32.
$$\overset{1\quad3}{1216}$$
$$\underline{\times\ 50}$$
$$60,80\underline{}$$

Multiply.

33. 23
    $\times\,3$

34. 41
    $\times\,2$

35. 52
    $\times\,4$

36. 63
    $\times\,2$

37. 52
    $\times\,9$

38. 58
    $\times\,3$

39. 59
    $\times\,6$

40. 39
    $\times\,8$

41. 22
    $\times\,78$

42. 16
    $\times\,33$

43. 94
    $\times\,50$

44. 70
    $\times\,75$

45. 605
    $\times\,40$

46. 740
    $\times\,80$

47. 153
    $\times\,33$

48. 407
    $\times\,89$

49. 6000
    $\times\,74$

50. 1681
    $\times\,60$

51. 4888
    $\times\,23$

52. 8737
    $\times\,91$

53. $4444 \cdot 270$

54. $2014 \cdot 515$

55. $3342 \cdot 951$

56. $3906 \cdot 550$

57. 25(915)

58. 34(333)

59. (37)(282)

60. (223)(4200)

Objective 1.4C   **Apply your knowledge**

61. What is 28 multiplied by 15?

62. What is twice 45,000?

63. How much are 12 calculators at $16 each?

64. What is the product of 54 and $50?

65. How much is 25 times 42 times 4?

66. Find the product of 16, 8, and 22.

67. David saves $30 per week from his part-time job. How much will he have saved in 26 weeks?

68. Soraya earns $8 per hour at Starbucks. How much does she earn in a 35-hour week?

69. Airbus Industries received an order from Delta Airlines for 13 Sky King commuter jets at a cost of $5,660,000 each. What was the total cost of the order?

70. According to the U.S. Postal Service, the average family receives 18 sales pitches, 3 bills, and 1 financial statement every week. Based on these figures, how many pieces of mail will the average family receive in one year? (There are 52 weeks in a year.)

71. Southside Bank requires that mortgage loan applicants have a monthly income of three times the amount of their monthly payment. How much must Maureen's monthly income be to qualify for a monthly payment of $1149?

72. The Bookworm sold 125 dictionaries last month at a price of $18 each. How much money did they take in on dictionary sales?

73. Worldwide, 7 people per second get on the Internet for the first time. How many new people get on in a 24-hour period?

74. If the average family in Martin City uses 33 gallons of water per day, how many gallons do they use in a 30-day month?

75. Toys Galore, a manufacturer of small plastic toys, uses molding machines that can produce 74 units per minute.

a. How many toys can a machine produce in 1 hour?

b. If the company has 9 of these machines, and they operate for 8 hours per day, what is the total output of toys per day?

76. A typical wallpaper hanger can cover 110 square feet of wall per hour.

a. How many square feet can he paper in a 7-hour day?

b. If a contractor hires 3 paper hangers for a large condominium project, how many square feet can they paper in a 5-day week?

77. A regulation tennis court for doubles play is 78 feet long and 36 feet wide.

a. What is the number of square feet of a doubles court?

b. A singles court is the same length but 9 feet shorter in width. What is the number of square feet of a singles court?

c. What is the difference between the area of a doubles court and the area of a singles court?

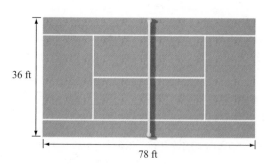

36 ft

78 ft

78. A regulation NCAA or NBA basketball court measures 94 feet long and 50 feet wide.

  a. What is the number of square feet of these courts?

  b. A regulation high school basketball court measures 84 feet long and 50 feet wide. How many square feet is this court?

  c. What is the difference between the area of an NCAA or NBA court and a high school court?

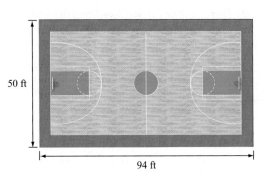

50 ft

94 ft

Use the bar graph *Average Value per Acre of U.S. Cropland* **for exercises 79–82.**

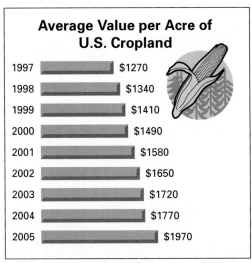

Average Value per Acre of U.S. Cropland

1997	$1270
1998	$1340
1999	$1410
2000	$1490
2001	$1580
2002	$1650
2003	$1720
2004	$1770
2005	$1970

Source: National Agricultural Statistics Service: data excludes Hawaii, Alaska

79. What was the value of a 300-acre farm in 2004?

80. What was the value of a 260-acre farm in 2005?

81. How much more was a 100-acre farm worth in 2001 compared with 1997?

82. How much less was a 100-acre farm worth in 1997 compared with 2002?

CUMULATIVE SKILLS REVIEW

1. Write 82,184 in word form. (1.1B)

2. Round 9228 to the nearest hundred. (1.1D)

3. Add 1550 + 122 + 892 + 30. (1.2B)

4. Subtract. (1.3A)

$$\begin{array}{r} 83 \\ -\ 19 \\ \hline \end{array}$$

5. How much is 422 increased by 110? (1.2B)

6. How much is 512 decreased by 125? (1.3B)

7. Last week you spent $22 for an oil change, $39 for tire rotation and balancing, and $9 for new windshield wiper blades. What was the total amount you spent on your car? (1.2C)

8. Tim loaded 48 cases of fruit in the morning and 43 cases in the afternoon. How many total cases did he load? (1.2C)

9. If 7485 tickets were originally available for a football game and 5795 were sold, how many tickets remain? (1.3B)

10. Sandy needs 64 credits to graduate with an associate's degree. If she has earned 22 credits to date, how many more credits does she need? (1.3B)

1.5 DIVIDING WHOLE NUMBERS

LEARNING OBJECTIVES

A. Use the division properties

B. Divide whole numbers

C. Apply your knowledge

Suppose that a 12-member group wants to rent kayaks for a river excursion. If each kayak can hold 3 people, how many kayaks are needed?

To determine the number of kayaks needed for the excursion, we can repeatedly subtract 3 people from the group of 12.

12-member group   canoe #1   canoe #2   canoe #3   canoe #4

division
The mathematical process of repeated subtraction of a value.

dividend
The number being divided.

divisor
The number by which the dividend is divided.

quotient
The result of dividing numbers.

Note that when we repeatedly subtract 3 people from the original group of 12, we ultimately divide the original group into 4 kayaks.

Another way of determining the number of kayaks needed is by using division. **Division** is the mathematical process of repeated subtraction of a specified value. In this example, we divide 12 by 3 to determine that 4 kayaks are needed to accommodate the group.

In a division problem, the ÷ symbol is called the division sign. The number being divided is called the **dividend**, the number by which it is divided is called the **divisor**, and the result of dividing numbers is known as the **quotient**.

$$12 \quad \div \quad 3 \quad = \quad 4$$

$$\text{dividend} \qquad \text{divisor} \qquad \text{quotient}$$

In general, division problems can be written in the following three ways.

$$\text{dividend} \div \text{divisor} \qquad \text{divisor} \overline{)\text{dividend}} \qquad \frac{\text{dividend}}{\text{divisor}}$$

Thus, $12 \div 3 = 4$ could also be written as follows.

$$3\overline{)12}^{\,4} \qquad \qquad \frac{12}{3} = 4$$

In the previous section, we learned that multiplication is the mathematical process of repeated addition. Since division is repeated subtraction, we say that multiplication and division are opposite operations. Thus, every division problem has a related multiplication problem. For example, the division problem $12 \div 3$ is related to the following multiplication problem.

What number times 3 equals 12?

Since $4 \cdot 3 = 12$, it follows that $12 \div 3 = 4$.

Objective 1.5A   Use the division properties

As with addition and multiplication, you should be aware of some useful properties when working division problems.

Dividing a Number by One

The quotient of any number and 1 is the number itself. That is, for any number a, we have the following.

$$a \div 1 = a$$

As some examples, consider the following.

$$18 \div 1 = 18 \qquad \frac{764}{1} = 764 \qquad 1\overline{)54}^{\,54}$$

Dividing a Number by Itself

The quotient of any nonzero number and itself is 1. That is, for any nonzero number a, we have the following.

$$a \div a = 1$$

Here are some examples of dividing a number by itself.

$$17 \div 17 = 1 \qquad \frac{248}{248} = 1 \qquad 39\overline{)39}^{\,1}$$

● *Learning Tip*

To remember the difference between dividing zero by a nonzero number and dividing a number by zero, the following may be useful.

0 divided by a number, K: $0 \div K$ is "okay," that is, we can do it. $0 \div K = 0$.

A number, N, divided by 0: $N \div 0$ is a "no-no," that is, we can't do it. $N \div 0$ is undefined.

Dividing Zero by a Nonzero Number

The quotient of zero and any nonzero number is zero. That is, for any nonzero number a, we have the following.

$$0 \div a = 0 \text{ where } a \neq 0$$

The following are some examples of dividing zero by a nonzero number.

$$0 \div 28 = 0 \qquad \frac{0}{355} = 0 \qquad 93\overline{)0}$$

Dividing a Number by Zero

Division by zero is undefined. That is, we can not divide by zero. That is, for any number a, we have the following.

$$a \div 0 \text{ is undefined.}$$

Here are some examples of dividing a number by zero.

$$43 \div 0 \text{ is undefined} \qquad \frac{549}{0} \text{ is undefined} \qquad 0\overline{)268} \text{ is undefined}$$

EXAMPLE 1   **Divide using the division properties**

Divide using the division properties.

a. $\dfrac{44}{1}$

b. $519 \div 519$

c. $93\overline{)0}$

d. $\dfrac{65}{0}$

SOLUTION STRATEGY

a. $\dfrac{44}{1} = 44$ Dividing a number by one equals the original number.

b. $519 \div 519 = 1$ Dividing a number by itself equals one.

c. $93\overline{)0}^{\,0}$ Zero divided by a number equals zero.

d. $\dfrac{65}{0}$ undefined   Dividing a number by zero is undefined.

TRY-IT EXERCISE 1

Divide.

a. $29 \div 1$ **b.** $\dfrac{285}{285}$

c. $0 \div 4$

d. $388 \div 0$

Check your answers with the solutions in Appendix A. ■

Objective 1.5B	**Divide whole numbers**

Consider the problem $20 \div 5$. We can determine the quotient by repeatedly subtracting 5 from 20.

$$
\begin{array}{r}
20 \\
-\ 5 \\
\hline
15 \\
-\ 5 \\
\hline
10 \\
-\ 5 \\
\hline
5 \\
-\ 5 \\
\hline
0
\end{array}
$$

Subtract 5 repeatedly 4 times

We are done!

Since we subtract 5 repeatedly 4 times, we see that $20 \div 5 = 4$.

While repeated subtraction allows us to determine the answer, we can also analyze the related multiplication problem. The related multiplication problem can be posed in the following way.

What number times 5 equals 20?

Since $4 \cdot 5 = 20$, it follows that $20 \div 5 = 4$.

Most multiplication problems are not quite as easy, especially those that contain larger numbers. As an example, consider $846 \div 2$. Certainly, we would not want to subtract 2 repeatedly from 846! Moreover, the related multiplication problem may not be any easier to analyze. Rather, we use long division formatting to determine the quotient. We perform the problem in the following way.

$2\overline{)846}$ Write the problem in long division format.

$\begin{array}{r} 4 \\ 2\overline{)846} \end{array}$ Divide 2 into 8. $8 \div 2 = 4$. Write 4 above 8 in the dividend. The 4 is referred to as *partial quotient*.

$\begin{array}{r} 42 \\ 2\overline{)846} \end{array}$ Divide 2 into 4. $4 \div 2 = 2$. Write the partial quotient, 2, above 4 in the dividend.

$\begin{array}{r} 423 \\ 2\overline{)846} \end{array}$ Divide 2 into 6. $6 \div 2 = 3$. Write the partial quotient, 3, above 6 in the dividend.

As another example, consider the problem $368 \div 4$. In working this problem, we show details that we shall use in working more difficult division problems.

$4\overline{)368}$ Write the problem in long division format.

$\begin{array}{r} 9 \\ 4\overline{)368} \end{array}$ Since $4 > 3$, consider 4 divided into 36. $36 \div 4 = 9$. Write the partial quotient, 9, above 6 in the dividend.

$$\frac{9}{4)368}$$
$$-36\downarrow$$
$$\overline{08}$$

Multiply 9 · 4. Write the product below 36 in the dividend.
Subtract. 36 − 36 = 0.
Bring down the 8.

$$\frac{92}{4)368}$$
$$\frac{36}{08}$$
$$\frac{-\ 8}{0}$$

Divide 4 into 8. 8 ÷ 4 = 2. Write the partial quotient, 2, above 8 in the dividend. Multiply 2 · 4. Write the product below 8. Subtract.

Let's consider more examples.

EXAMPLE 2 **Divide whole numbers**

Divide.

a. 963 ÷ 3   **b.** $\dfrac{459}{9}$

SOLUTION STRATEGY

a. $3)\overline{963}$ Write the problem using long division format.

$\dfrac{3}{3)963}$ Divide 3 into 9. 9 ÷ 3 = 3. Write the partial quotient, 3, above 9.

$\dfrac{32}{3)963}$ Divide 3 into 6. 6 ÷ 3 = 2. Write the partial quotient, 2, above 6.

$\dfrac{321}{3)963}$ Divide 3 into 3. 3 ÷ 3 = 1. Write the partial quotient, 1, above 3.

The quotient is 321.

b. $9)\overline{459}$ Write the problem using long division format.

$\dfrac{5}{9)459}$ Since 9 > 4, consider 9 divided into 45. 45 ÷ 9 = 5. Write the partial quotient, 5, above 5 in the dividend.

$$\frac{5}{9)459}$$
$$\frac{-45\downarrow}{09}$$

Multiply 5 · 9. Write the product below 45 in the dividend.
Subtract. 45 − 45 = 0. Bring down the 9.

$$\frac{51}{9)459}$$
$$\frac{-45}{09}$$
$$\frac{-\ 9}{0}$$

Divide 9 into 9. 9 ÷ 9 = 1.
Write the partial quotient, 1, above 9 in the dividend.

Multiply 1 · 9.
Subtract.

The quotient is 51.

TRY-IT EXERCISE 2

Divide.

a. 848 ÷ 4

b. 156 ÷ 3

Check your answers with the solutions in Appendix A. ■

> ### ● *Learning Tip*
>
> Since multiplication and division are opposite operations, we can check a division problem by multiplying the quotient by the divisor.
>
> quotient = divisor · dividend
>
> As an example, in the example to the right we see that
>
> 963 ÷ 3 = 321.
>
> To check, simply verify that 321 · 3 is, in fact, 963.
>
> 321 · 3 = 963

EXAMPLE 3   Divide whole numbers

Divide.

a. $513 \div 3$

b. $3604 \div 34$

SOLUTION STRATEGY

a. $3\overline{)513}$ with 1 above
Divide 3 into 5. Since 3 does not divide into 5 evenly, *estimate* the number of times 3 divides into 5. Our best estimate is 1. Write 1 above 5 in the dividend.

$$
\begin{array}{r}
1 \\
3\overline{)513} \\
-3\downarrow \\
\hline
21
\end{array}
$$
Multiply $1 \cdot 3$.
Subtract. $5 - 3 = 2$. Bring down the 1.

$$
\begin{array}{r}
17 \\
3\overline{)513} \\
-3 \\
\hline
21 \\
-21
\end{array}
$$
Divide 3 into 21. $21 \div 3 = 7$.
Write the partial quotient, 7, above 1 in the dividend.

Multiply $7 \cdot 3$.
Subtract. Bring down the 3.

$$
\begin{array}{r}
171 \\
3\overline{)513} \\
-3 \\
\hline
21 \\
-21 \\
\hline
03 \\
-3 \\
\hline
0
\end{array}
$$
Divide 3 into 3. $3 \div 3 = 1$.
Write the partial quotient, 1, above 3 in the dividend.

Multiply $1 \cdot 3$.
Subtract.

The quotient is 171.

b. $34\overline{)3604}$ with 1 above
Since $34 > 3$, consider 34 divided into 36. Since 34 does not divide into 36 evenly, estimate the number of times 34 divides into 36. Our best estimate is 1. Write 1 above 6 in the dividend.

$$
\begin{array}{r}
1 \\
34\overline{)3604} \\
-34\downarrow \\
\hline
20
\end{array}
$$
Multiply $1 \cdot 34$.
Subtract. $36 - 34 = 2$. Bring down the 0.

$$
\begin{array}{r}
10 \\
34\overline{)3604} \\
-34 \\
\hline
20 \\
-0\downarrow \\
\hline
-204
\end{array}
$$
Divide 34 into 20. Since 34 does not divide into 20 evenly, estimate that 34 divides into 21 zero times. Write 0 above 0 in the dividend.

Multiply $0 \cdot 34$.
Subtract. $20 - 0 = 20$. Bring down the 4.

$$
\begin{array}{r}
106 \\
34\overline{)3604} \\
-34 \\
\hline
20 \\
-0 \\
\hline
204 \\
-204 \\
\hline
0
\end{array}
$$
Divide 34 into 204. $204 \div 34 = 6$.
Write the partial quotient 6 above 4 in the dividend.

Multiply $6 \cdot 34$.
Subtract.

The quotient is 106.

TRY-IT EXERCISE 3

Divide.

a. $616 \div 4$

b. $4309 \div 31$

Check your answers with the solutions in Appendix A. ■

Frequently, the dividend does not divide evenly into the divisor. As an example, consider $19 \div 6$. We can repeatedly subtract 6 to find the quotient.

$$
\begin{array}{r}
19 \\
-\ 6 \\
\hline
13 \\
-\ 6 \\
\hline
7 \\
-\ 6 \\
\hline
1
\end{array}
$$

Subtract 6 repeatedly 3 times.

Can't subtract 6 anymore and get a whole number!

The quotient is 3 since we repeatedly subtract 6 a total of 3 times. But note that there is a number left over. That is, there is a number from which we can no longer subtract 6 and still get a whole number. Such a number is called a remainder. In general, a **remainder** is a number that remains after division is complete. When there is a remainder, we will write the quotient followed by the letter *R* followed by the remainder.

remainder
The number that remains after division is complete.

$$19 \div 6 = 3\,R\,1$$

We can write the previous problem in the following way using the long division format.

$$
\begin{array}{r}
3\,R\,1 \\
6\overline{)19}
\end{array}
$$

We generally work such a problem in the following way.

$$
\begin{array}{r}
3 \\
6\overline{)19}
\end{array}
$$

Consider 6 divided into 19. Since 6 does not divide evenly into 19, estimate the number of times 6 divides into 19. Since 6 divides into 19 approximately 3 times, write 3 above the 9 in the dividend.

$$
\begin{array}{r}
3 \\
6\overline{)19} \\
\underline{18} \\
1
\end{array}
$$

Multiply $3 \cdot 6$. Write the product below the dividend.
Subtract. $19 - 18 = 1$.

After we subtract 18 from 19, there is nothing in the dividend to bring down. Therefore, 1 is the remainder. Note that the remainder, 1, is less than the divisor, 6. In division problems with remainders, the remainder must always be less than the divisor. If it were larger, then the divisor would divide into the dividend at least one more time.

EXAMPLE 4   Divide whole numbers with a remainder

Divide.

a. 228 ÷ 30

b. $\dfrac{5356}{89}$

SOLUTION STRATEGY

a. $30\overline{)228}$ with 7 above

Since 30 > 2 and 30 > 22, consider 30 divided into 228. Since 30 does not divide into 228 evenly, estimate the number of times that 30 divides into 228. Our best estimate is 7. Write 7 above 8 in the dividend.

$$
\begin{array}{r}
7 \\
30\overline{)228} \\
-210 \\
\hline
18
\end{array}
$$

Multiply 7 · 30.
Subtract. 228 − 210 = 18.

$$
\begin{array}{r}
7\ R\ 18 \\
30\overline{)228}
\end{array}
$$

Because there is nothing left to bring down, the remainder is 18. Note that the remainder is less than the divisor.

b. $89\overline{)5356}$ with 6 above

Although 89 does not divide into 5 or 53, it does divide into 535. We estimate that 89 divides into 535 six times. Write 6 above the second 5 in the dividend.

$$
\begin{array}{r}
6 \\
89\overline{)5356} \\
-534\!\downarrow \\
\hline
16
\end{array}
$$

Multiply 6 · 89.
Subtract. 535 − 534 = 1. Bring down the 6.

$$
\begin{array}{r}
60 \\
89\overline{)5356} \\
-534 \\
\hline
16
\end{array}
$$

Divide 89 into 16. Since 89 divides into 16 zero times, write 0 above 6 in the dividend.

$$
\begin{array}{r}
-0 \\
\hline
16
\end{array}
$$

Multiply 0 · 89.
Subtract. 16 − 0 = 16.

$$
\begin{array}{r}
60\ R\ 16 \\
89\overline{)5356}
\end{array}
$$

Because there is nothing left to bring down, the remainder is 16. Note that the remainder is less than the divisor.

> **Learning Tip**
>
> Estimating the number of times that a number divides into another sometimes requires trial and error. For instance, we may initially guess that 30 divides into 228 six times. But note the following.
>
> $$
> \begin{array}{r}
> 6 \\
> 30\overline{)228} \\
> -180 \\
> \hline
> 48
> \end{array}
> $$
>
> In particular, note that the remainder, 48, is greater than the divisor, 30. When this happens, we know that the divisor must divide into the dividend at least one more time.

TRY-IT EXERCISE 4

Divide.

a. 574 ÷ 61

b. $\dfrac{6214}{73}$

Check your answers with the solutions in Appendix A. ■

| Objective 1.5C | **Apply your knowledge** |

As with addition, subtraction, and multiplication, there are key words and phrases that indicate when division is to be used.

divide	divided by	quotient	quotient of	divided into
goes into	ratio of	average of	per	equally divides

EXAMPLE 5   Solve an application problem using division

Sunflower Corporation has 35 employees on their production line. Last year they equally divided $42,000 in a profit sharing bonus. How much did each employee receive?

SOLUTION STRATEGY

$$
\begin{array}{r}
1200 \\
35\overline{)42{,}000} \\
-35 \\
\hline
70 \\
-70 \\
\hline
0
\end{array}
$$

The word *divided* indicates division.

Divide the amount of the bonus by the number of employees to determine the amount received by each employee.

Each employee received $1200.

TRY-IT EXERCISE 5

Donna purchased a stereo from Circuit City for $2520. The purchase was financed without interest over a 12-month period. What was the amount of Donna's payment each month?

Check your answer with the solution in Appendix A. ■

FIND AN AVERAGE OR ARITHMETIC MEAN OF A SET OF NUMBERS

Imagine a payroll manager being asked to describe the hourly wage of 400 clerical workers. The manager could provide a list of the 400 employees along with their hourly wages. This action answers the question, but it is extremely tedious.

A more appropriate response might be to calculate the average. An **average** or **arithmetic mean** is the value obtained by dividing the sum of all the values in a data set by the number of values in the set. The average of a set of values describes the set with a single value.

average or **arithmetic mean** The value obtained by dividing the sum of all the values in a data set by the number of values in the set.

Steps for Calculating an Average

Step 1. Find the sum of all the values in a data set.

Step 2. Divide the sum in step 1 by the number of values in the set.

$$\text{Average} = \frac{\text{Sum of values}}{\text{Number of values}}$$

EXAMPLE 6   Calculate an average

In a math class, Jose scored 72 on the first test, 94 on the second test, and 86 on the third test. What is Jose's average score for the three tests?

SOLUTION STRATEGY

$$\text{Average} = \frac{72 + 94 + 86}{3} = \frac{252}{3} = 84$$

Calculate the sum of the test scores.
Divide this sum by the number of tests.

The average score for the three tests is 84.

TRY-IT EXERCISE 6

On a recent sales trip, Nathan drove 184 miles on Monday, 126 miles on Tuesday, 235 miles on Wednesday, and 215 miles on Thursday. What is Nathan's average mileage for each of the four days?

Check your answer with the solution in Appendix A. ■

SECTION 1.5 REVIEW EXERCISES

Concept Check

1. The mathematical process of repeated subtraction of a value is called _____.

2. In a division problem, the number being divided is called the _____.

3. The number by which the dividend is divided is known as the _____.

4. The result of dividing numbers is called the _____.

5. Show three ways to express 8 divided by 4.

6. The quotient of any number and _____ is the number itself.

7. The quotient of any nonzero number and itself is _____.

8. The quotient of zero and any nonzero number is _____.

9. The quotient of any number and zero is _____.

10. The number that remains after division is complete is called the _____.

Objective 1.5A   Use the division properties

GUIDE PROBLEMS

11. $\dfrac{213}{1} =$ _____

12. $64 \div 64 =$ _____

13. $23\overline{)0}$

14. $\dfrac{42}{0} =$ _____

Divide using the division properties.

15. $18 \div 1$

16. $91 \div 1$

17. $51 \div 51$

18. $34 \div 34$

19. $0 \div 3$

20. $0 \div 23$

21. $54 \div 0$

22. $13 \div 0$

23. $\dfrac{67}{0}$

24. $\dfrac{49}{0}$

25. $\dfrac{0}{12}$

26. $\dfrac{0}{29}$

27. $76\overline{)0}$

28. $31\overline{)0}$

29. $0\overline{)210}$

30. $0\overline{)93}$

Objective 1.5B	Divide whole numbers

GUIDE PROBLEMS

31. $5\overline{)40}$
$\quad\ \ 40$

32. $15\overline{)50}$
$\quad\ \ \ 45$

33. $\begin{array}{r} 4 \\ 8\overline{)368} \\ 32 \\ \hline 4\ \ \end{array}$

34. $\begin{array}{r} 47\ R\ \underline{\quad} \\ 13\overline{)616} \\ 52 \\ \hline 96 \\ 91 \\ \hline 5 \end{array}$

Divide.

35. $16 \div 2$

36. $21 \div 7$

37. $8\overline{)48}$

38. $3\overline{)66}$

39. $55\overline{)495}$

40. $67\overline{)804}$

41. $675 \div 15$

42. $544 \div 32$

43. $2096 \div 16$

44. $3266 \div 46$

45. $23\overline{)2622}$

46. $12\overline{)5208}$

47. $23,400 \div 100$

48. $1,000,000 \div 1,000$

49. $34 \div 6$

50. $86 \div 9$

51. $9\overline{)78}$

52. $8\overline{)99}$

53. $\dfrac{766}{71}$

54. $\dfrac{502}{37}$

55. $\dfrac{460}{26}$

56. $\dfrac{841}{16}$

57. $19\overline{)910}$

58. $21\overline{)404}$

59. $937 \div 85$ **60.** $608 \div 11$ **61.** $13\overline{)688}$ **62.** $63\overline{)442}$

63. $\dfrac{9262}{343}$ **64.** $\dfrac{6192}{183}$ **65.** $\dfrac{4830}{169}$ **66.** $\dfrac{2949}{121}$

Objective 1.5C   Apply your knowledge

67. How much is 735 divided by 7?

68. How much is 1196 divided by 4?

69. What is the quotient of 3413 and 8?

70. What is 19 divided into 7610?

71. How many times does 88 go into 1056?

72. What is the quotient of 364 and 4?

73. An SAT test has five equally timed parts. If the entire test is 200 minutes long, how many minutes is each part of the test?

74. A 35-acre palm tree nursery has a total of 2380 trees. How many trees are there per acre?

75. The city of Denton has 2450 homes. The city recycling center took in 34,300 pounds of aluminum cans last month. On average, how many pounds of aluminum were recycled per home?

76. Del Monte packs ketchup in cases containing 36 bottles each. How many cases will be required to fill an order for 9000 bottles?

77. Captain Doug Black, dockmaster at Emerald Bay Marina purchased 1760 feet of mooring line.

   a. How many pieces, each 22 feet long, can be cut from the roll?

   b. If each boat requires 5 of these lines, how many boats can be furnished with mooring lines?

78. Nails and Pails Hardware had sales of $22,464 last week. The store had 468 transactions.

   a. What was the average amount per transaction?

   b. If the store was open for 6 days last week, what was the average amount in sales per day?

Use the graph *Auto Insurance Expenses* for exercises 79–82

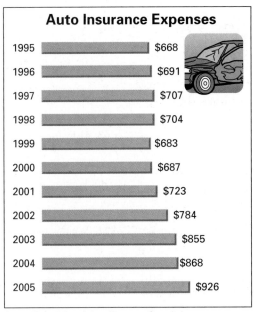

Auto Insurance Expenses

1995	$668
1996	$691
1997	$707
1998	$704
1999	$683
2000	$687
2001	$723
2002	$784
2003	$855
2004	$868
2005	$926

Source: National Association of Insurance Commissioners.
Insurance Information Institute estimates for 2001–2005

79. What was the average auto insurance rate for 1996 and 1997?

80. What was the average auto insurance rate for 2000 and 2001?

81. For 2001 through 2003, round each rate to the nearest hundred and find the average for those 3 years.

82. For 2002 through 2005, round each rate to the nearest ten, and find the average for those 4 years.

CUMULATIVE SKILLS REVIEW

1. Multiply 516 · 200. (1.4B)

2. Subtract 28 from 96. (1.3A)

3. How much is 954 increased by 181? (1.2B)

4. Round 1586 to the nearest hundreds. (1.1D)

5. Write 22,185 in expanded form. (1.1C)

6. What is 3 times 2200? (1.4C)

7. How much is 845 less 268? (1.3B)

8. Write 8965 in word form. (1.1B)

9. Tom worked 7 hours each day for 6 days straight. How many total hours did he work? (1.4C)

10. A school auditorium has 19 rows with 11 seats in each row. What is the total number of seats in the auditorium? (1.4C)

1.6 EVALUATING EXPONENTIAL EXPRESSIONS AND APPLYING ORDER OF OPERATIONS

Did you know there are about 100,000,000,000 stars in the galaxy? When dealing with such large numbers, it is useful to have a shorthand way of expressing them. **Exponential notation** is a shorthand way of expressing repeated multiplication. It is also a useful way of expressing very large or very small numbers. As we shall see in this section, the number of stars in the galaxy can be written in exponential notation in the following way.

$$10^{11}$$

In exponential notation, the **base** is the factor that is multiplied repeatedly. The **exponent** or **power** is the number that indicates how many times the base is to be used as a factor. The exponent is written as a superscript of the base. In the expression 2^3, 2 is the base and 3 is the exponent.

$$\text{base} \;\rightarrow\; 2^3 \;\leftarrow\; \text{exponent}$$
$$2^3 = 2 \cdot 2 \cdot 2$$

"two to the third power" or "two cubed"

The expression 2^3 is called an exponential expression since it has a base and an exponent.

Objective 1.6A   Read and write numbers in exponential notation

In mathematics, it is important to be able to read and write numbers in exponential notation.

The following chart illustrates how we read and write exponential expressions.

Exponential Notation	Read As
$4 = 4^1$	"four to the first power" or "four"
$4 \cdot 4 = 4^2$	"four to the second power" or "four squared"
$4 \cdot 4 \cdot 4 = 4^3$	"four to the third power" or "four cubed"
$4 \cdot 4 \cdot 4 \cdot 4 = 4^4$	"four to the fourth power"
$4 \cdot 4 \cdot 4 \cdot 4 \cdot 4 = 4^5$	"four to the fifth power"
$4 \cdot 4 \cdot 4 \cdot 4 \cdot 4 \cdot 4 = 4^6$	"four to the sixth power"

EXAMPLE 1   Write expressions in exponential notation

Write each expression in exponential notation and in word form.

a. $7 \cdot 7 \cdot 7$

b. $5 \cdot 5 \cdot 5 \cdot 5 \cdot 5$

c. $3 \cdot 3$

d. $2 \cdot 2 \cdot 8 \cdot 8 \cdot 8$

LEARNING OBJECTIVES

A. Read and write numbers in exponential notation

B. Evaluate an exponential expression

C. Use order of operations to simplify an expression

D. Apply your knowledge

exponential notation
A shorthand way of expressing repeated multiplication.

base
In exponential notation, the factor that is multiplied repeatedly.

exponent or **power**
In exponential notation, the number that indicates how many times the base is used as a factor.

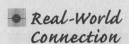

Real-World Connection

Albert Einstein's famous theory of relativity formula

$$E = mc^2$$

is an example of the scientific use of exponents.

SOLUTION STRATEGY

a. $7 \cdot 7 \cdot 7 = 7^3$ The base is 7 and the exponent is 3.

"seven to the third power" or "seven cubed"

b. $5 \cdot 5 \cdot 5 \cdot 5 \cdot 5 = 5^5$ The base is 5 and the exponent is 5.

"five to the fifth power"

c. $3 \cdot 3 = 3^2$ The base is 3 and the exponent is 2.

"three to the second power" or "three squared"

d. $2 \cdot 2 \cdot 8 \cdot 8 \cdot 8 = 2^2 \cdot 8^3$ The bases are 2 and 8 and the exponents are 2 and 3, respectively.

"two squared times eight cubed"

TRY-IT EXERCISE 1

Write each expression in exponential notation and in word form.

a. $9 \cdot 9 \cdot 9 \cdot 9$

b. $4 \cdot 4 \cdot 4 \cdot 4 \cdot 4 \cdot 4$

c. 6

d. $12 \cdot 12 \cdot 12 \cdot 16 \cdot 16$

Check your answers with the solutions in Appendix A. ∎

Objective 1.6B   **Evaluate an exponential expression**

Raising a number to the power of 1 or 0 yields some interesting results.

> **Raising a Number to the First Power**
>
> The result of raising a number to the first power is the number itself. That is, for any number a, we have the following.
>
> $$a^1 = a.$$

Learning Tip

The exponent 1 is usually not written. For example, 8^1 is written as simply 8.

Here are some examples.

$$16^1 = 16 \qquad 270^1 = 270 \qquad 1382^1 = 1382$$

> **Raising a Number to the Zero Power**
>
> The result of raising a nonzero number to the zero power is 1. That is, for any number a other than 0, we have the following.
>
> $$a^0 = 1$$

Some examples follow.

$$22^0 = 1 \qquad 659^0 = 1 \qquad 3489^0 = 1$$

EXAMPLE 2   Evaluate an expression using the exponential properties

Evaluate each exponential expression.

a. 4^0

b. 12^1

c. 8^0

d. 15^1

e. 1468^1

f. $17{,}000^0$

SOLUTION STRATEGY

a. $4^0 = 1$

b. $12^1 = 12$

c. $8^0 = 1$ These examples illustrate raising a number to the

d. $15^1 = 15$ first power and raising a number to the zero power.

e. $1468^1 = 1468$

f. $17{,}000^0 = 1$

TRY-IT EXERCISE 2

Evaluate each exponential expression.

a. 11^1

b. 26^1

c. 437^0

d. 10^0

e. 1899^1

f. $56{,}301^0$

Check your answers with the solutions in Appendix A. ■

The following steps are used to evaluate exponential expressions.

Steps for Evaluating Exponential Expressions

Step 1. Write the exponential expression as a product with the base appearing as a factor as many times as indicated by the exponent.

Step 2. Multiply.

EXAMPLE 3   Evaluate an exponential expression

Evaluate each exponential expression.

a. 3^4

b. 2^5

c. 10^3

SOLUTION STRATEGY

a. $3^4 = 3 \cdot 3 \cdot 3 \cdot 3 = 81$ Write the base 3 as a factor 4 times. Multiply.

b. $2^5 = 2 \cdot 2 \cdot 2 \cdot 2 \cdot 2 = 32$ Write the base 2 as a factor 5 times. Multiply.

c. $10^3 = 10 \cdot 10 \cdot 10 = 1000$ Write the base 10 as a factor 3 times. Multiply.

TRY-IT EXERCISE 3

Evaluate each exponential expression.

a. 4^3

b. 5^4

c. 10^7

Check your answers with the solutions in Appendix A. ■

> **Learning Tip**
>
> Many calculators have a
> $\boxed{y^x}$ or $\boxed{\wedge}$ key. To
> work example 2a using a
> calculator, use the follow-
> ing sequence.
>
>  = 81
>
> or
>
> $\boxed{3}$ $\boxed{\wedge}$ $\boxed{4}$ = 81

> **Learning Tip**
>
> In an exponential
> expression with base 10,
> the exponent tells us how
> many zeros there are in
> the number. For example,
> 10^3 has three zeros.
>
> $10^3 = 1000$.

Objective 1.6C   Use order of operations to simplify an expression

Sometimes numerical expressions require more than one operation. The result will differ depending on which operation is done first. For example, if we have the expression $6 + 5 \cdot 4$, how do we find the answer?

$$6 + 5 \cdot 4 \qquad\qquad 6 + 5 \cdot 4$$
$$11 \cdot 4 \qquad\qquad 6 + 20$$
$$44 \qquad\qquad\qquad 26$$

If we add first and then multiply, we get 44. If we multiply first and then add, we get 26. Which answer is correct? What happens if we also have parentheses or exponents in the expression?

To provide universal consistency in simplifying expressions, the mathematics community has agreed to a set of rules known as **order of operations**. These rules

order of operations
A set of rules that establishes the procedure for simplifying a mathematical expression.

establish the procedure for simplifying a mathematical expression. Today, these rules are even programmed into computers and most calculators.

According to the established rules for order of operations, the answer to the problem on page 66 is 26. Order of operations dictates that we multiply before we add. Here is the complete set of rules.

Order of Operations

Step 1. Perform all operations within grouping symbols: parentheses ( ), brackets [ ], and curly braces { }. When grouping symbols occur within grouping symbols, begin with the innermost grouping symbols.

Step 2. Evaluate all exponential expressions.

Step 3. Perform all multiplications and divisions as they appear in reading from left to right.

Step 4. Perform all additions and subtractions as they appear in reading from left to right.

● **Learning Tip**

Most calculators abide by the rules for order of operations. To check whether your calculator does so, consider the example $6 + 4 \cdot 5$. Enter the following in your calculator.

$$6 + 5 \times 4 =$$

If the result is 26, your calculator follows the rules set forth for order of operations. If the result is 44, your calculator does not follow the agreement, and you will have to enter the expression in the following way.

$$5 \times 4 + 6 =$$

EXAMPLE 4   Use order of operations to simplify an expression

Simplify each expression.

a. $46 \div 2 + 7$

b. $14 - 5 \div 5 \cdot 3 + 10$

c. $\dfrac{16 - 8}{10 - 6} + 25 \div 5$

SOLUTION STRATEGY

a. $46 \div 2 + 7$ There are no grouping symbols or exponents.

    $23\ \ + 7$ Divide. $46 \div 2 = 23$.

       30 Add. $23 + 7 = 30$.

b. $14 - 5 \div 5 \cdot 3 + 10$ There are no grouping symbols or exponents.

    $14 -\ \ 1\ \ \cdot 3 + 10$ Divide. $5 \div 5 = 1$.

    $14 -\ \ \ \ \ 3\ \ + 10$ Multiply. $1 \cdot 3 = 3$.

       $11\ \ \ \ \ \ \ \ \ \ + 10$ Subtract. $14 - 3 = 11$.

          21 Add. $11 + 10 = 21$.

c. $\dfrac{(16 - 8)}{(10 - 6)} + 25 \div 5$ When a division problem is written with a fraction bar, grouping symbols are understood to be around both the dividend and the divisor.

    $\dfrac{8}{4} + 25 \div 5$ Simplify the expressions in parentheses. $\dfrac{(16 - 8)}{(10 - 6)} = \dfrac{8}{4}$.

    $2 +\ \ \ \ \ 5$ Divide. $\dfrac{8}{4} = 2$. $25 \div 5 = 5$.

       7 Add. $2 + 5 = 7$.

TRY-IT EXERCISE 4

Simplify each expression.

a. $33 + 6 \div 2 - 7$

b. $6 \div 3 \cdot 7 - 6 + 3$

c. $20 \cdot 3 + 4 - \dfrac{112 \div 7}{21 - 17}$

Check your answers with the solutions in Appendix A. ■

EXAMPLE 5 **Use order of operations to simplify an expression**

Simplify each expression.

a. $6 \cdot 3 + (50 - 38) \div 6$

b. $9 + 6 - [(14 - 5) \div (2 + 1)]$

SOLUTION STRATEGY

a. $6 \cdot 3 + (50 - 38) \div 6$ Perform operations within parentheses first.

$6 \cdot 3 + \quad 12 \quad \div 6$ Subtract. $(50 - 38) = 12$.

$18 + \quad 12 \quad \div 6$ Multiply. $6 \cdot 3 = 18$.

$18 + \qquad\qquad 2$ Divide. $12 \div 6 = 2$.

20 Add. $18 + 2 = 20$.

b. $9 + 6 - [(14 - 5) \div (2 + 1)]$ Perform operations within grouping symbols first, beginning with the innermost parentheses.

$9 + 6 - [\quad 9 \quad \div \quad 3]$ Subtract. $(14 - 5) = 9$. Add. $(2 + 1) = 3$.

$9 + 6 - \qquad\quad 3$ Divide. $[9 \div 3] = 3$.

$15 - \qquad\qquad 3$ Add. $9 + 6 = 15$.

12 Subtract. $15 - 3 = 12$.

TRY-IT EXERCISE 5

Simplify each expression.

a. $(35 - 14) \div 7 + 4 \cdot 3$

b. $26 - [4 + (9 - 5)] \div 8$

Check your answers with the solutions in Appendix A. ■

EXAMPLE 6   Use order of operations to simplify an expression

Simplify each expression.

a. $43 + (8 - 5)^3 \div (34 - 5^2)$

b. $[(98 - 2) \div (3 \cdot 2^4)] + 6^2$

SOLUTION STRATEGY

a. $43 + (8 - 5)^3 \div (34 - 5^2)$ — Perform operations within parentheses first.

$43 + (8 - 5)^3 \div (34 - 25)$ — Evaluate the exponential expression within the parentheses. $5^2 = 25$.

$43 + (3)^3 \div 9$ — Subtract. $(8 - 5) = 3$. Subtract. $(34 - 25) = 9$.

$43 + 27 \div 9$ — Evaluate the exponential expression. $3^3 = 27$.

$43 + 3$ — Divide. $27 \div 9 = 3$.

46 — Add. $43 + 3 = 46$.

b. $[(98 - 2) \div (3 \cdot 2^4)] + 6^2$ — Perform operations within grouping symbols first, beginning with the innermost parentheses.

$[(98 - 2) \div (3 \cdot 16)] + 6^2$ — Evaluate the exponential expression. $2^4 = 16$.

$[96 \div 48] + 6^2$ — Subtract. $(98 - 2) = 96$. Multiply. $(3 \cdot 16) = 48$.

$2 + 6^2$ — Divide. $[96 \div 48] = 2$.

$2 + 36$ — Evaluate the exponential expression. $6^2 = 36$.

38 — Add. $2 + 36 = 38$.

TRY-IT EXERCISE 6

Simplify each expression.

a. $20 + 3(14 - 2^3) - (40 - 21)$

b. $40(3 - 8^0) \div [8 + (4 \cdot 3)]$

Check your answers with the solutions in Appendix A. ∎

Objective 1.6D   **Apply your knowledge**

THE AREA OF A SQUARE

One common application of exponents is finding the area of a square. If you have ever measured a room for carpeting or some other floor covering, you have already encountered the concept of area.

As we learned in Objective 1.4C, area is the measure associated with the interior of a closed, flat geometric figure. Measured in terms of "square units," area tells us the number of these units needed to cover the region. In Chapter 7, we will learn about the area of geometric shapes of all types, including triangles, rectangles, and circles. For now, let's see how the concept of area works for a square.

square
A rectangle with sides of equal length.

A **square** is a rectangle with sides of equal length. The area of a square is the length of a side squared. If A represents the area of a square and if s represents the length of one of its sides, then the following formula is used to calculate the area of a square.

$$A = s^2$$

Let's consider a square with sides of length 2 inches. The area of the square at the left is as follows.

$$A = (2 \text{ inches})^2 = 4 \text{ square inches}$$

EXAMPLE 7   Find the area of a square

A square room has a length of 9 feet.

a. What is the area of the room?

b. If ceramic tile costs $4 per square foot, how much will it cost to tile the room?

SOLUTION STRATEGY

a. $A = s^2$

$A = (9 \text{ feet})^2 = 81$ square feet

Because the room is in the shape of a square, we use the formula $A = s^2$ to calculate the area.

b. $\$4 \cdot 81 = \$321$

Multiply the cost per square foot by the number of square feet.

TRY-IT EXERCISE 7

You have just purchased a dining room table with a glass top. The table top is square, with sides that measure 48 inches.

a. What is the area of the table top?

b. If a protective pad for the glass top costs $5 per square foot, how much will the pad cost? Hint: One square foot equals 144 square inches.

Check your answers with the solutions in Appendix A. ■

SECTION 1.6 REVIEW EXERCISES

Concept Check

1. _____ notation is a shorthand way of expressing repeated multiplication.

2. In exponential notation, the factor that is repeatedly multiplied is called the _____.

3. In exponential notation, the _____ is the number that indicates how many times the base is used as a factor.

4. In the expression 10^6, the number 10 is known as the _____.

5. In the expression 4^3, the number 3 is known as the _____.

6. Write 5^4 in word form.

7. Write the number "15 cubed" using exponential notation.

8. The result of raising a number to the first power is the _____ itself.

9. The result of raising a nonzero number to the zero power is _____.

10. For each of the following, which operation is performed first according to order of operations?

    a. addition or division?

    b. evaluate exponential expressions or subtraction?

    c. multiplication or operations within parentheses?

Objective 1.6A	Read and write exponential notation

GUIDE PROBLEMS

11. $3 \cdot 3 \cdot 3 \cdot 3 = \underline{}^{4}$

12. $4 \cdot 4 = \underline{}^{2}$

13. $9 \cdot 9 \cdot 9 \cdot 9 \cdot 9 = 9{-}$

14. $12 \cdot 12 \cdot 12 = 12{-}$

15. $\underline{}\ \underline{}\ \underline{} = 8^{3}$

16. $\underline{}\ \underline{}\ \underline{}\ \underline{} = 15^{4}$

17. $5 \cdot 5 \cdot 3 \cdot 3 \cdot 3 = \underline{}^{2} \cdot \underline{}^{3}$

18. $6 \cdot 6 \cdot 6 \cdot 4 = 6{-} \cdot 4$

Write each expression in exponential notation and in word form.

19. $3 \cdot 3 \cdot 3$

20. $8 \cdot 8 \cdot 8 \cdot 8 \cdot 8$

21. $5 \cdot 5 \cdot 5 \cdot 5$

22. $4 \cdot 4 \cdot 4 \cdot 4 \cdot 4 \cdot 4 \cdot 4 \cdot 4$

23. 9

24. $12 \cdot 12$

25. $1 \cdot 1 \cdot 1$

26. $7 \cdot 7 \cdot 7 \cdot 7 \cdot 7 \cdot 7 \cdot 7$

Write each expression in exponential notation.

27. $4 \cdot 4 \cdot 4 \cdot 9 \cdot 9$

28. $2 \cdot 2 \cdot 2 \cdot 2 \cdot 6 \cdot 6 \cdot 6$

29. $3 \cdot 3 \cdot 4 \cdot 4 \cdot 4 \cdot 5$

30. $2 \cdot 5 \cdot 5 \cdot 6 \cdot 9 \cdot 9$

31. $5 \cdot 5 \cdot 8 \cdot 8 \cdot 8 \cdot 12$

32. $2 \cdot 2 \cdot 5 \cdot 7 \cdot 7 \cdot 7$

33. $2 \cdot 5 \cdot 5 \cdot 7 \cdot 9 \cdot 9 \cdot 9$

34. $3 \cdot 8 \cdot 20 \cdot 20$

Objective 1.6B	Evaluate an exponential notation

GUIDE PROBLEMS

35. $5{-} = 1$

36. $8^{1} = \underline{}$

37. $3{-} = 3 \cdot 3 \cdot 3 = \underline{}$

38. $2^{5} = \underline{} \cdot \underline{} \cdot \underline{} \cdot \underline{} \cdot \underline{} = \underline{}$

Evaluate each exponential expression.

39. 2^0 **40.** 11^0 **41.** 14^1 **42.** 21^1 **43.** 1^4 **44.** 1^{12}

45. 5^2 **46.** 6^2 **47.** 12^2 **48.** 7^2 **49.** 7^3 **50.** 5^4

51. 2^6 **52.** 2^7 **53.** 10^3 **54.** 6^3 **55.** 86^1 **56.** 350^1

57. 4^4 **58.** 3^5 **59.** 132^0 **60.** 2050^0 **61.** 15^2 **62.** 25^2

Objective 1.6C   **Use order of operations to simplify an expression**

GUIDE PROBLEMS

63. Simplify $67 + 3 \cdot 18$.
$67 + 3 \cdot 18$
$67 + \underline{}$

$\underline{}$

64. Simplify $(25 + 92) \div 13$.
$(25 + 92) \div 13$
$\underline{} \div 13$

$\underline{}$

65. Simplify $19 \cdot (4 + 21) - 2$.
$19 \cdot (4 + 21) - 2$
$19 \cdot \underline{} - 2$
$\underline{} - 2$

$\underline{}$

66. Simplify $3^4 - (3 \cdot 24)$.
$3^4 - (3 \cdot 24)$
$3^4 - \underline{}$
$\underline{} - \underline{}$

$\underline{}$

Simplify each expression.

67. $22 - (4 + 5)$ **68.** $(25 + 5) - 18$ **69.** $5 \cdot 4 + 2 \cdot 3$ **70.** $7 \cdot 3 + 4 \cdot 3$

71. $144 \div (100 - 76)$ **72.** $(18 + 32) \div 5$ **73.** $81 + 0 \div 3 + 9^2$ **74.** $8 + 0 \div 4 + 2^4$

75. $20 \div 5 + 3^3$ **76.** $4 + 10^2 \div 50$ **77.** $48 \div 2 - 11 \cdot 2$ **78.** $63 \div 9 \cdot 4 - 2 + 10$

79. $\dfrac{15 + 13}{9 - 2}$ **80.** $\dfrac{5 + 3^2 - 2^2}{10 \div 5}$ **81.** $42 + 3(6 - 2) + 5^2$ **82.** $18 \div 3^2 \cdot 5 - 2(8 - 3)$

83. $45 \cdot 2 - (6 + 1)^2$ **84.** $15 \cdot 9 - (4 + 1)^3$ **85.** $18 - 6 \cdot 2 + (2 + 4)^2 - 10$

86. $100 + (3 + 5)^2 - 50$ **87.** $2^4 \cdot 5 + 5 - 5^0$ **88.** $4^2 + 4^3 + 4^0 \cdot 16$

89. $23 + (15 - 12)^3 \div (134 - 5^3)$ **90.** $(15^2 + 15^2) \div 50$ **91.** $12 \div 4 \cdot 4[(6 - 2) + (5 - 3)]$

92. $[(5 - 3) \div 2] + 6 \cdot 3$ **93.** $\dfrac{3(14 + 3) - (20 - 5)}{6^2} + 1$ **94.** $\dfrac{16 \div 2^2}{17 - 15} + 88 \div (38 - 3^3)$

Objective 1.6D   Apply your knowledge

95. Find the area of a square serving dish, 15 inches on a side.

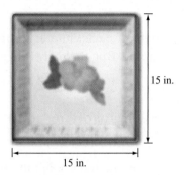

15 in.

15 in.

96. Find the area of a square plot of land, 12 miles on a side.

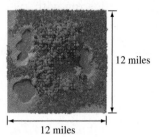

12 miles

12 miles

97. a. What is the area of a square living room floor with sides of length 20 feet?

 b. If WoodWorks, Inc. quotes a price of $9 per square foot for premium birchwood flooring, how much will it cost to install a wood floor in the living room?

 c. If Floormasters, Inc. quotes a cost of $7 per square foot for the same birchwood flooring, how much can be *saved* by taking the cheaper bid?

98. An office building has square glass windows, which measure 25 inches on each side.

 a. What is the area of each window?

 b. If the building has 60 of these windows, what is the total area of the windows?

 c. Given that each roll of window tinting material can cover 2500 square inches, how many rolls will be needed to tint all of the windows?

CUMULATIVE SKILLS REVIEW

1. Subtract 83,291 − 12,269. (1.3A)

2. Divide 1424 by 16. (1.5B)

3. Find the sum of 16,824 and 9542. (1.2B)

4. What is the average of 54, 36, and 24? (1.5C)

5. Multiply 1300 by 200. (1.4B)

6. How much is 4689 divided by 3? (1.5C)

7. Divide 0 ÷ 376. (1.5A)

8. Write one hundred sixty-two thousand, fifty-five in standard notation. (1.1B)

9. Belden Manufacturing employs 21 people in their warehouse. If they each received a $470 profit sharing bonus last year, what was the total amount of the bonuses? (1.4C)

10. Gifts Galore purchased 78 decorative oil lamps for a total of $3978. How much did they pay for each lamp? (1.5C)

1.7 SOLVING APPLICATION PROBLEMS

In mathematics, calculations are often part of real-world application problems dealing with everything from consumer and business math to advanced science and engineering.

Solving application problems is an important part of each chapter's subject matter and, as with other acquired skills, requires practice. But, the more you practice, the more at ease you will become.

| Objective 1.7A | **Solve an application problem involving addition, subtraction, multiplication, or division** |

In this section, we introduce the steps for solving application problems. Some problems require only one operation, while others require multiple operations.

Keep in mind that application problems contain key words and phrases that help you determine which operations to perform. We have already encountered many of these in the Apply Your Knowledge exercises in previous sections. Below is a list of several common ones. A list of key words and phrases indicating equality is also included.

KEY WORDS AND PHRASES FOR SOLVING APPLICATION PROBLEMS

ADDITION +	SUBTRACTION −	MULTIPLICATION ×	DIVISION ÷	EQUALS SIGN =
add	subtract	multiply	divide	equals
plus	minus	times	divided by	is
sum	difference	product	quotient	are
increased by	decreased by	product of	quotient of	yields
total of	take away	multiplied by	divided into	leaves
more than	reduced by	of	goes into	gives
greater than	deducted from	at	ratio of	makes
and	less than	twice	average of	results in
added to	fewer than	double	per	provides
gain of	subtracted from	triple	equally divided	produces

The following steps for solving application problems may be helpful to you as you proceed.

Steps for Solving Application Problems

Step 1. *Read and understand the problem.* You may have to read the problem several times. To visualize the problem, draw a picture if possible.

Step 2. *Take inventory.* Identify all of the parts of the situation. These can be dollars, people, boxes, dogs, miles, pies, anything! Separate the *knowns* (what is given) from the *unknowns* (what must be found).

Step 3. *Translate the problem.* Use the chart of key words and phrases to determine which operations are involved. Then, write the words of the problem statement in terms of numbers and mathematical operations.

Step 4. *Solve the problem.* Do the math. Express your answer using the appropriate units such as dollars, feet, pounds, miles, and so on.

Step 5. *Check the solution.*

EXAMPLE 1   Calculate the total amount spent on a shopping spree

On a recent trip to the mall you purchased a shirt for $34, a pair of slacks for $47, and a jacket for $102. You also had lunch for $6 and bought a CD for $13. What is the total amount of money you spent at the mall?

SOLUTION STRATEGY

Understand the situation.
We are given the dollar amounts for various purchases. We are asked to find a total.

shirt	$34
slacks	47
jacket	102
lunch	6
CD	+ 13
	$202

Take inventory.
The knowns are the purchase amounts.
The unknown is the total amount of the purchases.

Translate the problem.
The key word *total* indicates that we must add the amounts of the purchases.

shirt	$30
slacks	50
jacket	100
lunch	10
CD	+ 10
	$200

Solve the problem.
Add.

Check the solution.
To check, add again. Alternatively, estimate the solution by rounding the amount of each to the leftmost digit. Add. The estimate, $200, indicates that our solution is reasonable.

TRY-IT EXERCISE 1

At Office Warehouse you purchased a printer for $162, a black ink cartridge for $34, a color cartridge for $51, and a ream of paper for $5. What is the total amount of the purchase?

Check your answer with the solution in Appendix A. ■

EXAMPLE 2 **Calculate the difference between the heights of two buildings**

The John Hancock Building in Chicago stands 1127 feet tall, while Chicago's Sears Tower is 1451 feet tall. What is the difference between the heights of these buildings?

SOLUTION STRATEGY

Understand the situation.
We are given the heights of the John Hancock Building and the Sears Tower. We are asked to find the difference between their heights.

Take inventory.
The knowns are the heights of the buildings.
The unknown is the difference between their heights.

Translate the problem.
The key word *difference* indicates that we must subtract the heights of the buildings.

Sears Tower	1451
John Hancock	− 1127
	324

Solve the problem.
Subtract.

John Hancock	1127
difference	+ 324
	1451

Check the solution.
To check, add the height of the John Hancock Building to the difference. Since this sum is equal to the height of the Sears Tower, our answer checks.

TRY-IT EXERCISE 2

In January, American Mining produced 1474 tons of coal. In February, the company produced 188 fewer tons. How many tons were produced in February?

Check your answer with the solution in Appendix A. ∎

EXAMPLE 3 **Calculate total budget cost**

Marshall Industries purchased 31 computers loaded with special software for the accounting department at a cost of $2900 each. What is the total cost of the computers?

SOLUTION STRATEGY

Understand the situation.
We are given the fact that a company purchased a number of computers with special software at a given price. We are asked to find the total cost of the computers.

Take inventory.
The knowns are the number of computers and the cost of each computer.
The unknown is the total cost.

$$\begin{array}{r} \$2900 \\ \times\ 31 \\ \hline \$89{,}900 \end{array}$$

Translate the problem.
The key word *at* indicates that we must multiply the number of computers by the cost of each computer.

Solve the problem.
Multiply.

$$\begin{array}{r} \$3000 \\ \times\ 30 \\ \hline \$90{,}000 \end{array}$$

Check the solution.
To check, we can estimate the solution by rounding the cost of each computer and the total number of computers to the leftmost digit. Multiply. The estimate, $90,000, is close to our product, $89,900, indicating that our solution is reasonable.

TRY-IT EXERCISE 3

Before the beginning of the fall term, a college bookstore purchased 540 algebra textbooks from the publishing company for $89 each. What is the total amount of the textbook purchase?

Check your answer with the solution in Appendix A. ■

EXAMPLE 4   Devise a seating plan

You are in charge of setting up the seating plan for an outdoor concert at your school. A total of 1650 tickets have been sold. Your plan is to have 75 equal rows of seats. How many seats will be needed per row to accommodate the audience?

SOLUTION STRATEGY

Understand the situation.
We are given the fact that the total number of seats must be distributed evenly among a given number of rows. We are asked for the number of seats per row.

Take inventory.
The knowns are the total number of seats and the number of rows.

The unknown is the number of seats per row.

$$\begin{array}{r} 22 \\ 75{\overline{)1650}} \\ 150 \\ \hline 150 \\ 150 \\ \hline 0 \end{array}$$

Translate the problem.
The key word *per* indicates that we must divide the total number of seats by the number of rows.

Solve the problem.
Divide.

$$\begin{array}{r} 22 \\ \times\ 75 \\ \hline 110 \\ 1540 \\ \hline 1650 \end{array}$$

Check the solution.
To check, multiply the total number of rows by the quotient. Since this product equals the total number of seats, our solution checks.

TRY-IT EXERCISE 4

A company has allocated $300,000 to be evenly divided among 8 colleges for student scholarships. How much will each school receive?

Check your answer with the solution in Appendix A. ■

Objective 1.7B   **Solve an application problem involving more than one operation**

Frequently, application problems require more than one operation. The following example demonstrates such a problem.

EXAMPLE 5   **Determine weight of a container**

A cargo ship weighs 130 tons empty, and 394 tons when loaded with 22 equal-weight freight containers. How much does each container weigh?

SOLUTION STRATEGY

Understand the situation.
This problem has two parts.

Part 1: Find the total weight of the containers.

Part 2: Find the weight of each container.

We shall go through each step of the problem solving process for each part.

Part 1

Take inventory.
The knowns are the weight of the empty ship and the weight of the loaded ship.
The unknown is the weight of the containers.

Translate the problem.
Find the total weight of the containers by subtracting the weight of the empty ship from the weight of the loaded ship.

loaded ship	394
empty ship	− 130
	264

The total weight of the containers is 264 tons.

Solve the problem.
Subtract.

empty ship	130
difference	+ 264
	394

Check the solution.
Check by adding the weight of the empty ship to the difference. Since this sum is equal to the weight of the loaded ship, our answer checks.

Part 2

Take inventory.
The knowns are the total weight of the containers, 264 tons, and the number of containers, 22.
The unknown is the weight of each individual container.

$$\begin{array}{r} 12 \\ 22\overline{)264} \\ 22 \\ \hline 44 \\ 44 \\ \hline 0 \end{array}$$

Translate the problem.
Find the weight of each container by dividing the total weight of the containers by the number of containers.

Each container weighs 12 tons.

Solve the problem.
Divide.

$$
\begin{array}{r}
12 \\
\times\ 22 \\
\hline
24 \\
240 \\
\hline
264
\end{array}
$$

Check the solution.

To check, multiply the weight of each container by the total number of containers. Since this product equals the weight of the containers, our answer checks.

TRY-IT EXERCISE 5

First Alert Security Corporation charges $16 per hour for security guards. The guards are paid $11 per hour. Last week First Alert employed 25 guards, each working a 30-hour week. How much profit did the company make?

Check your answer with the solution in Appendix A. ■

SECTION 1.7 REVIEW EXERCISES

Concept Check

1. The keyword *total of* is used to indicate the operation of _____ in an application problem.

2. The phrase *decreased by* indicates the operation of _____.

3. *Of* and *at* are words used to indicate _____.

4. *Quotient* and *per* are used to indicate _____.

5. The words *is* and *are* indicate _____.

6. List the steps for solving application problems.

Objective 1.7A   Solve an application problem involving addition, subtraction, multiplication, or division

7. By adding a turbocharger, a race car's 460 horsepower engine was increased by 115 horsepower. What is the upgraded horsepower of the engine?

8. Creswell Corporation had 1342 employees last year. Due to an increase in business this year, they hired 325 new employees. How many people work for the company now?

9. A compact flash memory card for a digital camera has 512 megabytes of memory. If each photo requires 4 megabytes, how many photos can the card hold?

10. How many pills are in a prescription that calls for 2 tablets, 4 times a day, for 12 days?

11. Jan pays $385 per month in rent. How much does she pay in a year?

12. Bob paid $15,493 for a boat and $1322 for the trailer. How much did he pay for the boat and trailer?

13. Julie makes custom jewelry in her spare time. Last month she made 35 bracelets, 19 necklaces, and 12 anklets.

   a. How many total pieces of jewelry did she make?

   b. If she sold each piece for $30, how much money did she make last month?

   c. At the monthly rate from part b, how much will she make in a year?

15. You are interested in purchasing one of two pieces of property. The first is a 1350 square foot townhouse priced at $189,000. The second is a 950 square foot apartment priced at $166,250. Calculate the price per square foot for each to see which property is the best value, that is, determine which property has the lower price per square foot.

14. Max's Redland Farms produces 225 pounds of strawberries per acre each growing season.

   a. If he has 20 acres of strawberries, how many pounds can Max produce?

   b. If he sells the strawberries at a local farmer's market for $3 per pound, how much money does he make?

   c. If there are 3 growing seasons per year, how much does Max make in a year?

16. A delivery truck has a range of 660 miles on a tank of gasoline. If the tank holds 55 gallons of gasoline, how many miles can the truck travel on one gallon?

17. In 2003, the planet Mars was only 34,646,419 miles from Earth. That is the closest it has been in almost 60,000 years.

   a. Round this distance to the nearest ten thousand miles.

   b. If the "usual distance" from the Earth to Mars is approximately 60,000,000 miles, how much closer was it in 2003? (Use your rounded answer from part a for this calculation.)

18. The Sweet Tooth Ice Cream Company sold 495, 239, 290, 509, and 679 pints of ice cream over the past 5 days.

   a. Round each number to the nearest hundred to estimate the number of pints sold.

   b. What was the actual number of pints sold?

Use the table *Counting Calories* for exercises 19–22.

Counting Calories
The number of calories a 150-pound person would burn in 30 minutes of the following activities.

ACTIVITY	CALORIES
Jogging	338
Stair climbing	306
Tennis	275
Carrying a heavy load (e.g., bricks)	273
Weightlifting	234
Bicycling (flat surface)	221
Shoveling snow (manually)	205
Aerobics, low impact	171
Gardening	170
Mowing lawn (push power mower)	154
Ballroom dancing	153
Walking (briskly)	150

19. How many more calories are burned every 30 minutes playing tennis than gardening?

20. If a person does aerobics 1 hour per week, how many calories will be burned in a year?

21. If a person uses a stair climber 2 hours per week and does weightlifting 4 hours per week, how many calories will be burned in a one-week period?

22. How many more calories will be burned jogging 3 hours per week than walking briskly 4 hours per week?

Objective 1.7B   Solve an application problem that involves more than one operation

23. The IT department of Compton Corporation purchased 26 computers for $1590 each and 6 computers for $1850 each. What is the total amount of the purchase?

24. Seven friends ate dinner at the Lakeshore Restaurant. If the bill came to $157 and a $25 tip was added, how much should each person pay in order to split the bill evenly?

25. An inkjet printer can print 21 pages per minute in black and white and 8 pages per minute in color. What is the total time it will take to print a report containing 252 black and white pages and 104 color pages?

26. Carla started the month with a $391 balance on her Visa credit card. During the month she made purchases of $39, $144, $219, and $78. When the new bill arrived, she made a payment of $550. What is her new balance on the account?

27. The average cost per night for a room at the Ocean V Hotel on South Beach is currently $495. If this cost has tripled in the past 4 years, what is the difference between a 5-night stay now compared to 4 years ago?

28. Expenses at Galaxy Corporation for the month of June were $15,639 for salaries, $1960 for rent, $909 for electricity, $548 for insurance, $2300 for advertising, and $2150 for miscellaneous expenses. If the June expenses are representative of a typical month, what are the total expenses at Galaxy per year?

Photo by Robert Brechner

29. A roll of dental floss is 16 yards long. If the average length of floss people need per use is 16 inches, how many uses can they get from a roll? (There are 3 feet in one yard and 12 inches in one foot.)

30. James began a motorcycle trip with a full tank of gas. At the beginning of the trip, the odometer reading was 5339 miles and at the end it was 5689. If he used a total of 14 gallons of gasoline on the trip, how many miles per gallon did he get?

31. Last week, the Harper College bookstore sold 463 algebra textbooks at $85 each, 328 English textbooks at $67 each, and 139 economics textbooks at $45 each. What is the bookstore's total revenue from the sale of these books?

32. In a Miami Heat basketball game, Duane Wade scored 11 points in the first half and twice as many points in the second half. How many total points did he score in the game?

33. The town in which Toby lives increased in population from 18,408 to 35,418 in a 5-year period. What was the average increase per year?

34. Stan bowled three games last night. His scores were 165, 188, and 214. What was his average score for the three games?

35. A ferry from Vancouver to Seattle carries buses and cars. For loading purposes, buses are estimated to weigh 15,000 pounds each and cars are estimated at 2500 pounds each. By law, the maximum weight limit of cars and buses on ferries this size is 300,000 pounds.

a. If 12 buses and 40 cars are scheduled for next Thursday, will the total weight of this load be within the limits?

b. If the load is within limits, how many more vehicles could be accommodated? If it is not within the limits, how many vehicles should be eliminated?

36. The Canmore Mining Company produces 24 tons of coal in a 6-hour shift. The mine operates continuously— 4 shifts per day, 7 days per week.

a. How many tons of coal can be extracted in 9 weeks?

b. How many tons can be extracted in a year?

Use the following advertisement for exercises 37–39.

YOUR NEW FORD	WAS	SALE PRICE	LEASE PAYMENT
NEW FORD FOCUS 4-DOOR	~~$15,165~~	$11,495	$165 PER MO. 36 MO. LEASE
NEW F-150 SUPERCAB XLT	~~$27,120~~	$18,449	$219 PER MO. 36 MO. LEASE
NEW EXPLORER 4-DR.	~~$26,830~~	$19,699	$259 PER MO. 24 MO. LEASE
NEW SUPERCREW XLT	~~$28,965~~	$21,719	$247 PER MO. 36 MO. LEASE
NEW EXPEDITION XLT	~~$32,315~~	$24,496	$263 PER MO. 24 MO. LEASE

37. How much more will you pay on a lease over a 36-month period if you choose a Supercrew XLT over an F-150 Supercab XLT?

38. How much less will you pay on a lease over a 36-month period if you choose a Focus over an Explorer?

39. How much will you save by purchasing a Ford Focus at the sale price?

40. If you purchase three Ford Explorers and four Expeditions for your company, how much will you save by purchasing these cars at the advertised sale price over the original price?

CUMULATIVE SKILLS REVIEW

1. Divide $\dfrac{489}{3}$. (1.5B)

2. Simplify $3 \cdot 9^2 + \dfrac{[2(18 - 3)]^2}{9}$. (1.6C)

3. What is 59 subtracted from 83? (1.3B)

4. Write $6 \cdot 6 \cdot 7 \cdot 7 \cdot 7$ in exponential notation. (1.6A)

5. What is 982 more than 1563? (1.2C)

6. Identify the place value of the 4 in 24,339. (1.1A)

7. Simplify $48 + (3 + 2)^3$. (1.6C)

8. What is the area of a square with sides measuring 12 feet? (1.6D)

9. Write 1549 in expanded notation. (1.1C)

10. By how much is 542 less than 932? (1.3B)

10-MINUTE CHAPTER REVIEW

1.1 Understanding the Basics of Whole Numbers

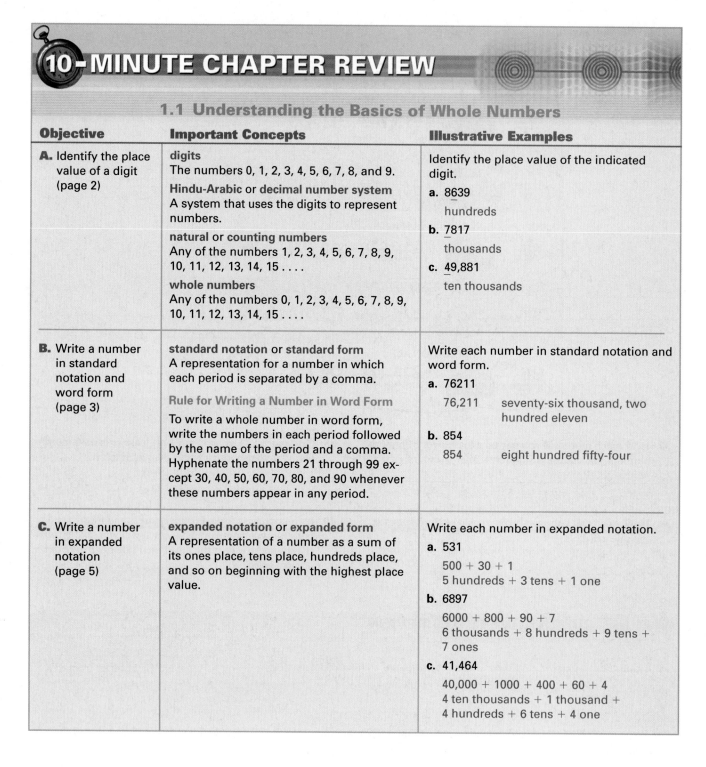

Objective	Important Concepts	Illustrative Examples
A. Identify the place value of a digit (page 2)	**digits** The numbers 0, 1, 2, 3, 4, 5, 6, 7, 8, and 9. **Hindu-Arabic** or **decimal number system** A system that uses the digits to represent numbers. **natural** or **counting numbers** Any of the numbers 1, 2, 3, 4, 5, 6, 7, 8, 9, 10, 11, 12, 13, 14, 15 . . . . **whole numbers** Any of the numbers 0, 1, 2, 3, 4, 5, 6, 7, 8, 9, 10, 11, 12, 13, 14, 15	Identify the place value of the indicated digit. **a.** 8639 hundreds **b.** 7817 thousands **c.** 49,881 ten thousands
B. Write a number in standard notation and word form (page 3)	**standard notation** or **standard form** A representation for a number in which each period is separated by a comma. **Rule for Writing a Number in Word Form** To write a whole number in word form, write the numbers in each period followed by the name of the period and a comma. Hyphenate the numbers 21 through 99 except 30, 40, 50, 60, 70, 80, and 90 whenever these numbers appear in any period.	Write each number in standard notation and word form. **a.** 76211 76,211 seventy-six thousand, two hundred eleven **b.** 854 854 eight hundred fifty-four
C. Write a number in expanded notation (page 5)	**expanded notation** or **expanded form** A representation of a number as a sum of its ones place, tens place, hundreds place, and so on beginning with the highest place value.	Write each number in expanded notation. **a.** 531 500 + 30 + 1 5 hundreds + 3 tens + 1 one **b.** 6897 6000 + 800 + 90 + 7 6 thousands + 8 hundreds + 9 tens + 7 ones **c.** 41,464 40,000 + 1000 + 400 + 60 + 4 4 ten thousands + 1 thousand + 4 hundreds + 6 tens + 4 one

D. Round a number to a specified place value (page 5)	**rounded number** An approximation of an exact number. Steps for Rounding Numbers to a Specified Place Value **Step 1.** Identify the place value to which the number is to be rounded. **Step 2.** If the digit to the right of the specified place value is 4 or less, the digit in the specified place value remains the same. If the digit to the right of the specified place value is 5 or more, increase the digit in the specified place value by one. **Step 3.** Change the digit in each place after the specified place value to zero.	Round each number to the specified place value. **a.** 6777 to the nearest hundreds 6800 **b.** 1011 to the nearest thousands 1000 **c.** 17,981 to the leftmost place value 20,000
E. Apply your knowledge (page 7)	**table** A collection of data arranged in rows and columns for ease of reference. Rule for Reading a Table Scan the titles of the columns to find the category in question. Then, scan down the column to find the row containing the information being sought.	**BOSTON RED SOX vs ATLANTA BRAVES** **AVERAGE ATTENDANCE PER GAME** | YEAR	BOSTON	ATLANTA
2003	33,631	30,393
2004	35,028	29,399
2005	35,166	31,519
2006	36,182	31,869 | **a.** What was the average attendance for the Atlanta Braves in 2004? 29,399 **b.** Rounded to the nearest thousand, what was the average attendance for the Boston Red Sox in 2006? 36,000

1.2 Adding Whole Numbers

Objective	Important Concepts	Illustrative Examples
A. Use the addition properties (page 14)	**addition** The mathematical process of combining two or more numbers to find the total. **addends** Numbers that are added together. **sum** The result of adding numbers. Addition Property of Zero Adding 0 to any number results in a sum equal to the original number. That is, for any number a, we have the following. $$a + 0 = a \quad \text{and} \quad 0 + a = a$$	**a.** Add. $3 + 0$. $3 + 0 = 3$

Commutative Property of Addition

Changing the order of the addends does not change the sum. That is, for any numbers a and b, we have the following.

$$a + b = b + a$$

b. Show that $8 + 2 = 2 + 8$.

$$8 + 2 = 2 + 8$$
$$10 = 10$$

Associative Property of Addition

Changing the grouping of addends does not change the sum. That is, for any numbers a, b, and c, we have the following.

$$(a + b) + c = a + (b + c)$$

c. Show that $(9 + 2) + 1 = 9 + (2 + 1)$.

$$(9 + 2) + 1 = 9 + (2 + 1)$$
$$11 + 1 = 9 + 3$$
$$12 = 12$$

B. Add whole numbers (page 15)

Steps for Adding Whole Numbers

Step 1. Write the digits of the addends in columns with the place values (ones, tens, hundreds, etc.) vertically aligned.

Step 2. Beginning with the ones column, add the digits in each column. If the sum of any column is a two-digit number, write the rightmost digit under the horizontal bar and carry the leftmost digit to the top of the next column to the left.

Step 3. Repeat this process until you reach the leftmost column. For that column, write the sum under the horizontal bar.

Add.

a. $8280 + 847$

$$\begin{array}{r} \overset{11}{8280} \\ +847 \\ \hline 9127 \end{array}$$

b. $5789 + 152$

$$\begin{array}{r} \overset{11}{5789} \\ +152 \\ \hline 5941 \end{array}$$

c. $3844 + 1450 + 1263$

$$\begin{array}{r} \overset{11}{3844} \\ 1450 \\ +1263 \\ \hline 6557 \end{array}$$

C. Apply your knowledge (page 18)

polygon
A closed, flat geometric figure in which all sides are line segments.

perimeter of a polygon
The sum of the lengths of its sides.

Find the perimeter of the triangle.

5 in.   6 in.   4 in.

$$4 \text{ in.} + 5 \text{ in.} + 6 \text{ in.} = 15 \text{ in.}$$

1.3 Subtracting Whole Numbers

Objective	Important Concepts	Illustrative Examples
A. Subtract whole numbers (page 26)	**subtraction** The mathematical process of taking away or deducting an amount from a given number. **minuend** The number from which another number is subtracted. **subtrahend** The number that is subtracted. **difference** The result of subtracting numbers.	Subtract. **a.** $6285 - 890$ $\begin{array}{r} 6285 \\ -890 \\ \hline 5395 \end{array}$ **b.** $3164 - 282$ $\begin{array}{r} 3164 \\ -282 \\ \hline 2882 \end{array}$

Steps for Subtracting Whole Numbers

Step 1. Write the digits of the minuend and subtrahend in columns with the place values vertically aligned.

Step 2. Beginning with the ones column, subtract the digits in each column. If the digits in a column cannot be subtracted to produce a whole number, borrow from the column to the left.

Step 3. Continue until you reach the last column on the left. For that column, write the difference under the horizontal bar.

c. $79{,}412 - 5745$

$$
\begin{array}{r}
79{,}412 \\
-\ \ 5{,}745 \\
\hline
73{,}667
\end{array}
$$

B. Apply your knowledge (page 29)

bar graph
A graphical representation of quantities using horizontal or vertical bars.

Below is a bar graph of Katie and Phillip's exercise schedule expressed in minutes and covering a three-week period.

a. How many minutes did Katie exercise during week 1?

80 minutes

b. During which week did Katie and Phillip exercise the same amount of time?

Week 2

c. In week 3, how many more minutes did Phillip exercise than Katie?

80 minutes $-$ 40 minutes $=$ 40 minutes

1.4 Multiplying Whole Numbers

Objective	Important Concepts	Illustrative Examples
A. Use the multiplication properties (page 36)	**multiplication** The mathematical process of repeated addition of a value a specified number of times. **factors** Numbers that are multiplied together. **product** The result of multiplying numbers. **Multiplication Property of Zero** The product of any number and 0 is 0. That is, for any real number a, we have the following. $$a \cdot 0 = 0 \cdot a = 0$$	**a.** Multiply $8 \cdot 0$. $8 \cdot 0 = 0$ **b.** Multiply $0 \cdot 6$. $0 \cdot 6 = 0$

Multiplication Property of One

The product of any number and 1 is the number itself. That is, for any real number a, we have the following.

$$a \cdot 1 = 1 \cdot a = a$$

Commutative Property of Multiplication

Changing the order of the factors does not change the product. That is, for any numbers a and b, we have the following.

$$a \cdot b = b \cdot a$$

Associative Property of Multiplication

Changing the grouping of the factors does not change the product. That is, for any numbers a, b, and c, we have the following.

$$(a \cdot b) \cdot c = a \cdot (b \cdot c)$$

Distributive Property of Multiplication over Addition or Subtraction

Multiplication distributes over addition and subtraction. That is, for any numbers a, b, and c, we have the following.

$$a(b + c) = ab + ac \text{ and } a(b - c) = ab - ac$$
$$(b + c)a = ba + ca \text{ and } (b - c)a = ba - ca$$

c. Multiply $36 \cdot 1$.
$$36 \cdot 1 = 36$$

d. Multiply $1 \cdot 92$.
$$1 \cdot 92 = 92$$

e. Show that $9 \cdot 4 = 4 \cdot 9$.
$$9 \cdot 4 = 4 \cdot 9$$
$$36 = 36$$

f. Show that $6(3 \cdot 8) = (6 \cdot 3) 8$.
$$6(3 \cdot 8) = (6 \cdot 3) 8$$
$$6(24) = 18(8)$$
$$144 = 144$$

g. Show that $8(4 + 9) = 8 \cdot 4 + 8 \cdot 9$.
$$8(4 + 9) = 8 \cdot 4 + 8 \cdot 9$$
$$8(13) = 32 + 72$$
$$104 = 104$$

h. Show that $3(6 - 3) = 3 \cdot 6 - 3 \cdot 3$.
$$3(6 - 3) = 3 \cdot 6 - 3 \cdot 3$$
$$3(3) = 18 - 9$$
$$9 = 9$$

B. Multiply whole numbers (page 39)

Product involving a single-digit whole number:

$$\begin{array}{r} {\scriptstyle 2} \\ 49 \\ \times\ 3 \\ \hline 7 \end{array}$$

$3 \cdot 9 = 27$.
Write 7 in the ones column.
Carry 2 to top of tens column.

$$\begin{array}{r} {\scriptstyle 2} \\ 49 \\ \times\ 3 \\ \hline 147 \end{array}$$

$3 \cdot 4 + 2 = 12 + 2 = 14$
Write 14 to the left of 7.

Product involving larger whole numbers:

$$\begin{array}{r} {\scriptstyle 2} \\ 49 \\ \times\ 13 \\ \hline 147 \end{array}$$

$3 \cdot 49 = 147$.
147 is a *partial product*.

$$\begin{array}{r} 49 \\ \times\ 13 \\ \hline 147 \\ 0 \end{array}$$

Below the partial product, write 0 in the ones column. This is a *placeholder*.

$$\begin{array}{r} 49 \\ \times\ 13 \\ \hline 147 \\ 490 \end{array}$$

$1 \cdot 49 = 49$.
Write 49 to the left of the placeholder.

Multiply.

a. $94 \cdot 5$

$$\begin{array}{r} 94 \\ \times\ 5 \\ \hline 470 \end{array}$$

b. 380×88

$$\begin{array}{r} 380 \\ \times\ 88 \\ \hline 3040 \\ 30400 \\ \hline 33{,}440 \end{array}$$

c. $43(9886)$

$$\begin{array}{r} 9886 \\ \times\ 43 \\ \hline 29658 \\ 395440 \\ \hline 425{,}098 \end{array}$$

$$\begin{array}{r} 49 \\ \times\ 13 \\ \hline 147 \\ +\ 490 \\ \hline 637 \end{array}$$ Add the partial products.

C. Apply your knowledge (page 43)	**area** The measure associated with the interior of closed, flat geometric figure. Area is measured in square units. Area of a rectangle is given by the formula $$A = l \cdot w.$$	The rectangular floor of a concert arena is 300 feet long and 225 feet wide. What is the area of the floor? $$\begin{array}{r} 300 \\ \times\ 225 \\ \hline 67{,}500 \end{array}$$ The area of the arena floor is 67,500 square feet.

1.5 Dividing Whole Numbers

Objective	Important Concepts	Illustrative Examples
A. Use the division properties (page 51)	**division** The mathematical process of repeated subtraction of a value. **dividend** The number being divided. **divisor** The number by which the dividend is divided. **quotient** The result of dividing numbers. **Dividing a Number by One** The quotient of any number and 1 is the number itself. That is, for any number a, we have the following. $$a \div 1 = a$$ **Dividing a Number by Itself** The quotient of any nonzero number and itself is 1. That is, for any nonzero number a, we have the following. $$a \div a = 1$$ **Dividing Zero by a Nonzero Number** The quotient of zero and any nonzero number is zero. That is, for any nonzero number a, we have the following. $$0 \div a = 0 \quad \text{where} \quad a \neq 0$$ **Dividing a Number by Zero** Division by zero is undefined. That is, we can not divide by zero. That is, for any number a, we have the following. $$a \div 0 \text{ is undefined.}$$	**a.** Divide. $4 \div 1$ $$4 \div 1 = 4$$ **b.** Divide. $7 \div 7$ $$7 \div 7 = 1$$ **c.** Divide. $0 \div 5$ $$0 \div 5 = 0$$ **d.** Divide. $12 \div 0$ $$12 \div 0 \text{ undefined}$$

B. Divide whole numbers (page 53)	**remainder**
	The number that remains after division is complete.
	
	Quotient of whole numbers:
	
	$\begin{array}{r} 141 \\ 4\overline{)564} \\ \underline{-4} \\ 16 \\ \underline{-16} \\ 04 \\ \underline{-4} \\ 0 \end{array}$ $1 \cdot 4 = 4.$
	   Subtract. Bring down the 6.
	   $4 \cdot 4 = 16.$
	   Subtract. Bring down the 4.
	   $1 \cdot 4 = 4.$
	   Subtract.
		Divide.
		a. $5\overline{)60}$
		
		$\begin{array}{r} 12 \\ 5\overline{)60} \\ \underline{-5} \\ 10 \\ \underline{-10} \\ 0 \end{array}$
		
		b. $304 \div 9$
		
		$\begin{array}{r} 33\,R\,7 \\ 9\overline{)304} \\ \underline{-27} \\ 34 \\ \underline{-27} \\ 7 \end{array}$

	$\begin{array}{r} 83\,R\,21 \\ 26\overline{)2179} \\ \underline{-208} \\ 99 \\ \underline{-78} \\ 21 \end{array}$ $8 \cdot 26 = 208.$
	   Subtract. Bring down the 9.
	   $3 \cdot 26 = 78.$
	   Subtract. The remainder is 21.	

C. Apply your knowledge (page 58)	**average** or **arithmetic mean** The value obtained by dividing the sum of all the values in a data set by the number of values in the set. **Steps for Calculating an Average** **Step 1.** Find the sum of all the values in a data set. **Step 2.** Divide the sum in step 1 by the number of values in the set. $$\text{Average} = \frac{\text{Sum of values}}{\text{Number of values}}$$	Sarah has just finished training for a race. During a three-week period, she ran 16 miles the first week, 18 miles the second week, and 23 miles the third week. What is Sarah's average mileage per each week of the three-week period? $$\text{Average} = \frac{16 + 18 + 23}{3} = \frac{57}{3} = 19 \text{ miles}$$

1.6 Evaluating Exponential Expressions and Applying Order of Operations

Objective	Important Concepts	Illustrative Examples

A. Read and write numbers in exponential notation (page 63)	**exponential notation**
	A shorthand way of expressing repeated multiplication.
	
	base
	In exponential notation, the factor that is multiplied repeatedly.
	
	exponent or **power**
	In exponential notation, the number that indicates how many times the base is used as a factor.
		Write each expression in exponential notation and in word form.
		a. $8 \cdot 8 \cdot 8$
		   8^3, eight to the third power
		b. $3 \cdot 3 \cdot 3 \cdot 3 \cdot 3 \cdot 3$
		   3^6, three to the sixth power
		c. $2 \cdot 2 \cdot 2 \cdot 2 \cdot 2$
		   2^5, two to the fifth power

B. Evaluate an exponential expression (page 64)	**Raising a Number to the First Power** The result of raising a number to the first power is the number itself. That is, for any number a, we have the following. $$a^1 = a.$$ **Raising a Number to the Zero Power** The result of raising a nonzero number to the zero power is 1. That is, for any number a other than 0, we have the following. $$a^0 = 1$$ **Steps for Evaluating Exponential Expressions** **Step 1.** Write the exponential expression as a product with the base appearing as a factor as many times as indicated by the exponent. **Step 2.** Multiply.	Examples of the Exponential Properties **a.** Evaluate. 452^1 $452^1 = 452$ **b.** Evaluate 59^0 $59^0 = 1$ Evaluate each exponential expression. **a.** 3^8 $3 \cdot 3 \cdot 3 \cdot 3 \cdot 3 \cdot 3 \cdot 3 \cdot 3 = 6561$ **b.** 7^4 $7 \cdot 7 \cdot 7 \cdot 7 = 2401$
C. Use the order of operations to simplify an expression (page 66)	**order of operations** A set of rules that establishes the procedure for simplifying a mathematical expression. **Order of Operations** **Step 1.** Perform all operations within grouping symbols: parentheses ( ), brackets [ ], and curly braces { }. When grouping symbols occur within grouping symbols, begin with the innermost grouping symbols. **Step 2.** Evaluate all exponential expressions **Step 3.** Perform all multiplications and divisions as they appear in reading from left to right. **Step 4.** Perform all additions and subtractions as they appear in reading from left to right.	Simplify each expression. **a.** $37 + (5 \cdot 2^3) \div 10 - 25$ $37 + (5 \cdot 8) \div 10 - 25$ $37 + 40 \div 10 - 25$ $37 + 4 - 25$ $41 - 25$ 16 **b.** $[27 \div 9 - 2] + 65 \cdot 2$ $[3 - 2] + 65 \cdot 2$ $1 + 65 \cdot 2$ $1 + 130$ 131
D. Apply your knowledge (page 69)	**square** A rectangle that has all four sides of equal length. Area of a rectangle is given by the formula $$A = s^2$$	What is the area of a square wall that has sides measuring 15 feet each? 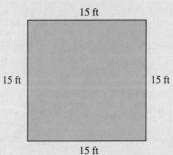 $A = (15 \text{ feet})^2 = 225$ square feet

Section 1.7 Solving Application Problems

Objective	Important Concepts	Illustrative Examples

A. Solve an application problem involving addition, subtraction, multiplication, or division (page 74)	**Steps for Solving Application Problems**
	
	Step 1. *Read and understand the problem.* You may have to read the problem several times. To visualize the problem, draw a picture if possible.
	
	Step 2. *Take inventory.* Identify all of the parts of the situation. These can be dollars, people, boxes, dogs, miles, pies, anything! Separate the *knowns* (what is given) from the *unknowns* (what must be found).
	
	Step 3. *Translate the problem.* Use the chart of key words and phrases to determine which operations are involved. Then, write the words of the problem statement in terms of numbers and mathematical operations.
	
	Step 4. *Solve the problem.* Do the math. Express your answer using the appropriate units such as dollars, feet, pounds, miles, and so on.
	
	Step 5. *Check the solution.*
		a. Jenny and Dave took a road trip last week. They drove 135 miles on Monday, 151 miles on Tuesday, and 222 miles on Wednesday. What was the total number of miles they drove?
		
		Monday 135
		Tuesday 151
		Wednesday + 222
		————————
		                  508 miles
		
		Check the solution for reasonableness by rounding the miles traveled each day to the leftmost digit.
		
		Monday 100
		Tuesday 200
		Wednesday + 200
		————————
		                  500
		
		b. Nancy's annual income last year was $35,000. This year she was promoted and received a raise. Now she is making $45,500. How much more is Nancy making this year?
		
		this year $45,500
		last year − 35,000
		————————
		              $10,500
		
		Check the solution by adding.
		
		        $10,500
		      + 35,000
		      ————————
		        $45,500

B. Solve an application problem involving more than one operation (page 78)	On average, Johnson Farm Equipment sells three $5000 tractors each week.
	
	a. What are the total annual sales of tractors?
	
	$5000 $15,000
	× 3 × 52
	———————— ————————
	$15,000 per week $780,000 annual sales
	
	b. What are the average monthly tractor sales?
	
	$\overline{\$65,000}$
	$12)\overline{780,000}$
	$\underline{-72}$
	   60
	$\underline{-60}$
	    0	

Numerical Facts of Life

The Personal Balance Sheet

Personal financial statements are an important indicator of your personal financial position. A personal balance sheet provides a "financial picture" of how much wealth you have accumulated as of a certain date. It specifically lists your *assets*, what you own, and your *liabilities*, what you owe. Your *net worth* is the difference between the assets and the liabilities.

$$\text{Net worth} = \text{Assets} - \text{Liabilities}$$

Todd and Claudia have asked for your help in preparing a personal balance sheet. They have listed the following assets and liabilities: savings account, $4720; current value of their home, $225,500; automobiles, $32,300; personal property, $6400; boat loan balance, $4580; stocks and bonds, $25,550; automobile loans, $13,200; mutual funds, $15,960; checking account balance, $3,640; store charge account balances, $1940; certificates of deposit, $18,640; TV's, stereo equipment, and computers, $7630; Visa and MasterCard balances, $8660; home mortgage balance, $165,410; 401(k) retirement plan, $67,880; sailboat, $12,100.

Use the data provided and the template below to prepare a personal balance sheet for Todd and Claudia.

ASSETS			LIABILITIES		
CURRENT ASSETS			**CURRENT LIABILITIES**		
Checking account	_____		Store charge accounts	_____	
Savings account	_____		Credit card accounts	_____	
Certificates of deposit	_____		Other current debt	_____	
Total Current Assets		_____	**Total Current Liabilities**		_____
LONG-TERM ASSETS			**LONG-TERM LIABILITIES**		
Investments			Home mortgage	_____	
Retirement plans	_____		Automobile loans	_____	
Stocks and bonds	_____		Other loans	_____	
Mutual funds	_____		**Total Long-Term Liabilities**		_____
Personal			**TOTAL LIABILITIES**		_____
Home	_____				
Automobiles	_____				
Personal property	_____				
Other	_____		**NET WORTH**		
Other	_____		Total Assets	_____	
Total Long-Term Assets		_____	Total Liabilities	_____	
TOTAL ASSETS		_____	**NET WORTH**		_____

CHAPTER REVIEW EXERCISES

Identify the place value of the indicated digit. (1.1A)

1. 54,220

2. 727

3. 78,414,645

4. 3341

5. 35,686

6. 18,286,719

Write each number in standard notation and in word form. (1.1B)

7. 336   **8.** 8475   **9.** 784341

10. 380633   **11.** 62646   **12.** 1326554

13. 10102   **14.** 6653634   **15.** 4022407508

Write each number in expanded notation. (1.1C)

16. 23   **17.** 532   **18.** 109

19. 26,385   **20.** 2,148   **21.** 1,928,365

Round each number to the specified place value. (1.1D)

22. 363,484 to the nearest thousand   **23.** 18,136 to the nearest ten   **24.** 86,614 to the nearest ten thousand

25. 601,927 to the nearest hundred   **26.** 4,829,387 to the nearest million   **27.** 3,146,844 to the nearest hundred thousand

28. 81,084 to the nearest ten   **29.** 196,140 to the nearest thousand   **30.** 42,862,785 to the nearest ten million

Add. (1.2A, B)

31.
$$\begin{array}{r} 30 \\ + 59 \\ \hline \end{array}$$

32.
$$\begin{array}{r} 45 \\ + 68 \\ \hline \end{array}$$

33.
$$\begin{array}{r} 319 \\ + 60 \\ \hline \end{array}$$

34.
$$\begin{array}{r} 916 \\ + 35 \\ \hline \end{array}$$

35.
$$\begin{array}{r} 414 \\ + 181 \\ \hline \end{array}$$

36.
$$\begin{array}{r} 360 \\ 971 \\ + 964 \\ \hline \end{array}$$

37.
$$\begin{array}{r} 43,814 \\ + 71,658 \\ \hline \end{array}$$

38.
$$\begin{array}{r} 1700 \\ 130 \\ 421 \\ 81 \\ + 237 \\ \hline \end{array}$$

39. $59 + 294 + 1100 + 10$ **40.** $853 + 121 + 0 + 2912$ **41.** $25 + 0 + 53 + 180 + 0$ **42.** $9 + 0 + 71 + 0 + 312$

Subtract. (1.3A)

43.
$$\begin{array}{r} 67 \\ -\ 3 \\ \hline \end{array}$$

44.
$$\begin{array}{r} 16 \\ -\ 7 \\ \hline \end{array}$$

45.
$$\begin{array}{r} 89 \\ -\ 62 \\ \hline \end{array}$$

46.
$$\begin{array}{r} 55 \\ -\ 32 \\ \hline \end{array}$$

47.
$$\begin{array}{r} 695 \\ -\ 12 \\ \hline \end{array}$$

48.
$$\begin{array}{r} 386 \\ -\ 24 \\ \hline \end{array}$$

49.
$$\begin{array}{r} 649 \\ -\ 226 \\ \hline \end{array}$$

50.
$$\begin{array}{r} 867 \\ -\ 253 \\ \hline \end{array}$$

51.
$$\begin{array}{r} 7332 \\ -\ 499 \\ \hline \end{array}$$

52.
$$\begin{array}{r} 1565 \\ -\ 360 \\ \hline \end{array}$$

53.
$$\begin{array}{r} 4300 \\ -\ 31 \\ \hline \end{array}$$

54.
$$\begin{array}{r} 7500 \\ -\ 973 \\ \hline \end{array}$$

Multiply. (1.4A, B)

55.
$$\begin{array}{r} 64 \\ \times\ 1 \\ \hline \end{array}$$

56.
$$\begin{array}{r} 72 \\ \times\ 0 \\ \hline \end{array}$$

57.
$$\begin{array}{r} 63 \\ \times\ 25 \\ \hline \end{array}$$

58.
$$\begin{array}{r} 78 \\ \times\ 55 \\ \hline \end{array}$$

59.
$$\begin{array}{r} 39 \\ \times\ 95 \\ \hline \end{array}$$

60.
$$\begin{array}{r} 342 \\ \times\ 37 \\ \hline \end{array}$$

61. $318 \cdot 40$

62. 55×111

63. $18(45)$ **64.** $(64)(270)$ **65.** $815 \cdot 60$ **66.** $328 \cdot 2900$

Divide. (1.5A, B)

67. $48 \div 0$ **68.** $0 \div 63$ **69.** $\dfrac{46}{1}$ **70.** $\dfrac{79}{79}$

71. $49\overline{)784}$ **72.** $42\overline{)882}$ **73.** $4\overline{)46}$ **74.** $29\overline{)635}$

75. $\dfrac{284}{14}$ **76.** $6192 \div 182$ **77.** $11\overline{)46}$ **78.** $3\overline{)95}$

Write each expression in exponential notation. (1.6A)

79. $7 \cdot 7 \cdot 7 \cdot 7$ **80.** $13 \cdot 13 \cdot 13$ **81.** 17 **82.** $5 \cdot 5 \cdot 5 \cdot 5 \cdot 5 \cdot 5$

83. $3 \cdot 3 \cdot 5 \cdot 5 \cdot 5 \cdot 11 \cdot 11$ **84.** $5 \cdot 5 \cdot 7 \cdot 17 \cdot 17 \cdot 19$ **85.** $2 \cdot 2 \cdot 2 \cdot 2 \cdot 23 \cdot 23 \cdot 29$ **86.** $11 \cdot 11 \cdot 11 \cdot 19 \cdot 19$

Evaluate each exponential expression. (1.6B)

87. 7^2

88. 2^4

89. 39^1

90. 3^5

91. 10^3

92. 66^0

93. 19^2

94. 1^{20}

95. 10^6

96. 6^3

97. 0^7

98. 2^9

Simplify each expression. (1.6C)

99. $9 + 17 \cdot 20$

100. $34 \div 2 + 9(20 + 5)$

101. $20 \div 2^2 + (5 \cdot 4)$

102. $\dfrac{360 \div 6^2}{35 - 25} + 5^3$

103. $8^2 - (8 - 4)^3$

104. $5 + \left(\dfrac{300}{12} - 4^2\right)^2$

105. $50 \cdot 8^2 \div (10 + 30)^2$

106. $12 + 2[6 - (5 - 2)]$

107. $\dfrac{(4 \cdot 3^2)}{18 - 12} \cdot 10$

108. $111{,}000 - 500(12 - 6)^3$

109. $3[100 - 8(4) + 9 \div 3 + 7]$

110. $\dfrac{7^2 - 6^2}{(7 + 6)} + 19$

Solve each application problem. (1.8A, 1.8B)

111. In one year, a fleet of airplanes used 453,229 gallons of aviation fuel. A report to the vice president of operations requires that this number be rounded to the nearest hundred.

    a. What number should be reported?

    b. Write the result of part a in word form.

112. Londonderry Farm has 450 acres of corn, 259 acres of wheat, 812 acres of soybeans, and 18 acres of assorted vegetables. In addition, there are 22 acres of grazing pasture and 6 acres for the farmhouse and barnyard.

    a. What is the total acreage of the farm?

    b. If they sold 329 acres of the farm, how many acres would be left?

113. Stewart Creek Golf Course has 18 holes. There are six par-3 holes that average 175 yards each, seven par-4 holes that average 228 yards each, and five par-5 holes that average 340 yards each. What is the total yardage for the golf course?

114. Bayside Realty, Inc. sold four parcels of land for $32,500 each: one condominium apartment for $55,600 and two homes, one for $79,200 and one for $96,200. What are the company's total sales?

Photo by Robert Brechner

115. The Frame Factory charges $3 per inch of perimeter to frame artwork in a standard frame and $4 per inch for a deluxe frame. You are interested in framing a painting that measures 22 inches wide by 14 inches high.

    a. How much will it cost to frame the painting in a standard frame?

    b. How much more will it cost for a deluxe frame?

116. You have been put in charge of planning the annual reunion party for your alumni association. The food will cost $16 per person, the entertainment will cost $1250, and the rental fee for the ballroom is $700. In addition, the invitation printing and postage charges are $328 and flowers are $382. Other miscellaneous expenses amount to $1500.

    a. If 160 alumni are expected, what is the total cost of the party?

    b. What is the cost per person?

Use the graph *How Teens Spend Their Time* for exercises 117–122.

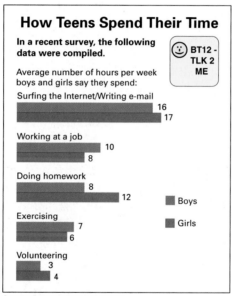

Source: Buzzllar's Market Research

117. How many total hours per week do girls work and do homework?

118. How many total hours per week do boys exercise and work?

119. How many more hours per year do girls surf the Net and write email than boys?

120. How many fewer hours per year do girls work compared to boys?

121. On average, how many hours per year do kids (boys and girls) surf the Net and write email?

122. What is the average number of hours per week that kids (boys and girls) do homework?

Identify the place value of the indicated digit.

1. 68$\underline{7}$7

2. 2,3$\underline{3}$6,029

Write each number in standard notation and in word form.

3. $10,000 + 5000 + 800 + 60 + 2$

4. $100,000 + 20,000 + 3000 + 500 + 9$

Write each number in expanded notation.

5. 475

6. 1397

Round each number to the specified place value.

7. 34,771 to the nearest thousand

8. 6,529,398 to the nearest hundred thousand

Add.

9. $\begin{array}{r} 463 \\ + 25 \\ \hline \end{array}$

10. $652 + 0 + 257 + 576$

Subtract.

11. $\begin{array}{r} 51 \\ - 34 \\ \hline \end{array}$

12. $782 - 41$

Multiply.

13. $\begin{array}{r} 318 \\ \times \ 36 \\ \hline \end{array}$

14. $3132 \cdot 58$

Divide.

15. $2142 \div 34$

16. $7\overline{)99}$

Write each expression in exponential notation.

17. $13 \cdot 13 \cdot 13$

18. $3 \cdot 3 \cdot 5 \cdot 5 \cdot 5 \cdot 5 \cdot 7$

Evaluate each exponential expression.

19. 6^2

20. 2^4

Simplify each expression.

21. $6 + 7 \cdot 2$

22. $64 \div 2^3 + (5 \cdot 7)$

Solve each application problem.

23. Alice drove 238 miles on Tuesday and 287 miles on Wednesday. If her odometer was at 23,414 miles before the two trips, what was the odometer reading after the trips?

24. A $2,520,000 lottery grand prize is evenly split among 14 people. How much does each person receive?

25. You are the chef at the Spaghetti Factory restaurant.

    a. How many 4-ounce portions of pasta can be made from an industrial-sized carton containing 420 ounces of pasta?

    b. If the restaurant serves 225 pasta meals per night, how many cartons will be used each 7-day week?

26. The Mars rover *Opportunity* is a $400 million robotic explorer. Part of the rover's mission is to photograph a rectangular-shaped section of martian surface that measures 150 feet long and 110 feet wide.

    a. What is the perimeter of the Mars section to be photographed?

    b. What is the area of the Mars section to be photographed?

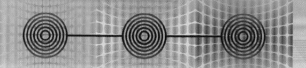
Fractions

Culinary Arts

To create cuisine with the ideal flavor, chefs and bakers must know how to appropriately combine different ingredients. They need to know exactly how much of each ingredient must be added to a particular recipe. Adding too much baking soda to a cake recipe will result in a cake that is hard as a rock. Adding too little garlic to shrimp scampi will result in a bland dish.

Many recipes involve fractions. For instance, a recipe may call for $\frac{1}{3}$ cup of sugar or $\frac{1}{2}$ teaspoon of vanilla. More sophisticated recipes may require very small fractional amounts. A recipe may require a pinch of salt, which is traditionally defined as $\frac{1}{8}$ teaspoon.

Often, chefs need to adjust recipes. For example, a chef may want to make only half of a recipe, or she may have to double it. Consequently, anyone working in the culinary arts must be proficient at manipulating fractions. Try Example 4 of Section 2.4 about cutting a recipe in half.

2.1 FACTORS, PRIME FACTORIZATIONS, AND LEAST COMMON MULTIPLES

We begin this chapter with a discussion of factors, prime numbers, and least common multiples. Although these concepts relate to natural numbers, they are important ideas in our work with fractions.

| **Objective 2.1A** | **Find the factors of a natural number** |

In Section 1.4, Multiplying Whole Numbers, we learned that factors are numbers being multiplied. In the product $3 \cdot 6 = 18$, both 3 and 6 are factors. More precisely, we say that 3 and 6 are factors of 18.

An alternate way of expressing the concept of a factor is in terms of division. When one number divides another number evenly so that the remainder is 0, both the divisor and the quotient are factors of the dividend. For example, we know that $18 \div 3 = 6$. Because the divisor 3 divides the dividend 18 evenly so that the remainder is 0, both the divisor 3 and the quotient 6 are factors of 18. We also say that 18 is *divisible* by both 3 and 6.

Certainly, there are numbers other than 3 and 6 that, when multiplied together, give us 18. That is, there are other factors of 18. Let's find all the factors of 18. To do this, let's divide 18 by the natural numbers, 1, 2, 3, and so on.

$18 \div 1 = 18$	1 and 18 are factors of 18.
$18 \div 2 = 9$	2 and 9 are factors of 18.
$18 \div 3 = 6$	3 and 6 are factors of 18.
$18 \div 4$	Does not divide evenly.
$18 \div 5$	Does not divide evenly.
$18 \div 6 = 3$	6 and 3 are factors of 18. (We have already made this observation.)

Once the factors begin to repeat, we have found all of the factors. We see that 1, 2, 3, 6, 9, and 18 are the factors of 18.

In general, we do the following in order to determine the factors of a natural number.

Rule for Finding Factors of a Natural Number

Divide the natural number by each of the numbers 1, 2, 3, and so on. If the natural number is divisible by one of these numbers, then both the divisor and the quotient are factors of the natural number. Continue until the factors begin to repeat.

To determine whether one number divides another number wholly, it is often helpful to use the following rules of divisibility. Note that all numbers are divisible by 1; the result of dividing any number by 1 is the number itself. Therefore, 1 is a factor of every number, and each number is a factor of itself.

Rules for Divisibility

A NUMBER IS DIVISIBLE BY	IF
2	The number is even (that is, the last digit is 0, 2, 4, 6, or 8).
3	The sum of the digits is divisible by 3.
4	The number named by the last two digits is divisible by 4.
5	The last digit is either 0 or 5.
6	The number is even and the sum of the digits is divisible by 3.
8	The number named by the last three digits is divisible by 8.
9	The sum of the digits is divisible by 9.
10	The last digit is 0.

> **Learning Tip**
>
> If 4 is a factor of a number, then so is 2. For example, 4 is a factor of 16, and since 2 is a factor of 4, it follows that 2 is also a factor of 16.
>
> The reverse is not necessarily true. That is, just because 2 is a factor of a number does not mean that 4 is also a factor. As an example, 2 is a factor of 10, but 4 is not.
>
> Similar statements hold for each of the following.
>
> - 6 and 3
> - 6 and 2
> - 8 and 4
> - 8 and 2
> - 9 and 3
> - 10 and 5

EXAMPLE 1   Find the factors of a natural number

Find the factors of each number.

a. 32   **b.** 60

SOLUTION STRATEGY

a. $32 \div 1 = 32$ 1 and 32 are factors.   Divide 32 by 1, 2, 3, and so on.
$32 \div 2 = 16$ 2 and 16 are factors.
$32 \div 3$ Does not divide evenly.
$32 \div 4 = 8$ 4 and 8 are factors.
$32 \div 5$ Does not divide evenly.
$32 \div 6$ Does not divide evenly.
$32 \div 7$ Does not divide evenly.
$32 \div 8 = 4$ 8 and 4 are factors.   8 and 4 are repeat factors. Stop!

The factors of 32 are 1, 2, 4, 8, 16, and 32.   List the factors in ascending order.

b. $60 \div 1 = 60$ 1 and 60 are factors.   Divide 60 by 1, 2, 3, and so on.
$60 \div 2 = 30$ 2 and 30 are factors.
$60 \div 3 = 20$ 3 and 20 are factors.
$60 \div 4 = 15$ 4 and 15 are factors.
$60 \div 5 = 12$ 5 and 12 are factors.
$60 \div 6 = 10$ 6 and 10 are factors.
$60 \div 7$ Does not divide evenly.
$60 \div 8$ Does not divide evenly.
$60 \div 9$ Does not divide evenly.
$60 \div 10$ 10 and 6 are factors.   10 and 6 are repeat factors. Stop!

The factors of 60 are 1, 2, 3, 4, 5, 6, 10, 12, 15, 20, 30, and 60.   List the factors in ascending order.

TRY-IT EXERCISE 1

Find the factors of each number.

a. 24   **b.** 120

Check your answers with the solutions in Appendix A. ■

| **Objective 2.1B** | **Determine whether a number is prime, composite, or neither** |

A natural number greater than 1 that has only two factors (divisors), namely, 1 and itself, is called a **prime number**. We say that such a number is **prime**. The number 7, for example, is prime because its only two factors (divisors) are 1 and 7. The number 2 is the smallest prime number. It is also the only even prime number.

A natural number greater than 1 that has more than two factors (divisors) is known as a **composite number**. Every natural number greater than 1 is either prime or composite depending on the numbers of factors (divisors) it has. Note that 0 and 1 are neither prime nor composite (0 is not a natural number and, by definition, prime and composite numbers are greater than 1).

To determine whether a number is a composite number, divide the number by smaller prime numbers. If we can divide without a remainder, then the number is composite.

For reference, the prime numbers less than 100 are listed below.

> 2, 3, 5, 7, 11, 13, 17, 19, 23, 29, 31, 37, 41, 43, 47, 53, 59, 61, 67, 71, 73, 79, 83, 89, 97

prime number or **prime**
A natural number greater than 1 that has only two factors (divisors), namely, 1 and itself.

composite number
A natural number greater than 1 that has more than two factors (divisors).

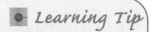
Learning Tip

Every even number, except for 2, is composite because each is divisible by 2.

Real-World Connection

For centuries, mathematicians have searched for larger and larger prime numbers. At the time of this printing, the largest known prime had over 9,800,000 digits!

EXAMPLE 2 **Determine whether a number is prime, composite, or neither**

Determine whether each number is prime, composite, or neither.

a. 14   **b.** 11   **c.** 23

d. 36   **e.** 0   **f.** 19

SOLUTION STRATEGY

14	composite	14 is composite because its factors are 1, 2, 7, and 14.
11	prime	11 is prime because its only factors are 1 and itself.
23	prime	23 is prime because its only factors are 1 and itself.
36	composite	36 is composite because its factors are 1, 2, 3, 4, 6, 9, 12, 18, and 36.
0	neither	By definition, 0 is neither prime nor composite.
19	prime	19 is prime because its only factors are 1 and itself.

TRY-IT EXERCISE 2

Determine whether each number is prime, composite, or neither.

a. 29   **b.** 1   **c.** 44   **d.** 18   **e.** 100   **f.** 43

Check your answers with the solutions in Appendix A. ■

Objective 2.1C	**Find the prime factorization of a composite number**

The term *factor* can also be defined as a verb. As a verb, to **factor** means to express a quantity as a product of factors. Such a product is called a factorization.

factor
To express a quantity as a product of factors.

As an example, consider the number 18. There are three two-number factorizations.

$$1 \cdot 18 = 18 \qquad 2 \cdot 9 = 18 \qquad 3 \cdot 6 = 18$$

Because 18 can be factored in any of the three ways listed above, the numbers 1, 2, 3, 6, 9, and 18 are all factors of 18.

A **prime factorization** of a whole number is a factorization in which each factor is prime. None of the factorizations of 18 listed above are prime factorizations. Note, for instance, that $2 \cdot 9$ is not a prime factorization because 9 is a composite number. But, if we factor the 9 as $3 \cdot 3$, we then get the prime factorization of 18.

prime factorization
A factorization of a whole number in which each factor is prime.

$$2 \cdot 3 \cdot 3 = 2 \cdot 3^2 = 18$$

A **factor tree** is an illustration used to determine the prime factorization of a composite number. To see how to construct a factor tree, let's once again factor 18. We begin by seeking a two-number factorization of 18 in which 1 is not a factor. Let's use $2 \cdot 9$. Extend two branches from 18 and write 2 at the end of one branch and 9 at the end of the other.

factor tree
An illustration used to determine the prime factorization of a composite number.

Because 2 is prime, circle it. The remaining factor, 9, is composite, and so we extend two branches from 9 and seek a two-number factorization. Since $9 = 3 \cdot 3$, write 3 at the end of each branch. Moreover, since 3 is prime, circle each 3.

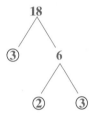

At this point, we have a prime number at the end of each branch. The prime factorization of 18 is simply the product of the circled primes.

$$18 = 2 \cdot 3 \cdot 3 = 2 \cdot 3^2$$

It should be noted that the prime factorization of a composite number is unique. Therefore, no matter which two-number factorization we begin with, we will always end up with the same prime factorization. So, if we begin with the fact that $18 = 3 \cdot 6$, we end up with the same prime factors.

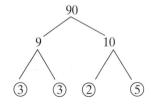

EXAMPLE 3   **Find the prime factorization of a composite number**

Find the prime factorization of each number.

a. 45   **b.** 90   **c.** 288

SOLUTION STRATEGY

a.

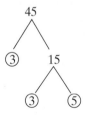

The prime factorization of 45 is $3 \cdot 3 \cdot 5 = 3^2 \cdot 5$.

Write a two-number factorization for 45. We choose $3 \cdot 15$, but any two-number factorization in which 1 is not a factor can be used.
Circle the prime factor 3.

Write a two-number factorization for 15.
Circle the prime factors 3 and 5.

The prime factorization is the product of the prime numbers.

b.

90
9   10
③ ③   ②   ⑤

The prime factorization of 90 is $2 \cdot 3 \cdot 3 \cdot 5 = 2 \cdot 3^2 \cdot 5$.

Write a two-number factorization for 90. We choose $9 \cdot 10$, but any two-number factorization in which 1 is not a factor can be used.

Write a two-number factorization for 9.
Write a two-number factorization for 10.
Circle the prime factors 3, 2, and 5.

The prime factorization is the product of these prime numbers.

c.

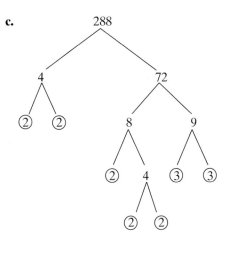

Write a two-number factorization for 288. We choose $4 \cdot 72$, but any two-number factorization in which 1 is not a factor can be used.

Write a two-number factorization for 4.
Write a two-number factorization for 72.
Circle each prime factor 2.

Write a two-number factorization for 8.
Write a two-number factorization for 9.
Circle the prime factors 2 and 3.

Write a two-number factorization for 4.
Circle each prime factor 2.

The prime factorization of 288 is $2^5 \cdot 3^2$.

The prime factorization is the product of these prime numbers.

TRY-IT EXERCISE 3

Find the prime factorization of each number.

a. 42 **b.** 88 **c.** 286

Check your answers with the solutions in Appendix A. ■

Objective 2.1D **Find the least common multiple (LCM) of a set of numbers**

A **multiple of a number** is the product of the number and any natural number. For example, multiples of 2 include 2, 4, 6, 8, and 10. In particular, note the following:

$$2 \cdot 1 = 2, \quad 2 \cdot 2 = 4, \quad 2 \cdot 3 = 6, \quad 2 \cdot 4 = 8, \quad 2 \cdot 5 = 10$$

We can create a list of multiples for any number by multiplying it by each natural number. Because there are infinitely many natural numbers, the list of the multiples is infinitely long. Therefore, we commonly write only the first few multiples of a given number.

A **common multiple** is a multiple that is shared by a set of two or more natural numbers. For example, let's find some common multiples of 4 and 6.

Multiples of 4 are 4, 8, 12, 16, 20, 24, 28, 32, 36, 40, ...

Multiples of 6 are 6, 12, 18, 24, 30, 36, 42, 48, 54, 60, ...

Comparing the first 10 multiples of each number, we see that 12, 24, and 36 are common.

multiple of a number
The product of the number and any natural number.

common multiple
A multiple that is shared by a set of two or more natural numbers.

least common multiple or LCM
The smallest multiple shared by a set of two or more numbers.

While there are infinitely many common multiples, we are generally interested in a single common multiple. The one we are most interested in is called the least common multiple. The **least common multiple** or **LCM** is the smallest multiple shared by a set of two or more numbers. In the previous example, because 12 is the least of the common multiples, we say that 12 is the LCM of 4 and 6.

EXAMPLE 4   Find the LCM of a set of numbers by listing multiples

Find the LCM of 2, 4, and 5 by listing multiples.

SOLUTION STRATEGY

Multiples of 2 are 2, 4, 6, 8, 10, 12, 14, 16, 18, $\boxed{20}$, . . .   List the multiples of each number.

Multiples of 4 are 4, 8, 12, 16, $\boxed{20}$, 24, 28, 32, 36, 40, . . .

Multiples of 5 are 5, 10, 15, $\boxed{20}$, 25, 30, 35, 40, 45, 50, . . .   The least common multiple is the smallest nonzero multiple shared by these numbers.

      The LCM of 2, 4, and 5 is 20.

TRY-IT EXERCISE 4

Find the LCM of 2, 5, and 6.

Check your answer with the solution in Appendix A. ∎

The process of finding the LCM of a set of numbers by listing multiples can be extremely tedious, especially when the numbers are large. Another method uses the concept of prime factorization. We outline the steps for this method below.

Steps for Finding the LCM Using Prime Factorization

Step 1. Write the prime factorization of each number.

Step 2. Write the product of the prime factors with each factor appearing the greatest number of times that it occurs in any one factorization.

To demonstrate this method, let's search for the LCM of 8 and 12. We begin by writing the prime factorization of each number.

$$8 = 2 \cdot 2 \cdot 2$$
$$12 = 2 \cdot 2 \cdot 3$$

Next, we write the product of the prime factors with each factor appearing the greatest number of times that it occurs in any one factorization.

$$2 \cdot 2 \cdot 2 \cdot 3$$

Note that 2 occurs three times in the prime factorization of 8 and twice in the prime factorization of 12. Therefore, we include the prime factor 2 a total of three times in our product. Next, we note that 3 is a prime factor of 12. Because it occurs only one time, we include the factor 3 once in our product. The LCM is the product of these factors.

$$\text{LCM} = 2 \cdot 2 \cdot 2 \cdot 3 = 24$$

EXAMPLE 5   Find the LCM of a set of numbers using prime factorization

Find the LCM of 4, 6, and 10 using prime factorization.

SOLUTION STRATEGY

$4 = 2 \cdot 2$	Find the prime factorization of each number.
$6 = 2 \cdot 3$	
$10 = 2 \cdot 5$	
$2 \cdot 2 \cdot 3 \cdot 5$	Write the product of prime factors with each factor occurring the greatest number of times that it occurs in any one factorization.
	The greatest number of times 2 occurs in any factorization is two times.
	The greatest number of times that 3 occurs is one time. The greatest number of times that 5 occurs is one time.
The LCM of 4, 6, and 10 is $2 \cdot 2 \cdot 3 \cdot 5 = 60$.	The LCM is the product of all factors in the list.

TRY-IT EXERCISE 5

Find the LCM of 18, 15, and 12 using prime factorization.

Check your answer with the solution in Appendix A. ■

We now detail an alternate method. To demonstrate this approach, let's once again search for the LCM of 8 and 12. To begin, list the numbers 8 and 12 in a row as shown below.

$$\underline{|8 \quad 12}$$

Now, find a factor of one or both of these numbers. Since 8 and 12 are even, we know that 2 is a factor of each number. Write 2 to the left of the numbers.

$$2 \, \underline{|8 \quad 12}$$

Divide 8 by 2 and write the quotient, 4, directly below 8; divide 12 by 2 and write the quotient, 6, directly below 12.

$$2 \, \underline{|8 \quad 12}$$
$$\underline{|4 \quad 6}$$

Now, repeat the process: find a factor of one or both of the numbers 4 and 6. Once again, 2 is a factor of each number. Write 2 to the left of the numbers.

$$2 \, \underline{|8 \quad 12}$$
$$2 \, \underline{|4 \quad 6}$$

Divide 4 by 2 and write the quotient, 2, directly below 4; divide 6 by 2 and write the quotient, 3, directly below 6.

```
2 |8   12
2 |4    6
  |2    3
```

Once again, repeat the process: find a factor of one or both numbers. This time, 2 is a factor of 2 but not of 3. Write 2 to the left of the numbers.

```
2 |8   12
2 |4    6
2 |2    3
```

Divide 2 by 2 and write the quotient, 1, directly below 2. Since 2 does not go into 3 evenly, simply rewrite 3 below itself.

```
2 |8   12
2 |4    6
2 |2    3
  |1    3
```

Repeat the process one last time. This time, note that 3 is a factor of itself. Write 3 to the left of 1 and 3.

```
2 |8   12
2 |4    6
2 |2    3
3 |1    3
```

Because 3 does not go into 1, simply rewrite 1 below itself. Divide 3 by 3 and write the quotient, 1, directly below 3.

```
2 |8   12
2 |4    6
2 |2    3
3 |1    3
  |1    1
```

At this point, a row of ones remains, and so we are finished. The LCM of 8 and 12 is the product of the factors.

$$LCM = 2 \cdot 2 \cdot 2 \cdot 3 = 24$$

In general, follow these steps to determine the LCM using this alternate method.

Steps for Finding the LCM: Alternate Method

Step 1. List the numbers for which we are trying to find the LCM in a row. Draw a "half-box" around the numbers.

Step 2. Find a prime factor other than 1 for at least one of these numbers. Write this factor to the left of the numbers.

Step 3. Consider the quotient of each number in the half-box and the prime factor from step 2. If the number is evenly divisible by the factor, write the quotient below the number. If not, rewrite the number itself. Place a half-box around this new row of numbers.

Step 4. Repeat steps 2 and 3 until a row of ones remains.

Step 5. Calculate the product of the prime factors to the left of each half-box. This is the LCM.

EXAMPLE 6   Find the LCM of a set of numbers using the alternate method

Find the LCM of 4, 6, and 10 using the alternate method.

SOLUTION STRATEGY

$\underline{|4\quad 6\quad 10}$ List the numbers in a row.

$2\underline{|4\quad 6\quad 10}$ 2 is a prime factor of 4, 6, and 10. Write 2 to the left of the numbers.

$\underline{|2\quad 3\quad 5}$ Write the quotients of the numbers and 2 directly below each number.

$2\underline{|2\quad 3\quad 5}$ Note that 2 is a prime factor of 2. Write 2 to the left of the numbers.

$\underline{|1\quad 3\quad 5}$ Write the quotient of 2 and itself directly below 2.
Because 2 is not a factor of either 3 or 5, rewrite 3 and 5.

$3\underline{|1\quad 3\quad 5}$ Note that 3 is a prime factor of itself. Write 3 to the left of the numbers.

$\underline{|1\quad 1\quad 5}$ Write the quotient of 3 and itself directly below 3. Because 3 is not a factor of 1 or 5, rewrite 1 and 5 below each number.

$5\underline{|1\quad 1\quad 5}$ Note that 5 is a prime factor of itself. Write 5 to the left of the numbers.

$\underline{|1\quad 1\quad 1}$ Write the quotient of 5 and 5 directly below 5. Rewrite 1 and 1 below each number.

Because a row of ones remains, the process is complete.

The LCM of 4, 6,   The LCM is the product of the prime factors.
and 10 is
$2 \cdot 2 \cdot 3 \cdot 5 = 60$.

TRY-IT EXERCISE 6

Find the LCM of 18, 15, and 12 using the alternate method.

Check your answer with the solution in Appendix A. ■

Consider two special cases when finding the LCM of a set of numbers. The first of these cases applies when finding the LCM of a set of prime numbers. In this case, the LCM is simply the product of these numbers. As an example, consider 3 and 5. Because the numbers are prime, the LCM is simply the product of the two numbers.

$$LCM = 3 \cdot 5 = 15$$

The second case pertains to a collection of numbers in which each of the smaller numbers divides evenly into the largest number. In this case, the LCM is simply the largest number. As an example, consider 3 and 15. Because 3 divides evenly into 15, the LCM of 3 and 15 is the larger of the two numbers.

$$LCM = 15$$

Objective 2.1E **Apply your knowledge**

EXAMPLE 7 Apply your knowledge

You have volunteered to be the "barbeque chef" for a school party. From experience, you know that hot dogs should be turned every 2 minutes and hamburgers should be turned every 3 minutes. How often will they be turned at the same time?

SOLUTION STRATEGY

$2 = 1 \cdot 2$ In this example, we are looking for the least common
$3 = 1 \cdot 3$ multiple of 2 and 3.

The LCM of 2 and 3 is $2 \cdot 3 = 6$.

The hamburgers and hot dogs will be turned at the same time every 6 minutes.

TRY-IT EXERCISE 7

A Formula I race car can complete one lap of a road race every 3 minutes, while a Formula Jr. race car completes one lap every 4 minutes. If they maintain these speeds throughout a race, how often will they complete a lap at the same time?

Check your answer with the solution in Appendix A. ∎

SECTION 2.1 REVIEW EXERCISES

Concept Check

1. A _____ number is a natural number greater than 1 that has only two factors (divisors), namely, 1 and itself.

2. A _____ number is a natural number greater than 1 that has more than two factors (divisors).

3. To _____ a quantity is to express it as a product of factors.

4. A factorization of a whole number in which each factor is prime is known as a _____ _____ .

5. An illustration used to determine the prime factorization of a composite number is known as a _____ _____ .

6. A _____ of a number is the product of the number and any natural number.

7. A nonzero multiple that is shared by a set of two or more whole numbers is called a _____ multiple.

8. The smallest multiple shared by a set of two or more numbers is called the _____ _____ _____ or _____ .

Objective 2.1A   Find the factors of a natural number

GUIDE PROBLEMS

9. Find the factors of 40.

$40 \div 1 = 40$

$40 \div 2 = 20$

$40 \div 3$

$40 \div 4 = 10$

$40 \div 5 = 8$

$40 \div 6 =$

$40 \div 7 =$

$40 \div 8 = 5$

The factors of 40 are ___, ___, ___, ___, ___, ___, ___, and ___ .

10. Find the factors of 25.

$25 \div 1 = 25$

$25 \div 2$

$25 \div 3$

$25 \div 4$

$25 \div 5 = 5$

The factors of 25 are ___, ___, and ___ .

Find the factors of each number.

11. 5

12. 11

13. 6

14. 9

15. 49

16. 21

17. 29

18. 41

19. 77

20. 34

21. 28

22. 18

23. 61

24. 83

25. 75

26. 50

27. 54

28. 32

29. 100

30. 84

Objective 2.1B	Determine whether a number is prime, composite, or neither

GUIDE PROBLEMS

31. Determine whether 40 is prime, composite, or neither.

The factors of 40 are 1, 2, 4, 5, 8, 10, 20, and 40.
Therefore, 40 is _____.

32. Determine whether 31 is prime, composite, or neither.

The factors of 31 are 1 and 31.
Therefore, 31 is _____.

Determine whether each number is prime, composite, or neither.

33. 43   **34.** 16   **35.** 1   **36.** 61

37. 0   **38.** 95   **39.** 28   **40.** 14

41. 165   **42.** 125   **43.** 17   **44.** 37

45. 81   **46.** 54   **47.** 83   **48.** 67

Objective 2.1C	Find the prime factorization of a composite number

GUIDE PROBLEMS

49. Find the prime factorization of 30.

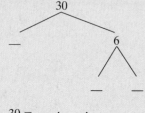

30 = ___ · ___ · ___

50. Find the prime factorization of 24.

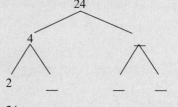

24 = ___ · ___ · ___ · ___ = ___ · ___

Find the prime factorization of each number.

51. 10   **52.** 14   **53.** 51   **54.** 77

55. 42   **56.** 70   **57.** 49   **58.** 25

59. 12   **60.** 18   **61.** 16   **62.** 32

63. 81

64. 64

65. 108

66. 360

67. 175

68. 250

69. 135

70. 225

71. 150

72. 525

73. 400

74. 2000

Objective 2.1D	Find the least common multiple (LCM) of a set of numbers

GUIDE PROBLEMS

75. Find the LCM of 4 and 6 by listing multiples.

   a. List the first few multiples of each denominator.

     4: 4, 8, ___, ___, ___, ___, . . .

     6: 6, 12, ___, ___, ___, ___, . . .

   b. The LCM is the smallest multiple common to each list. What is the LCM?

     The LCM of 4 and 6 is ___.

76. Find the LCM of 3, 4, and 8 by listing multiples.

   a. List the first few multiples of each denominator.

     3: 3, 6, ___, ___, ___, ___, ___, ___, . . .

     4: 4, 8, ___, ___, ___, ___, . . .

     8: 8, 16, ___, ___, ___, ___, . . .

   b. The LCM is the smallest multiple common to each list. What is the LCM?

     The LCM of 3, 4, and 8 is ___.

77. Find the LCM of 8 and 18 using prime factorization.

   a. Find the prime factorization of each number.

     ___ $\cdot$ ___ $\cdot$ ___ = ___ $\cdot$ ___

   b. The LCM is the product of those prime factors occurring the greatest number of times in any one factorization. What is the LCM?

     The greatest number of times that 2 appears in either factorization is _____ times.

     The greatest number of times that 3 appears in either factorization is _____ times.

     The LCM of 8 and 18 is

     ___ $\cdot$ ___ $\cdot$ ___ $\cdot$ ___ $\cdot$ ___ = ___.

78. Find the LCM of 12 and 30 using prime factorization.

   a. Find the prime factorization of each number.

     $12 = 2 \cdot 2 \cdot 3 = 2^2 \cdot 3$

     $30 = $ ___ $\cdot$ ___ $\cdot$ ___

   b. The LCM is the product of those prime factors occurring the greatest number of times in any one factorization. What is the LCM?

     The greatest number of times that 2 appears in either factorization is _____ times.

     The greatest number of times that 3 appears in either factorization is _____ time.

     The greatest number of times that 5 appears in either factorization is _____ time.

     The LCM of 12 and 30 is ___ $\cdot$ ___ $\cdot$ ___ $\cdot$ ___ = ___.

Find the LCM of each set of numbers.

79. 2, 9

80. 3, 8

81. 4, 5

82. 4, 7

83. 6, 9

84. 9, 12

85. 8, 9

86. 24, 40

87. 8, 16   **88.** 8, 20   **89.** 15, 20   **90.** 12, 18

91. 2, 3, 16   **92.** 5, 8, 16   **93.** 12, 14, 21   **94.** 7, 21, 24

95. 2, 6, 33   **96.** 2, 12, 16   **97.** 8, 9, 12, 18   **98.** 8, 12, 16, 18

Objective 2.1E **Apply your knowledge**

99. In the summer, Tony goes to the beach every fourth day. Kathy goes to the beach every sixth day. How often do they see each other at the beach?

100. Joe works on an assembly line that fills boxes with various toy trinkets. Every sixth box gets a red ball and every eighth box gets a blue whistle. How often does a box get both a red ball and a blue whistle?

101. Thomas takes a break from his work every 20 minutes while Elaine takes a break every 30 minutes. How often do they take a break at the same time assuming that they start work together?

102. In a certain factory, a bell rings every 30 minutes and a buzzer sounds every 40 minutes. If Tami hears them both at the same time, how long will it be before she hears them sound together again?

CUMULATIVE SKILLS REVIEW

1. Simplify $30 - (4 - 2)^2 \cdot 7$. (1.6C)

2. Write three hundred twenty-one thousand fourteen in standard notation. (1.1B)

3. Add $18,255 + 1399 + 415$. (1.2B)

4. Evaluate 8^3. (1.6B)

5. Subtract $105 - 26$. (1.3A)

6. Divide $\dfrac{1068}{12}$. (1.5B)

7. Write $6 \cdot 6 \cdot 7 \cdot 7 \cdot 7$ in exponential notation. (1.6A)

8. Multiply $299 \cdot 1000$. (1.4B)

9. Hallmark Industries had profits of $34,232,900 last year. Round this number to the nearest thousand. (1.1D)

10. Write $7540 in word form. (1.1B)

2.2 INTRODUCTION TO FRACTIONS AND MIXED NUMBERS

In the previous chapter, we discussed whole numbers and used them in a variety of applications. But there are other types of numbers aside from just whole numbers. Among these are the fractions. In this section, we discuss fractions and give some common interpretations of them. In later sections, we will learn how to add, subtract, multiply, and divide fractions.

LEARNING OBJECTIVES

A. Identify a fraction and distinguish proper fractions, improper fractions, and mixed numbers

B. Use a fraction to represent a part of a whole

C. Convert between an improper fraction and a mixed or whole number

D. Apply your knowledge

| **Objective 2.2A** | **Identify a fraction and distinguish proper fractions, improper fractions, and mixed numbers** |

In order to properly define a fraction, let's draw part of a *number line*, a line in which each point uniquely corresponds to some number.

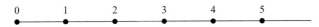

On the part of the number line shown above, the whole numbers correspond to *equally* spaced points. Notice the gaps between 0 and 1, between 1 and 2, between 2 and 3, and so on. Each gap is called an *interval*. In each interval are other numbers including fractions. To obtain fractions, we break each interval into smaller intervals. For example, let's break each interval into two smaller equal-length intervals. We then name each point in the following way.

$$\frac{0}{2} \quad \frac{1}{2} \quad \frac{2}{2} \quad \frac{3}{2} \quad \frac{4}{2} \quad \frac{5}{2} \quad \frac{6}{2} \quad \frac{7}{2} \quad \frac{8}{2} \quad \frac{9}{2} \quad \frac{10}{2} \quad \frac{11}{2}$$

Each point corresponds to a number known as a fraction. Formally, a **fraction** is a number written in the form $\frac{a}{b}$ where a and b are whole numbers and b is not zero.

The top number in a fraction is called the **numerator**, while the bottom number in a fraction is called the **denominator**. The line between the numerator and the denominator is called the **fraction bar**.

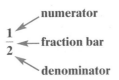

Each fraction on the number line above has a denominator of 2. To obtain fractions with a denominator of 3, we would break each interval into 3 equal intervals. To obtain fractions with a denominator of 4, we would break each interval into 4 equal intervals. Continuing in this way, we could obtain any fraction with any whole number denominator other than 0.

On the number line above, notice that $\frac{0}{2}$ corresponds to 0, $\frac{2}{2}$ corresponds to 1, $\frac{4}{2}$ corresponds to 2, $\frac{6}{2}$ corresponds to 3, and so on. This suggests that a fraction can represent division. In general, $\frac{a}{b} = a \div b$. We shall explore this and another common interpretation of fractions below.

 Learning Tip

The word fraction comes from the Latin word *fractum*, the past participle of the Latin verb *frangere* meaning *to break*. Fractions can be used to represent the parts of something that has been broken up into several smaller equal pieces.

fraction
A number written in the form $\frac{a}{b}$ where a and b are whole numbers and b is not zero.

numerator
The top number in a fraction.

denominator
The bottom number in a fraction.

fraction bar
The line between the numerator and the denominator.

proper fraction or **common fraction**
A fraction in which the numerator is less than the denominator.

A fraction in which the numerator is less than the denominator is called a **proper fraction** or a **common fraction**. Some other examples of proper fractions are as follows:

$$\frac{1}{2} \qquad \frac{3}{16} \qquad \frac{9}{32}$$

improper fraction
A fraction in which the numerator is greater than or equal to the denominator.

A fraction in which the numerator is greater than or equal to the denominator is called an **improper fraction**. Therefore, an improper fraction is always greater than or equal to 1. Some examples of improper fractions are as follows:

$$\frac{15}{11} \qquad \frac{19}{7} \qquad \frac{2}{2}$$

mixed number
A number that combines a whole number with a fraction.

A number that combines a whole number with a fraction is known as a **mixed number**. An example of a mixed number is $2\frac{3}{5}$. It represents $2 + \frac{3}{5}$. Some other examples of mixed numbers are as follows:

$$1\frac{3}{8} \qquad 7\frac{11}{16} \qquad 15\frac{13}{28}$$

We shall soon see that improper fractions and mixed numbers are closely related.

complex fraction
A quotient of the form $\frac{A}{B}$ where A or B or both are fractions and where B is not zero.

A **complex fraction** is a quotient of the form $\frac{A}{B}$ where A or B or both are fractions and where B is not zero. An example of a complex fraction is $\frac{1/2}{4/5}$. Note that both the numerator and denominator are fractions. We will briefly refer to complex fractions when we discuss division of fractions in Section 2.5 and percents in Section 5.1.

EXAMPLE 1   **Classify as a proper fraction, improper fraction, or mixed number**

Classify each as a proper fraction, an improper fraction, or a mixed number.

   a. $\dfrac{45}{16}$

   b. $14\dfrac{2}{5}$

   c. $\dfrac{11}{12}$

SOLUTION STRATEGY

a. $\dfrac{45}{16}$ is an improper fraction.   This is an improper fraction because the numerator, 45, is greater than the denominator, 16.

b. $14\dfrac{2}{5}$ is a mixed number.   This is a mixed number because it combines the whole number 14 with the fraction $\dfrac{2}{5}$.

c. $\dfrac{11}{12}$ is a proper fraction.   This is a proper fraction because the numerator, 11, is less than the denominator, 12.

TRY-IT EXERCISE 1

Classify each as a proper fraction, an improper fraction, or a mixed number.

a. $76\dfrac{3}{4}$ **b.** $\dfrac{3}{5}$ **c.** $\dfrac{23}{18}$

Check your answers with the solutions in Appendix A. ■

Objective 2.2B   **Use a fraction to represent a part of a whole**

While a fraction is really just a number, we frequently use fractions to represent a part of a whole. To understand what we mean, consider a chocolate candy bar divided into 8 equal pieces. Each of the 8 pieces can be represented by the fraction $\dfrac{1}{8}$, or, in words, one-eighth or an eighth. If you ate 3 of the 8 pieces, you would have consumed 3 of the eighths, and so you would use the fraction $\dfrac{3}{8}$ to represent the portion of the candy bar that you ate.

As another example, consider a pizza cut into 12 equal slices. Each of the 12 slices represents $\dfrac{1}{12}$, or, in words, one-twelfth or a twelfth, of the pizza. If you and your friends ate 7 slices, then 7 of the twelfths were consumed. You would use the fraction $\dfrac{7}{12}$ to represent this portion.

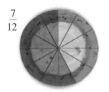

EXAMPLE 2   **Write a fraction or mixed number to represent a shaded portion**

Write a fraction or mixed number to represent the shaded portion of each figure.

a.

b.

c.

SOLUTION STRATEGY

a.

$$\frac{3}{7}$$

There are 3 parts shaded out of a total of 7 parts. The fraction is $\frac{3}{7}$.

b.

$$\frac{9}{16}$$

Each inch on a ruler is divided into 16 equal parts. Since 9 of these parts are highlighted, the fraction $\frac{9}{16}$ represents the shaded portion.

c.

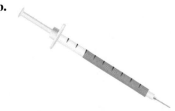

$$\frac{11}{8} \text{ or } 1\frac{3}{8}$$

Each pie is divided into 8 pieces. Thus, 1 piece represents $\frac{1}{8}$ or an *eighth* of a pie. Since 8 pieces of the first pie and 3 pieces of the second pie are shaded, a total of 11 of the *eighths* are shaded. We can use the fraction $\frac{11}{8}$ to represent the shaded portion. Alternatively, because the first pie is entirely shaded and 3 of the 8 pieces of the second pie are shaded, we could use the mixed number $1\frac{3}{8}$ to represent the shaded portion.

TRY-IT EXERCISE 2

Write a fraction or mixed number to represent the shaded portion of each figure.

a.

b.

c.

Check your answers with the solutions in Appendix A. ∎

Objective 2.2C	Convert between an improper fraction and a mixed or whole number

As we saw in Section 1.5, Dividing Whole Numbers, a fraction is frequently used to represent the operation of division. As an example, consider the fraction $\frac{35}{7}$. This fraction can be interpreted as $35 \div 7$. Thus, we write $\frac{35}{7} = 5$. In general, $\frac{a}{b} = a \div b$. We can use this fact to write an improper fraction as either a mixed or whole number.

Steps for Writing an Improper Fraction as a Mixed or Whole Number

Step 1. Divide the numerator by the denominator.

Step 2. a. If there is no remainder, then the improper fraction is equal to the whole number quotient found in step 1.

b. If there is a remainder, then the improper fraction can be written as follows:

$$\text{Quotient} \, \frac{\text{Remainder}}{\text{Divisor}}$$

EXAMPLE 3   **Write an improper fraction as a mixed or whole number**

Write each improper fraction as a mixed or whole number.

a. $\frac{30}{5}$

b. $\frac{9}{2}$

SOLUTION STRATEGY

a. $\frac{30}{5} = 30 \div 5 = 6$ Divide 30 by 5.

b. $\frac{9}{2} = 9 \div 2$ Divide 9 by 2.

$$
\begin{array}{r}
4 \\
2\overline{)9} \\
-8 \\
\hline
1
\end{array}
$$

Use long division.

$\frac{9}{2} = 4\frac{1}{2}$ The quotient, 4, is the whole number part of the mixed number. The remainder, 1, is the numerator of the fractional part. The denominator is 2.

TRY-IT EXERCISE 3

Write each improper fraction as a mixed or whole number.

a. $\dfrac{7}{3}$ **b.** $\dfrac{27}{4}$ **c.** $\dfrac{39}{3}$

Check your answers with the solutions in Appendix A. ■

A nonzero whole number can always be written as an improper fraction. To do so, simply write the number over 1. For example, the whole number 5 can be written as $\dfrac{5}{1}$.

A mixed number can also be written as an improper fraction.

Steps for Writing Mixed Numbers as Improper Fractions

Step 1. Multiply the whole number part by the denominator of the fraction part and add the numerator of the fraction part to this product.

Step 2. Write an improper fraction. The numerator is the result of step 1. The denominator is the original denominator.

EXAMPLE 4   **Write a mixed number as an improper fraction**

Write each mixed number as an improper fraction.

a. $5\dfrac{2}{3}$ **b.** $9\dfrac{5}{6}$

SOLUTION STRATEGY

a. $5\dfrac{2}{3} = \dfrac{5 \cdot 3 + 2}{3}$ Multiply the whole number, 5, by the denominator, 3, and add the numerator, 2, to this product. Place over the original denominator, 3.

$= \dfrac{17}{3}$

b. $9\dfrac{5}{6} = \dfrac{9 \cdot 6 + 5}{6}$ Multiply the whole number, 9, by the denominator, 6, and add the numerator, 5, to this product. Place over the original denominator, 6.

$= \dfrac{59}{6}$

TRY-IT EXERCISE 4

Write each mixed number as an improper fraction.

a. $2\dfrac{3}{4}$

b. $9\dfrac{1}{5}$

c. $22\dfrac{5}{8}$

d. $5\dfrac{4}{7}$

Check your answers with the solutions in Appendix A. ■

Objective 2.2D	**Apply your knowledge**

EXAMPLE 5   Represent data using fractions

An accounting office has 23 employees. Nine of the employees are certified public accountants and the rest are support staff.

a. What fraction of the total do accountants represent?

b. What fraction of the total do support staffers represent?

SOLUTION STRATEGY

a. $\dfrac{9}{23}$ The denominator, 23, represents the total number of employees. The numerator, 9, represents the part of the total to which we are referring—in this case, the number of accountants.

b. $23 - 9 = 14$ To find the number of support staff personnel, subtract the number of accountants, 9, from the total number of employees, 23.

$\dfrac{14}{23}$ The denominator, 23, represents the total number of employees. The numerator, 14, represents the part of the total to which we are referring—in this case, the number of support staffers.

TRY-IT EXERCISE 5

A football team has 55 players. Nineteen play offense, 23 play defense, and the rest are on special teams. What fraction of the total does each category of player represent?

a. Offense

b. Defense

c. Special teams

Check your answers with the solutions in Appendix A. ■

EXAMPLE 6　**Represent time using fractions**

What fraction of an hour does each of the following represent?

a. 23 minutes

b. 91 minutes

SOLUTION STRATEGY

a. $\dfrac{23}{60}$　The denominator, 60, defines the total number of minutes in an hour. The numerator, 23, defines the number to which we are referring.

b. $\dfrac{91}{60}$　In this case, the numerator, 91, is larger than the denominator, 60, resulting in the improper fraction $\dfrac{91}{60}$. As a mixed number, the answer is $1\dfrac{31}{60}$.

TRY-IT EXERCISE 6

What fraction of a year does each of the following represent?

a. 201 days

b. 365 days

c. 448 days

Check your answers with the solutions in Appendix A. ■

SECTION 2.2 REVIEW EXERCISES

Concept Check

1. A _____ is a number written in the form $\dfrac{a}{b}$ where a and b are whole numbers and b is not zero.

2. The top number in a fraction is called the _____.

3. The bottom number in a fraction is called the _____.

4. The line between the numerator and the denominator is known as the _____ _____.

5. A fraction in which the numerator is less than the denominator is known as a _____ fraction.

6. A fraction in which the numerator is greater than or equal to the denominator is known as an _____ fraction.

7. A _____ _____ is a number that combines a whole number with a fraction.

8. A _____ _____ is a quotient of the form $\dfrac{A}{B}$ where A and B are both fractions and where B is not zero.

Objective 2.2A   **Identify a fraction and distinguish proper fractions, improper fractions, and mixed numbers**

GUIDE PROBLEMS

9. Classify each as a proper fraction, an improper fraction, or a mixed number.

   a. $\dfrac{5}{19}$

   The numerator is less than the denominator, which means $\dfrac{5}{19}$ is a(n) _____ .

   b. $\dfrac{13}{8}$

   The numerator is greater than the denominator, which means $\dfrac{13}{8}$ is a(n) _____ .

   c. $3\dfrac{1}{7}$

   Because $3\dfrac{1}{7}$ is a whole number plus a proper fraction, $3\dfrac{1}{7}$ is a _____ .

10. Classify each as a proper fraction, an improper fraction, or a mixed number.

    a. $\dfrac{3}{3}$ is a(n) _____ .

    b. $2\dfrac{3}{10}$ is a(n) _____ .

    c. $\dfrac{9}{22}$ is a(n) _____ .

Classify each as a proper fraction, an improper fraction, or a mixed number.

11. $\dfrac{3}{8}$ 12. $\dfrac{1}{16}$ 13. $\dfrac{9}{9}$ 14. $\dfrac{5}{3}$

15. $4\dfrac{1}{5}$ 16. $12\dfrac{15}{17}$ 17. $\dfrac{33}{6}$ 18. $\dfrac{54}{11}$

19. $\dfrac{7}{7}$ 20. $\dfrac{153}{155}$ 21. $5\dfrac{2}{3}$ 22. $8\dfrac{2}{9}$

Objective 2.2B   **Use a fraction to represent a part of a whole**

GUIDE PROBLEMS

23. Write a fraction or mixed number to represent the shaded portion of each figure.

    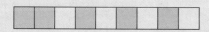

    The rectangle is divided into ____ squares.

    ____ squares are shaded.

    The fraction ____ represents the shaded portion.

24. Write a fraction or mixed number to represent the shaded portion of each figure.

    One inch of the ruler is divided into ____ equal parts. ____ of these equal parts are shaded.

    The fraction ____ represents the shaded portion.

Write a fraction or mixed number to represent the shaded portion of each figure.

25.

26.

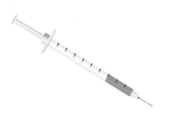

27.

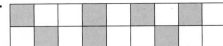

28.

29.

30.

31.

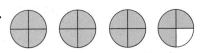

32.

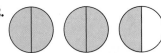

33.

34.

35. What fraction represents the fish in this group of animals?

36. What fraction represents the hammers in this group of tools?

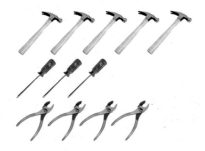

| **Objective 2.2C** | **Convert between an improper fraction and a mixed or whole number** |

GUIDE PROBLEMS

37. Write $\dfrac{54}{9}$ as a mixed or whole number.

$$9\overline{)54}\ \ \leftarrow \text{quotient}$$

$$\leftarrow \text{remainder}$$

$$\frac{54}{9} = \underline{\ \ }$$

38. Write $\dfrac{73}{8}$ as a mixed or whole number.

$$8\overline{)73}\ \ \leftarrow \text{quotient}$$

$$\leftarrow \text{remainder}$$

$$\frac{73}{8} = \underline{\ \ }\frac{\ \ }{8}$$

39. Write $8\dfrac{3}{5}$ as an improper fraction.

$$8\frac{3}{5} = \frac{8 \cdot \underline{\ } + \underline{\ }}{5} = \frac{\ \ }{5}$$

40. Write $9\dfrac{1}{3}$ as an improper fraction.

$$9\frac{1}{3} = \frac{\underline{\ } \cdot \underline{\ } + \underline{\ }}{\underline{\ }} = \frac{\ \ }{\underline{\ }}$$

Write each improper fraction as a mixed or whole number.

41. $\dfrac{90}{9}$ **42.** $\dfrac{48}{8}$ **43.** $\dfrac{13}{2}$ **44.** $\dfrac{114}{11}$

45. $\dfrac{88}{9}$ **46.** $\dfrac{43}{6}$ **47.** $\dfrac{130}{10}$ **48.** $\dfrac{54}{3}$

49. $\dfrac{15}{8}$ **50.** $\dfrac{63}{7}$ **51.** $\dfrac{40}{3}$ **52.** $\dfrac{26}{3}$

53. $\dfrac{31}{3}$ **54.** $\dfrac{124}{17}$ **55.** $\dfrac{131}{12}$ **56.** $\dfrac{104}{11}$

Write each mixed number as an improper fraction.

57. $10\dfrac{3}{7}$ **58.** $7\dfrac{2}{3}$ **59.** $11\dfrac{3}{5}$ **60.** $2\dfrac{5}{8}$

61. $7\dfrac{3}{10}$ **62.** $6\dfrac{2}{3}$ **63.** $8\dfrac{4}{5}$ **64.** $6\dfrac{5}{6}$

65. $12\frac{2}{3}$　　　　**66.** $7\frac{2}{13}$　　　　**67.** $12\frac{1}{10}$　　　　**68.** $13\frac{1}{4}$

69. $10\frac{8}{13}$　　　　**70.** $12\frac{2}{9}$　　　　**71.** $9\frac{1}{7}$　　　　**72.** $7\frac{1}{10}$

Objective 2.2D　　**Apply your knowledge**

73. An English class with 37 students has 21 females.

　a. What fraction of the total do female students represent?

　b. What fraction of the total do male students represent?

74. On a 40-question chemistry test, you answer 33 questions correctly.

　a. What fraction of the total do the correct answers represent?

　b. What fraction of the total do the wrong answers represent?

75. Your college football team has a total of 55 players. If 14 are freshmen, what fraction of the total do the freshman players represent?

76. If you attended 5 hours of class on Tuesday, what fraction of the day represents the time you were in class?

77. What fraction of a week does each of the following represent?

　a. 3 days?

　b. 11 days?

78. A digital memory card holds 215 pictures. If you took 71 pictures at a party last night, what fraction of the total do the remaining exposures represent?

79. While at the mall, you spent $24 on a pair of jeans, $17 on a shirt, and $42 on a jacket. You had budgeted to spend $200 that day.

　a. What fraction of your budget do your spendings represent?

　b. What fraction of your budget remains?

80. Your associate's degree requires 63 credits. You have already completed four 3-credit courses and three 4-credit courses.

　a. What fraction of the required credits have you completed?

　b. What fraction of required credits remain before you can graduate?

81. A charity has raised $11,559 of its $30,000 goal.

    a. What fraction of the goal amount represents the amount that still needs to be raised?

    b. What fraction of the goal amount would have been raised if the goal amount were changed to $36,000?

82. An office building has 10,950 square feet of office space. If 3373 square feet are rented, what fraction of the total space is still available?

83. You currently appear in a play at your school's drama theater beginning next Monday and running for 7 days. There is one performance each day at 8 PM, and on Friday and Saturday there is an additional afternoon show at 3 PM. What fraction of the total number of performances have you given after Thursday's show?

84. According to the College Board, the estimated cost of one year of college including tuition, fees, room, and board during the 2006–2007 academic year was $12,796 for a public 4-year school and $30,367 for a private 4-year school.

    a. What fraction represents public school expenses as a portion of private school expenses?

    b. What type of fraction is the answer to part a?

    c. What fraction represents private school expenses as a portion of public school expenses?

    d. What type of fraction is the answer to part c?

CUMULATIVE SKILLS REVIEW

1. Find the factors of 16. (2.1A)

2. Subtract $452 - 199$. (1.3A)

3. Simplify $48 + (3 + 2)3$. (1.6C)

4. Evaluate 7^3. (1.6B)

5. Round 132,596 to the nearest thousand. (1.1D)

6. Evaluate $322 \div 14$. (1.5B)

7. Is 65 prime, composite, or neither? (2.1B)

8. Multiply $22 \cdot 15$. (1.4B)

9. Write 125662 in standard notation and in words. (1.1B)

10. Multiply $143 \cdot 10,000$. (1.4B)

2.3 EQUIVALENT FRACTIONS

LEARNING OBJECTIVES

A. Simplify a fraction

B. Write an equivalent fraction with a larger denominator

C. Compare fractions using the least common denominator (LCD)

D. Apply your knowledge

equivalent fractions
Fractions that represent the same quantity.

fraction simplified to lowest terms
A fraction in which the numerator and denominator have no common factor other than 1.

From the illustrations below, we can see that $\frac{8}{12}$ and $\frac{2}{3}$ represent the same quantity. However, because the second fraction involves smaller numbers in each of the numerator and denominator, we generally prefer to use $\frac{2}{3}$ rather than $\frac{8}{12}$, especially when expressing a final result. Fractions that represent the same quantity are called **equivalent fractions**.

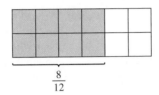
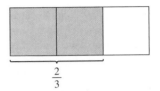

$$\frac{8}{12} \qquad\qquad \frac{2}{3}$$

Objective 2.3A **Simplify a fraction**

A fraction in which the numerator and denominator have no common factor other than 1 is called a **fraction simplified to lowest terms**. To simplify a fraction to lowest terms, we can write the prime factorization for each of the numerator and denominator. We then divide the numerator and denominator by each common factor.

As an example, let's consider the fraction $\frac{6}{9}$. In order to simplify this fraction, we write each of the numerator and denominator in terms of its prime factorization.

$$\frac{6}{9} = \frac{2 \cdot 3}{3 \cdot 3}$$

Then, we divide the numerator and denominator by each common factor. In this case, the only common factor is 3. To divide out a common factor, use the convention of crossing out the numbers in each of the numerator and denominator that share a common factor.

$$\frac{6}{9} = \frac{2 \cdot \overset{1}{\cancel{3}}}{3 \cdot \underset{1}{\cancel{3}}} = \frac{2 \cdot 1}{3 \cdot 1}$$

Finally, we multiply the remaining factors in the numerator and denominator to determine the simplified fraction.

$$\frac{6}{9} = \frac{2 \cdot 1}{3 \cdot 1} = \frac{2}{3}$$

The following steps summarize the process for simplifying fractions.

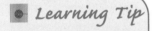

Learning Tip

In this chapter, "simplify" means "simplify to lowest terms." Fractions simplified to lowest terms may also be referred to as follows.

- reduced
- reduced to lowest terms
- in lowest terms
- simplified
- simplified completely

Steps for Simplifying a Fraction Using Prime Factorization

Step 1. Write the prime factorizations of the numerator and denominator.

Step 2. Divide out any factors common to the numerator and denominator.

Step 3. Multiply the remaining factors in the numerator and denominator to determine the simplified fraction.

EXAMPLE 1   Simplify a fraction using prime factorizations

Simplify each fraction using the prime factorizations of the numerator and denominator.

a. $\dfrac{28}{50}$

b. $\dfrac{63}{210}$

SOLUTION STRATEGY

a. $\dfrac{28}{50} = \dfrac{2 \cdot 2 \cdot 7}{2 \cdot 5 \cdot 5}$

Write the prime factorizations of the numerator and denominator.

$= \dfrac{\overset{1}{2} \cdot 2 \cdot 7}{\underset{1}{2} \cdot 5 \cdot 5}$

Divide out the common factor, 2.

$= \dfrac{1 \cdot 2 \cdot 7}{1 \cdot 5 \cdot 5} = \dfrac{14}{25}$

Multiply the remaining factors in the numerator and denominator to determine the simplified fraction.

b. $\dfrac{63}{210} = \dfrac{3 \cdot 3 \cdot 7}{2 \cdot 3 \cdot 5 \cdot 7}$

Write the prime factorizations of the numerator and denominator.

$= \dfrac{\overset{1}{3} \cdot 3 \cdot \overset{1}{7}}{2 \cdot \underset{1}{3} \cdot 5 \cdot \underset{1}{7}}$

Divide out the common factors, 3 and 7.

$= \dfrac{1 \cdot 3 \cdot 1}{2 \cdot 1 \cdot 5 \cdot 1} = \dfrac{3}{10}$

Multiply the remaining factors in the numerator and denominator to determine the simplified fraction.

TRY-IT EXERCISE 1

Simplify each fraction using the prime factorizations of the numerator and denominator.

a. $\dfrac{30}{55}$

b. $\dfrac{72}{148}$

Check your answers with the solutions in Appendix A. ∎

It is not necessary to write the prime factorizations of the numerator and denominator in order to simplify a fraction. Rather, it is often easier to inspect the fraction for a factor common to both the numerator and denominator. For example, we could simplify the fraction $\dfrac{6}{10}$ by noting that 2 is a factor common to both the numerator and denominator. We then simplify the fraction by dividing both the numerator and denominator by 2.

$$\frac{6}{10} = \frac{\overset{3}{6}}{\underset{5}{10}} = \frac{3}{5}$$

To simplify the fraction $\frac{6}{10}$, divide both the numerator and denominator by the common factor, 2. We can explicitly indicate this division as follows.

$$\frac{6}{10} = \frac{6 \div 2}{10 \div 2} = \frac{3}{5}$$

Likewise, to simplify the fraction $\frac{8}{12}$, divide both the numerator and denominator by the common factor, 4. We can explicitly indicate this division as follows.

$$\frac{8}{12} = \frac{8 \div 4}{12 \div 4} = \frac{2}{3}$$

In this text, we will use the convention of crossing out the numerator and denominator when dividing out a common factor.

greatest common factor or **GCF**
The largest factor common to two or more numbers.

A fraction referred to as *reduced* does not mean that the fraction is smaller. It simply means that smaller numbers are used to describe the fraction.

As another example, consider $\frac{8}{12}$. Note that 4 is a factor common to both 8 and 12. We can simplify the fraction by dividing both the numerator and denominator by 4.

$$\frac{8}{12} = \frac{\overset{2}{\cancel{8}}}{\underset{3}{\cancel{12}}} = \frac{2}{3}$$

In simplifying fractions, we often seek the largest factor that is common to both the numerator and denominator. The **greatest common factor** or **GCF** is the largest factor common to two or more numbers.

Sometimes, the GCF isn't obvious. In such cases, divide out any common factors until the fraction is simplified completely.

Steps for Simplifying a Fraction

Step 1. Identify and divide out any factors common to the numerator and the denominator. Use the greatest common factor if you can identify it.

Step 2. If a common factor remains in the numerator and denominator of the resulting fraction, repeat step 1 until the fraction is simplified to lowest terms.

EXAMPLE 2   Simplify a fraction

Simplify each fraction.

a. $\dfrac{48}{54}$ **b.** $\dfrac{30}{75}$

SOLUTION STRATEGY

a. $\dfrac{48}{54} = \dfrac{\overset{24}{\cancel{48}}}{\underset{27}{\cancel{54}}} = \dfrac{24}{27}$ 2 is a factor common to the numerator and the denominator. Divide out the common factor, 2.

$\dfrac{24}{27} = \dfrac{\overset{8}{\cancel{24}}}{\underset{9}{\cancel{27}}} = \dfrac{8}{9}$ 3 is a factor common to the numerator and the denominator. Divide out the common factor, 3.

The only factor common to 8 and 9 is 1.

b. $\dfrac{30}{75} = \dfrac{\overset{6}{\cancel{30}}}{\underset{15}{\cancel{75}}} = \dfrac{6}{15}$ 5 is a factor common to the numerator and the denominator. Divide out the common factor, 5.

$\dfrac{6}{15} = \dfrac{\overset{2}{\cancel{6}}}{\underset{5}{\cancel{15}}} = \dfrac{2}{5}$ 3 is a factor common to the numerator and the denominator. Divide out the common factor, 3.

The only factor common to 2 and 5 is 1.

TRY-IT EXERCISE 2

Simplify each fraction.

a. $\dfrac{18}{42}$

b. $\dfrac{45}{80}$

Check your answers with the solutions in Appendix A. ■

| Objective 2.3B | **Write an equivalent fraction with a larger denominator** |

Aside from simplifying fractions, we can also create an equivalent fraction by rewriting the fraction with a larger denominator. To do this, divide the new denominator by the original denominator and multiply the numerator and denominator of the original fraction by this quotient.

As an example, let's write $\dfrac{3}{4}$ as an equivalent fraction with a denominator of 8. To do this, divide the new denominator, 8, by the original denominator, 4. Since $8 \div 4 = 2$, multiply both the numerator and denominator of the original fraction by 2.

$$\frac{3}{4} = \frac{3 \cdot 2}{4 \cdot 2} = \frac{6}{8}$$

Thus, $\dfrac{3}{4}$ is equivalent to $\dfrac{6}{8}$.

In the preceding example, when we multiply both the numerator and denominator by 2, we are actually multiplying the fraction by 1 in the form of $\dfrac{2}{2}$. The multiplication property of 1 tells us that the result of multiplying any number by 1 is the original number. Consequently, when we multiply $\dfrac{3}{4}$ by 1 in the form of $\dfrac{2}{2}$, the value of the fraction does not change even though its form does. We will see how to multiply fractions in the next section.

Rule for Writing an Equivalent Fraction with a Larger Denominator

To find an equivalent fraction for $\dfrac{a}{b}$ with a larger denominator, multiply both the numerator and denominator by the same nonzero whole number, n. In general, we have the following.

$$\frac{a}{b} = \frac{a \cdot n}{b \cdot n}$$

EXAMPLE 3   Write an equivalent fraction with a larger denominator

Write each fraction as an equivalent fraction with the indicated denominator.

a. $\dfrac{2}{3}$ with a denominator of 15

b. $\dfrac{3}{5}$ with a denominator of 40

SOLUTION STRATEGY

a. $\dfrac{2}{3} = \dfrac{2 \cdot 5}{3 \cdot 5} = \dfrac{10}{15}$ Multiply the numerator and denominator of the original fraction by 5.

b. $\dfrac{3}{5} = \dfrac{3 \cdot 8}{5 \cdot 8} = \dfrac{24}{40}$ Multiply the numerator and the denominator of the original fraction by 8.

TRY-IT EXERCISE 3

Write each fraction as an equivalent fraction with the indicated denominator.

a. $\dfrac{3}{4}$ with a denominator of 12

b. $\dfrac{5}{8}$ with a denominator of 56

Check your answer with the solutions in Appendix A. ■

Objective 2.3C   ### Compare fractions using the least common denominator (LCD)

Sometimes it is necessary to compare fractions. For example, we may know that three-fifths of the respondents to a survey prefer warm vacation getaways, while two-fifths of the survey participants prefer cold vacation adventures. To decide which type of vacation is preferred most by respondents to the survey, we must compare the fractions three-fifths and two-fifths. To do so, consider the following figures that represent the fractions in question.

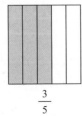

$$\dfrac{3}{5}$$

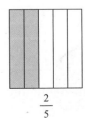

$$\dfrac{2}{5}$$

We see that the larger fraction corresponds to the larger shaded portion of each figure. Thus, $\frac{3}{5} > \frac{2}{5}$. Recall that "<" means "is less than" and ">" means "is greater than."

Fractions with the same denominator are called **like fractions**. In general, to compare like fractions, simply compare the numerators.

Suppose that $\frac{4}{5}$ of the students passed a test in one class and $\frac{5}{6}$ passed the same test in another class. Which class has the lower pass rate? To answer this question, we need to determine which fraction is smaller, $\frac{4}{5}$ or $\frac{5}{6}$. In this case, the fractions are not like, so we cannot simply compare the numerators. When it is difficult to determine which fraction has the smaller or larger value, writing equivalent fractions with the same denominator will make the answer evident. To do this, we must determine a common denominator.

In general, a **common denominator** is a common multiple of all the denominators for a set of fractions. There are many such common denominators, but usually we use the smallest one. The **least common denominator** or **LCD** is the least common multiple (LCM) of all the denominators for a set of fractions. For example, to determine the smaller of the fractions $\frac{4}{5}$ and $\frac{5}{6}$, we must determine the LCD, that is, the LCM of the denominators. Refer back to Section 2.1 for a review of LCMs.

The LCM of 5 and 6 is 30, and so the LCD of $\frac{4}{5}$ and $\frac{5}{6}$ is 30. For each of these fractions, write an equivalent fraction with a denominator of 30.

$$\frac{4}{5} = \frac{4 \cdot 6}{5 \cdot 6} = \frac{24}{30} \qquad \text{Multiply the numerator and denominator by 6.}$$

$$\frac{5}{6} = \frac{5 \cdot 5}{6 \cdot 5} = \frac{25}{30} \qquad \text{Multiply the numerator and denominator by 5.}$$

We note that 24 is less than 25, and so $\frac{24}{30}$ is less than $\frac{25}{30}$. Thus, $\frac{4}{5}$ is less than $\frac{5}{6}$.

$$\frac{4}{5} < \frac{5}{6} \quad \text{or} \quad \frac{5}{6} > \frac{4}{5}$$

Use the following steps to list fractions in order of value.

like fractions
Fractions with the same denominator.

common denominator
A common multiple of all the denominators for a set of fractions.

least common denominator or LCD
The least common multiple (LCM) of all the denominators for a set of fractions.

Steps for Comparing Fractions

Step 1. Find the LCD of the fractions.

Step 2. Write each fraction as an equivalent fraction with a denominator equal to the LCD.

Step 3. Compare the numerators.

EXAMPLE 4   Compare fractions

Compare the fractions.

a. $\dfrac{2}{3}, \dfrac{5}{8}$ b. $\dfrac{3}{4}, \dfrac{3}{5}, \dfrac{7}{10}$

SOLUTION STRATEGY

a. $\dfrac{2}{3} = \dfrac{2 \cdot 8}{3 \cdot 8} = \dfrac{16}{24}$ The LCD of $\dfrac{2}{3}$ and $\dfrac{5}{8}$ is 24.

$\dfrac{5}{8} = \dfrac{5 \cdot 3}{8 \cdot 3} = \dfrac{15}{24}$ Write each fraction as an equivalent fraction with a denominator of 24.

$\dfrac{5}{8} < \dfrac{2}{3}$ Because $15 < 16$, $\dfrac{15}{24} < \dfrac{16}{24}$. Thus, $\dfrac{5}{8} < \dfrac{2}{3}$.

b. $\dfrac{3}{4} = \dfrac{3 \cdot 5}{4 \cdot 5} = \dfrac{15}{20}$ The LCD of $\dfrac{3}{4}, \dfrac{3}{5}$, and $\dfrac{7}{10}$ is 20.

$\dfrac{3}{5} = \dfrac{3 \cdot 4}{5 \cdot 4} = \dfrac{12}{20}$ Write each fraction as an equivalent fraction with a denominator of 20.

$\dfrac{7}{10} = \dfrac{7 \cdot 2}{10 \cdot 2} = \dfrac{14}{20}$ Because $12 < 14 < 15$, $\dfrac{12}{20} < \dfrac{14}{20} < \dfrac{15}{20}$.

$\dfrac{3}{5} < \dfrac{7}{10} < \dfrac{3}{4}$ Thus, $\dfrac{3}{5} < \dfrac{7}{10} < \dfrac{3}{4}$.

TRY-IT EXERCISE 4

Compare the fractions.

a. $\dfrac{2}{5}, \dfrac{3}{7}$ b. $\dfrac{3}{8}, \dfrac{2}{5}, \dfrac{1}{4}$

Check your answer with the solutions in Appendix A. ■

Objective 2.3D   ## Apply your knowledge

EXAMPLE 5   Compare fractions in an application problem

Frank's instructor said that on a recent math test, 12 of 28 students in the class received a grade of B.

a. What fraction represents the portion of the class that received Bs on the math test? Simplify this fraction.

b. What fraction represents the portion of the class that did not receive Bs? Simplify this fraction.

SOLUTION STRATEGY

a. $\dfrac{12}{28}$

The number of students who received a B on the math test is 12. The total number of students who took the test is 28.

$\dfrac{12}{28} = \dfrac{\overset{3}{\cancel{12}}}{\underset{7}{\cancel{28}}} = \dfrac{3}{7}$

The greatest common factor of 12 and 28 is 4.
Divide out the common factor, 4.

b. $28 - 12 = 16$

$\dfrac{16}{28}$

To find the number of students who did not receive a B, subtract 12, the number of students who received a B, from 28, the total number of students.

$\dfrac{16}{28} = \dfrac{\overset{4}{\cancel{16}}}{\underset{7}{\cancel{28}}} = \dfrac{4}{7}$

The greatest common factor of 16 and 28 is 4.
Divide out the common factor, 4.

TRY-IT EXERCISE 5

At a recent boat show, 160 of the 582 boats on display were sailboats.

a. What fraction represents the portion of the boats that were sailboats at the show? Simplify this fraction.

b. What fraction represents the portion of the boats that were not sailboats? Simplify this fraction.

Check your answers with the solutions in Appendix A. ■

SECTION 2.3 REVIEW EXERCISES

Concept Check

1. Fractions that represent the same quantity are called _____ fractions.

2. A fraction in which the numerator and denominator have no common factor other than 1 is a fraction _____ to lowest terms.

3. The largest factor common to two or more numbers is known as the _____ _____ _____ or _____.

4. To simplify fractions to lowest terms, _____ _____ any factors common to the numerator and denominator. Use the greatest common factor if you can identify it.

5. When we multiply the numerator and denominator of a fraction by the same nonzero number, we are actually multiplying the fraction by _____.

6. To find an equivalent fraction with a larger denominator, _____ the numerator and denominator by the same nonzero whole number.

7. A _____ _____ is a common multiple of all the denominators for a set of fractions.

8. The _____ _____ _____ or _____ is the least common multiple (LCM) of all the denominators for a set of fractions.

9. To list fractions in order of value, first find the _____ of the fractions. Then, write each fraction as an _____ fraction with this denominator. Then, list the fractions in order by comparing their _____.

10. The inequality symbol "$<$" means "is _____ than," while the inequality symbol "$>$" means "is _____ than."

Objective 2.3A	Simplify a fraction

GUIDE PROBLEMS

11. Consider the fraction $\dfrac{20}{24}$.

    a. Write the prime factorization of the numerator.

    $20 = \underline{} \cdot \underline{} \cdot \underline{}$

    b. Write the prime factorization of the denominator.

    $24 = \underline{} \cdot \underline{} \cdot \underline{} \cdot \underline{}$

    c. Simplify $\dfrac{20}{24}$ by dividing out the factors common to the numerator and denominator.

    $\dfrac{20}{24} = \dfrac{\underline{}}{\underline{}} = \dfrac{\underline{}}{\underline{}}$

12. Consider the fraction $\dfrac{16}{36}$.

    a. Write the prime factorization of 16.

    $16 = \underline{} \cdot \underline{} \cdot \underline{} \cdot \underline{}$

    b. Write the prime factorization of 36.

    $36 = \underline{} \cdot \underline{} \cdot \underline{} \cdot \underline{}$

    c. Simplify $\dfrac{16}{36}$ by dividing out the factors common to the numerator and denominator.

    $\dfrac{16}{36} = \dfrac{\underline{}}{\underline{}} = \dfrac{\underline{}}{\underline{}}$

13. Consider the fraction $\dfrac{12}{20}$.

    a. What is the greatest common factor (GCF) of the numerator and denominator of $\dfrac{12}{20}$?

    b. Simplify $\dfrac{12}{20}$ by dividing out the GCF.

    $\dfrac{\overline{12}}{\underset{\underline{}}{20}} = \dfrac{}{}$

14. Consider the fraction $\dfrac{18}{60}$.

    a. What is the greatest common factor (GCF) of the numerator and denominator of $\dfrac{18}{60}$?

    b. Simplify $\dfrac{18}{60}$ by dividing out the GCF.

    $\dfrac{\overline{18}}{\underset{\underline{}}{60}} = \dfrac{}{}$

Simplify each fraction.

15. $\dfrac{6}{14}$

16. $\dfrac{9}{24}$

17. $\dfrac{6}{36}$

18. $\dfrac{3}{27}$

19. $\dfrac{8}{36}$

20. $\dfrac{6}{15}$

21. $\dfrac{2}{22}$

22. $\dfrac{7}{77}$

23. $\dfrac{16}{20}$

24. $\dfrac{24}{64}$

25. $\dfrac{7}{19}$

26. $\dfrac{13}{23}$

27. $\dfrac{9}{90}$

28. $\dfrac{16}{80}$

29. $\dfrac{32}{56}$

30. $\dfrac{30}{48}$

31. $\dfrac{48}{80}$

32. $\dfrac{32}{48}$

33. $\dfrac{7}{24}$

34. $\dfrac{3}{17}$

35. $\dfrac{9}{75}$

36. $\dfrac{9}{39}$

37. $\dfrac{26}{40}$

38. $\dfrac{77}{84}$

39. $\dfrac{28}{60}$

40. $\dfrac{63}{78}$

41. $\dfrac{43}{79}$

42. $\dfrac{13}{53}$

43. $\dfrac{44}{80}$

44. $\dfrac{48}{78}$

45. $\dfrac{40}{78}$

46. $\dfrac{60}{62}$

47. $\dfrac{62}{70}$

48. $\dfrac{46}{72}$

49. $\dfrac{65}{79}$

50. $\dfrac{37}{79}$

Objective 2.3B	Write an equivalent fraction with a larger denominator

GUIDE PROBLEMS

51. Write $\frac{2}{3}$ as an equivalent fraction with a denominator of 30.

$$\frac{2}{3} = \frac{2 \cdot}{3 \cdot 10} = \frac{}{30}$$

52. Write $\frac{3}{5}$ as an equivalent fraction with a denominator of 35.

$$\frac{3}{5} = \frac{3 \cdot}{5 \cdot 7} = \frac{}{35}$$

53. Write $\frac{5}{6}$ as an equivalent fraction with a denominator of 24.

$$\frac{5}{6} = \frac{5 \cdot}{6 \cdot} = \frac{}{24}$$

54. Write $\frac{7}{8}$ as an equivalent fraction with a denominator of 48.

$$\frac{7}{8} = \frac{7 \cdot}{8 \cdot \underline{}} = \frac{}{48}$$

Write each fraction as an equivalent fraction with the indicated denominator.

55. $\dfrac{1}{8} = \dfrac{?}{56}$

56. $\dfrac{3}{4} = \dfrac{?}{24}$

57. $\dfrac{5}{8} = \dfrac{?}{64}$

58. $\dfrac{1}{10} = \dfrac{?}{70}$

59. $\dfrac{5}{8} = \dfrac{?}{48}$

60. $\dfrac{1}{8} = \dfrac{?}{32}$

61. $\dfrac{7}{11} = \dfrac{?}{99}$

62. $\dfrac{1}{3} = \dfrac{?}{24}$

63. $\dfrac{1}{3} = \dfrac{?}{27}$

64. $\dfrac{7}{13} = \dfrac{?}{65}$

65. $\dfrac{1}{13} = \dfrac{?}{78}$

66. $\dfrac{1}{4} = \dfrac{?}{32}$

67. $\dfrac{11}{13} = \dfrac{?}{78}$

68. $\dfrac{8}{11} = \dfrac{?}{77}$

69. $\dfrac{5}{13} = \dfrac{?}{52}$

70. $\dfrac{3}{11} = \dfrac{?}{99}$

71. $\dfrac{9}{14} = \dfrac{?}{98}$

72. $\dfrac{1}{8} = \dfrac{?}{64}$

73. $\dfrac{3}{4} = \dfrac{?}{28}$

74. $\dfrac{2}{3} = \dfrac{?}{120}$

75. $\dfrac{5}{8} = \dfrac{?}{40}$

76. $\dfrac{3}{5} = \dfrac{?}{60}$

77. $\dfrac{2}{13} = \dfrac{?}{65}$

78. $\dfrac{9}{10} = \dfrac{?}{300}$

79. $\dfrac{11}{14} = \dfrac{?}{70}$ **80.** $\dfrac{2}{9} = \dfrac{?}{180}$ **81.** $\dfrac{7}{16} = \dfrac{?}{48}$ **82.** $\dfrac{5}{12} = \dfrac{?}{96}$

83. $\dfrac{16}{17} = \dfrac{?}{34}$ **84.** $\dfrac{9}{13} = \dfrac{?}{39}$ **85.** $\dfrac{5}{14} = \dfrac{?}{84}$ **86.** $\dfrac{6}{11} = \dfrac{?}{55}$

Objective 2.3C	Compare fractions using the least common denominator (LCD)

GUIDE PROBLEMS

87. List the fractions $\dfrac{3}{5}$ and $\dfrac{5}{9}$ in ascending order.

    a. Find the LCD of the fractions.

        The LCD of $\dfrac{3}{5}$ and $\dfrac{5}{9}$ is ___.

    b. Write each fraction as an equivalent fraction with the denominator determined in part a.

        $\dfrac{3}{5} = \dfrac{3\cdot\rule{1em}{0.4pt}}{5\cdot\rule{1em}{0.4pt}} = \dfrac{}{} = \dfrac{}{}$

        $\dfrac{5}{9} = \dfrac{5\cdot\rule{1em}{0.4pt}}{9\cdot\rule{1em}{0.4pt}} = \dfrac{}{} = \dfrac{}{}$

    c. Compare the fractions.

        $\dfrac{}{} = \dfrac{}{}$ or, in lowest terms, as $\dfrac{5}{9}$ $\dfrac{}{}$.

88. List the fractions $\dfrac{4}{9}, \dfrac{1}{3}, \dfrac{5}{6}$ in ascending order.

    a. Find the LCD of the fractions.

        The LCD of $\dfrac{4}{9}, \dfrac{1}{3}$, and $\dfrac{5}{6}$ is ___.

    b. Write each fraction as an equivalent fraction with the denominator determined in part a.

        $\dfrac{4}{9} = \dfrac{4\cdot\rule{1em}{0.4pt}}{9\cdot\rule{1em}{0.4pt}} = \dfrac{}{} = \dfrac{}{}$

        $\dfrac{1}{3} = \dfrac{1\cdot\rule{1em}{0.4pt}}{3\cdot\rule{1em}{0.4pt}} = \dfrac{}{} = \dfrac{}{}$

        $\dfrac{5}{6} = \dfrac{5\cdot\rule{1em}{0.4pt}}{6\cdot\rule{1em}{0.4pt}} = \dfrac{}{} = \dfrac{}{}$

    c. Compare the fractions.

        $\dfrac{}{} < \dfrac{}{} < \dfrac{}{}$ or, in lowest terms, as

        $\dfrac{1}{3} < \dfrac{}{} < \dfrac{}{}$.

Compare the fractions.

89. $\dfrac{7}{10}, \dfrac{5}{8}$ **90.** $\dfrac{3}{4}, \dfrac{11}{15}$ **91.** $\dfrac{1}{14}, \dfrac{3}{8}$ **92.** $\dfrac{7}{12}, \dfrac{11}{18}$

93. $\dfrac{1}{4}, \dfrac{1}{6}, \dfrac{1}{2}$ **94.** $\dfrac{9}{16}, \dfrac{5}{8}, \dfrac{7}{12}$ **95.** $\dfrac{5}{6}, \dfrac{1}{2}, \dfrac{2}{3}$ **96.** $\dfrac{1}{6}, \dfrac{1}{4}, \dfrac{3}{8}$

97. $\dfrac{9}{16}, \dfrac{8}{32}, \dfrac{5}{24}$ **98.** $\dfrac{1}{5}, \dfrac{3}{7}, \dfrac{57}{70}$ **99.** $\dfrac{7}{12}, \dfrac{1}{18}, \dfrac{4}{9}, \dfrac{7}{8}$ **100.** $\dfrac{4}{7}, \dfrac{3}{14}, \dfrac{5}{12}, \dfrac{8}{9}$

101. If 240 of 380 students in a lecture class are females, what fraction represents the males in the class? Simplify.

102. If 435 of 1830 students at a small college are juniors, what fraction represents the students that are not juniors? Simplify.

103. Sandy bought a car for $16,000 and paid $6000 down. Write a fraction to express the down payment as a part of the sales price. Simplify.

104. A box contains 50 high-density computer diskettes, and 18 of them are used for a project.

    a. What fraction represents the portion used for the project? Simplify.

    b. What fraction represents the portion of diskettes remaining?

105. Sergio worked 26 hours so far this week. He normally works a 40-hour week. What fraction represents the portion of hours he has worked? Simplify.

106. A box of 24 assorted chocolates contains 8 pieces with nuts, 10 pieces with cream filling, and the rest split evenly between light and dark solid chocolate. What fraction represents the portion that is dark solid chocolate? Simplify.

107. In a shipment of 40 cartons of merchandise, a store received 12 cartons on time, 20 cartons late, and the rest never arrived. What fraction represents the cartons that did not arrive?

108. An automobile dealership sold 25 cars and 35 sport utility vehicles (SUVs) last week.

    a. What fraction of the total number of vehicles represents the cars sold?

    b. What fraction of the total number of vehicles represents the SUVs sold?

109. A company has 8 warehouses in California, 7 in Texas, 4 in Missouri, 2 in Virginia, 5 in New York, 1 in Georgia, and 1 in Florida. What fraction represents the warehouses in Virginia, Georgia, and Florida combined?

110. Last week you earned $130 at a part-time job. If you spent $65 to repair your car and $19 for school supplies, what fraction represents the portion of your earnings that you have left?

111. According to industry figures from the Consumer Electronics Association, consumer electronics sales in the United States reached $136 billion in 2006, up from $122 billion in 2005. What fraction represents the 2005 sales as a portion of the 2006 sales? Simplify.

112. Jane's recipe for brownies calls for $\frac{2}{3}$ cup of flour. Terri has a similar recipe that calls for $\frac{3}{4}$ cup of flour. Which recipe calls for the most flour?

113. Thomas wishes to order some washers from a parts list. The two washers measure $\frac{5}{12}$ inches and $\frac{3}{8}$ inches. What is the size of the smaller washer?

114. Roxy orders three individual items weighing $\frac{5}{6}$ pound, $\frac{2}{3}$ pound, and $\frac{3}{5}$ pound, respectively. What is the weight of the lightest item?

115. Three trucks are loaded with gravel weighing $1\frac{5}{8}$ tons, $1\frac{2}{3}$, and $1\frac{7}{10}$ tons, respectively. What is the weight of the heaviest load?

CUMULATIVE SKILLS REVIEW

1. Write $\frac{55}{12}$ as a mixed number. (2.2C)

2. Find the sum of 789, 502, and 1851. (1.2C)

3. What is the average of 32, 34, 16, and 62? (1.5C)

4. Simplify $\frac{3(14 - 2) + 3^2}{5}$. (1.6C)

5. What is the area of a square with sides measuring 12 feet? (1.6D)

6. Write 16607 in standard notation and in word form. (1.1B)

7. Write $4\frac{8}{15}$ as an improper fraction. (2.1C)

8. What fraction of an hour is 23 minutes? (2.2D)

9. In your garden, one plant is watered every 2 days while another is watered every 3 days. How often are they watered on the same day? (2.1E)

10. Subtract $31,400 - 451$. (1.3A)

2.4 MULTIPLYING FRACTIONS AND MIXED NUMBERS

LEARNING OBJECTIVES

A. Multiply fractions

B. Multiply fractions, mixed numbers, or whole numbers

C. Apply your knowledge

Suppose a certain cookie recipe requires $\frac{1}{3}$ cup of brown sugar. If you want to make half the number of cookies, how many cups of brown sugar would you need? As we will see in Example 4a, this is a problem that involves multiplication of fractions.

Objective 2.4A   Multiply fractions

The following steps are used to multiply fractions.

Steps for Multiplying Fractions

Step 1. Multiply the numerators to form the new numerator.

Step 2. Multiply the denominators to form the new denominator.

Step 3. Simplify, if possible.

EXAMPLE 1   Multiply fractions

Multiply. Simplify, if possible.

a. $\dfrac{5}{7} \cdot \dfrac{3}{4}$

b. $\dfrac{2}{3} \cdot \dfrac{7}{9}$

c. $\dfrac{1}{4} \cdot \dfrac{6}{7}$

SOLUTION STRATEGY

a. $\dfrac{5}{7} \cdot \dfrac{3}{4} = \dfrac{15}{28}$ Multiply $5 \cdot 3$ to form the new numerator.

Multiply $7 \cdot 4$ to form the new denominator.

b. $\dfrac{2}{3} \cdot \dfrac{7}{9} = \dfrac{14}{27}$ Multiply $2 \cdot 7$ to form the new numerator.

Multiply $3 \cdot 9$ to form the new denominator.

c. $\dfrac{1}{4} \cdot \dfrac{6}{7} = \dfrac{6}{28}$ Multiply $1 \cdot 6$ to form the new numerator.

Multiply $4 \cdot 7$ to form the new denominator.

$= \dfrac{\overset{3}{\cancel{6}}}{\underset{14}{\cancel{28}}} = \dfrac{3}{14}$ 2 is a factor common to both the numerator and the denominator. Divide out the common factor, 2.

TRY-IT EXERCISE 1

Multiply. Simplify, if possible.

a. $\dfrac{2}{5} \cdot \dfrac{6}{7}$

b. $\dfrac{5}{8} \cdot \dfrac{3}{4}$

c. $\dfrac{4}{15} \cdot \dfrac{3}{5}$

Check your answers with the solutions in Appendix A. ■

When multiplying fractions, it is often necessary to simplify the result to lowest terms. Example 1c demonstrates such a situation. In this example, we had to simplify $\frac{6}{28}$. We did so by dividing both the numerator and denominator by the common factor, 2.

Instead of simplifying a product *after* we perform the multiplication, we can use a shortcut whereby we divide out common factors *before* we multiply the fractions. To see how this works, consider once again the product $\frac{1}{4} \cdot \frac{6}{7}$. Note that 4, the denominator of the first fraction, and 6, the numerator of the second fraction, have a common factor of 2. We can divide out the common factor and then multiply the resulting fractions.

> **Learning Tip**
>
> In multiplication, another name for dividing out is canceling.

$$\frac{1}{\overset{}{\underset{2}{4}}} \cdot \frac{\overset{3}{6}}{7} = \frac{1}{2} \cdot \frac{3}{7} = \frac{3}{14}$$

This procedure is summarized below.

Steps for Simplifying before Multiplying Fractions

Step 1. Find a common factor that divides evenly into one of the numerators and one of the denominators. Divide the identified numerator and denominator by this common factor.

Step 2. Repeat step 1 until there are no more common factors.

Step 3. Multiply the remaining factors in the numerators and in the denominators.

EXAMPLE 2   Multiply fractions

Multiply. Simplify, if possible.

a. $\frac{2}{3} \cdot \frac{7}{8}$ **b.** $\frac{5}{21} \cdot \frac{7}{11}$

SOLUTION STRATEGY

a. $\frac{2}{3} \cdot \frac{7}{8} = \frac{\overset{1}{2}}{3} \cdot \frac{7}{\underset{4}{8}}$

2 is a common factor of 2, the numerator of the first fraction, and 8, the denominator of the second fraction.

Divide 2 and 8 by the common factor, 2.

$= \frac{1}{3} \cdot \frac{7}{4}$

$= \frac{7}{12}$

Multiply 1 · 7 to form the new numerator.
Multiply 3 · 4 to form the new denominator.

b. $\dfrac{5}{21} \cdot \dfrac{7}{8} = \dfrac{5}{\overset{}{\underset{3}{\cancel{21}}}} \cdot \dfrac{\overset{1}{\cancel{7}}}{11}$ 7 is a common factor of 21, the denominator of the first fraction, and 7, the numerator of the second fraction. Divide 21 and 7 by the common factor, 7.

$= \dfrac{5}{3} \cdot \dfrac{1}{11}$

$= \dfrac{5}{33}$ Multiply 5 · 1 to form the new numerator.
Multiply 3 · 11 to form the new denominator.

TRY-IT EXERCISE 2

Multiply. Simplify, if possible.

a. $\dfrac{2}{9} \cdot \dfrac{3}{10}$

b. $\dfrac{15}{32} \cdot \dfrac{4}{5}$

Check your answers with the solutions in Appendix A. ■

Objective 2.4B   **Multiply fractions, mixed numbers, or whole numbers**

In multiplication problems involving fractions, mixed numbers, or whole numbers, change each whole number or mixed number to an improper fraction. Recall that a whole number, n, can be written as $\dfrac{n}{1}$.

EXAMPLE 3   **Multiply fractions, mixed numbers, or whole numbers**

Multiply. Simplify, if possible.

a. $3\dfrac{3}{4} \cdot 5\dfrac{1}{2}$

b. $12\dfrac{5}{6} \cdot 4$

SOLUTION STRATEGY

a. $3\dfrac{3}{4} \cdot 5\dfrac{1}{2} = \dfrac{15}{4} \cdot \dfrac{11}{2}$ Express each mixed number as an improper fraction.

$= \dfrac{15 \cdot 11}{4 \cdot 2}$ Multiply the numerators. Multiply the denominators.

$= \dfrac{165}{8} = 20\dfrac{5}{8}$ Write the result as a mixed number.

b. $12\dfrac{5}{6} \cdot 4 = \dfrac{77}{6} \cdot \dfrac{4}{1}$ Express each factor as an improper fraction.

$\qquad = \dfrac{77}{\underset{3}{6}} \cdot \dfrac{\overset{2}{\cancel{4}}}{1}$ 2 is a common factor of 6, the denominator of the first fraction, and 4, the numerator of the second fraction. Divide 6
and 4 by the common factor, 2.

$\qquad = \dfrac{77 \cdot 2}{3 \cdot 1}$ Multiply the numerators. Multiply the denominators.

$\qquad = \dfrac{154}{3} = 51\dfrac{1}{3}$ Write the result as a mixed number.

TRY-IT EXERCISE 3

Multiply. Simplify, if possible.

a. $8\dfrac{2}{5} \cdot 6\dfrac{1}{4}$

b. $5\dfrac{4}{9} \cdot 2\dfrac{1}{4}$

Check your answers with the solutions in Appendix A. ■

Objective 2.4C	**Apply your knowledge**

To solve application problems involving multiplication of fractions, use the same procedures learned in Chapter 1. Remember to read the question carefully. Be sure to identify what information is given and what we need to find.

As with whole numbers, key words and phrases should be identified to determine what mathematical operations to perform.

EXAMPLE 4   Multiply fractions in an application problem

a. A chocolate chip cookie recipe requires $\dfrac{2}{3}$ cup of brown sugar. If you want to make half the number of cookies, how many cups of brown sugar would you need?

b. Suppose that the same cookie recipe requires $2\dfrac{1}{4}$ cups of flour. If you want to make half the number of cookies, how many cups of flour would you need?

SOLUTION STRATEGY

a. $\dfrac{2}{3} \cdot \dfrac{1}{2}$ The problem contains the key word *half* indicating multiplication by $\dfrac{1}{2}$.

$$\frac{2}{3} \cdot \frac{1}{2} = \frac{\overset{1}{\cancel{2}}}{3} \cdot \frac{1}{\underset{1}{\cancel{2}}}$$ 2 is a common factor of the numerator of the first fraction and the denominator of the second fraction. Divide each by the common factor, 2.

$$= \frac{1}{3} \cdot \frac{1}{1}$$ Multiply the numerators. Multiply the denominators.

$$= \frac{1}{3} \text{ cup}$$

b. $2\frac{1}{4} \cdot \frac{1}{2} = \frac{9}{4} \cdot \frac{1}{2}$ Express the mixed number as an improper fraction.

$$= \frac{9}{8}$$ Multiply the numerators. Multiply the denominators.

$$= 1\frac{1}{8} \text{ cups}$$ Write the result as a mixed number.

TRY-IT EXERCISE 4

a. A paving crew can lay $1\frac{5}{8}$ miles of asphalt on a highway per day. How many miles of highway can they pave in half a day?

b. Working at this rate, how many miles of highway could the crew pave in 3 days?

Check your answers with the solutions in Appendix A. ■

SECTION 2.4 REVIEW EXERCISES

Concept Check

1. To multiply fractions, multiply the _____ to form the new numerator and multiply the _____ to form the new denominator.

2. In multiplying fractions it is often necessary to _____ the result to lowest terms.

3. To simplify fractions before multiplying, find a _____ that divides evenly into one of the numerators and one of the denominators. Then, _____ the identified numerator and denominator by this common factor.

4. In multiplication problems involving a combination of fractions, mixed numbers, and whole numbers, change each mixed number or whole number to an _____ fraction. Recall that a whole number n can be written as _____.

Objective 2.4A	Multiply fractions

GUIDE PROBLEMS

5. Multiply $\dfrac{3}{5} \cdot \dfrac{7}{8}$. Simplify, if possible.

$$\dfrac{3}{5} \cdot \dfrac{7}{8} = \dfrac{}{40}$$

6. Multiply $\dfrac{3}{4} \cdot \dfrac{1}{8}$. Simplify, if possible.

$$\dfrac{3}{4} \cdot \dfrac{1}{8} = \dfrac{}{}$$

7. Multiply $\dfrac{2}{3} \cdot \dfrac{9}{14}$. Simplify the fractions before multiplying.

$$\dfrac{2}{3} \cdot \dfrac{9}{14} = \dfrac{2}{\overset{}{\underset{1}{3}}} \cdot \dfrac{\overset{3}{9}}{14} = \dfrac{}{1} \cdot \dfrac{3}{} = \dfrac{}{}$$

8. Multiply $\dfrac{5}{12} \cdot \dfrac{8}{15}$. Simplify the fractions before multiplying.

$$\dfrac{5}{12} \cdot \dfrac{8}{15} = \dfrac{\overset{}{5}}{\underset{}{12}} \cdot \dfrac{\overset{}{8}}{\underset{}{15}} = \dfrac{}{} \cdot \dfrac{}{} = \dfrac{}{}$$

Multiply. Simplify, if possible.

9. $\dfrac{1}{2} \cdot \dfrac{1}{3}$

10. $\dfrac{1}{3} \cdot \dfrac{1}{5}$

11. $\dfrac{1}{5} \cdot \dfrac{4}{7}$

12. $\dfrac{3}{5} \cdot \dfrac{1}{4}$

13. $\dfrac{2}{3} \cdot \dfrac{4}{5}$

14. $\dfrac{3}{5} \cdot \dfrac{2}{7}$

15. $\dfrac{5}{7} \cdot \dfrac{3}{8}$

16. $\dfrac{4}{9} \cdot \dfrac{5}{7}$

17. $\dfrac{4}{7} \cdot \dfrac{6}{11}$

18. $\dfrac{2}{5} \cdot \dfrac{8}{9}$

19. $\dfrac{7}{8} \cdot \dfrac{3}{10}$

20. $\dfrac{5}{6} \cdot \dfrac{7}{12}$

21. $\dfrac{1}{2} \cdot \dfrac{2}{3}$

22. $\dfrac{5}{9} \cdot \dfrac{4}{5}$

23. $\dfrac{2}{11} \cdot \dfrac{11}{25}$

24. $\dfrac{13}{22} \cdot \dfrac{7}{13}$

25. $\dfrac{3}{6} \cdot \dfrac{4}{11}$

26. $\dfrac{7}{8} \cdot \dfrac{2}{3}$

27. $\dfrac{5}{12} \cdot \dfrac{8}{9}$

28. $\dfrac{4}{9} \cdot \dfrac{6}{13}$

29. $\dfrac{3}{8} \cdot \dfrac{4}{5}$

30. $\dfrac{5}{4} \cdot \dfrac{2}{7}$

31. $\dfrac{4}{9} \cdot \dfrac{5}{12}$

32. $\dfrac{7}{12} \cdot \dfrac{3}{5}$

33. $\dfrac{4}{3} \cdot \dfrac{3}{8}$

34. $\dfrac{2}{5} \cdot \dfrac{5}{8}$

35. $\dfrac{5}{14} \cdot \dfrac{14}{25}$

36. $\dfrac{19}{24} \cdot \dfrac{8}{19}$

37. $\dfrac{5}{12} \cdot \dfrac{9}{10}$

38. $\dfrac{4}{9} \cdot \dfrac{3}{16}$

39. $\dfrac{5}{21} \cdot \dfrac{14}{25}$

40. $\dfrac{5}{24} \cdot \dfrac{18}{25}$

41. $\dfrac{5}{9} \cdot \dfrac{9}{16} \cdot \dfrac{7}{5}$

42. $\dfrac{21}{5} \cdot \dfrac{5}{4} \cdot \dfrac{4}{21}$

43. $\dfrac{8}{13} \cdot \dfrac{1}{4} \cdot \dfrac{1}{3}$

44. $\dfrac{2}{6} \cdot \dfrac{1}{12} \cdot \dfrac{3}{5}$

45. $\dfrac{3}{10} \cdot \dfrac{12}{16} \cdot \dfrac{4}{15}$

46. $\dfrac{6}{7} \cdot \dfrac{1}{3} \cdot \dfrac{3}{14}$

47. $\dfrac{5}{8} \cdot \dfrac{2}{3} \cdot \dfrac{4}{9} \cdot \dfrac{7}{20}$

48. $\dfrac{1}{3} \cdot \dfrac{9}{11} \cdot \dfrac{3}{15} \cdot \dfrac{5}{6}$

Objective 2.4B   **Multiply fractions, mixed numbers, and whole numbers**

GUIDE PROBLEMS

49. Multiply $6 \cdot \dfrac{2}{3}$.

  a. Change each whole number or mixed number to an improper fraction.

  $6 = \dfrac{\overline{}}{1}$

  b. Multiply the fractions. Simplify, if possible. Express your answer as a whole number or mixed number, if possible.

  $\dfrac{\overset{\_}{\cancel{6}}}{1} \cdot \dfrac{2}{3} = \dfrac{\overline{}}{1} \cdot \dfrac{2}{\underline{}} = \dfrac{\overline{}}{\underline{}} = \dfrac{}{\underline{}}$

50. Multiply $1\dfrac{2}{5} \cdot 3\dfrac{1}{3}$.

  a. Change each whole number or mixed number to an improper fraction.

  $1\dfrac{2}{5} = \dfrac{\overline{}}{5}, 3\dfrac{1}{3} = \dfrac{\overline{}}{3}$

  b. Multiply the fractions. Simplify, if possible. Express your answer as a whole number or mixed number, if possible.

  $\dfrac{7}{\cancel{5}} \cdot \dfrac{\overset{\_}{\cancel{10}}}{3} = \dfrac{7}{\underline{}} \cdot \dfrac{\overline{}}{3} = \dfrac{\overline{}}{\underline{}} = 4\dfrac{\overline{}}{3}$

Multiply. Simplify, if possible.

51. $2\dfrac{2}{3} \cdot 2\dfrac{1}{4}$

52. $1\dfrac{2}{3} \cdot 2\dfrac{2}{5}$

53. $7\dfrac{1}{2} \cdot 3\dfrac{1}{5}$

54. $\dfrac{1}{7} \cdot 2$

55. $\dfrac{1}{2} \cdot \dfrac{1}{3} \cdot 6$
    1

56. $\dfrac{2}{15} \cdot 4\dfrac{6}{11}$

57. $2\dfrac{1}{2} \cdot 16\dfrac{2}{3}$

58. $3\dfrac{1}{3} \cdot 5\dfrac{1}{4}$

59. $\dfrac{3}{4} \cdot 4\dfrac{2}{3}$

60. $4 \cdot \dfrac{5}{8}$

61. $\dfrac{1}{2} \cdot 18$

62. $24 \cdot \dfrac{1}{6}$

63. $7 \cdot \dfrac{9}{14}$

64. $3\dfrac{4}{5} \cdot 3\dfrac{3}{4}$

65. $\dfrac{4}{7} \cdot 3\dfrac{1}{4}$

66. $3\dfrac{3}{11} \cdot 2\dfrac{1}{5}$

67. $5\dfrac{3}{4} \cdot 7\dfrac{2}{3}$

68. $\dfrac{2}{11} \cdot 5$

69. $2\dfrac{3}{4} \cdot 1\dfrac{1}{3}$

70. $2\dfrac{3}{13} \cdot 3$

71. $4\dfrac{1}{3} \cdot 2 \cdot 3\dfrac{1}{2}$

72. $3\dfrac{1}{2} \cdot 3\dfrac{3}{4} \cdot \dfrac{1}{5}$

73. $7 \cdot \dfrac{1}{4} \cdot \dfrac{8}{21}$

74. $2\dfrac{1}{2} \cdot 5 \cdot 2\dfrac{3}{5}$

Objective 2.4C   **Apply your knowledge**

75. A school has 8500 students. If $\dfrac{3}{4}$ of the students are from out of state, how many students are from out of state?

76. A tanker truck holds 5200 gallons of liquid propane fully loaded.

  a. If the tank is $\dfrac{3}{16}$ full, how many gallons are on board?

  b. If the truck picks up an additional $\dfrac{1}{4}$ of a tank, how many gallons are now on board?

77. Last year you earned \$12,300 at a part-time job. If $\dfrac{1}{5}$ was withheld for income tax, Medicare, and social security, how much was left for you to spend?

78. A department store sells television sets for a regular price of \$460.

  a. If they are on sale at $\dfrac{1}{4}$ off the regular price, what is the sale price?

  b. If a television set is scratched or dented, the store is offering an additional $\dfrac{1}{4}$ of the regular price off the sale price. What is the selling price of a scratched or dented set?

79. A recipe for brownies requires $2\dfrac{2}{3}$ cups of flour. If you want to make 6 times that amount for a bake sale, how much flour will you need?

80. Lloyd earns \$120 per day. If he worked only $\dfrac{5}{8}$ of a day on Friday, how much did he earn?

81. In a market research survey, $\dfrac{3}{16}$ of the people interviewed responded positively. If 6000 people were interviewed, how many responded positively?

82. An Amtrak train travels at an average speed of 88 miles per hour. How many miles will the train travel in $3\dfrac{3}{4}$ hours?

83. A road map has a scale of $\frac{5}{8}$ inches for every 125 miles. How many inches would be needed to represent 1000 miles on the map?

84. The Number Crunchers, an accounting firm, has 161 employees. If $\frac{3}{7}$ of them are certified public accountants, how many CPAs are in the firm?

85. Clarissa's flower garden measures $5\frac{2}{3}$ feet long by $6\frac{3}{4}$ feet wide. If the area of a rectangle is length times width, what is the area of this garden?

86. A blueprint of a house has a scale in which 1 inch equals $4\frac{1}{2}$ feet. If the living room wall measures $5\frac{1}{4}$ inches on the drawing, what is the actual length of the wall?

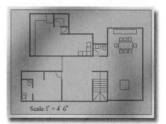

87. A company has a warehouse with 3600 square feet of storage space. If a new warehouse is planned with $3\frac{5}{16}$ times as much space, how many square feet will it contain?

88. Stan increased his earnings by $\frac{1}{5}$ from last year. If he made $25,500 last year, how much more did he make this year?

89. A union takes $\frac{1}{25}$ of Mario's wages as dues. If he made $825 last week, how much was deducted for dues?

90. Three-fifths of the cars in a parking lot are Ford vehicles. If 4800 cars are in the lot, how many Fords are there?

91. What is the cost of $2\frac{2}{3}$ pounds of imported ham at $6.00 per pound?

92. A computer hard drive has 140 gigabytes of storage space. You are asked to partition the drive into two parts, C and D. Drive C is to get $\frac{2}{5}$ of the space and drive D is to get $\frac{3}{5}$ of the space.

  a. How many gigabytes would drive C have?

  b. How many gigabytes would drive D have?

93. A lottery of $260,000 is split among 65 winners. Each will receive $\frac{1}{65}$ of the prize. How much does each person receive?

94. Carpet Magic, Inc. is bidding on a job at the Colony Hotel. Each of the 60 rooms requires $25\frac{3}{4}$ square yards of carpeting.

  a. How many total square yards will be required for the job?

  b. If the padding costs $2 per square yard and carpeting costs $8 per square yard, what is the total cost of the job?

95. Freddie Fast can make $6\frac{4}{5}$ chairs per hour on a furniture assembly line. Warren Weary makes $4\frac{1}{2}$ chairs per hour. In a 10-hour shift, how many more chairs does Freddie make than Warren?

96. Alice has a recipe for cherry noodle pudding that serves 4 people. She wants to make the pudding for 15 people at a dinner party. Calculate the new amount for each ingredient.

INGREDIENT	QUANTITY (4 PEOPLE)	QUANTITY (15 PEOPLE)
cooked noodles	24 ounces	**a.**
sour cream	$2\frac{4}{5}$ cups	**b.**
sugar	$\frac{2}{3}$ cup	**c.**
pitted cherries	$7\frac{1}{2}$ ounces	**d.**
vanilla	$\frac{3}{4}$ teaspoon	**e.**
eggs	2 eggs	**f.**

97. Nutritionists advise that calcium can prevent osteoporosis and control blood pressure. Based on this information, you always try to have the recommended 1300 milligrams of calcium each day. Today you have already had 2 calcium supplements, a glass of skim milk, and 8 ounces of nonfat yogurt. Together, these represent $\frac{5}{8}$ of the daily dosage.

a. How many milligrams of calcium have you had?

b. How many more milligrams of calcium should you take to consume the recommended 1300 milligrams?

c. What fraction represents the milligrams of calcium you still must take today to reach the recommended dosage?

   CUMULATIVE SKILLS REVIEW

1. Divide $1716 \div 11$. (1.5B)

2. Subtract $4393 - 1220$. (1.3A)

3. What fraction represents the shaded portion of the following illustration? (2.1B)

4. Warren ate 5 pieces of a pizza that had a total of 12 pieces. What fraction represents the part of the whole pizza that remains? (2.2B)

5. Multiply $1318 \cdot 612$. (1.4B)

6. Find the prime factorization of 108. (2.1C)

7. Simplify $\frac{24}{56}$. (2.3A)

8. Simplify $\frac{9}{72}$. (2.3A)

9. Write $8\frac{2}{5}$ as an improper fraction. (2.2C)

10. Yesterday morning you had $520 in your checking account. During the day you wrote a check for $55 for concert tickets and $160 for a new outfit. What fraction represents the portion of the original balance you have left in the account? (2.3C)

2.5 DIVIDING FRACTIONS AND MIXED NUMBERS

LEARNING OBJECTIVES

A. Divide fractions

B. Divide fractions, mixed numbers, or whole numbers

C. Apply your knowledge

How many metal plates, each $2\frac{3}{4}$ inches thick, will fit in a storage container that is $27\frac{1}{2}$ inches high? In Example 3 of this section, we will see how to find the answer to problems of this type by dividing fractions.

When we divide numbers, it is important to identify which number is the dividend and which is the divisor. Remember that the number that precedes the ÷ sign is the dividend, and the number that follows the ÷ sign is the divisor. For example, in the division problem $\frac{3}{4} \div \frac{2}{3}$, $\frac{3}{4}$ is the dividend and $\frac{2}{3}$ is the divisor.

We can also write $\frac{3}{4} \div \frac{2}{3}$ as the complex fraction $\dfrac{\frac{3}{4}}{\frac{2}{3}}$. In this section, however, we'll prefer to write division problems involving fractions in the first way.

Objective 2.5A   Divide fractions

Division of fractions is achieved by multiplication. Thus, if we know how to multiply fractions, then we know how to divide them.

In order to discuss division of fractions, we must first introduce the reciprocal of a fraction. The **reciprocal of the fraction $\dfrac{a}{b}$**, where $a \neq 0$ and $b \neq 0$, is the fraction $\dfrac{b}{a}$. Thus, to find the reciprocal of a fraction, simply interchange the numerator and denominator. For example, the reciprocal of $\frac{1}{3}$ is $\frac{3}{1}$, and the reciprocal of $\frac{4}{11}$ is $\frac{11}{4}$.

reciprocal of the fraction $\dfrac{a}{b}$

The fraction $\dfrac{b}{a}$ where $a \neq 0$ and $b \neq 0$.

To divide two fractions, we multiply the dividend by the reciprocal of the divisor. As an example, consider the division problem $\frac{2}{7} \div \frac{1}{3}$.

$$\frac{2}{7} \div \frac{1}{3} = \frac{2}{7} \cdot \frac{3}{1} \qquad \text{Multiply the dividend } \frac{2}{7} \text{ by } \frac{3}{1}, \text{ the reciprocal of the divisor } \frac{1}{3}.$$

$$= \frac{6}{7}$$

Steps for Dividing by a Fraction

Step 1. Multiply the dividend by the reciprocal of the divisor, that is,

$$\frac{a}{b} \div \frac{c}{d} = \frac{a}{b} \cdot \frac{d}{c}$$

where $b, c,$ and d are not zero.

Step 2. Simplify, if possible.

EXAMPLE 1   Divide fractions

Divide. Simplify, if possible.

a. $\dfrac{4}{5} \div \dfrac{2}{3}$

b. $\dfrac{7}{10} \div \dfrac{1}{5}$

SOLUTION STRATEGY

a. $\dfrac{4}{5} \div \dfrac{2}{3} = \dfrac{4}{5} \cdot \dfrac{3}{2}$ Multiply $\dfrac{4}{5}$ by $\dfrac{3}{2}$, the reciprocal of $\dfrac{2}{3}$.

$\qquad = \dfrac{\overset{2}{\cancel{4}}}{5} \cdot \dfrac{3}{\underset{1}{\cancel{2}}}$ Divide 4, the numerator of the first fraction, and 2, the denominator of the second fraction, by the common factor, 2.

$\qquad = \dfrac{6}{5} = 1\dfrac{1}{5}$ Multiply. Express the improper fraction as a mixed number.

b. $\dfrac{7}{10} \div \dfrac{1}{5} = \dfrac{7}{10} \cdot \dfrac{5}{1}$ Multiply $\dfrac{7}{10}$ by $\dfrac{5}{1}$, the reciprocal of $\dfrac{1}{5}$.

$\qquad = \dfrac{7}{\underset{2}{\cancel{10}}} \cdot \dfrac{\overset{1}{\cancel{5}}}{1}$ Divide 10, the denominator of the first fraction, and 5, the numerator of the second fraction, by the common factor, 5.

$\qquad = \dfrac{7}{2} = 3\dfrac{1}{2}$ Multiply. Express the improper fraction as a mixed number.

TRY-IT EXERCISE 1

Divide. Simplify, if possible.

a. $\dfrac{1}{8} \div \dfrac{5}{6}$

b. $\dfrac{1}{3} \div \dfrac{5}{9}$

c. $\dfrac{3}{7} \div \dfrac{3}{7}$

d. $\dfrac{5}{16} \div \dfrac{1}{8}$

Check your answers with the solutions in Appendix A. ∎

Objective 2.5B   ## Divide fractions, mixed numbers, or whole numbers

In division problems involving fractions, whole numbers, or mixed numbers, change each whole number and mixed number to an improper fraction.

EXAMPLE 2   Divide fractions, mixed numbers, or whole numbers

Divide. Simplify, if possible.

a. $12\frac{1}{6} \div 3$ **b.** $6\frac{3}{8} \div 2\frac{1}{2}$

SOLUTION STRATEGY

a. $12\frac{1}{6} \div 3 = \frac{73}{6} \div \frac{3}{1}$ Write the dividend and divisors as improper fractions.

$\qquad = \frac{73}{6} \cdot \frac{1}{3} = \frac{73}{18}$ Multiply $\frac{73}{6}$ by $\frac{1}{3}$, the reciprocal of $\frac{3}{1}$.

$\qquad = 4\frac{1}{18}$ Express the improper fraction as a mixed number.

b. $6\frac{3}{8} \div 2\frac{1}{2} = \frac{51}{8} \div \frac{5}{2}$ Write the dividend and divisors as improper fractions.

$\qquad = \frac{51}{8} \cdot \frac{2}{5}$ Multiply $\frac{51}{8}$ by $\frac{2}{5}$, the reciprocal of $\frac{5}{2}$.

$\qquad = \frac{51}{\overset{}{\underset{4}{8}}} \cdot \frac{\overset{1}{2}}{5}$ Divide 2 in the numerator and 8 in the denominator by the common factor 2.

$\qquad = \frac{51}{20}$ Multiply.

$\qquad = 2\frac{11}{20}$ Express the improper fraction as a mixed number.

TRY-IT EXERCISE 2

Divide. Simplify, if possible.

a. $10 \div \frac{6}{7}$

b. $2\frac{3}{16} \div 4\frac{1}{4}$

c. $9 \div 5\frac{3}{5}$

d. $3\frac{3}{8} \div 6$

Check your answers with the solutions in Appendix A. ∎

Objective 2.5C   **Apply your knowledge**

To solve application problems involving division of fractions, use the same procedures learned in Chapter 1. Remember to read the question carefully. Be sure to identify what information is given and what you need to find.

As with whole numbers, key words and phrases should be used to determine what mathematical operations to perform.

EXAMPLE 3   Divide fractions in an application problem

How many metal plates, each $2\frac{3}{4}$ inches thick, will fit in a storage container that is $27\frac{1}{2}$ inches high?

SOLUTION STRATEGY

$27\frac{1}{2} \div 2\frac{3}{4}$ To find the number of plates that will fit in the container, divide the height of the container by the thickness of each plate.

$= \dfrac{55}{2} \div \dfrac{11}{4}$ Write the mixed numbers as improper fractions.

$= \dfrac{55}{2} \cdot \dfrac{4}{11}$ Multiply $\dfrac{55}{2}$ by $\dfrac{4}{11}$, the reciprocal of $\dfrac{4}{11}$.

$= \dfrac{\overset{5}{55}}{\underset{1}{2}} \cdot \dfrac{\overset{2}{4}}{\underset{1}{11}}$ Divide 2, the denominator of the first fraction, and 4, the numerator of the second fraction, by the common factor, 2. Also, divide 55, the numerator of the first fraction, and 11, the denominator of the second fraction, by the common factor, 11.

$= \dfrac{10}{1} = 10$ Multiply.

TRY-IT EXERCISE 3

The Candy Connection packages multicolored jelly beans in $3\frac{1}{2}$-pound bags. How many bags can be made from 280 pounds of candy?

Check your answer with the solutions in Appendix A. ■

SECTION 2.5 REVIEW EXERCISES

Concept Check

1. In the division problem $\dfrac{a}{b} \div \dfrac{c}{d}$, the fraction $\dfrac{a}{b}$ is called the _____ and the fraction $\dfrac{c}{d}$ is called the _____.

2. The _____ of the fraction $\dfrac{a}{b}$ is the fraction $\dfrac{b}{a}$ where $a \neq 0$ and $b \neq 0$.

3. To divide fractions, _____ the dividend by the _____ of the divisor and simplify if possible.

4. To divide a combination of fractions, whole numbers, or mixed numbers, change any whole numbers or mixed numbers to _____ fractions.

Objective 2.5A	**Divide fractions**

GUIDE PROBLEMS

5. Divide $\dfrac{3}{5} \div \dfrac{9}{11}$.

    a. Identify the reciprocal of the divisor.

    The reciprocal of $\dfrac{9}{11}$ is $\dfrac{\;\;\;}{\;\;\;}$.

    b. Rewrite the division problem as a multiplication problem.

$$\frac{3}{5} \div \frac{9}{11} = \frac{3}{5} \cdot \frac{\;\;\;}{\;\;\;}$$

    c. Multiply the dividend by the reciprocal of the divisor.

$$\frac{3}{5} \cdot \frac{\;\;\;}{\;\;\;} = \frac{3}{5} \cdot \frac{\overset{1}{\cancel{3}}}{\cancel{\;\;\;}}$$

$$= \frac{1}{5} \cdot \frac{\;\;\;}{\;\;\;} = \frac{\;\;\;}{\;\;\;}$$

6. Divide $\dfrac{5}{8} \div \dfrac{15}{16}$.

    a. Identify the reciprocal of the divisor.

    The reciprocal of $\dfrac{15}{16}$ is $\dfrac{\;\;\;}{\;\;\;}$.

    b. Rewrite the division problem as a multiplication problem.

$$\frac{5}{8} \div \frac{15}{16} = \frac{5}{8} \cdot \frac{\;\;\;}{\;\;\;}$$

    c. Multiply the dividend by the reciprocal of the divisor.

$$\frac{5}{8} \cdot \frac{\;\;\;}{\;\;\;} = \frac{\overset{1}{\cancel{5}}}{\underset{1}{\cancel{8}}} \cdot \frac{\cancel{\;\;\;}}{\cancel{\;\;\;}}$$

$$= \frac{1}{1} \cdot \frac{\;\;\;}{\;\;\;} = \frac{\;\;\;}{\;\;\;}$$

Divide. Simplify, if possible.

7. $\dfrac{9}{16} \div \dfrac{3}{4}$

8. $\dfrac{12}{13} \div \dfrac{8}{13}$

9. $\dfrac{2}{3} \div \dfrac{2}{7}$

10. $\dfrac{6}{11} \div \dfrac{4}{5}$

11. $\dfrac{7}{14} \div \dfrac{1}{7}$

12. $\dfrac{1}{3} \div \dfrac{2}{3}$

13. $\dfrac{1}{3} \div \dfrac{1}{6}$

14. $\dfrac{1}{2} \div \dfrac{1}{3}$

15. $\dfrac{4}{11} \div \dfrac{5}{11}$

16. $\dfrac{4}{7} \div \dfrac{8}{11}$

17. $\dfrac{3}{5} \div \dfrac{2}{3}$

18. $\dfrac{1}{3} \div \dfrac{4}{5}$

19. $\dfrac{3}{4} \div \dfrac{1}{8}$

20. $\dfrac{1}{9} \div \dfrac{2}{3}$

21. $\dfrac{5}{12} \div \dfrac{25}{36}$

22. $\dfrac{3}{5} \div \dfrac{12}{25}$

23. $\dfrac{1}{3} \div \dfrac{1}{9}$

24. $\dfrac{1}{4} \div \dfrac{5}{9}$

25. $\dfrac{1}{10} \div \dfrac{6}{11}$

26. $\dfrac{4}{9} \div \dfrac{1}{9}$

27. $\dfrac{8}{9} \div \dfrac{4}{5}$

28. $\dfrac{1}{5} \div \dfrac{1}{8}$

29. $\dfrac{4}{7} \div \dfrac{4}{7}$

30. $\dfrac{2}{3} \div \dfrac{1}{4}$

31. $\dfrac{6}{7} \div \dfrac{3}{5}$

32. $\dfrac{5}{12} \div \dfrac{5}{6}$

33. $\dfrac{7}{8} \div \dfrac{3}{4}$

34. $\dfrac{3}{4} \div \dfrac{1}{12}$

| Objective 2.5B | Divide fractions, mixed numbers, or whole numbers |

GUIDE PROBLEMS

35. Divide $\dfrac{3}{4} \div 9$.

  a. Change each whole number or mixed number to an improper fraction.

  $9 = \dfrac{}{1}$

  b. Identify the reciprocal of the divisor.

  The reciprocal of $\dfrac{9}{1}$ is $\dfrac{}{}$.

  c. Rewrite the division problem as a multiplication problem.

  $\dfrac{3}{4} \div \dfrac{9}{1} = \dfrac{3}{4} \cdot \dfrac{}{}$

  d. Multiply the dividend by the reciprocal of the divisor.

  $\dfrac{3}{4} \cdot \dfrac{}{} = \dfrac{\overset{1}{\cancel{3}}}{4} \cdot \dfrac{}{\cancel{}}$

  $= \dfrac{1}{4} \cdot \dfrac{1}{} = \dfrac{}{}$

36. Divide $8\dfrac{8}{9} \div 6\dfrac{2}{3}$.

  a. Change each whole number or mixed number to an improper fraction.

  $8\dfrac{8}{9} = \dfrac{}{9}, 6\dfrac{2}{3} = \dfrac{}{3}$

  b. Identify the reciprocal of the divisor.

  The reciprocal of $\dfrac{}{3}$ is $\dfrac{}{}$.

  c. Rewrite the division problem as a multiplication problem.

  $\dfrac{80}{9} \div \dfrac{20}{3} = \dfrac{80}{9} \cdot \dfrac{}{}$

  d. Multiply the dividend by the reciprocal of the divisor.

  $\dfrac{80}{9} \cdot \dfrac{}{} = \dfrac{\overset{4}{\cancel{80}}}{\underset{3}{\cancel{9}}} \cdot \dfrac{\cancel{}}{\cancel{}}$

  $= \dfrac{4}{3} \cdot \dfrac{}{} = \dfrac{}{} = 1\dfrac{}{}$

Divide. Simplify, if possible

37. $5\dfrac{3}{4} \div 1\dfrac{1}{2}$

38. $31\dfrac{1}{2} \div 1\dfrac{1}{2}$

39. $5\dfrac{3}{8} \div 2\dfrac{3}{4}$

40. $3\dfrac{1}{2} \div 2\dfrac{4}{5}$

41. $1\dfrac{3}{4} \div \dfrac{1}{2}$

42. $178\dfrac{1}{2} \div 3\dfrac{1}{2}$

43. $\dfrac{2}{3} \div 2\dfrac{1}{3}$

44. $\dfrac{2}{3} \div 1\dfrac{2}{5}$

45. $112 \div 2\dfrac{1}{3}$

46. $45 \div 1\dfrac{1}{2}$

47. $22\dfrac{1}{2} \div 2\dfrac{1}{4}$

48. $2 \div 3\dfrac{1}{6}$

49. $3\dfrac{3}{5} \div 2$

50. $\dfrac{3}{2} \div 3$

51. $71\dfrac{2}{3} \div 1\dfrac{2}{3}$

52. $84\dfrac{1}{3} \div 3\dfrac{2}{3}$

53. $2\dfrac{2}{3} \div 3\dfrac{1}{2}$

54. $36\dfrac{2}{3} \div 3\dfrac{2}{3}$

55. $51 \div 1\dfrac{1}{2}$

56. $\dfrac{3}{8} \div 1$

57. $49 \div 1\dfrac{3}{4}$

58. $50 \div 2\dfrac{1}{2}$

59. $2 \div \dfrac{1}{6}$

60. $\dfrac{2}{3} \div 4\dfrac{2}{3}$

Objective 2.5C **Apply your knowledge**

61. On a recent trip, you drove 730 miles on $33\dfrac{1}{3}$ gallons of gasoline.

   a. How many miles per gallon did your car average on this trip?

   b. How many gallons would be required for your car to travel 1095 miles?

62. To mix fertilizer for your lawn, the instructions are to combine $\dfrac{3}{8}$ ounces of concentrate for each gallon of water. How many gallons can you mix from a bottle containing $4\dfrac{1}{2}$ ounces of concentrate?

63. A farmer wants to divide $126\dfrac{7}{8}$ acres of fertile land into 5 equal plots. How many acres will each plot contain?

64. Vanity Homes, Inc., a builder of custom homes, owns $126\dfrac{1}{2}$ acres of undeveloped land. If each home is to be constructed on a $1\dfrac{3}{8}$ acre parcel of land, how many homesites can be developed?

65. Fleming's Warehouse contains 19,667 square feet. If a storage bin requires $35\dfrac{1}{2}$ square feet, how many bins can the warehouse accommodate?

66. Home-Mart Hardware buys nails in bulk from the manufacturer and packs them into $3\dfrac{4}{5}$-pound boxes. How many boxes will 608 pounds of nails fill?

67. You are the chef at the Sizzling Steakhouse. You have $131\dfrac{1}{4}$ pounds of sirloin steak on hand for Saturday night. If each portion is $10\dfrac{1}{2}$ ounces, how many sirloin steak dinners can be served? (There are 16 ounces in a pound.)

68. Engineers at Liberty Electronics use special silver wire to manufacture fuzzy logic circuit boards. The wire comes in 840-foot rolls that cost $2400 each. Each board requires $4\dfrac{1}{5}$ feet of wire.

   a. How many circuit boards can be made from each roll?

   b. What is the cost of wire per circuit board?

69. Brilliant Signs, Inc. makes speed limit signs for the state department of transportation. By law, these signs must be displayed every $\frac{7}{8}$ of a mile. How many signs will be required on a new highway that is $38\frac{1}{2}$ miles long?

70. Fancy Fruit Wholesalers purchases 350 crates of apples from Sun-Ripe Orchard. They intend to repack the apples in smaller boxes to be shipped to supermarkets. If each box contains $\frac{5}{8}$ of a crate, how many boxes can be packed?

71. Bakers at the Golden Flake Bakery use $12\frac{3}{4}$ ounces of flour for each loaf of bread. If 7650 ounces of flour were used for bread last week, how many loaves were baked?

CUMULATIVE SKILLS REVIEW

1. Multiply $192 \cdot 102$. (1.4B)

2. What type of fraction is $\frac{3}{52}$? (2.1A)

3. Multiply $\frac{25}{81} \cdot \frac{3}{75}$. (2.4A)

4. What is the total of 143, 219, and 99? (1.2C)

5. Find the prime factorization of 90. (2.1C)

6. Simplify $\frac{105}{135}$. (2.3A)

7. Multiply $\frac{6}{7} \cdot \frac{2}{3} \cdot 1\frac{1}{2}$. (2.4B)

8. Subtract $5637 - 5290$. (1.3A)

9. A pasta recipe requires $3\frac{2}{3}$ cups of spaghetti. If you want to make five times that amount for a dinner party, how many cups of spaghetti will you need? (2.4C)

10. On a 600-mile automobile trip, you drove 215 miles yesterday and 150 miles today. What simplified fraction represents the portion of the trip remaining? (2.3D)

2.6 ADDING FRACTIONS AND MIXED NUMBERS

Now that we have learned to simplify fractions to lowest terms, create equivalent fractions with larger denominators, and find least common denominators, we are ready to add and subtract fractions.

Objective 2.6A   **Add fractions with the same denominator**

Suppose that you ate one-eighth of a pizza and your friend ate two-eighths of the same pizza. Together, how much of the pizza did you and your friend eat? Study the figure below.

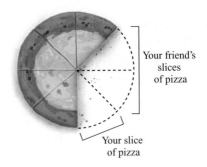

In total, you and your friend ate three slices of pizza. Therefore, it seems reasonable to conclude that together, you and your friend ate three-eighths of the pizza.

This example suggests that to add fractions with the same denominator, all we have to do is add the numerators and leave the common denominator alone.

$$\frac{1}{8} + \frac{2}{8} = \frac{1 + 2}{8} = \frac{3}{8}$$

Note that the denominators are the same. Fractions with the same denominator are called **like fractions**. The following steps are used to add like fractions.

Steps for Adding Like Fractions

Step 1. Add the numerators and write this sum over the common denominator.

Step 2. Simplify, if possible.

EXAMPLE 1   **Add fractions with the same denominator**

Add. Simplify, if possible.

a. $\frac{3}{8} + \frac{4}{8}$

b. $\frac{4}{15} + \frac{1}{15} + \frac{1}{15}$

c. $\frac{4}{21} + \frac{5}{21} + \frac{11}{21} + \frac{8}{21}$

SOLUTION STRATEGY

a. $\dfrac{3}{8} + \dfrac{4}{8} = \dfrac{3+4}{8} = \dfrac{7}{8}$

Add the numerators and write this sum over the common denominator.

b. $\dfrac{4}{15} + \dfrac{1}{15} + \dfrac{1}{15} = \dfrac{4+1+1}{15} = \dfrac{6}{15}$

Add the numerators and write this sum over the common denominator.

$\dfrac{6}{15} = \dfrac{2}{5}$

Simplify to lowest terms.

c. $\dfrac{4}{21} + \dfrac{5}{21} + \dfrac{11}{21} + \dfrac{8}{21} = \dfrac{28}{21}$

Add the numerators and write this sum over the common denominator.

$\dfrac{28}{21} = \dfrac{4}{3} = 1\dfrac{1}{3}$

Simplify to lowest terms.

TRY-IT EXERCISE 1

Add. Simplify, if possible.

a. $\dfrac{3}{25} + \dfrac{9}{25}$

b. $\dfrac{4}{9} + \dfrac{1}{9} + \dfrac{3}{9}$

c. $\dfrac{5}{16} + \dfrac{11}{16} + \dfrac{7}{16} + \dfrac{13}{16}$

Check your answers with the solutions in Appendix A. ■

Objective 2.6B   **Add fractions with different denominators**

To add fractions with different denominators, we must first create equivalent fractions with a common denominator. We choose the least common denominator or LCD. Recall that the LCD is the LCM of all the denominators.

The steps for adding fractions with different denominators are given below.

Steps for Adding Fractions with Different Denominators

Step 1. Find the LCD of the fractions.

Step 2. Write each fraction as an equivalent fraction with the LCD found in step 1.

Step 3. Follow the steps for adding like fractions.

EXAMPLE 2   Add fractions with different denominators

Add. Simplify, if possible.

a. $\dfrac{5}{6} + \dfrac{3}{4}$ **b.** $\dfrac{3}{8} + \dfrac{5}{7} + \dfrac{1}{2}$

SOLUTION STRATEGY

a. $\dfrac{5}{6} + \dfrac{3}{4} = \dfrac{5 \cdot 2}{6 \cdot 2} + \dfrac{3 \cdot 3}{4 \cdot 3}$

The smallest multiple of 6 that is also a multiple of 4 is 12. Therefore, LCD = 12.

$= \dfrac{10}{12} + \dfrac{9}{12}$

Write each fraction as an equivalent fraction with denominator 12.

$= \dfrac{10 + 9}{12} = \dfrac{19}{12} = 1\dfrac{7}{12}$

Add the numerators and write the sum over the LCD.

b. $\dfrac{3}{8} + \dfrac{5}{7} + \dfrac{1}{2} = \dfrac{3 \cdot 7}{8 \cdot 7} + \dfrac{5 \cdot 8}{7 \cdot 8} + \dfrac{1 \cdot 28}{2 \cdot 28}$

The smallest multiple of 8 that is also a multiple of 7 and of 2 is 56. Therefore, LCD = 56.

$= \dfrac{21}{56} + \dfrac{40}{56} + \dfrac{28}{56}$

Write each fraction as an equivalent fraction with denominator 56.

$= \dfrac{21 + 40 + 28}{56} = \dfrac{89}{56} = 1\dfrac{33}{56}$

Add the numerators and write the sum over the LCD.

TRY-IT EXERCISE 2

Add. Simplify, if possible.

a. $\dfrac{3}{8} + \dfrac{5}{6}$

b. $\dfrac{1}{6} + \dfrac{3}{5} + \dfrac{2}{3}$

c. $\dfrac{3}{4} + \dfrac{1}{6} + \dfrac{7}{15}$

Check your answers with the solutions in Appendix A. ■

Objective 2.6C   **Add mixed numbers**

To add mixed numbers, we first add the fractions and then the whole numbers. As an example, consider $3\dfrac{1}{5} + 6\dfrac{3}{5}$.

$$
\begin{array}{r}
3\dfrac{1}{5} \\
+\,6\dfrac{3}{5} \\
\hline
\dfrac{4}{5} \\
\uparrow
\end{array}
\qquad\qquad
\begin{array}{r}
3\dfrac{1}{5} \\
+\,6\dfrac{3}{5} \\
\hline
9\dfrac{4}{5} \\
\uparrow
\end{array}
$$

Add the fractions.   Add the whole numbers.

EXAMPLE 3   Add mixed numbers

Add. Simplify, if possible.

a. $5\dfrac{1}{7} + 6\dfrac{5}{7}$

b. $4\dfrac{1}{8} + 5\dfrac{3}{8}$

SOLUTION STRATEGY

a.

$$
\begin{array}{r}
5\dfrac{1}{7} \\[4pt]
+\ 6\dfrac{5}{7} \\[4pt]
\hline
11\dfrac{6}{7}
\end{array}
$$
    Add the fractions. Then, add the whole numbers.

b.

$$
\begin{array}{r}
4\dfrac{1}{8} \\[4pt]
+\ 5\dfrac{3}{8} \\[4pt]
\hline
9\dfrac{4}{8} = 9\dfrac{1}{2}
\end{array}
$$
    Add the fractions. Then, add the whole numbers.
Simplify the fraction part.

TRY-IT EXERCISE 3

Add. Simplify, if possible.

a. $4\dfrac{1}{9} + 8\dfrac{4}{9}$

b. $5\dfrac{1}{12} + 9\dfrac{5}{12}$

Check your answers with the solutions in Appendix A. ■

Often, in an addition problem involving mixed numbers, the fraction parts of the addends have different denominators. In such addition problems, we must find the LCD. As an example, consider $3\dfrac{1}{2} + 5\dfrac{2}{5}$.

$$
3\dfrac{1}{2} \rightarrow \quad 3\dfrac{1\cdot 5}{2\cdot 5} \rightarrow \quad 3\dfrac{5}{10}
$$
    LCD = 10.

$$
+\,5\dfrac{2}{5} \rightarrow +\,5\dfrac{2\cdot 2}{5\cdot 2} \rightarrow +\,5\dfrac{4}{10}
$$
    Write the fraction part of each mixed number as an equivalent fraction with denominator 10.

$$
8\dfrac{9}{10}
$$
    Add the fraction parts. Then, add the whole numbers.

● Learning Tip

Alternate Method for Adding Mixed Numbers

Step 1. Change each mixed number to an improper fraction.

Step 2. Find the LCD, and write each fraction as an equivalent fraction with the LCD.

Step 3. Follow the rules for adding like fractions.

Step 4. Convert the answer to a mixed number and simplify.

Examples

$$
3\dfrac{1}{5} + 6\dfrac{3}{5} = \dfrac{16}{5} + \dfrac{33}{5}
$$

$$
= \dfrac{49}{5} = 9\dfrac{4}{5}
$$

$$
3\dfrac{1}{2} + 5\dfrac{2}{5} = \dfrac{7}{2} + \dfrac{27}{5}
$$

$$
= \dfrac{35}{10} + \dfrac{54}{10}
$$

$$
= \dfrac{89}{10} = 8\dfrac{9}{10}
$$

EXAMPLE 4   Add mixed numbers

Add. Simplify, if possible.

a. $15\frac{3}{4} + 18\frac{1}{8}$ **b.** $23\frac{1}{3} + 12\frac{3}{7}$

SOLUTION STRATEGY

a. $15\frac{3}{4} + 18\frac{1}{8}$ LCD = 8.

$15\frac{3 \cdot 2}{4 \cdot 2} \rightarrow 15\frac{6}{8}$ Write each fraction as an equivalent fraction with denominator 8.

$\dfrac{+ 18\frac{1}{8} \rightarrow + 18\frac{1}{8}}{\qquad\qquad 33\frac{7}{8}}$ Add the fraction parts. Then add the whole numbers.

b. $23\frac{1}{3} + 12\frac{3}{7}$ LCD = 21.

$23\frac{1 \cdot 7}{3 \cdot 7} \rightarrow 23\frac{7}{21}$ Write each fraction as an equivalent fraction with denominator 21.

$\dfrac{+ 12\frac{3 \cdot 3}{7 \cdot 3} \rightarrow + 12\frac{9}{21}}{\qquad\qquad 35\frac{16}{21}}$ Add the fraction parts. Then add the whole numbers.

TRY-IT EXERCISE 4

Add. Simplify, if possible.

a. $4\frac{1}{4} + 6\frac{5}{12}$

b. $12\frac{1}{3} + 18\frac{2}{5}$

Check your answers with the solutions in Appendix A. ∎

Sometimes when we add fractions, we obtain an improper fraction. In such a case, we must change the improper fraction to a mixed number. Then, add the whole number to the mixed number. As an example, consider $6\frac{2}{3} + 5\frac{1}{2}$.

$6\frac{2 \cdot 2}{3 \cdot 2} \rightarrow 6\frac{4}{6}$ LCD = 6.

$\dfrac{+ 5\frac{1 \cdot 3}{2 \cdot 3} \rightarrow + 5\frac{3}{6}}{11\frac{7}{6} = 11 + \frac{7}{6}}$ Add the fraction part. Then, add the whole numbers.

$= 11 + 1\frac{1}{6}$ Change $\frac{7}{6}$ to a mixed number.

$= 12\frac{1}{6}$ Add the whole number and the mixed number.

◉ Learning Tip

To find the sum $11 + 1\frac{5}{12}$, we can do the following.

$11 \rightarrow 11\frac{0}{12}$

$\dfrac{+ 1\frac{5}{12} \rightarrow + 1\frac{5}{12}}{12\frac{5}{12}}$

In general, to add a whole number and a mixed number, add the whole numbers and keep the fraction.

EXAMPLE 5   Add mixed numbers

Add. Simplify, if possible.

a. $8\frac{3}{4} + 9\frac{5}{6}$ **b.** $4\frac{5}{6} + 11 + 5\frac{7}{8}$

SOLUTION STRATEGY

a. $8\frac{3}{4} + 9\frac{5}{6}$ LCD = 12.

$$8\frac{3 \cdot 3}{4 \cdot 3} \rightarrow 8\frac{9}{12}$$

Write each fraction as an equivalent fraction with denominator 12.

$$+ 9\frac{5 \cdot 2}{6 \cdot 2} \rightarrow + 9\frac{10}{12}$$

$$17\frac{19}{12}$$

Add the fraction parts. Then add the whole numbers.

$$17\frac{19}{12} = 17 + \frac{19}{12}$$

Write the mixed number as the sum of the whole number and the fraction part.

$$= 17 + 1\frac{7}{12}$$

Write the fraction part as a mixed number.

$$= 18\frac{7}{12}$$

Add the whole number and the mixed number.

b. $4\frac{5}{6} + 11 + 5\frac{7}{8}$ LCD = 24.

$$4\frac{5 \cdot 4}{6 \cdot 4} \rightarrow 4\frac{20}{24}$$

Write each fraction as an equivalent fraction with denominator 24.

$$11 \quad \rightarrow \quad 11$$

$$+ 5\frac{7 \cdot 3}{8 \cdot 3} \rightarrow + 5\frac{21}{24}$$

$$20\frac{41}{24}$$

Add the fraction parts. Then add the whole numbers.

$$20\frac{41}{24} = 20 + \frac{41}{24}$$

Write the mixed number as the sum of the whole number and the fraction part.

$$= 20 + 1\frac{17}{24}$$

Write the fraction part as a mixed number.

$$= 21\frac{17}{24}$$

Add the whole number and the mixed number.

TRY-IT EXERCISE 5

Add. Simplify, if possible.

a. $2\frac{3}{4} + 6\frac{5}{12}$

b. $10\frac{3}{5} + 13\frac{7}{8}$

Check your answers with the solutions in Appendix A. ∎

We summarize the steps for adding mixed numbers.

Steps for Adding Mixed Numbers

Step 1. If the denominators of the fraction parts differ, write each fraction part as an equivalent fraction with the LCD of the original fractions.

Step 2. Add the fraction parts.

Step 3. Add the whole number parts.

Step 4. If the fraction part is an improper fraction, rewrite the mixed number as the sum of a whole number and an improper fraction expressed as a mixed number. Add the whole number and the mixed number.

Step 5. Simplify, if possible.

| Objective 2.6D | **Apply your knowledge** |

Now let's take a look at some application problems that employ what we have learned about adding fractions and mixed numbers. Recall that some of the key words and phrases that indicate addition are *and, increased by, total of, plus, more than, the sum of,* and *added to.*

EXAMPLE 6   Add mixed numbers in an application problem

Roberta ran $3\frac{1}{2}$ miles on Monday, $2\frac{1}{4}$ miles on Tuesday, and $4\frac{2}{3}$ miles on Wednesday. How many total miles did Roberta run?

SOLUTION STRATEGY

$$3\frac{1 \cdot 6}{2 \cdot 6} \rightarrow 3\frac{6}{12}$$
Because we are looking for a total, add the three distances together.

$$2\frac{1 \cdot 3}{4 \cdot 3} \rightarrow 2\frac{3}{12}$$
LCD = 12. Write each fraction as an equivalent fraction with denominator 12.

$$+ 4\frac{2 \cdot 4}{3 \cdot 4} \rightarrow + 4\frac{8}{12}$$

$$9\frac{17}{12}$$
Add the fraction parts. Add the whole numbers.

$$9\frac{17}{12} = 9 + \frac{17}{12}$$
Write the mixed number as the sum of the whole number and the fraction part.

$$= 9 + 1\frac{5}{12}$$
Write the fraction part as a mixed number.

$$= 10\frac{5}{12}$$
Add the whole number and the mixed number.

Roberta ran $10\frac{5}{12}$ miles.

TRY-IT EXERCISE 6

Michael caught a grouper weighing $6\frac{3}{8}$ pounds and two snappers weighing $7\frac{1}{2}$ and $5\frac{3}{4}$ pounds. What was the total weight of the three fish?

Check your answer with the solution in Appendix A. ∎

SECTION 2.6 REVIEW EXERCISES

Concept Check

1. Fractions with the same denominator are known as _____ fractions.

2. To add like fractions, add the _____ and write this sum over the common _____. Simplify, if possible.

3. When adding fractions with different denominators, we must find the _____ of the fractions, write each fraction as an _____ fraction with this denominator, and then add the resulting like fraction.

4. When adding mixed numbers, we first add the _____ parts and then add the _____.

5. When the sum of two mixed numbers contains an improper fraction, we must change the improper fraction to a _____ and then add the whole number to it.

6. An alternate method for adding mixed numbers is to change each mixed number to an _____ fraction and then add.

Objective 2.6A   **Add fractions with the same denominator**

GUIDE PROBLEMS

7. Add $\dfrac{4}{9} + \dfrac{1}{9}$.

$$\dfrac{4}{9} + \dfrac{1}{9} = \dfrac{+}{9} = \dfrac{}{9}$$

8. Add $\dfrac{3}{17} + \dfrac{8}{17}$.

$$\dfrac{3}{17} + \dfrac{8}{17} = \dfrac{+}{17} = \dfrac{}{17}$$

Add. Simplify, if possible.

9. $\dfrac{1}{7} + \dfrac{4}{7}$

10. $\dfrac{5}{9} + \dfrac{2}{9}$

11. $\dfrac{8}{13} + \dfrac{3}{13}$

12. $\dfrac{4}{15} + \dfrac{9}{15}$

13. $\dfrac{1}{12} + \dfrac{5}{12}$

14. $\dfrac{7}{18} + \dfrac{1}{18}$

15. $\dfrac{2}{21} + \dfrac{7}{21}$

16. $\dfrac{7}{36} + \dfrac{11}{36}$

17. $\dfrac{7}{10} + \dfrac{3}{10}$

18. $\dfrac{5}{14} + \dfrac{9}{14}$

19. $\dfrac{8}{9} + \dfrac{5}{9}$

20. $\dfrac{4}{5} + \dfrac{3}{5}$

21. $\dfrac{1}{3} + \dfrac{2}{3} + \dfrac{1}{3}$

22. $\dfrac{5}{6} + \dfrac{5}{6} + \dfrac{3}{6}$

23. $\dfrac{2}{5} + \dfrac{3}{5} + \dfrac{1}{5}$

24. $\dfrac{8}{9} + \dfrac{4}{9} + \dfrac{7}{9}$

Objective 2.6B **Add fractions with different denominators**

GUIDE PROBLEMS

25. Add $\dfrac{1}{3} + \dfrac{3}{4}$.

   a. Find the LCD of the fractions.

     LCD = ___

   b. Write each fraction as an equivalent fraction with the LCD found in part a.

     $\dfrac{1}{3} \cdot \dfrac{}{} = \dfrac{}{} = \dfrac{}{}$

     $\dfrac{3}{4} \cdot \dfrac{}{} = \dfrac{}{} = \dfrac{}{}$

   c. Add the fractions.

     $\dfrac{\overline{}}{12} + \dfrac{\overline{}}{12} = \dfrac{\overline{}}{12} =$ ___

26. Add $\dfrac{3}{8} + \dfrac{5}{6}$.

   a. Find the LCD of the fractions.

     LCD = ___

   b. Write each fraction as an equivalent fraction with the LCD found in part a.

     $\dfrac{3}{8} \cdot \dfrac{}{} = \dfrac{}{} = \dfrac{}{}$

     $\dfrac{5}{6} \cdot \dfrac{}{} = \dfrac{}{} = \dfrac{}{}$

   c. Add the fractions.

     $\dfrac{\overline{}}{24} + \dfrac{\overline{}}{24} = \dfrac{\overline{}}{24} =$ ___

Add. Simplify, if possible.

27. $\dfrac{7}{16} + \dfrac{9}{24}$

28. $\dfrac{3}{7} + \dfrac{1}{14}$

29. $\dfrac{1}{6} + \dfrac{1}{8}$

30. $\dfrac{5}{8} + \dfrac{5}{24}$

31. $\dfrac{5}{6} + \dfrac{1}{18}$

32. $\dfrac{1}{6} + \dfrac{1}{12}$

33. $\dfrac{3}{4} + \dfrac{7}{16}$

34. $\dfrac{1}{4} + \dfrac{7}{8}$

35. $\dfrac{1}{3} + \dfrac{5}{6} + \dfrac{8}{9}$

36. $\dfrac{4}{5} + \dfrac{5}{6} + \dfrac{1}{10}$

37. $\dfrac{4}{5} + \dfrac{7}{8} + \dfrac{9}{20}$

38. $\dfrac{2}{3} + \dfrac{3}{6} + \dfrac{4}{9}$

39. $\dfrac{1}{5} + \dfrac{1}{9} + \dfrac{13}{15}$

40. $\dfrac{3}{8} + \dfrac{4}{5} + \dfrac{11}{20}$

41. $\dfrac{5}{6} + \dfrac{2}{9} + \dfrac{4}{15}$

42. $\dfrac{1}{6} + \dfrac{11}{12} + \dfrac{8}{15}$

Objective 2.6C   **Add mixed numbers**

GUIDE PROBLEMS

43. Add $8\dfrac{2}{3} + 7\dfrac{3}{4}$.

    a. Find the LCD of the fraction parts.

        LCD = ___

    b. Write the fraction part of each mixed number as an equivalent fraction with the LCD found in part a.

$$8\dfrac{2}{3} = 8\dfrac{2 \cdot \underline{}}{3 \cdot \underline{}} = 8\dfrac{\underline{}}{\underline{}}$$

$$7\dfrac{3}{4} = 7\dfrac{3 \cdot \underline{}}{4 \cdot \underline{}} = 7\dfrac{\underline{}}{\underline{}}$$

    c. Add the fraction parts and then add the whole number parts. Simplify, if possible.

$$\begin{aligned}8&\dfrac{\underline{}}{\underline{}} \\ +\,7&\dfrac{\underline{}}{\underline{}} \\ \hline 15&\dfrac{\underline{}}{\underline{}}\end{aligned} = 15 + \dfrac{\underline{}}{\underline{}} = 15 + 1\dfrac{\underline{}}{\underline{}} = 16\dfrac{\underline{}}{\underline{}}$$

44. Add $11\dfrac{1}{2} + 17\dfrac{3}{5}$.

    a. Find the LCD of the fraction parts.

        LCD = ___

    b. Write the fraction part of each mixed number as an equivalent fraction with the LCD found in part a.

$$11\dfrac{1}{2} = 11\dfrac{1 \cdot \underline{}}{2 \cdot \underline{}} = 11\dfrac{\underline{}}{\underline{}}$$

$$17\dfrac{3}{5} = 17\dfrac{3 \cdot \underline{}}{5 \cdot \underline{}} = 17\dfrac{\underline{}}{\underline{}}$$

    c. Add the fraction parts and then add the whole number parts. Simplify, if possible.

$$\begin{aligned}11&\dfrac{\underline{}}{\underline{}} \\ +\,17&\dfrac{\underline{}}{\underline{}} \\ \hline 28&\dfrac{\underline{}}{\underline{}}\end{aligned} = 28 + \dfrac{\underline{}}{\underline{}} = 28 + 1\dfrac{\underline{}}{\underline{}} = 29\dfrac{\underline{}}{\underline{}}$$

Add. Simplify, if possible.

45. $\dfrac{4}{15} + 3\dfrac{9}{25}$

46. $\dfrac{3}{7} + 2\dfrac{3}{14}$

47. $\dfrac{3}{8} + 1\dfrac{3}{10}$

48. $\dfrac{7}{15} + 2\dfrac{13}{18}$

49. $\dfrac{3}{4} + 2\dfrac{3}{8}$

50. $\dfrac{2}{7} + 5\dfrac{1}{2}$

51. $1\dfrac{2}{5} + \dfrac{3}{16}$

52. $\dfrac{12}{35} + 2\dfrac{1}{10}$

53. $4\dfrac{7}{24} + 8\dfrac{7}{18}$

54. $4\dfrac{13}{100} + 2\dfrac{7}{10}$

55. $7\dfrac{1}{2} + 7\dfrac{3}{4}$

56. $6\dfrac{1}{8} + 6\dfrac{3}{4}$

57. $2\dfrac{4}{7} + 3\dfrac{7}{9}$

58. $12\dfrac{1}{3} + 4\dfrac{1}{6}$

59. $3\dfrac{2}{5} + 3\dfrac{5}{8}$

60. $22\dfrac{1}{2} + 38\dfrac{2}{3} + 17\dfrac{1}{3}$

61. $1\dfrac{3}{8} + 1\dfrac{1}{3} + 3\dfrac{1}{4}$

62. $5\dfrac{1}{3} + 10\dfrac{1}{2} + 15\dfrac{1}{2}$

63. $\dfrac{5}{30} + \dfrac{3}{40} + 2\dfrac{1}{8}$

64. $3\dfrac{3}{5} + 2\dfrac{1}{4} + 5\dfrac{3}{10}$

65. $\dfrac{2}{5} + \dfrac{2}{15} + 2\dfrac{1}{10}$

66. $1\dfrac{2}{5} + 1\dfrac{5}{6} + 6\dfrac{1}{2}$

67. $2\dfrac{1}{4} + 4\dfrac{5}{8} + 1\dfrac{1}{6}$

68. $\dfrac{1}{5} + 2\dfrac{1}{3} + 1\dfrac{1}{4}$

69. $\dfrac{1}{3} + 2\dfrac{3}{5} + 5\dfrac{1}{5}$

70. $1\dfrac{1}{3} + 1\dfrac{3}{8} + 5\dfrac{19}{24}$

71. $\dfrac{1}{3} + \dfrac{5}{12} + 5\dfrac{4}{5}$

Objective 2.6D   Apply your knowledge

72. Sandra went to Gardner's Market and bought $\dfrac{1}{2}$ pound of bananas and $\dfrac{2}{3}$ pounds of peaches. What is the total weight of her purchase?

73. James rode his bike $\dfrac{3}{4}$ miles to school, $\dfrac{5}{16}$ miles to the mall, and $\dfrac{7}{8}$ miles back home. What is the total distance he rode?

74. A building contractor completes $\dfrac{1}{8}$ of a job the first week, $\dfrac{1}{5}$ of the job the second week, and $\dfrac{1}{4}$ of the job the third week. What fraction of the job has been completed?

75. Lester's Landscape Service sent three workers to mow a golf course. Alfred mowed $16\dfrac{1}{5}$ acres, Larry mowed $17\dfrac{2}{3}$ acres, and Howard mowed $15\dfrac{1}{12}$ acres. How many acres did Alfred, Larry, and Howard mow together?

76. While on a diet, Alicia lost $4\dfrac{1}{2}$ pounds in May, $3\dfrac{3}{8}$ pounds in June, and $6\dfrac{3}{4}$ pounds in July. How much total weight did she lose?

77. Tropical Glass received an order for a rectangular piece of glass measuring $29\dfrac{5}{16}$ inches by $44\dfrac{7}{8}$ inches with a beveled edge around the perimeter. How many total inches of bevel are required on the glass? (Use the formula: Perimeter = 2 · length + 2 · width)

78. During a recent storm, $3\frac{7}{8}$ inches of rain fell in the morning and $4\frac{3}{8}$ inches of rain fell in the afternoon. What was the total amount of rainfall for the day?

79. A farm has $125\frac{1}{3}$ acres of soybeans, $65\frac{4}{5}$ acres of wheat, and $88\frac{3}{4}$ acres of canola. What is the total acreage of the crops?

Photo by Robert Brechner

80. Jennifer works part time as a legal assistant. Last week she worked $4\frac{3}{5}$ hours on Tuesday, $3\frac{3}{4}$ hours on Thursday, and 5 hours on Friday.

  a. How many hours did she work last week?

  b. This week Jennifer plans to work $7\frac{1}{2}$ hours more than last week. How many hours will she work this week?

  c. What will be her total hours for the 2-week period?

81. To paint his house, Peter used $5\frac{1}{2}$ gallons of paint on the interior walls, $8\frac{4}{5}$ gallons on the exterior walls, $2\frac{5}{6}$ gallons on the wood trim, and $4\frac{2}{3}$ gallons on the roof.

  a. How many total gallons of paint did Peter use on the house?

  b. What was the total cost of the paint if it cost $20 per gallon?

CUMULATIVE SKILLS REVIEW

1. Round 12,646 to the nearest ten. (1.1D)

2. LCD is the abbreviation for _____ _____ _____. (2.3C)

3. Three packages weigh $25\frac{2}{5}$ pounds, $25\frac{4}{15}$ pounds, and $25\frac{7}{20}$ pounds. What is the weight of the lightest package? (2.3D)

4. Multiply $\frac{3}{4} \cdot \frac{5}{12}$. (2.4A)

5. Write $\frac{11}{14}$ as an equivalent fraction with a denominator of 84. (2.3B)

6. Find the prime factorization of 66. (2.1C)

7. Compare $4\frac{9}{16}$ and $4\frac{7}{12}$ using the symbols $<$ or $>$. (2.3C)

8. True or false: $(3 + 8) + 7 = 3 + (8 + 7)$. (1.2A)

9. Find the LCD of $\frac{2}{3}$ and $\frac{1}{7}$. (2.3C)

10. A painter used $4\frac{1}{6}$ gallons of paint on a roof. If the next job is $3\frac{1}{2}$ times as large, how much paint will be required? (2.4C)

2.7 SUBTRACTING FRACTIONS AND MIXED NUMBERS

LEARNING OBJECTIVES

A. Subtract fractions with the same denominator

B. Subtract fractions with different denominators

C. Subtract mixed numbers

D. Apply your knowledge

Procedures for subtracting fractions and mixed numbers are very similar to those we used for addition. However, some modification of our approach is required, especially when subtracting mixed numbers.

> **Objective 2.7A**   **Subtract fractions with the same denominator**

In Section 2.6, Adding Fractions and Mixed Numbers, we began by using an example involving pizza. Let's use a similar example here. Suppose that you ate three-eighths of a pizza. What part of the pizza remains? Study the figure below.

Because you ate three of the eight slices of pizza, five slices remain. Therefore, we conclude that five-eighths of the pizza remains.

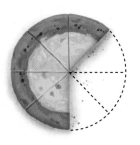

To get this answer, we could subtract $\frac{3}{8}$, the portion of the pizza you ate, from $\frac{8}{8}$, the fraction representing the entire pizza. The fact that the answer is $\frac{5}{8}$ suggests that we simply subtract the numerators and leave the common denominator alone.

$$\frac{8}{8} - \frac{3}{8} = \frac{8 - 3}{8} = \frac{5}{8}$$

The following steps are used to subtract like fractions.

Steps for Subtracting Like Fractions

Step 1. Subtract the second numerator from the first numerator and write this difference over the common denominator.

Step 2. Simplify, if possible.

EXAMPLE 1   Subtract fractions with the same denominators

Subtract. Simplify, if possible.

a. $\dfrac{9}{16} - \dfrac{5}{16}$

b. $\dfrac{20}{21} - \dfrac{11}{21}$

SOLUTION STRATEGY

a. $\dfrac{9}{16} - \dfrac{5}{16} = \dfrac{9-5}{16} = \dfrac{4}{16}$ Subtract the second numerator from the first numerator and write this difference over the common denominator.

$\dfrac{4}{16} = \dfrac{1}{4}$ Simplify.

b. $\dfrac{20}{21} - \dfrac{11}{21} = \dfrac{20-11}{21} = \dfrac{9}{21}$ Subtract the second numerator from the first numerator and write this difference over the common denominator.

$\dfrac{9}{21} = \dfrac{3}{7}$ Simplify.

TRY-IT EXERCISE 1

Subtract. Simplify, if possible.

a. $\dfrac{11}{25} - \dfrac{6}{25}$

b. $\dfrac{13}{14} - \dfrac{5}{14}$

Check your answers with the solutions in Appendix A. ■

Objective 2.7B   **Subtract fractions with different denominators**

To subtract fractions with different denominators, first create equivalent fractions with the same denominator. The steps for subtracting fractions with different denominators are given below.

Steps for Subtracting Fractions with Different Denominators

Step 1. Find the LCD of the fractions.

Step 2. Write each fraction as an equivalent fraction with the LCD found in step 1.

Step 3. Follow the steps for subtracting like fractions.

EXAMPLE 2 **Subtract fractions with different denominators**

Subtract. Simplify, if possible.

a. $\dfrac{7}{9} - \dfrac{1}{2}$ **b.** $\dfrac{2}{3} - \dfrac{3}{8}$

SOLUTION STRATEGY

a. $\dfrac{7}{9} - \dfrac{1}{2} = \dfrac{7 \cdot 2}{9 \cdot 2} - \dfrac{1 \cdot 9}{2 \cdot 9}$ The LCD is 18. Write each fraction as an equivalent fraction with denominator 18.

$= \dfrac{14}{18} - \dfrac{9}{18}$

$= \dfrac{14 - 9}{18} = \dfrac{5}{18}$ Subtract the second numerator from the first numerator and write the difference over the common denominator.

b. $\dfrac{2}{3} - \dfrac{3}{8} = \dfrac{2 \cdot 8}{3 \cdot 8} - \dfrac{3 \cdot 3}{8 \cdot 3}$ The LCD is 24. Write each fraction as an equivalent fraction with denominator 24.

$= \dfrac{16}{24} - \dfrac{9}{24}$

$= \dfrac{16 - 9}{24} = \dfrac{7}{24}$ Subtract the second numerator from the first numerator and write the difference over the common denominator.

TRY-IT EXERCISE 2

Subtract. Simplify, if possible.

a. $\dfrac{5}{12} - \dfrac{2}{9}$

b. $\dfrac{7}{16} - \dfrac{1}{6}$

c. $\dfrac{6}{7} - \dfrac{3}{21}$

Check your answers with the solutions in Appendix A. ■

Objective 2.7C **Subtract mixed numbers**

To subtract mixed numbers, first subtract the fraction parts and then the whole numbers. As an example, consider $8\dfrac{6}{7} - 3\dfrac{2}{7}$.

$$8\dfrac{6}{7}$$
$$-\,3\dfrac{2}{7}$$
$$\overline{\dfrac{4}{7}}$$
$$\uparrow$$

$$8\dfrac{6}{7}$$
$$-\,3\dfrac{2}{7}$$
$$\overline{5\dfrac{4}{7}}$$
$$\uparrow$$

Subtract the fractions.   Subtract the whole numbers.

If the fraction parts of the mixed numbers have different denominators, find the LCD. As an example, consider $3\frac{3}{4} - 2\frac{1}{6}$.

$$3\frac{3}{4} \rightarrow 3\frac{3 \cdot 3}{4 \cdot 3} \rightarrow 3\frac{9}{12}$$

$$-2\frac{1}{6} \rightarrow -2\frac{1 \cdot 2}{6 \cdot 2} \rightarrow -2\frac{2}{12}$$

$$1\frac{7}{12}$$

LCD = 12.
Write the fraction part of each mixed number as an equivalent fraction with denominator 12.

Subtract the fraction parts. Then, add the whole numbers.

EXAMPLE 3   Subtract mixed numbers

Subtract. Simplify, if possible.

a. $15\frac{5}{12} - 9\frac{1}{12}$ **b.** $7\frac{3}{5} - 2\frac{1}{8}$

SOLUTION STRATEGY

a.
$$15\frac{5}{12}$$
$$-9\frac{1}{12}$$
$$6\frac{4}{12} = 6\frac{1}{3}$$

Subtract the fraction parts. Then, subtract the whole numbers. Simplify.

b.
$$7\frac{3 \cdot 8}{5 \cdot 8} \rightarrow 7\frac{24}{40}$$
$$-2\frac{1 \cdot 5}{8 \cdot 5} \rightarrow -2\frac{5}{40}$$
$$5\frac{19}{40}$$

LCD = 40. Write each fraction as an equivalent fraction with denominator 40.

Subtract the fraction parts. Then, subtract the whole numbers. Simplify.

TRY-IT EXERCISE 3

Subtract. Simplify, if possible.

a. $12\frac{7}{8} - 5\frac{3}{8}$ **b.** $8\frac{5}{12} - 3\frac{1}{4}$

Check your answers with the solutions in Appendix A. ■

> **◉ Learning Tip**
>
> **Alternate Method for Subtracting Mixed Numbers**
>
> **Step 1.** Change each mixed number to an improper fraction.
>
> **Step 2.** Find the LCD, and write each fraction as an equivalent fraction with the LCD.
>
> **Step 3.** Follow the rules for subtracting like fractions.
>
> **Step 4.** Convert the answer to a mixed number and simplify.
>
> **Examples**
>
> $$8\frac{6}{7} - 3\frac{2}{7} = \frac{62}{7} - \frac{23}{7}$$
> $$= \frac{39}{7} = 5\frac{4}{7}$$
>
> $$3\frac{3}{4} - 2\frac{1}{6} = \frac{15}{4} - \frac{13}{6}$$
> $$= \frac{15 \cdot 3}{4 \cdot 3} - \frac{13 \cdot 2}{6 \cdot 2}$$
> $$= \frac{45}{12} - \frac{26}{12}$$
> $$= \frac{19}{12} = 1\frac{7}{12}$$

As another example, consider $5\frac{3}{10} - 2\frac{7}{10}$. When subtracting the fractions, we encounter the problem of taking $\frac{7}{10}$ away from something smaller, $\frac{3}{10}$. We can remedy this situation by borrowing, just as we do in subtraction problems involving whole numbers. To do so, first recognize that $5\frac{3}{10}$ is the same as $5 + \frac{3}{10}$. Moreover, notice that 5 is the same as $4 + 1$.

$$5\frac{3}{10} = 5 + \frac{3}{10} = 4 + 1 + \frac{3}{10}$$

We can now add 1 and $\frac{3}{10}$. If we wish to do so, we must first write 1 as a fraction with the same denominator as $\frac{3}{10}$. That is, we must write 1 as $\frac{10}{10}$.

$$4 + 1 + \frac{3}{10} = 4 + \frac{10}{10} + \frac{3}{10} = 4 + \frac{13}{10} = 4\frac{13}{10}$$

From this we see that $5\frac{3}{10} = 4\frac{13}{10}$. Thus, our problem can be worked in the following way.

$$5\frac{3}{10} \rightarrow 4 + 1 + \frac{3}{10} \rightarrow 4 + \frac{10}{10} + \frac{3}{10} \rightarrow \quad 4\frac{13}{10}$$
$$-2\frac{7}{10} \rightarrow \qquad -2\frac{7}{10} \rightarrow \qquad -2\frac{7}{10} \rightarrow -2\frac{7}{10}$$
$$\overline{\qquad\qquad} \qquad \overline{\qquad\qquad} \qquad \overline{\qquad\qquad} \qquad \overline{\qquad\qquad}$$
$$2\frac{6}{10} = 2\frac{3}{5}$$

Since $\frac{3}{10}$ is less than $\frac{7}{10}$, borrow 1 from 5. Add 1 in the form of $\frac{10}{10}$ to $\frac{3}{10}$.

Subtract the fraction parts. Subtract the whole numbers. Simplify the fraction.

EXAMPLE 4   Subtract mixed numbers

Subtract. Simplify, if possible.

a. $11\frac{1}{6} - 5\frac{3}{4}$

b. $32\frac{3}{8} - 16\frac{5}{12}$

c. $18 - 6\frac{3}{7}$

SOLUTION STRATEGY

a. $11\frac{1 \cdot 2}{6 \cdot 2} \rightarrow \quad 11\frac{2}{12}$
$ -5\frac{3 \cdot 3}{4 \cdot 3} \rightarrow -5\frac{9}{12}$
$ \overline{\qquad\qquad} \qquad \overline{\qquad\qquad}$

LCD = 12. Write each fraction as an equivalent fraction with denominator 12.

$$11\frac{2}{12} \rightarrow 10 + 1 + \frac{2}{12} \rightarrow 10 + \frac{12}{12} + \frac{2}{12} \rightarrow 10\frac{14}{12}$$
$$-5\frac{9}{12} \rightarrow \qquad -5\frac{9}{12} \rightarrow \qquad -5\frac{9}{12} \rightarrow -5\frac{9}{12}$$
$$\overline{\qquad\qquad} \qquad \overline{\qquad\qquad} \qquad \overline{\qquad\qquad} \qquad \overline{\qquad\qquad}$$
$$5\frac{5}{12}$$

Since $\frac{2}{12}$ is less than $\frac{9}{12}$, borrow 1 from 11. Add 1 in the form of $\frac{12}{12}$ to $\frac{2}{12}$.

Subtract the fraction parts. Then, subtract the whole numbers.

b.
$$32\frac{3 \cdot 3}{8 \cdot 3} \rightarrow 32\frac{9}{24}$$
$$-16\frac{5 \cdot 2}{12 \cdot 2} \rightarrow -16\frac{10}{24}$$

LCD = 24. Write each fraction as an equivalent fraction with denominator 24.

$$32\frac{9}{24} \rightarrow 31 + 1 + \frac{9}{24} \rightarrow 31 + \frac{24}{24} + \frac{9}{24} \rightarrow 31\frac{33}{24}$$
$$-16\frac{10}{24} \rightarrow \quad -16\frac{10}{24} \rightarrow \quad -16\frac{10}{24} \rightarrow -16\frac{10}{24}$$
$$15\frac{23}{24}$$

Since $\frac{9}{24}$ is less than $\frac{10}{24}$, borrow 1 from 32. Add 1 in the form of $\frac{24}{24}$ to $\frac{9}{24}$.

Subtract the fraction parts. Then, subtract the whole numbers.

c.
$$18 \rightarrow 17 + 1 \rightarrow 17 + \frac{7}{7} \rightarrow 17\frac{7}{7}$$
$$-6\frac{3}{7} \rightarrow -6\frac{3}{7} \rightarrow -6\frac{3}{7} \rightarrow -6\frac{3}{7}$$
$$11\frac{4}{7}$$

Since 18 is a whole number, write 18 as 17 + 1. Write 1 in the form of $\frac{7}{7}$.

Subtract the fraction parts. Then, subtract the whole numbers.

TRY-IT EXERCISE 4

Subtract. Simplify, if possible.

a. $11\frac{2}{7} - 8\frac{3}{5}$ **b.** $42\frac{2}{9} - 7\frac{8}{15}$ **c.** $21 - 13\frac{8}{11}$

Check your answers with the solutions in Appendix A. ■

We summarize the steps for subtracting mixed numbers.

Steps for Subtracting Mixed Numbers

Step 1. If the denominators of the fractions are different, write each fraction as an equivalent fraction with the LCD of the original fractions.

Step 2. a. If the fraction part of the first mixed number is less than the fraction part of the second mixed number, then borrow 1 from the whole number of the first mixed number and add it in the form of $\frac{LCD}{LCD}$ to the fraction part.

b. If the first number is a whole number, borrow a 1 from the whole number and add this in the form of $\frac{LCD}{LCD}$ to one less than the whole number.

Step 3. Subtract the fraction parts.

Step 4. Subtract the whole number parts.

Step 5. Simplify.

Objective 2.7D **Apply your knowledge**

Now let's take a look at some application problems that require us to use what we have learned about subtracting fractions and mixed numbers. Recall that some of the key words and phrases that indicate subtraction are the *difference of, decreased by, take away, less than, fewer than,* and *subtracted from.*

EXAMPLE 5 **Subtract mixed numbers in an application problem**

Dan prepares to mail a package weighing $20\frac{1}{4}$ pounds. At the last minute, he removes some items weighing $7\frac{2}{3}$ pounds. How much does the package weigh now?

SOLUTION STRATEGY

$$20\frac{1 \cdot 3}{4 \cdot 3} \rightarrow 20\frac{3}{12}$$
$$-7\frac{2 \cdot 4}{3 \cdot 4} \rightarrow -7\frac{8}{12}$$

The key word *remove* indicates subtraction.
LCD = 12. Write each fraction as an equivalent fraction with denominator 12.

$$20\frac{3}{12} \rightarrow 19 + 1 + \frac{3}{12} \rightarrow 19 + \frac{12}{12} + \frac{3}{12} \rightarrow 19\frac{15}{12}$$
$$-7\frac{8}{12} \rightarrow -7\frac{8}{12} \rightarrow -7\frac{8}{12} \rightarrow -7\frac{8}{12}$$
$$\phantom{-7\frac{8}{12}} \qquad \qquad \qquad \qquad 12\frac{7}{12}$$

Because $\frac{3}{12}$ is less than $\frac{8}{12}$, borrow 1 from 20. Add in the form of $\frac{12}{12}$ to $\frac{3}{12}$.
Subtract the fractional parts.
Subtract the whole numbers.

TRY-IT EXERCISE 5

Rose is hiking a trail in Banff National Park that is 8 miles long. She stops for a snack when she reaches a sign that indicates that she has $3\frac{2}{5}$ miles to go. How far has she hiked to this point?

Check your answer with the solution in Appendix A. ∎

Photo by Robert Brechner

SECTION 2.7 REVIEW EXERCISES

Concept Check

1. To subtract like fractions, subtract the second _____ from the first numerator and write this difference over the common _____ . Simplify, if possible.

2. When subtracting fractions with different denominators, we must find the _____ of the fractions, write each fraction as an _____ fraction with this denominator, and then subtract the resulting like fractions.

3. When subtracting mixed numbers, we first subtract the _____ parts and then subtract the _____ .

4. When subtracting mixed numbers, if the fraction part of the first mixed number is less than the fraction part of the second mixed number, then borrow 1 from the whole number of the first mixed number and add it in the form of _____ to the fraction part.

5. When subtracting a mixed number from a whole number, we must borrow 1 from the whole number part and add this in the form of _____ to one less than the whole number part.

6. An alternate method for adding mixed numbers is to change each mixed number to an _____ fraction and then add.

Objective 2.7A **Subtract fractions with the same denominators**

GUIDE PROBLEMS

7. Subtract $\dfrac{7}{11} - \dfrac{3}{11}$.

$$\frac{7}{11} - \frac{3}{11} = \frac{-}{11} = \frac{}{11}$$

8. Subtract $\dfrac{6}{7} - \dfrac{1}{7}$.

$$\frac{6}{7} - \frac{1}{7} = \frac{-}{7} = \frac{}{7}$$

Subtract. Simplify, if possible.

9. $\dfrac{9}{10} - \dfrac{3}{10}$

10. $\dfrac{25}{36} - \dfrac{18}{36}$

11. $\dfrac{9}{14} - \dfrac{4}{14}$

12. $\dfrac{7}{12} - \dfrac{1}{12}$

13. $\dfrac{3}{17} - \dfrac{1}{17}$

14. $\dfrac{5}{6} - \dfrac{1}{6}$

15. $\dfrac{11}{61} - \dfrac{10}{61}$

16. $\dfrac{18}{37} - \dfrac{14}{37}$

17. $\dfrac{16}{25} - \dfrac{11}{25}$

18. $\dfrac{11}{36} - \dfrac{5}{36}$

19. $\dfrac{17}{48} - \dfrac{7}{48}$

20. $\dfrac{19}{56} - \dfrac{11}{56}$

Objective 2.7B **Subtract fractions with different denominators**

GUIDE PROBLEMS

21. Subtract $\dfrac{3}{4} - \dfrac{1}{3}$.

a. Find the LCD of the fractions.

LCD = ____

b. Write each fraction as an equivalent fraction with the LCD found in part a.

$$\frac{3}{4} \cdot \frac{}{} = \frac{}{} = \frac{}{}$$

$$\frac{1}{3} \cdot \frac{}{} = \frac{}{} = \frac{}{}$$

c. Subtract the fractions.

$$\frac{}{12} - \frac{}{12} = \frac{}{12}$$

22. Subtract $\dfrac{3}{5} - \dfrac{1}{4}$.

a. Find the LCD of the fractions.

LCD = ____

b. Write each fraction as an equivalent fraction with the LCD found in part a.

$$\frac{3}{5} \cdot \frac{}{} = \frac{}{} = \frac{}{}$$

$$\frac{1}{4} \cdot \frac{}{} = \frac{}{} = \frac{}{}$$

c. Subtract the fractions.

$$\frac{}{} - \frac{}{} = \frac{}{} = \frac{}{}$$

Subtract and simplify, if possible.

23. $\dfrac{5}{6} - \dfrac{5}{8}$

24. $\dfrac{7}{8} - \dfrac{15}{32}$

25. $\dfrac{1}{6} - \dfrac{1}{8}$

26. $\dfrac{1}{2} - \dfrac{7}{20}$

27. $\dfrac{14}{15} - \dfrac{8}{9}$

28. $\dfrac{9}{14} - \dfrac{3}{8}$

29. $\dfrac{4}{5} - \dfrac{3}{10}$

30. $\dfrac{3}{5} - \dfrac{1}{2}$

31. $\dfrac{19}{25} - \dfrac{11}{50}$

32. $\dfrac{3}{8} - \dfrac{1}{6}$

33. $\dfrac{7}{16} - \dfrac{1}{12}$

34. $\dfrac{9}{10} - \dfrac{7}{8}$

Objective 2.7C   **Subtract mixed numbers**

GUIDE PROBLEMS

35. Subtract $15\dfrac{3}{4} - 8\dfrac{1}{4}$.

$$15\dfrac{3}{4}$$
$$-\ 8\dfrac{1}{4}$$
$$\overline{\qquad}$$
$$7\dfrac{\ \ }{\ \ } = 7\dfrac{\ \ }{\ \ }$$

36. Subtract $28\dfrac{5}{8} - 5\dfrac{1}{8}$.

$$28\dfrac{5}{8}$$
$$-\ 5\dfrac{1}{8}$$
$$\overline{\qquad}$$
$$\dfrac{\ \ }{\ \ } = \dfrac{\ \ }{\ \ }$$

Subtract. Simplify, if possible.

37. $2\dfrac{4}{5} - 1\dfrac{1}{5}$

38. $4\dfrac{11}{15} - 1\dfrac{1}{15}$

39. $5\dfrac{11}{12} - 3\dfrac{7}{12}$

40. $2\dfrac{16}{17} - \dfrac{12}{17}$

41. $2\dfrac{5}{6} - 1\dfrac{2}{6}$

42. $2\dfrac{5}{8} - \dfrac{3}{8}$

43. $12\dfrac{13}{27} - 7\dfrac{5}{27}$

44. $7\dfrac{1}{7} - 2\dfrac{1}{7}$

GUIDE PROBLEMS

45. Subtract $14\frac{1}{4} - 3\frac{3}{4}$.

    a. Because the fraction part of the first mixed number is less than the fraction part of the second mixed number, borrow 1 from the whole number of the first mixed number in the form of $\frac{LCD}{LCD}$ and add it to the fraction part of the first mixed number.

$$14\frac{1}{4} = 14 + \frac{1}{4} = 13 + \frac{}{} + \frac{1}{4} = 13\frac{}{}$$

    b. Subtract the fraction parts and then subtract the whole number parts. Simplify, if possible.

$$\begin{array}{r} 13\frac{}{} \\ -\ 3\frac{3}{4} \\ \hline 10\frac{}{} = \underline{}\frac{}{} \end{array}$$

46. Subtract $16\frac{1}{8} - 9\frac{3}{8}$.

    a. Because the fraction part of the first mixed number is less than the fraction part of the second mixed number, borrow 1 from the whole number of the first mixed number in the form of $\frac{LCD}{LCD}$ and add it to the fraction part of the first mixed number.

$$16\frac{1}{8} = 16 + \frac{1}{8} = 15 + \frac{}{} + \frac{1}{8} = 15\frac{}{}$$

    b. Subtract the fraction parts and then subtract the whole number parts. Simplify, if possible.

$$\begin{array}{r} 15\frac{}{} \\ -\ 9\frac{3}{8} \\ \hline \underline{}\frac{}{} = \underline{}\frac{}{} \end{array}$$

Subtract. Simplify, if possible.

47. $4\frac{1}{8} - 2\frac{3}{8}$

48. $19\frac{3}{8} - 5\frac{5}{8}$

49. $6\frac{1}{9} - 2\frac{4}{9}$

50. $9\frac{2}{5} - 1\frac{3}{5}$

51. $14\frac{1}{7} - 3\frac{5}{7}$

52. $17\frac{2}{11} - 5\frac{5}{11}$

53. $21\frac{3}{8} - 16\frac{5}{8}$

54. $15\frac{9}{16} - 14\frac{11}{16}$

GUIDE PROBLEMS

55. Subtract $17\frac{2}{3} - 4\frac{1}{4}$.

    a. Find the LCD of the fraction parts.

      LCD = ___

    b. Write the fractional part of each mixed number as an equivalent fraction with the LCD found in part a.

$$17\frac{2}{3} = 17\frac{2 \cdot }{3 \cdot } = 17\frac{}{}$$

$$4\frac{1}{4} = 4\frac{1 \cdot }{4 \cdot } = 4\frac{}{}$$

    c. Subtract the fraction parts and then subtract the whole number parts. Simplify, if possible.

$$\begin{array}{r} 17\frac{}{} \\ -\ 4\frac{}{} \\ \hline 13\frac{}{} \end{array}$$

56. Subtract $8\dfrac{3}{4} - 2\dfrac{1}{3}$.

a. Find the LCD of the fractional parts.

LCD = ___

b. Write the fraction part of each mixed number as an equivalent fraction with the LCD found in part a.

$$8\dfrac{3}{4} = 8\dfrac{3 \cdot }{4 \cdot } = 8\dfrac{}{}$$

$$2\dfrac{1}{3} = 2\dfrac{1 \cdot }{3 \cdot } = 2\dfrac{}{}$$

c. Subtract the fraction parts and then subtract the whole number parts. Simplify if possible.

$$8\dfrac{}{}$$
$$-\,2\dfrac{}{}$$
$$\overline{}$$
$$6\dfrac{}{}$$

Subtract. Simplify, if possible.

57. $1\dfrac{11}{12} - \dfrac{3}{20}$

58. $25\dfrac{1}{2} - 20\dfrac{1}{6}$

59. $2\dfrac{5}{6} - \dfrac{3}{5}$

60. $2\dfrac{13}{16} - \dfrac{5}{12}$

61. $29\dfrac{3}{5} - 20\dfrac{14}{15}$

62. $3\dfrac{13}{18} - \dfrac{7}{12}$

63. $7\dfrac{2}{3} - 5\dfrac{1}{2}$

64. $2\dfrac{15}{16} - \dfrac{5}{12}$

65. $3\dfrac{5}{6} - \dfrac{1}{8}$

66. $18\dfrac{1}{2} - 2\dfrac{5}{12}$

67. $30\dfrac{3}{4} - 10\dfrac{3}{10}$

68. $3\dfrac{11}{15} - \dfrac{2}{5}$

69. $15\dfrac{5}{6} - 8\dfrac{8}{10}$

70. $5\dfrac{3}{8} - 3\dfrac{5}{16}$

71. $3\dfrac{1}{4} - 1\dfrac{1}{8}$

72. $5\dfrac{33}{40} - \dfrac{7}{24}$

73. $9\dfrac{13}{18} - 1\dfrac{7}{15}$

74. $18\dfrac{7}{10} - 8\dfrac{1}{4}$

75. $56\dfrac{2}{3} - 4\dfrac{1}{2}$

76. $4\dfrac{47}{60} - 1\dfrac{17}{24}$

GUIDE PROBLEMS

77. Subtract $18\frac{1}{3} - 5\frac{1}{2}$.

   a. Find the LCD of the fraction parts.

     LCD = ___

   b. Write the fraction part of each mixed number as an equivalent fraction with the LCD found in part a.

$$18\frac{1}{3} = 18\frac{1 \cdot }{3 \cdot } = 18\frac{}{}$$

$$5\frac{1}{2} = 5\frac{1 \cdot }{2 \cdot } = 5\frac{}{}$$

   c. Because the fraction part of the first mixed number is less than the fraction part of the second mixed number, borrow 1 from the whole number of the first mixed number in the form of $\dfrac{\text{LCD}}{\text{LCD}}$ and add it to the fraction part of the first mixed number.

$$18\frac{}{} = 18 + \frac{}{} = 17 + \frac{}{} + \frac{}{} = 17\frac{}{}$$

   d. Subtract the fraction parts and then subtract the whole number parts. Simplify, if possible.

$$\begin{array}{r} 17\frac{}{} \\ -\,5\frac{}{} \\ \hline \frac{}{} \end{array}$$

78. Subtract $24\frac{1}{4} - 3\frac{4}{5}$.

   a. Find the LCD of the fraction parts.

     LCD = ___

   b. Write the fraction part of each mixed number as an equivalent fraction with the LCD found in part a.

$$24\frac{1}{4} = 24\frac{1 \cdot }{4 \cdot } = 24\frac{}{}$$

$$3\frac{4}{5} = 3\frac{4 \cdot }{5 \cdot } = 3\frac{}{}$$

   c. Because the fraction part of the first mixed number is less than the fraction part of the second mixed number, borrow 1 from the whole number of the first mixed number in the form of $\dfrac{\text{LCD}}{\text{LCD}}$ and add it to the fraction part of the first mixed number.

$$24\frac{}{} = 24 + \frac{}{} = 23 + \frac{}{} + \frac{}{} = 23\frac{}{}$$

   d. Subtract the fraction parts and then subtract the whole number parts. Simplify, if possible.

$$\begin{array}{r} 23\frac{}{} \\ -\,3\frac{}{} \\ \hline \frac{}{} \end{array}$$

Subtract. Simplify, if possible.

79. $5\frac{2}{5} - 1\frac{14}{15}$

80. $10\frac{1}{6} - 5\frac{1}{2}$

81. $13 - 1\frac{5}{18}$

82. $37\frac{1}{6} - 10\frac{1}{2}$

83. $69\frac{1}{4} - 38\frac{1}{2}$

84. $7\frac{1}{5} - 4\frac{11}{15}$

85. $17\frac{1}{8} - \frac{3}{4}$

86. $51\frac{1}{3} - 26\frac{5}{6}$

87. $11\frac{5}{16} - 8\frac{3}{4}$

88. $31 - 9\frac{3}{4}$

89. $4 - \frac{1}{3}$

90. $14\frac{1}{6} - 4\frac{7}{8}$

91. $10\frac{5}{16} - 4\frac{7}{12}$

92. $19 - 5\frac{4}{9}$

93. $12 - 9\frac{15}{16}$

94. $5 - 2\frac{1}{10}$

Objective 2.7D   **Apply your knowledge**

95. A canister contained $\frac{7}{8}$ pound of sugar. If Samantha used $\frac{3}{5}$ pound to make a batch of cookies, how much sugar was left in the canister?

96. Robert is $67\frac{1}{2}$ inches tall, and his brother Howard is $71\frac{3}{4}$ inches tall. How many inches taller is Howard than Bob?

97. A $9\frac{5}{8}$-inch piece is cut from a $27\frac{1}{4}$-inch pipe. What is the length of the remaining pipe?

98. A land developer sold $2\frac{3}{5}$ acres of his $18\frac{1}{4}$ acres. How many acres does he have left?

99. A Boy Scout troop stopped for lunch after walking $8\frac{3}{4}$ miles of a $15\frac{1}{2}$-mile hike. How much further do they have to go to complete the hike?

100. At Petro Chemicals, Inc., $\frac{7}{32}$ of an inch is removed from a piece of $\frac{3}{8}$-inch thick copper sheeting during a chemical etching process. What is the new thickness of the copper sheeting?

101. At Mel's Diner, a meatloaf weighed $3\frac{9}{16}$ pounds before cooking and $2\frac{7}{8}$ pounds after. How much weight was lost in cooking?

102. Two years ago, interest rates on a 30-year mortgage averaged $6\frac{3}{4}$ percent. Last year they averaged $7\frac{5}{16}$ percent. By how much did the rate increase?

103. A Starbucks Cafe began the morning with $22\frac{3}{8}$ pounds of Kona Coast coffee. By noon, there were only $6\frac{1}{3}$ pounds left. How many pounds of Kona Coast coffee were sold?

104. Tom owns $\frac{1}{4}$ of a business, Anna owns $\frac{1}{3}$, and Jill owns the rest. What fraction represents the portion owned by Jill?

105. A picture frame is $14\frac{3}{4}$ inches wide. If the matte and frame on each side of the photo is $2\frac{1}{8}$ inches, how wide is the photo?

106. On the 6-hour mode of a DVD, you record a program for $1\frac{3}{10}$ hours and another for $3\frac{3}{5}$ hours.

    a. What is the total recording time for the two programs?

    b. How much time is left on the tape?

107. From a 63-foot roll of rubber hose, you cut lengths of $15\frac{3}{8}$ feet, $8\frac{4}{5}$ feet, and $12\frac{1}{6}$ feet. How much hose is left on the roll?

108. Lynn budgets two-fifths of her income for food and clothing, one-fourth of her income for housing, and one-eighth for transportation. What fraction of her income is left for entertainment and savings?

109. From the illustration below, find the unknown length.

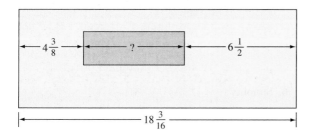

110. For a party, you purchased $3\frac{3}{4}$ pounds of peppermint patty candies. After the party, there were $2\frac{1}{5}$ pounds left. Since George really likes these candies, he took $\frac{1}{2}$ pound home. How many pounds do you have left?

111. Susan started a diet weighing $134\frac{3}{4}$ pounds. The first week she lost $2\frac{1}{4}$ pounds, the second week she lost $1\frac{1}{2}$ pounds, and the third week she gained $1\frac{1}{8}$ pounds. How much did she weigh at the end of the third week?

112. A boat hull weighs $1658\frac{1}{2}$ pounds, and the outboard motor weighs $645\frac{1}{4}$ pounds. A standard trailer has a weight limit of 2170 pounds.

    a. Is this a safe combination, or will a heavy-duty trailer be necessary?

    b. By how many pounds is the load over or under the limit?

Photo by Robert Brechner

113. Robert has two suitcases weighing $51\frac{1}{3}$ pounds and $28\frac{1}{4}$ pounds respectively. He is allowed a maximum of 80 pounds.

a. Is the total weight of the suitcases within the 80-pound limit?

b. By how many pounds is the total weight over or under the limit?

114. When you left home this morning, you filled the fuel tank in your car. By noon you had used one-fourth of a tank. By late afternoon you used an additional five-sixteenths of a tank. What fraction represents the fuel remaining in the tank?

CUMULATIVE SKILLS REVIEW

1. Write $\frac{7}{12}$ as an equivalent fraction with a denominator of 60. (2.3B)

2. Add $\frac{4}{15} + \frac{2}{15}$. Simplify, if possible. (2.6A)

3. A service station started the day with 7560 gallons of high octane gasoline. During the day 2334 gallons were sold. How many gallons remain? (1.3B)

4. Add $18\frac{3}{7} + 45\frac{1}{2}$. Simplify if possible. (2.6C)

5. Find the LCD of $\frac{3}{7}, \frac{2}{5}, \frac{8}{9}$. (2.3C)

6. Simplify $\frac{8}{144}$. (2.3A)

7. Simplify $89 + (4 + 8)^2 - 12$. (1.6C)

8. Multiply $8\frac{1}{3} \cdot 2\frac{2}{5}$. Simplify, if possible. (2.4B)

9. Find the LCD of $\frac{1}{12}$ and $\frac{7}{8}$. (2.3C)

10. A construction job requires pipes of length $34\frac{1}{2}$ inches, $18\frac{3}{8}$ inches, and $12\frac{1}{4}$ inches. What is the total length of the pipes needed for the job? (2.6D)

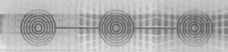

10-MINUTE CHAPTER REVIEW

2.1 Factors, Prime Factorizations, and Least Common Multiples

Objective	Important Concepts	Illustrative Examples
A. Find the factors of a natural number (page 102)	**Rule for Finding Factors of a Natural Number** Divide the natural number by each of the numbers 1, 2, 3, and so on. If the natural number is divisible by one of these numbers, then both the divisor and the quotient are factors of the natural number. Continue until the factors begin to repeat. **Rules for Divisibility** A number is | DIVISIBLE BY	IF
---	---
2	The number is even (that is, the last digit is 0, 2, 4, 6, or 8).
3	The sum of the digits is divisible by 3.
4	The number named by the last two digits is divisible by 4.
5	The last digit is either 0 or 5.
6	The number is even and the sum of the digits is divisible by 3.
8	The number named by the last three digits is divisible by 8.
9	The sum of the digits is divisible by 9.
10	The last digit is 0.		Find all the factors of 28. $28 \div 1 = 28$ 1 and 28 are factors. $28 \div 2 = 14$ 2 and 14 are factors. $28 \div 3$ Does not divide evenly. $28 \div 4 = 7$ 4 and 7 are factors. $28 \div 5$ Does not divide evenly. $28 \div 6$ Does not divide evenly. $28 \div 7 = 4$ 7 and 4 are repeat factors. Stop! The factors of 28 are 1, 2, 4, 7, 14, and 28. Find the factors of 45. $45 \div 1 = 45$ 1 and 45 are factors. $45 \div 2$ Does not divide evenly. $45 \div 3 = 15$ 3 and 15 are factors. $45 \div 4$ Does not divide evenly. $45 \div 5 = 9$ 5 and 9 are factors. $45 \div 6$ Does not divide evenly. $45 \div 7$ Does not divide evenly. $45 \div 8$ Does not divide evenly. $45 \div 9 = 5$ 9 and 5 are repeat factors. Stop! The factors of 45 are 1, 3, 5, 9, 15, and 45.

B. Determine whether a number is prime, composite, or neither (page 104)	**prime number** or **prime**
	A natural number greater than 1 that has only two factors (divisors), namely, one and itself.
	
	composite number
	A natural number greater than 1 that has more than two factors (divisors).
		Determine whether each number is prime, composite, or neither.
		
		a. 22
		   composite
		
		b. 0
		   neither
		
		c. 61
		   prime

C. Find the prime factorization of a composite number (page 105)

factor
To express a quantity as a product of factors.

prime factorization
A factorization of a whole number in which each factor is prime.

factor tree
An illustration used to determine the prime factorization of a composite number.

Find the prime factorization of each number.

a. 63

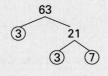

$63 = 3 \cdot 3 \cdot 7 = 3^2 \cdot 7$

b. 91

$91 = 7 \cdot 13$

D. Find the least common multiple (LCM) of a set of numbers (page 107)

multiple of a number
The product of the number and any natural number.

common multiple
A multiple that is shared by a set of two or more natural numbers.

least common multiple or **LCM**
The smallest multiple shared by a set of two or more numbers.

Steps for Finding the LCM Using Prime Factorization

Step 1. Write the prime factorization of each number.

Step 2. Write the product of the prime factors with each factor appearing the greatest number of times that it occurs in any one factorization.

Steps for Finding the LCM: Alternate Method

Step 1. List the numbers for which we are trying to find the LCM in a row. Draw a "half-box" around the numbers.

Step 2. Find a factor other than 1 for at least one of these numbers. Write this factor to the left of the numbers.

Step 3. Consider the quotient of each number in the half-box and the factor from step 2. If the number is evenly divisible by the factor, write the quotient below the number. If not, rewrite the number itself. Place a half-box around this new row of numbers.

Step 4. Repeat steps 2 and 3 until a row of ones remain.

Step 5. Calculate the product of the factors to the left of each half-box. This is the LCM.

Find the LCM of 4, 8, and 10 by listing multiples.

Multiples of 4 are 4, 8, 12, 16, 20, 24, 28, 32, 36, 40, 44, . . .

Multiples of 8 are 8, 16, 24, 32, 40, 48, 56 . . .

Multiples of 10 are 10, 20, 30, 40, 50, 60, . . .

The LCM of 4, 8, and 10 is 40.

Find the LCM of 4, 8, and 10 using prime factorization.

$4 = 2 \cdot 2$

$8 = 2 \cdot 2 \cdot 2$

$10 = 2 \cdot 5$

$2 \cdot 2 \cdot 2 \cdot 5 = 40$

The LCM of 4, 8, and 10 is 40.

Find the LCM of 4, 8, and 10 using the alternate method.

```
2 | 4   8   10
2 | 2   4    5
2 | 1   2    5
5 | 1   1    5
  | 1   1    1
```

$2 \cdot 2 \cdot 2 \cdot 5 = 40$

The LCM of 4, 8, and 10 is 40.

E. Apply your knowledge (page 112)	If a plane takes off every 4 minutes on one runway while a plane lands every 6 minutes on a parallel one, how often will a plane land while another simultaneously takes off? $4 = 2 \cdot 2$ $6 = 2 \cdot 3$ The LCM of 4 and 6 is $2 \cdot 2 \cdot 3 = 12$. Two planes will land and take off simultaneously every 12 minutes.

2.2 Introduction to Fractions and Mixed Numbers

Objective	Important Concepts	Illustrative Examples

A. Identify a fraction and distinguish proper fractions, improper fractions, and mixed numbers (page 117)	**fraction**
	A number that can be written in the form $\frac{a}{b}$ where a and b are whole numbers and b is not zero.
	numerator
	The top number in a fraction.
	denominator
	The bottom number in a fraction.
	fraction bar
	The line between the numerator and the denominator.
	proper fraction or **common fraction**
	A fraction in which the numerator is less than the denominator.
	improper fraction
	A fraction in which the numerator is greater than or equal to the denominator.
	mixed number
	A number that combines a whole number with a fraction.
	complex fraction
	A quotient of the form $\frac{A}{B}$ where A or B or both are both fractions and where B is not zero.
		Classify each as a proper fraction, an improper fraction, or a mixed number.
		
		a. $12\frac{5}{6}$
		
		    mixed number
		
		b. $\frac{2}{7}$
		
		    proper fraction
		
		c. $\frac{21}{9}$
		
		    improper fraction

B. Use a fraction to represent a part of a whole (page 119)	Write the number of shaded parts as the numerator and the total number of parts as the denominator.	Write a fraction or mixed number to represent the shaded portion of each figure. **a.** $\frac{2}{5}$ **b.** $2\frac{1}{2}$
C. Convert between an improper fraction and a mixed or whole number (page 121)	**Steps for Writing an Improper Fraction as a Mixed or Whole Number** **Step 1.** Divide the numerator by the denominator. **Step 2. a.** If there is no remainder, then the improper fraction is equal to the whole number quotient found in step 1.	Write each improper fraction as a whole or mixed number. **a.** $\frac{28}{4}$ **b.** $\frac{12}{5}$ 7 $2\frac{2}{5}$

b. If there is a remainder, then the improper fraction can be written as follows:

$$\text{Quotient } \frac{\text{Remainder}}{\text{Divisor}}$$

Steps for Writing Mixed Numbers as Improper Fractions

Step 1. Multiply the whole number part by the denominator of the fraction part and add the numerator of the fraction part to this product.

Step 2. Write an improper fraction. The numerator is the result of step 1. The denominator is the original denominator.

Write each mixed number as an improper fraction.

a. $2\frac{3}{7}$ **b.** $8\frac{2}{5}$

$$8\frac{2}{5} = \frac{8 \cdot 5 + 2}{5} = \frac{42}{5}$$

$$2\frac{3}{7} = \frac{2 \cdot 7 + 3}{7} = \frac{17}{7}$$

D. Apply your knowledge (page 123)

The AquaClear Pool Company has 23 service trucks. Nine are Fords, eight are GMCs, and the rest are Dodges. What fraction of the total number of vehicles represents Dodge trucks?

Total number of Fords and GMCs: $9 + 8 = 17$

Number of Dodges: $23 - 17 = 6$

$$\frac{6}{23}$$

2.3 Simplifying Fractions to Lowest Terms

Objective	Important Concepts	Illustrative Examples
A. Simplify a fraction (page 130)	**equivalent fractions** Fractions that represent the same quantity.	Simplify $\frac{60}{126}$ using the prime factorization of the numerator and denominator.
	fraction simplified to lowest terms A fraction in which the numerator and denominator have no common factor other than 1.	$\frac{60}{126} = \frac{2 \cdot 2 \cdot 3 \cdot 5}{2 \cdot 3 \cdot 3 \cdot 7}$
	Steps for Simplifying a Fraction Using Prime Factorization	$= \frac{\overset{1}{\cancel{2}} \cdot 2 \cdot \overset{1}{\cancel{3}} \cdot 5}{\underset{1}{\cancel{2}} \cdot \underset{1}{\cancel{3}} \cdot 3 \cdot 7}$
	Step 1. Write the prime factorization of the numerator and denominator.	$= \frac{1 \cdot 2 \cdot 1 \cdot 5}{1 \cdot 1 \cdot 3 \cdot 7} = \frac{10}{21}$
	Step 2. Divide out any factors common to the numerator and denominator.	Simplify each fraction.
	Step 3. Multiply the remaining factors in the numerator and denominator to determine the simplified fraction.	**a.** $\frac{12}{21}$
	greatest common factor or **GCF** The largest factor common to two or more numbers.	GCF = 3 $$\frac{12}{21} = \frac{\overset{4}{\cancel{12}}}{\underset{7}{\cancel{21}}} = \frac{4}{7}$$

	Steps for Simplifying a Fraction	
	Step 1. Identify and divide out any factor common to the numerator and the denominator. Use the greatest common factor if you can identify it.	**b.** $\dfrac{75}{90}$ GCF = 15
	Step 2. If a common factor remains in the numerator and denominator of the resulting fraction, repeat step 1 until the fraction is simplified to lowest terms.	$\dfrac{75}{90} = \dfrac{\overset{5}{\cancel{75}}}{\underset{6}{\cancel{90}}} = \dfrac{5}{6}$
B. Write an equivalent fraction with a larger denominator (page 133)	**Rule for Writing an Equivalent Fraction with a Larger Denominator** To find an equivalent fraction for $\dfrac{a}{b}$ with a larger denominator, multiply both the numerator and denominator by the same nonzero whole number, n. In general, we have the following. $$\dfrac{a}{b} = \dfrac{a \cdot n}{b \cdot n}$$	Write $\dfrac{5}{8}$ fraction as an equivalent fraction with a denominator of 56. $$\dfrac{5}{8} = \dfrac{5 \cdot 7}{8 \cdot 7} = \dfrac{35}{56}$$
C. Compare fractions using the least common denominator (LCD) (page 134)	**common denominator** A common multiple of all the denominators for a set of fractions. **least common denominator** or **LCD** The least common multiple (LCM) of all the denominators for a set of fractions. **Steps for Comparing Fractions** **Step 1.** Find the LCD of the fractions. **Step 2.** Write each fraction as an equivalent fraction with denominator equal to the LCD. **Step 3.** Compare the fractions.	Compare $\dfrac{4}{7}$ and $\dfrac{5}{8}$. LCD of $\dfrac{4}{7}$ and $\dfrac{5}{8}$ is 56. $\dfrac{4}{7} = \dfrac{4 \cdot 8}{7 \cdot 8} = \dfrac{32}{56}$ $\dfrac{5}{8} = \dfrac{5 \cdot 7}{8 \cdot 7} = \dfrac{35}{56}$ $\dfrac{4}{7} < \dfrac{5}{8}$
D. Apply your knowledge (page 136)	Twenty-six of 65 students in an economics class are married. Express this as a fraction in simplified form. $\dfrac{26}{65} = \dfrac{2}{5}$ What fraction represents those students who are not married? Simplify, if possible. $\dfrac{39}{65} = \dfrac{3}{5}$	

2.4 Multiplying Fractions and Mixed Numbers

Objective	Important Concepts	Illustrative Examples
A. Multiply fractions (page 144)	**Steps for Multiplying Fractions** **Step 1.** Multiply the numerators to form the new numerator. **Step 2.** Multiply the denominators to form the new denominator. **Step 3.** Simplify, if possible. **Steps for Simplifying before Multiplying Fractions** **Step 1.** Find a common factor that divides evenly into one of the numerators and one of the denominators. Divide the identified numerator and denominator by this common factor. **Step 2.** Repeat step 1 until there are no more common factors. **Step 3.** Multiply the remaining factors in the numerators and in the denominators.	Multiply $\dfrac{5}{8} \cdot \dfrac{2}{5}$. Simplify, if possible. $\dfrac{5}{8} \cdot \dfrac{2}{5} = \dfrac{5 \cdot 2}{8 \cdot 5} = \dfrac{10}{40} = \dfrac{1}{4}$ The same problem can be done by simplifying before multiplying. $\dfrac{5}{8} \cdot \dfrac{2}{5} = \dfrac{\overset{1}{\cancel{5}}}{\underset{4}{\cancel{8}}} \cdot \dfrac{\overset{1}{\cancel{2}}}{\underset{1}{\cancel{5}}} = \dfrac{1}{4} \cdot \dfrac{1}{1} = \dfrac{1}{4}$
B. Multiply fractions, mixed numbers, or whole numbers (page 146)	In multiplication problems involving fractions, mixed numbers, or whole numbers, change each whole number and mixed number to an improper fraction. Recall that a whole number, n, can be written as $\dfrac{n}{1}$.	Multiply $2\dfrac{1}{4} \cdot 4\dfrac{5}{6}$. Simplify, if possible. $2\dfrac{1}{4} \cdot 4\dfrac{5}{6} = \dfrac{9}{4} \cdot \dfrac{29}{6}$ $\dfrac{\overset{3}{\cancel{9}}}{4} \cdot \dfrac{29}{\underset{2}{\cancel{6}}} = \dfrac{3}{4} \cdot \dfrac{29}{2} = \dfrac{87}{8}$ $\dfrac{87}{8} = 10\dfrac{7}{8}$
C. Apply your knowledge (page 147)	A box of kitchen floor tiles covers $8\dfrac{1}{2}$ square feet. How many square feet can you cover if you have $6\dfrac{3}{4}$ boxes? $8\dfrac{1}{2} \cdot 6\dfrac{3}{4} = \dfrac{17}{2} \cdot \dfrac{27}{4} = \dfrac{459}{8} = 57\dfrac{3}{8}$ square feet	

2.5 Dividing Fractions and Mixed Numbers

Objective	Important Concepts	Illustrative Examples
A. Divide fractions (page 154)	**reciprocal of the fraction** $\dfrac{a}{b}$ The fraction $\dfrac{b}{a}$ where $a \neq 0$ and $b \neq 0$.	Divide $\dfrac{7}{16} \div \dfrac{3}{4}$. Simplify, if possible.

	Steps for Dividing by a Fraction	$\frac{7}{16} \div \frac{3}{4} = \frac{7}{\overset{}{\underset{4}{16}}} \cdot \frac{\overset{1}{4}}{3} = \frac{7}{12}$
	Step 1. Multiply the dividend by the reciprocal of the divisor, that is,	
	$$\frac{a}{b} \div \frac{c}{d} = \frac{a}{b} \cdot \frac{d}{c}$$	
	where b, c, and d are not zero.	
	Step 2. Simplify, if possible.	
B. Divide fractions, mixed numbers, or whole numbers (page 155)	In division problems involving fractions, whole numbers, or mixed numbers, change each whole number and mixed number to an improper fraction.	Divide $2\frac{5}{8} \div 1\frac{1}{3}$. Simplify, if possible. $$2\frac{5}{8} \div 1\frac{1}{3} = \frac{21}{8} \div \frac{4}{3}$$ $$= \frac{21}{8} \cdot \frac{3}{4} = \frac{63}{32} = 1\frac{31}{32}$$
C. Apply your knowledge (page 157)	An architect is building a model that requires several $2\frac{3}{8}$-inch pieces of piping. How many pieces can be cut from a pipe that is $52\frac{1}{4}$ inches long? $$52\frac{1}{4} \div 2\frac{3}{8} = \frac{209}{4} \div \frac{19}{8} = \frac{\overset{11}{209}}{\underset{1}{4}} \cdot \frac{\overset{2}{8}}{\underset{1}{19}} = \frac{11}{1} \cdot \frac{2}{1} = \frac{22}{1} = 22 \text{ pieces of piping}$$	

2.6 Adding Fractions and Mixed Numbers

Topic	Important Concepts	Illustrative Examples
A. Add fractions with the same denominator (page 162)	**like fractions** Fractions with the same denominator. **Steps for Adding Like Fractions** **Step 1.** Add the numerators and write this sum over the common denominator. **Step 2.** Simplify, if possible.	Add $\frac{5}{18} + \frac{11}{18}$. Simplify, if possible. $$\frac{5}{18} + \frac{11}{18} = \frac{5 + 11}{18} = \frac{16}{18} = \frac{8}{9}$$
B. Add fractions with different denominators (page 163)	**Steps for Adding Fractions with Different Denominators** **Step 1.** Find the LCD of the fractions. **Step 2.** Write each fraction as an equivalent fraction with the LCD found in step 1. **Step 3.** Follow the steps for adding like fractions.	Add $\frac{4}{15} + \frac{3}{4}$. Simplify, if possible. $$\frac{4}{15} + \frac{3}{4} = \frac{4 \cdot 4}{15 \cdot 4} + \frac{3 \cdot 15}{4 \cdot 15}$$ $$= \frac{16}{60} + \frac{45}{60} = \frac{61}{60} = 1\frac{1}{60}$$
C. Add mixed numbers (page 164)	**Steps for Adding Mixed Numbers** **Step 1.** If the denominators of the fraction parts are different, write each fraction part as an equivalent fraction with the LCD of the original fractions. **Step 2.** Add the fraction parts. **Step 3.** Add the whole number parts.	Add. Simplify, if possible. **a.** $5\frac{1}{5} + 9\frac{7}{15}$ $$\begin{array}{rcl} 5\frac{1}{5} & \rightarrow & 5\frac{3}{15} \\ +9\frac{7}{15} & \rightarrow & +9\frac{7}{15} \\ \hline & & 14\frac{10}{15} = 14\frac{2}{3} \end{array}$$

Step 4. If the fraction part is an improper fraction, rewrite the mixed number as the sum of a whole number and an improper fraction expressed as a mixed number. Add the whole number and the mixed number.

Step 5. Simplify, if possible.

b. $4\dfrac{3}{5} + 3\dfrac{1}{2}$.

$$4\dfrac{3}{5} \rightarrow 4\dfrac{3 \cdot 2}{5 \cdot 2} \rightarrow 4\dfrac{6}{10}$$

$$+ 3\dfrac{1}{2} \rightarrow + 3\dfrac{1 \cdot 5}{2 \cdot 5} \rightarrow + 3\dfrac{5}{10}$$

$$7\dfrac{11}{10} = 7 + \dfrac{11}{10}$$
$$= 7 + 1\dfrac{1}{10}$$
$$= 8\dfrac{1}{10}$$

D. Apply your knowledge (page 168)

What is the total height of a bar stool if the legs are $33\dfrac{1}{2}$ inches high and seat cushion is $4\dfrac{3}{4}$ inch high?

$$33\dfrac{1}{2} \rightarrow 33\dfrac{2}{4}$$
$$+ 4\dfrac{3}{4} \rightarrow + 4\dfrac{3}{4}$$

$$37\dfrac{5}{4} = 37 + 1\dfrac{1}{4} = 38\dfrac{1}{4} \text{ inches}$$

2.7 Subtracting Fractions and Mixed Numbers

Topic	Important Concepts	Illustrative Examples
A. Subtract fractions with the same denominator (page 174)	**Steps for Subtracting Like Fractions** **Step 1.** Subtract the second numerator from the first numerator and write this difference over the common denominator. **Step 2.** Simplify, if possible.	Subtract $\dfrac{5}{12} - \dfrac{1}{12}$. Simplify, if possible. $$\dfrac{5}{12} - \dfrac{1}{12} = \dfrac{5-1}{12} = \dfrac{4}{12} = \dfrac{1}{3}$$
B. Subtract fractions with different denominators (page 176)	**Steps for Subtracting Fractions with Different Denominators** **Step 1.** Find the LCD of the fractions. **Step 2.** Write each fraction as an equivalent fraction with the LCD found in step 1. **Step 3.** Follow the steps for subtracting like fractions.	Subtract $\dfrac{3}{5} - \dfrac{1}{8}$. Simplify, if possible. $$\dfrac{3}{5} - \dfrac{1}{8} = \dfrac{3 \cdot 8}{5 \cdot 8} - \dfrac{1 \cdot 5}{8 \cdot 5} = \dfrac{24}{40} - \dfrac{5}{40} = \dfrac{19}{40}$$

C. Subtract mixed numbers (page 176)

Steps for Subtracting Mixed Numbers

Step 1. If the denominators of the fractions are different, write each fraction as an equivalent fraction with the LCD of the original fractions.

Step 2. a. If the fraction part of the first mixed number is less than the fraction part of the second mixed number, then borrow 1 from the whole number of the first mixed number and add it in the form of $\frac{LCD}{LCD}$ to the fraction part.

b. If the first number is a whole number, borrow a 1 from the whole number and add this in the form of $\frac{LCD}{LCD}$ to one less than the whole number.

Step 3. Subtract the fraction parts.

Step 4. Subtract the whole number parts.

Step 5. Simplify.

Subtract. Simplify, if possible.

a. $4\frac{1}{6} - 2\frac{3}{5}$

$$4\frac{1}{6} \rightarrow 4\frac{5}{30} = 3\frac{35}{30}$$
$$-2\frac{3}{5} \rightarrow -2\frac{18}{30} = -2\frac{18}{30}$$
$$\overline{1\frac{17}{30}}$$

b. $9 - 6\frac{5}{8}$

$$9 \rightarrow 8\frac{8}{8}$$
$$-6\frac{5}{8} \rightarrow -6\frac{5}{8}$$
$$\overline{2\frac{3}{8}}$$

D. Apply your knowledge (page 180)

The back wall of a house is $37\frac{1}{8}$ feet wide. If windows on that wall measure $22\frac{5}{6}$ feet, how many feet of wall do not have windows?

$$37\frac{1}{8} \rightarrow 37\frac{3}{24} = 36 + \frac{24}{24} + \frac{3}{24} = 36\frac{27}{24}$$
$$-22\frac{5}{6} \rightarrow -22\frac{20}{24} \qquad\qquad\qquad -22\frac{20}{24}$$
$$\overline{14\frac{7}{24}\text{ feet}}$$

Numerical Facts of Life

Chocolate Chip Cookies

$\frac{1}{2}$ cup butter, softened

$\frac{2}{3}$ cup brown sugar, packed

$\frac{1}{2}$ cup sugar

4 large eggs

1 teaspoon vanilla

$2\frac{1}{4}$ cup unsifted flour

1 teaspoon baking powder

$\frac{1}{2}$ teaspoon baking soda

1 teaspoon espresso powder

1 cup pecans, finely chopped

1 pinch of salt

$11\frac{1}{2}$ ounces milk chocolate chips

Increasing a Recipe

The chocolate chip cookie recipe to the left yields 4 dozen cookies. Suppose that you need to make 12 dozen cookies for a large party.

1. What factor must you multiply each amount by in order to make 12 dozen cookies?

2. How much butter is required in the increased recipe? Express your answer as both an improper fraction and a mixed number.

3. How much brown sugar is required in the increased recipe?

4. How much flour is required in the increased recipe? Express your answer as both an improper fraction and a mixed number.

5. How many ounces of chocolate chips are required in the increased recipe? Express your answer as both an improper fraction and as a mixed number.

6. If a pinch is $\frac{1}{8}$ of a teaspoon, how many teaspoons of salt would be required for the increased recipe?

CHAPTER REVIEW EXERCISES

Find the factors of each number. (2.1A)

1. 10 **2.** 15 **3.** 44 **4.** 48

5. 46 **6.** 85 **7.** 89 **8.** 61

9. 24   **10.** 63   **11.** 66   **12.** 112

Determine whether each number is prime, composite, or neither. (2.1B)

13. 41   **14.** 50   **15.** 1   **16.** 91

17. 125   **18.** 0   **19.** 57   **20.** 97

21. 12   **22.** 37   **23.** 81   **24.** 13

Find the prime factorization of each number. (2.1C)

25. 75   **26.** 40   **27.** 57   **28.** 62

29. 88   **30.** 105   **31.** 625   **32.** 90

33. 1000   **34.** 120   **35.** 50   **36.** 504

Find the LCM of each set of numbers. (2.1D)

37. 3, 11   **38.** 13, 26   **39.** 2, 43   **40.** 8, 20

41. 6, 8, 9, 12   **42.** 8, 12, 14, 18   **43.** 6, 7, 12, 16   **44.** 8, 12, 16, 18

45. 6, 8, 12, 14   **46.** 6, 9, 12, 14   **47.** 7, 8, 9, 16   **48.** 3, 7, 13, 22

Classify each as a proper fraction, an improper fraction, or a mixed number. (2.2A)

49. $\dfrac{14}{5}$ **50.** $4\dfrac{7}{9}$ **51.** $\dfrac{8}{15}$

52. $2\dfrac{5}{8}$ **53.** $\dfrac{9}{13}$ **54.** $\dfrac{33}{7}$

Write a fraction or mixed number to represent the shaded portion of each figure. (2.2B)

55.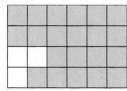

56.

57.

58.

59.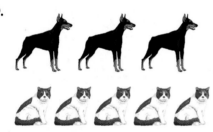

   a. What fraction of the total number of animals do the dogs represent?

   b. What fraction of the total number of animals do the cats represent?

60.

   a. What fraction of the total number of vehicles do the buses represent?

   b. What fraction of the total number of vehicles do the cars represent?

Write each improper fraction as a mixed or whole number. (2.2C)

61. $\dfrac{25}{2}$ **62.** $\dfrac{37}{8}$ **63.** $\dfrac{49}{7}$

64. $\dfrac{107}{6}$ **65.** $\dfrac{55}{5}$ **66.** $\dfrac{78}{7}$

Write each mixed number as an improper fraction. (2.2C)

67. $2\dfrac{3}{5}$

68. $14\dfrac{8}{9}$

69. $7\dfrac{3}{8}$

70. $22\dfrac{1}{5}$

71. $45\dfrac{2}{15}$

72. $10\dfrac{6}{17}$

Simplify each fraction. (2.3A)

73. $\dfrac{9}{72}$

74. $\dfrac{25}{125}$

75. $\dfrac{15}{24}$

76. $\dfrac{20}{32}$

77. $\dfrac{12}{36}$

78. $\dfrac{18}{60}$

79. $\dfrac{25}{90}$

80. $\dfrac{54}{90}$

Write each fraction as an equivalent fraction with the indicated denominator. (2.3B)

81. $\dfrac{3}{14} = \dfrac{?}{56}$

82. $\dfrac{1}{10} = \dfrac{?}{80}$

83. $\dfrac{2}{11} = \dfrac{?}{44}$

84. $\dfrac{3}{8} = \dfrac{?}{64}$

Compare the fractions. (2.3C)

85. $\dfrac{11}{12}, \dfrac{5}{6}$

86. $\dfrac{5}{6}, \dfrac{7}{9}$

87. $\dfrac{5}{8}, \dfrac{11}{12}, \dfrac{13}{16}$

88. $\dfrac{7}{9}, \dfrac{5}{6}, \dfrac{7}{8}$

Multiply. Simplify, if possible. (2.4A)

89. $\dfrac{7}{9} \cdot \dfrac{3}{9}$

90. $\dfrac{2}{16} \cdot \dfrac{3}{6}$

91. $\dfrac{2}{3} \cdot \dfrac{10}{11}$

92. $\dfrac{2}{5} \cdot \dfrac{1}{3}$

93. $\dfrac{4}{5} \cdot \dfrac{1}{4}$

94. $\dfrac{12}{27} \cdot \dfrac{5}{19}$

95. $\dfrac{9}{80} \cdot \dfrac{7}{72}$

96. $\dfrac{7}{8} \cdot \dfrac{5}{7}$

Multiply. Simplify, if possible. (2.4B)

97. $3\frac{5}{7} \cdot 2\frac{7}{8}$

98. $4\frac{1}{3} \cdot 7\frac{3}{4}$

99. $2\frac{1}{4} \cdot 19\frac{1}{2}$

100. $6\frac{3}{4} \cdot 5\frac{1}{2}$

101. $4\frac{8}{9} \cdot 1\frac{5}{6}$

102. $3\frac{12}{15} \cdot 4\frac{7}{9}$

103. $2\frac{1}{5} \cdot 12\frac{1}{6}$

104. $18\frac{2}{3} \cdot 5\frac{6}{7}$

Divide. Simplify, if possible. (2.5A)

105. $\frac{2}{4} \div \frac{1}{8}$

106. $\frac{5}{14} \div \frac{1}{2}$

107. $\frac{2}{6} \div \frac{5}{6}$

108. $\frac{1}{3} \div \frac{2}{13}$

109. $\frac{6}{10} \div \frac{2}{5}$

110. $\frac{1}{3} \div \frac{7}{8}$

111. $\frac{2}{3} \div \frac{5}{6}$

112. $\frac{3}{4} \div \frac{1}{2}$

Divide. Simplify, if possible. (2.5B)

113. $1\frac{3}{5} \div 2\frac{5}{6}$

114. $29\frac{1}{3} \div 2\frac{2}{3}$

115. $20\frac{3}{4} \div 2\frac{1}{4}$

116. $5\frac{3}{5} \div 6\frac{2}{3}$

117. $14\frac{2}{5} \div 1\frac{2}{7}$

118. $10\frac{1}{3} \div 3\frac{1}{5}$

119. $24\frac{2}{9} \div 5\frac{1}{3}$

120. $15\frac{13}{23} \div 6\frac{1}{2}$

Add. Simplify, if possible. (2.6A, B)

121. $\frac{1}{4} + \frac{1}{5}$

122. $\frac{3}{4} + \frac{1}{4}$

123. $\frac{2}{5} + \frac{1}{10}$

124. $\frac{5}{8} + \frac{7}{12}$

125. $\frac{6}{7} + \frac{1}{5}$

126. $\frac{8}{9} + \frac{2}{7}$

127. $\frac{5}{12} + \frac{1}{3}$

128. $\frac{7}{15} + \frac{5}{6}$

Add. Simplify, if possible. (2.7C)

129. $26\frac{1}{2} + 28\frac{2}{3}$

130. $1\frac{2}{3} + 5\frac{5}{12}$

131. $23\frac{1}{4} + 20\frac{2}{5}$

132. $37\frac{1}{5} + 30\frac{2}{3}$

133. $17\frac{1}{3} + 2\frac{11}{12}$

134. $1\frac{5}{8} + 9\frac{13}{24}$

135. $30\frac{1}{3} + 24\frac{1}{2}$

136. $12\frac{4}{7} + 15\frac{5}{6}$

Subtract. Simplify, if possible. (2.7A, B)

137. $\frac{4}{5} - \frac{3}{5}$

138. $\frac{14}{15} - \frac{4}{9}$

139. $\frac{7}{20} - \frac{4}{12}$

140. $\frac{2}{5} - \frac{1}{6}$

141. $\frac{5}{9} - \frac{7}{18}$

142. $\frac{3}{4} - \frac{1}{16}$

143. $\frac{3}{4} - \frac{1}{2}$

144. $\frac{5}{9} - \frac{5}{12}$

Subtract. Simplify, if possible. (2.7C)

145. $52\frac{1}{6} - 14\frac{2}{3}$

146. $50\frac{4}{7} - 11\frac{5}{21}$

147. $35\frac{7}{16} - 13\frac{5}{8}$

148. $49\frac{1}{3} - 12\frac{4}{6}$

149. $32\frac{3}{4} - 23\frac{1}{2}$

150. $57\frac{8}{13} - 21\frac{15}{26}$

151. $35\frac{2}{3} - 28\frac{11}{12}$

152. $56\frac{1}{6} - 38\frac{2}{3}$

Solve each application problem.

153. What fraction of an hour is 18 minutes? Simplify the fraction.

154. Twenty out of 85 stocks went up yesterday. What fraction of the stocks went up?

155. Randy goes to the grocery store and buys $2\frac{3}{4}$ pounds of bananas. He returns to buy $3\frac{5}{7}$ pounds more. How many total pounds of bananas did he purchase?

156. A recipe calls for $18\frac{3}{4}$ ounces of flour. If you want to cut the recipe in half, how many ounces of flour should be used?

157. A sweater requires $\frac{4}{7}$ yards of material. How many yards will be required for 23 sweaters?

158. Carolina has $3\frac{4}{9}$ feet of paper. Victor has 3 times as many feet of paper as Carolina. How many feet of paper does Victor have?

159. Granny Nell has made 50 pints of blueberry preserves. How many $\frac{4}{5}$ pint jars can she fill?

160. The Lopez family spends three-eighths of their monthly income on rent and utilities. If their monthly income is $4800, how much do they spend on rent and utilities?

161. What is the area of a floor that measures $45\frac{1}{2}$ feet long by $15\frac{3}{4}$ feet wide?

162. Guillermo's car gets $24\frac{1}{6}$ miles per gallon. How far can he travel on 9 gallons?

163. How much shorter is a $3\frac{5}{16}$-inch piece of wire than a $5\frac{1}{4}$-inch piece?

164. During a 7-hour rainstorm, $12\frac{4}{5}$ inches of rain fell. On average, how many inches fell per hour?

165. A dining room set cost $3\frac{1}{4}$ times as much as a sofa. If the sofa costs $580, how much does the dining room set cost?

166. In Telluride, Colorado, it snowed $15\frac{7}{8}$ inches in January, $9\frac{5}{8}$ inches in February, and 18 inches in March. What is the average snowfall per month for the 3-month period?

ASSESSMENT TEST

Find the factors of each number.

1. 31

2. 64

Determine whether each number is prime, composite, or neither.

3. 75

4. 43

Find the prime factorization of each number.

5. 12

6. 81

Find the LCM of each set of numbers.

7. 6, 9

8. 7, 8, 14

Classify each as a proper fraction, an improper fraction, or a mixed number.

9. $\frac{14}{5}$

10. $4\frac{7}{9}$

11. $\frac{8}{15}$

Write a fraction or mixed number to represent the shaded portion of each figure.

12.    **13.**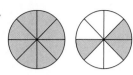

Write each improper fraction as a mixed or whole number.

14. $\dfrac{23}{6}$ **15.** $\dfrac{159}{35}$ **16.** $\dfrac{81}{27}$

Write each mixed number as an improper fraction.

17. $7\dfrac{4}{5}$ **18.** $2\dfrac{11}{16}$ **19.** $21\dfrac{1}{3}$

Simplify each fraction.

20. $\dfrac{15}{18}$ **21.** $\dfrac{21}{49}$ **22.** $\dfrac{36}{81}$ **23.** $\dfrac{16}{60}$

Write each fraction as an equivalent fraction with the indicated denominator.

24. $\dfrac{5}{8} = \dfrac{?}{48}$ **25.** $\dfrac{2}{9} = \dfrac{?}{81}$ **26.** $\dfrac{15}{6} = \dfrac{?}{24}$

Compare the fractions.

27. $\dfrac{4}{7}, \dfrac{1}{2}, \dfrac{5}{8}$ **28.** $\dfrac{22}{35}, \dfrac{37}{70}, \dfrac{6}{10}$

Multiply. Simplify, if possible.

29. $\dfrac{7}{9} \cdot \dfrac{3}{5}$ **30.** $\dfrac{1}{5} \cdot \dfrac{5}{10} \cdot 1\dfrac{2}{3}$ **31.** $3\dfrac{3}{4} \cdot 8\dfrac{1}{2} \cdot 2$

Divide. Simplify, if possible.

32. $\dfrac{11}{18} \div \dfrac{5}{6}$

33. $4\dfrac{1}{3} \div 2\dfrac{1}{5}$

34. $120 \div \dfrac{5}{6}$

Add. Simplify, if possible.

35. $\dfrac{5}{9} + \dfrac{1}{2}$

36. $\dfrac{4}{6} + 3\dfrac{5}{8} + \dfrac{7}{12}$

37. $\dfrac{1}{10} + 3\dfrac{2}{5} + 1\dfrac{5}{6} + \dfrac{1}{15}$

Subtract. Simplify, if possible.

38. $6\dfrac{3}{5} - 4\dfrac{1}{2}$

39. $12\dfrac{1}{3} - 5\dfrac{3}{4}$

40. $15\dfrac{18}{25} - 10\dfrac{7}{15}$

Solve each application problem.

41. A math class has 25 students from within the state, 22 students from out-of-state, and 8 students from out of the country.

    a. What fraction of students represents out-of-state students?

    b. What fraction of students represents out-of-country students?

    c. What fraction represents the in-state and out-of-state students combined?

42. Highway directional signs are placed every $\dfrac{5}{8}$ of a mile on Interstate 89. How many signs are there on a 75-mile stretch of that highway?

43. A race car completed 54 laps around a $3\dfrac{3}{5}$-mile race course before blowing a tire. How many miles did the race car travel?

44. A $12\dfrac{3}{4}$-inch plant grew $2\dfrac{1}{6}$ inches last month and $3\dfrac{1}{2}$ inches this month. How tall is the plant now?

45. A company spends two-thirds of its revenue on expenses. If the revenue last month was $54,000, how much were the expenses?

46. A chemical etching process reduces a piece of $1\dfrac{13}{16}$ centimeters copper by $\dfrac{35}{64}$ of a centimeter. What is the thickness of the copper after the etching process?

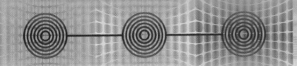

Decimals

Sports Statistics

On May 28, 2006, Sam Hornish Jr. won the Indianapolis 500 auto race, finishing six hundred thirty-five ten-thousandths (0.0635) of a second ahead of rookie Marco Andretti. This was the second-closest Indy 500 margin of victory ever!

Decimals are used extensively in our everyday lives, in everything from keeping sports statistics to situations involving money. In this chapter, we will learn about decimals and how to perform arithmetic operations using decimals. Once these basic skills have been mastered, we will learn to solve numerous real world applications using the principles of decimal computation.

3.1 UNDERSTANDING DECIMALS

LEARNING OBJECTIVES

A. Identify the place value of a digit in a decimal

Suppose that you went to the store and the total amount of your purchase was $3.67. If you wanted to pay using exact change, you might begin by pulling out 3 one-dollar bills. In order to pay the remaining 67 cents *exactly*, you could not

B. Write a decimal in word form and standard form

C. Convert a decimal to a fraction or mixed number

D. Compare decimals

E. Round a decimal to a specified place value

F. Apply your knowledge

decimal fraction
A fraction whose denominator is a power of 10.

decimal number or **decimal**
A number written in decimal notation.

just hand over another dollar bill. That's because the 67 cents, or $0.67, represents a fraction of a dollar bill. In particular, it represents $\frac{67}{100}$ of a dollar.

The fraction $\frac{67}{100}$ is an example of a decimal fraction. A **decimal fraction** is a fraction whose denominator is a power of 10 (that is, a fraction whose denominator is one of the numbers 10, 100, 1000, and so on). Other examples include $\frac{1}{10}, \frac{57}{100}$, and $\frac{341}{1000}$.

Decimal fractions can also be written in *decimal notation*. The decimal notation for each of the fractions $\frac{1}{10}, \frac{57}{100}$, and $\frac{341}{1000}$ is 0.1, 0.57, and 0.341, respectively. A number written in decimal notation is called a **decimal number** or a **decimal**.

Objective 3.1A   **Identify the place value of a digit in a decimal**

Decimals have a whole number side and a decimal side separated by a dot known as a *decimal point*. For example, consider 12.48.

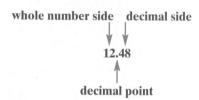

whole number side   decimal side

12.48

decimal point

In a decimal where the whole number is 0, such as 0.57, we may or may not include the 0. We could write either 0.57 or .57, but 0.57 is generally preferred.

A whole number, such as 34, is understood to have a decimal point to the right of the digit in the ones place. We could write 34 as either 34. or 34.0. Generally, 34 or 34.0 are preferred.

Each digit in a decimal has a place value. The place values to the left of the decimal point are powers of 10: 1, 10, 100, and so on. Recall that these place values are the ones place, the tens place, the hundreds place, and so on. The place values to the right of the decimal point are fractions whose *denominators* are powers of 10: $\frac{1}{10}, \frac{1}{100}, \frac{1}{1000}$, and so on. The first digit to the right of the decimal point is in the tenths place, the next digit to the right is in the hundredths place, the next digit to the right is in the thousandths place, and so on. Note that the names of the place values to the right of the decimal point end in -*ths*. The following chart shows the place values in the decimal 241.3759.

Learning Tip

While whole numbers are usually written without the decimal point, they are understood to have a decimal point located to the right of the digit in the ones place. For example, the whole number 55 may be written in any of the following ways.

     55   55.   55.0

We prefer to write it as either 55 or 55.0.

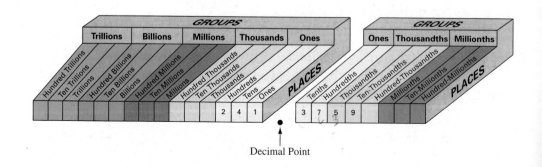

Decimal Point

EXAMPLE 1   Identify the place value of a digit

Identify the place value of the indicated digit.

a. 1.5̲32

b. 10.87̲6

c. 741.4359̲2

d. 0.12001̲3

e. 8.236̲12

SOLUTION STRATEGY

a. 1.5̲32   tenths

b. 10.87̲6   hundredths

c. 741.4359̲2   ten-thousandths

d. 0.12001̲3   hundred-thousandths

e. 8.236̲12   thousandths

TRY-IT EXERCISE 1

Identify the place value of the indicated digit.

a. 2.16̲7

b. 3.8̲349

c. 1084.315̲97

d. 0.00148̲9

e. 11.0031427̲98

Check your answers with the solutions in Appendix A. ■

Objective 3.1B   **Write a decimal in word form and standard form**

Now that we understand the place value system, we can write decimals in words.

Steps for Writing a Decimal in Word Form

Step 1. Write the whole number part in words.

Step 2. Write the word *and* in place of the decimal point.

Step 3. Write the decimal part in words as though it were a whole number without any commas followed by the name of the place value of the last digit.

Below are some examples.

3.78	three and seventy-eight hundredths
11.412	eleven and four hundred twelve thousandths
251.089	two hundred fifty-one and eighty-nine thousandths
0.7829	seven thousand eight hundred twenty-nine ten-thousandths

Notice that the word *and* represents the decimal point. When reading or writing numbers in words, this is the only time we use the word *and*. Also, notice that the decimal side is followed by the name of the place value of the last digit. Finally, notice that when the whole number side is zero, we do not read or write 0 followed by the word *and*.

EXAMPLE 2 **Write a decimal in word form**

Write each decimal in word form.

a. 0.419   **b.** 0.0274   **c.** 8.65   **d.** 75.928   **e.** 724.8709

SOLUTION STRATEGY

a. 0.419   four hundred nineteen thousandths

b. 0.0274   two hundred seventy-four ten-thousandths

c. 8.65   eight and sixty-five hundredths

d. 75.928   seventy-five and nine hundred twenty-eight thousandths

e. 724.8709   seven hundred twenty-four and eight thousand seven hundred nine ten-thousandths

TRY-IT EXERCISE 2

Write each decimal in word form.

a. 0.52

b. 0.83465

c. 19.25

d. 90.0273

Check your answers with the solutions in Appendix A. ■

A decimal written in words can be written in decimal notation by reversing each step of the procedure outlined above. Here are some examples.

two hundred thirty-seven and two hundred sixty-eight thousandths	237.268
four hundred nineteen and twenty-one hundredths	419.21

In writing decimals in standard notation, we must make sure that the last digit is in the correct place. We do so by inserting zeros as placeholders when necessary.

thirteen and nine hundred forty-five ten-thousandths   13.0945

Insert 0 in the tenths place as a placeholder
so that the last digit is in the ten-thousandths place

EXAMPLE 3   **Write a decimal in decimal notation**

Write each number in decimal notation.

a. sixteen hundredths

b. two hundred forty-nine and six hundred seventy-nine thousandths

c. forty-eight and thirty-one ten-thousandths

SOLUTION STRATEGY

a. sixteen hundredths = 0.16

b. two hundred forty-nine and six hundred seventy-nine thousandths = 249.679

c. forty-eight and thirty-one ten-thousandths = 48.0031   Insert zeros in the tenths place and hundredths place as placeholders.

TRY-IT EXERCISE 3

Write each number in decimal notation.

a. three hundred thirty-one thousandths

b. one and five hundredths

c. fifteen and eleven ten-thousandths

Check your answers with the solutions in Appendix A. ■

Objective 3.1C   **Convert a decimal to a fraction or mixed number**

Just as we can write a whole number in expanded notation, we can also write a decimal in expanded notation using the place value system. For example, consider 0.57. In this decimal, there are 0 ones, 5 tenths, and 7 hundredths. In expanded notation, we write this as follows.

$$0 + \frac{5}{10} + \frac{7}{100}$$

We can add the fractions by adding equivalent fractions using the LCD, 100.

$$\frac{5}{10} + \frac{7}{100} = \frac{50}{100} + \frac{7}{100} = \frac{57}{100}$$

Thus, 0.57 is equivalent to the fraction $\dfrac{57}{100}$.

As another example, consider 18.023. In this decimal, there are 1 ten, 8 ones, 0 tenths, 2 hundredths, and 3 thousandths. In expanded notation, we write the decimal as follows.

$$10 + 8 + \frac{0}{10} + \frac{2}{100} + \frac{3}{1000}$$

We can add the fractions by adding equivalent fractions using the LCD, 1000.

$$18 + \frac{0}{1000} + \frac{20}{1000} + \frac{3}{1000} = 18 + \frac{23}{1000} = 18\frac{23}{1000}$$

Thus, 18.023 is equivalent to $18\dfrac{23}{1000}$.

In each example above, notice that the number of places to the right of the decimal point is the same as the number of zeros in the denominator of the decimal fraction.

$$0.57 = \frac{57}{100} \qquad\qquad 18.023 = 18\frac{23}{1000}$$

2 places   2 zeros   3 places   3 zeros

This suggests the following rule for writing a decimal as a fraction.

Rule for Converting a Decimal to a Fraction

To convert a decimal to a fraction, write the whole number formed by the digits to the right of the decimal point as the numerator, and write the power of 10 that has as many zeros as place values in the decimal as the denominator.

EXAMPLE 4   Convert a decimal to a fraction

Convert each decimal to a fraction or mixed number. Simplify, if possible.

a. 0.23   **b.** 0.007   **c.** 12.5   **d.** 43.025

SOLUTION STRATEGY

a. $0.23 = \dfrac{23}{100}$

Write 23 as the numerator. Since there are two places after the decimal point, write 100 as the denominator.

b. $0.007 = \dfrac{7}{1000}$

Write 7 as the numerator. Since there are three places after the decimal point, write 1000 as the denominator.

c. $12.5 = 12\dfrac{5}{10} = 12\dfrac{1}{2}$

Write as a mixed number. Write 5 as the numerator of the fraction part. Since there is one place after the decimal point, write 10 as the denominator. Simplify the fraction part.

d. $43.025 = 43\dfrac{25}{1000} = 43\dfrac{1}{40}$

Write as a mixed number. Write 25 as the numerator of the fraction part. Since there are three places after the decimal point, write 1000 as the denominator. Simplify the fraction part.

TRY-IT EXERCISE 4

Convert each decimal to a fraction or mixed number. Simplify, if possible.

a. 0.31

b. 0.0019

c. 57.8

d. 132.075

Check your answers with the solutions in Appendix A. ■

From the examples above, you already know how to write a fraction whose denominator is a power of 10 as a decimal. Later in the chapter, we will learn how to write any fraction as a decimal.

Objective 3.1D   Compare decimals

It is important to be able to compare decimal numbers. Many everyday applications rely on your ability to know which of two decimal numbers is larger.

One way to compare decimals is to use a number line. For example, if we wanted to compare the decimals 0.4 and 0.7, we could graph them as follows.

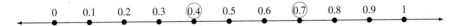

Note that 0.4 is to the left of 0.7 on the number line. This means that 0.4 is less than 0.7. Recall that "<" means "is less than" and ">" means "is greater than." Therefore, we write $0.4 < 0.7$.

Perhaps the easiest way to apply these steps is to write the decimals one above another and then compare corresponding place values. The following steps outline how to do this.

Steps for Comparing Two Decimal Numbers

Step 1. Write the decimals one above another so that their decimal points are vertically aligned.

Step 2. Compare the whole number sides. If one is greater than the other, then the entire decimal is greater. If they are equal, continue to the next step.

Step 3. Compare the digits to the right of the decimal point in the corresponding place values from left to right.

    a. If the digits are the same, move right one place to the next digit. If necessary, insert zeros after the last digit to the right of the decimal point to continue the comparison.

    b. If the digits are not the same, the larger digit corresponds to the larger number.

EXAMPLE 5 **Compare decimals**

Insert the symbol $<$, $>$, or $=$ to form a true statement.

a. 3.465 ____ 3.545   **b.** 0.012544 ____ 0.0125

SOLUTION STRATEGY

a. 3.465
3.545

Write the decimals one above another so that their decimal points are aligned. The whole number sides are equal. Continue.

3.465
3.545

The digits in the tenths places are different. Since $4 < 5$, $3.465 < 3.545$.

3.465 < 3.545

b. 0.012544
0.0125

Write the decimals one above another so that their decimal points are aligned. The whole number sides are equal. Continue.

0.012544
0.0125

The digits in the tenths places are the same. Continue.

0.012544
0.0125

The digits in the hundredths places are the same. Continue.

0.012544
0.0125

The digits in the thousandths places are the same.

0.012544
0.01250

Insert a 0 to the right of the last digit in 0.0125 to continue the comparison.

The digits in the ten-thousandths places are different. Since $4 > 0$, $0.012544 > 0.01250$.

0.012544 > 0.0125

TRY-IT EXERCISE 5

Insert the symbol $<$, $>$, or $=$ to form a true statement.

a. 0.9384 ____ 0.93870   **b.** 143.00502 ____ 143.005

Check your answers with the solutions in Appendix A. ∎

Objective 3.1E **Round a decimal to a specified place value**

Rounding decimals is important because numbers commonly contain more decimal places than are required for a particular situation. We use the following steps to round decimals.

Steps for Rounding Decimals to a Specified Place Value

Step 1. Identify the place value to the right of the decimal point to which the decimal is to be rounded.

Step 2. If the digit to the right of the specified place value is 4 or less, the digit in the specified place value remains the same.
If the digit to the right of the specified place value is 5 or more, increase the digit in the specified place value by one. Carry, if necessary

Step 3. Delete the digit in each place after the specified place value.

In rounding a number to a specified place, only include digits up to that place—no more, no less. Here are some examples of rounding decimals.

EXAMPLE 6   Round a decimal to a specified place value

Round each decimal to the specified place value.

a. 0.43698 to the nearest thousandth

b. 0.0093837 to the nearest hundred-thousandth

c. 32.898 to the nearest hundredth

d. 7.3381 to the nearest tenth

SOLUTION STRATEGY

a. 0.43698

0.437

The digit in the thousandths place is 6. Since the digit to the right of the 6 is 9, increase 6 to 7 and delete the digit in each place thereafter.

b. 0.0093837

0.00938

The digit in the hundred-thousandths place is 8. Since the digit to the right of the 8 is 3, keep the 8 and delete the digit in each place thereafter.

c. 32.898

32.90

The digit in the hundredths place is 9. Since the digit to the right of the 9 is 8, increase 9 to 10. Since we cannot write 10 in the hundredths place, record 0 in the hundredths place and carry the 1 to the tenths place.

d. 7.3381

7.3

The digit in the tenths place is 3. Since the digit to the right of the 3 is 3, keep the 3 in the tenths place and delete the digit in each place thereafter.

TRY-IT EXERCISE 6

Round each number to the specified place value.

a. 0.18188 to the nearest hundredth

b. 0.0555035 to the nearest ten-thousandth

c. 6.718 to the nearest tenth

d. 337.871632 to the nearest hundred-thousandth

Check your answers with the solutions in Appendix A. ■

Objective 3.1F **Apply your knowledge**

WRITE THE MONETARY AMOUNT ON A CHECK

When writing a check, you must write the amount in both decimal notation and in partial word form. In writing the words on the check, the cents portion is written as $\frac{\text{cents}}{100}$ dollars. For example, if the amount of the check was $89.53, we would write, "eighty-nine and $\frac{53}{100}$ dollars."

> ● **Real-World Connection**
>
> If a check is written and the amount written in word form differs from the amount in decimal notation, the word form is considered as the official amount.

EXAMPLE 7 **Write the monetary amount on a check**

a. You are writing a check for three hundred fifty-seven dollars and twenty-one cents. Write the decimal notation for this amount.

b. You are writing a check for $184.76. Write the word form for this amount.

SOLUTION STRATEGY

a. $357.21

b. one hundred eighty-four and $\frac{76}{100}$ dollars

TRY-IT EXERCISE 7

a. You are writing a check for two thousand eighty-five dollars and sixty-three cents. Write the decimal notation for this amount.

b. You are writing a check for $3244.19. Write the word form for this amount.

Check your answers with the solutions in Appendix A. ■

SECTION 3.1 REVIEW EXERCISES

Concept Check

1. A _____ _____ is a fraction whose denominator is a power of 10.

2. In decimal notation, the decimal fraction $\frac{31}{100}$ is written as _____.

3. A number written in decimal notation is called a _____.

4. The place values to the left of the decimal point are powers of 10, while the place values to the right of the decimal point are fractions whose _____ are powers of 10.

5. The names of the place values to the right of the decimal point end in -_____.

6. When writing a decimal in word form, write the word _____ in place of the decimal point.

7. To convert a decimal to a fraction, write the _____ to the right of the decimal point in the numerator, and write the power of 10 that has as many zeros as _____ _____ in the decimal in the denominator.

8. The symbol > means _____ _____. The symbol < means _____ _____.

9. When rounding, if the digit to the right of the specified place value is _____ or less, the digit in the specified place value remains the same, whereas if the digit to the right of the specified place value is _____ or more, increase the digit in the specified place value by one.

10. A decimal rounded to the nearest thousandth has _____ decimal places.

Objective 3.1A   **Identify the place value of a digit in a decimal**

GUIDE PROBLEMS

11. In the decimal 23.5618, identify the digit in each place.

   a. ones place ____

   b. tenths place ____

   c. thousandths place ____

   d. ten-thousandths place ____

12. In the decimal 72.916, identify the name of each place value.

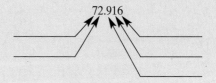

Identify the place value of the indicated digit.

13. 453.23

14. 327.41

15. 3.961

16. 21.374

17. 2.876452

18. 6.08072601

19. 13.9014365

20. 123.0870763581

Objective 3.1B   **Write a decimal in word form and standard form**

GUIDE PROBLEMS

21. Write 16.74 in word form.

   a. Write the whole number portion of 16.74 in word form.

   b. Write the word representing the decimal point.

   c. How many decimal places are in the number?

   d. The number of decimal places in part c indicates the _____ place.

   e. Write the decimal part of the number in word form.

   f. Write the entire number in word form.

22. Write 134.029 in word form.

   a. Write the whole number portion of 134.029 in word form.

   b. Write the word representing the decimal point.

   c. How many decimal places are in the number?

   d. The number of decimal places in part c indicates the _____ place.

   e. Write the decimal part of the number in word form.

   f. Write the entire number in word form.

Write each decimal in word form.

23. 0.9

24. 0.4

25. 0.0054

26. 0.071

27. 1.34

28. 3.8

29. 25.3652

30. 99.4038

31. The diameter of a fiber optic cable measures 0.0062 inches.

32. A sheet of paper measures 0.089 inches thick.

33. A car gets 15.7 miles per gallon.

34. A package weighs 133.28 pounds.

GUIDE PROBLEMS

35. Write the number sixty-seven and fifteen ten-thousandths in decimal notation.

   a. Write the whole number part of the number in decimal notation.

   b. Write the decimal part of the number in decimal notation.

   c. Write the entire number in decimal notation.

36. Write the number two hundred thirty-six and eleven thousandths in decimal notation.

   a. Write the whole number part of the number in decimal notation.

   b. Write the decimal part of the number in decimal notation.

   c. Write the entire number in decimal notation.

Write each number in decimal notation.

37. one hundred eighty-three thousandths

38. two thousand six hundred forty-five ten-thousandths

39. fifteen ten-thousandths

40. twenty-nine thousandths

41. five hundred ninety-eight and eight tenths

42. four thousand six hundred twenty-three and eleven hundredths

43. forty-six and three hundredths

44. twelve and four thousandths

45. Last week in Canmore, it snowed a total of fourteen and thirty-five hundredths inches.

46. A metal plate is three hundred eighty-two thousandths of an inch thick.

47. An industrial process uses a plastic film that measures twenty-nine hundred-thousandths of a meter.

48. A ceramic cup holds six and twenty-three hundredths ounces.

| **Objective 3.1C** | **Convert a decimal to a fraction or mixed number** |

GUIDE PROBLEMS

49. Consider the decimal 0.51.

 a. To write 0.51 as a decimal fraction, what whole number do we write as the numerator?

 b. What power of 10 do we write as the denominator?

 c. Write 0.51 as a decimal fraction. Simplify, if possible.
$$0.51 = \frac{51}{\underline{\quad}}$$

50. Consider the decimal 0.024.

 a. To write 0.024 as a decimal fraction, what whole number do we write as the numerator?

 b. What power of 10 do we write as the denominator?

 c. Write 0.024 as a decimal fraction. Simplify, if possible.
$$0.024 = \frac{\underline{\quad}}{\underline{\quad}} = \frac{\underline{\quad}}{\underline{\quad}}$$

51. Consider the decimal 28.37.

 a. To write 28.37 as a mixed number, what whole number do we write as the numerator of the fraction part?

 b. What power of 10 do we write as the denominator of the fraction part?

 c. Write 28.37 as a decimal fraction. Simplify, if possible.
$$28.37 = 28\frac{\underline{\quad}}{\underline{\quad}}$$

52. Consider the decimal 7.0125.

 a. To write 7.0125 as a mixed number, what whole number do we write as the numerator of the fraction part?

 b. What power of 10 do we write as the denominator of the fraction part?

 c. Write 7.0125 as a decimal fraction. Simplify, if possible.
$$7.0125 = \underline{\quad}\frac{\underline{\quad}}{\underline{\quad}} = \underline{\quad}\frac{\underline{\quad}}{\underline{\quad}}$$

Write each decimal as a fraction or mixed number. Simplify, if possible.

53. 0.7

54. 0.13

55. 0.001

56. 0.0009

57. 0.64   **58.** 0.425   **59.** 3.75   **60.** 12.375

61. 26.088   **62.** 7.268   **63.** 14.5003   **64.** 17.0041

Objective 3.1D   **Compare decimals**

GUIDE PROBLEMS

65. Use the symbol $<$, $>$, or $=$ to compare 4.596 and 4.587.

Write 4.596 and 4.587 one above another so that the decimal points are aligned. (Insert zeros, as needed.)

4.596
4.587

a. Compare the digits of each number. Which is the first place value where there is a difference?

b. Which number is larger?

c. Use the symbol $<$, $>$, or $=$ to write a true statement for the numbers.

66. Use the symbol $<$, $>$, or $=$ to compare 0.0038 and 0.00387.

Write 0.0038 and 0.00387 one above another so that the decimal points are aligned. (Insert zeros, as needed.)

0.00380
0.00387

a. Compare the digits of each number. Which is the first place value where there is a difference?

b. Which number is larger?

c. Use the symbol $<$, $>$, or $=$ to write a true statement for the numbers.

Insert the symbol $<$, $>$, or $=$ to form a true statement.

67. 0.57 _____ 0.62   **68.** 1.287 _____ 1.278   **69.** 4.017 _____ 4.170

70. 0.694 _____ 0.685   **71.** 0.0023 _____ 0.00230   **72.** 64.001 _____ 64.010

73. 243.33 _____ 242.33   **74.** 85.003 _____ 0.85003   **75.** 133.52 _____ 133.5

76. 0.920200 _____ 0.9202   **77.** 0.730 _____ 0.7299   **78.** 2.05070 _____ 2.05700

79. 0.564, 0.5654, and 0.5 in ascending order   **80.** 12.0049, 12.0094, and 12.0 in descending order

81. 4.57, 4.576, and 4.6 in descending order   **82.** 0.0026, 0.2669, and 0.00267 in ascending order

83. 1.379, 1.3879, 1.3856, and 1.3898 in ascending order

84. 7.678, 7.6781, 7.7681, and 7.79 in descending order

| Objective 3.1E | Round a decimal to a specified place value |

GUIDE PROBLEMS

85. Round 3.07869 to the nearest thousandth.

   a. What digit is in the thousandths place?

   b. What digit is to the right of the digit in the thousandths place?

   c. Explain what to do next.

   d. Write the rounded number.

86. Round 22.1437 to the nearest hundredth.

   a. What digit is in the hundredths place?

   b. What number is to the right of the digit in the hundredths place?

   c. Explain what to do next.

   d. Write the rounded number.

Round each number to the specified place value.

87. 14.5734 to the nearest thousandth

88. 907.2987 to the nearest tenth

89. 8.328 to the nearest tenth

90. 37.603 to the nearest one

91. 235.88 to the nearest ten

92. 404.4838 to the nearest one

93. 841.9844 to the nearest tenth

94. 48.9837 to the nearest thousandth

95. 0.00394875 to the nearest millionth

96. 31.8015 to the nearest hundredth

97. 10.3497 to the nearest thousandth

98. 685.992 to the nearest tenth

| Objective 3.1F | Apply your knowledge |

99. Adult human hair grows 0.34 millimeters per day. Write this measurement in word form.

100. In converting from the metric to the U. S. system, one liter is equal to 1.056 quarts. Write this measurement in word form.

101. A piece of copper on an electronic circuit board is three and thirty-four hundredths inches long. Write this measurement in decimal notation.

102. The coating on a piece of safety glass is thirteen ten-thousandths of an inch thick. Write this measurement in decimal notation.

103. For three runs at a drag strip, a dragster covered a quarter mile in the following times: 5.4132 seconds, 5.4318 seconds, and 5.399 seconds. List these times in descending order.

104. On an assembly line quality control test, pencil leads measured 0.612 mm, 0.6188 mm, and 0.603 mm. List these diameters in ascending order.

105. At Circuit City, a computer monitor sells for $349.95. Round this price to the nearest dollar.

106. A washing machine spins at a rate of 433.57 rpm (revolutions per minute). Round this figure to the nearest one.

107. A candy wrapper is 0.0441 inches thick. Round this measurement to the nearest hundredth.

108. The Bow River is 243.58 miles long. Round this distance to the nearest mile.

109. a. You are writing a check for $17.68. Write the word form for this amount.

b. You are writing a check for two hundred fifty-one dollars and ten cents. Write the decimal notation for this amount.

110. a. You are writing a check for $6744.03. Write the word form for this amount.

b. You are writing a check for eleven dollars and fifteen cents. Write the decimal notation for this amount.

CUMULATIVE SKILLS REVIEW

1. Round 34,572 to the nearest hundred. (1.1D)

2. Write 5936 in expanded notation and in word form. (1.1B, 1.1C)

3. Add $398 + 436 + 19$. (1.2A)

4. Subtract $277 - 39$. (1.3A)

5. Find the LCM of 12 and 18. (2.1D)

6. Find the LCD of $\dfrac{5}{6}, \dfrac{5}{14}$, and $\dfrac{10}{21}$. (2.3C)

7. Find the prime factorization of 20. Express your answer in standard and exponential notation. (2.1C)

8. Write $7 \cdot 7 \cdot 3 \cdot 3 \cdot 3$ in exponential notation. (1.6A)

9. Write $5\dfrac{3}{10}$ as an improper fraction. (2.2C)

10. A road paving crew for Acme Asphalt completed $1\dfrac{3}{5}$ miles of road on Tuesday and $2\dfrac{2}{3}$ miles of road on Wednesday. If the job was a total of 7 miles, how much more is left to pave? (2.7D)

3.2 ADDING AND SUBTRACTING DECIMALS

Calculations with decimals are common in our everyday activities. We go shopping, put gas in the car, measure or weigh something, or write a check. Each one of these situations requires working with decimals.

The operations of addition, subtraction, multiplication, and division with decimals follow the same procedures used with whole numbers. In this section, we will learn to add and subtract decimals.

LEARNING OBJECTIVES

A. Add decimals

B. Subtract decimals

C. Estimate when adding or subtracting decimals

D. Apply your knowledge

Objective 3.2A	Add decimals

As with whole numbers, alignment of place values is very important when adding decimals. To ensure proper alignment, we line up the decimal points vertically.

Steps for Adding Decimals

Step 1. Write the decimals so that the decimal points are vertically aligned. If necessary, insert extra zeros to the right of the last digit after the decimal point so that each addend has the same number of decimal places.

Step 2. Add as with whole numbers. Carry, if necessary.

Step 3. Place the decimal point in the sum so that it is vertically aligned with the decimal points of the addends.

 *Learning Tip*

Inserting extra zeros as placeholders to the right of the last digit after the decimal point does not change the value of the number.

EXAMPLE 1   **Add decimals**

Add.

a. $1.45 + 3.2$ **b.** $0.5873 + 7.006$

SOLUTION STRATEGY

a.
$$\begin{array}{r} 1.45 \\ + 3.20 \\ \hline \end{array}$$
Vertically align the decimal points.
Insert a 0 as a placeholder in the second addend.

$$\begin{array}{r} 1.45 \\ + 3.20 \\ \hline 4.65 \end{array}$$
Add the digits from right to left as with whole numbers.
Place the decimal point in the sum so that it is vertically aligned with the decimal points of the addends.

b.
$$\begin{array}{r} 0.5873 \\ + 7.0060 \\ \hline \end{array}$$
Vertically align the decimal points.
Insert a 0 as a placeholder in the second addend.

$$\begin{array}{r} {\scriptstyle 1} \\ 0.5873 \\ + 7.0060 \\ \hline 7.5933 \end{array}$$
Add the digits from right to left.
Place the decimal point in the sum so that it is vertically aligned with the decimal points of the addends.

TRY-IT EXERCISE 1

Add.

a. 3.229 + 0.66

b. 0.00282 + 1.6541

Check your answers with the solutions in Appendix A. ■

EXAMPLE 2   **Add decimals**

Add.

a. 4.33 + 16.0192 + 0.938   **b.** 65 + 12.344 + 8.29

SOLUTION STRATEGY

a.
```
   4.3300
  16.0192
+  0.9380
```
Vertically align the decimal points.
Insert two zeros in the first addend and one 0 in the third addend as placeholders.

```
  1  1
   4.3300
  16.0192
+  0.9380
  21.2872
```
Add the digits from right to left.
Place the decimal point in the sum so that it is vertically aligned with the decimal points of the addends.

b.
```
  65.000
  12.344
+  8.290
```
Vertically align the decimal points.
Insert three zeros in the first addend and one 0 in the third addend as placeholders.

```
  1  1
  65.000
  12.344
+  8.290
  85.634
```
Add the digits from right to left.
Place the decimal point in the sum so that it is vertically aligned with the decimal points of the addends.

TRY-IT EXERCISE 2

Add.

a. 5.069 + 0.00918 + 4

b. 0.8847 + 0.34221 + 0.19 + 1.3

Check your answers with the solutions in Appendix A. ■

| Objective 3.2B | **Subtract decimals** |

Steps for Subtracting Decimals

Step 1. Write the decimals so that the decimal points are vertically aligned. If necessary, insert extra zeros to the right of the decimal point where needed so that each value has the same number of decimal places.

Step 2. Subtract as with whole numbers. Borrow, if necessary.

Step 3. Place the decimal point in the difference so that it is vertically aligned with the decimal points of the minuend and subtrahend.

EXAMPLE 3   **Subtract decimals**

Subtract.

a. $3.4899 - 1.364$ **b.** $0.0057 - 0.00132$ **c.** $9 - 5.231$

SOLUTION STRATEGY

a.
$$\begin{array}{r} 3.4899 \\ -\ 1.3640 \\ \end{array}\quad \begin{array}{l}\text{minuend} \\ \text{subtrahend}\end{array}$$

Vertically align the decimal points.
Insert a 0 as a placeholder in the subtrahend.

$$\begin{array}{r} 3.4899 \\ -\ 1.3640 \\ \hline 2.1259 \end{array}$$

Subtract the digits from right to left.
Place the decimal point in the difference so that it is vertically aligned with the decimal points of the minuend and subtrahend.

b.
$$\begin{array}{r} 0.00570 \\ -\ 0.00132 \\ \end{array}\quad \begin{array}{l}\text{minuend} \\ \text{subtrahend}\end{array}$$

Vertically align the decimal points.
Insert a 0 as a placeholder in the minuend.

$$\begin{array}{r} \overset{6\ 10}{0.0057\cancel{0}} \\ -\ 0.00132 \\ \hline 0.00438 \end{array}$$

Subtract the digits from right to left.
Place the decimal point in the difference so that it is vertically aligned with the decimal points of the minuend and subtrahend.

c.
$$\begin{array}{r} 9.000 \\ -\ 5.231 \\ \end{array}\quad \begin{array}{l}\text{minuend} \\ \text{subtrahend}\end{array}$$

Vertically align the decimal points.
Insert three zeros as placeholders in the minuend.

$$\begin{array}{r} \overset{\overset{9\ \ 9}{8\ \ \cancel{10}\cancel{10}\cancel{10}}}{9.000} \\ -\ 5.321 \\ \hline 3.679 \end{array}$$

Subtract the digits from right to left.
Place the decimal point in the difference so that it is vertically aligned with the decimal points of the minuend and subtrahend.

TRY-IT EXERCISE 3

Subtract.

a. $4.3178 - 2.1001$

b. $0.0872 - 0.04635$

c. $12 - 3.4485$

Check your answers with the solutions in Appendix A. ■

Objective 3.2C   **Estimate when adding or subtracting decimals**

Estimating is a handy way to check math calculations to see whether or not an answer is reasonable. To estimate when adding or subtracting decimals, we use the following steps.

Steps for Estimating When Adding or Subtracting Decimals

Step 1. Round each decimal to the specified place.

Step 2. Add or subtract.

EXAMPLE 4   **Estimate when adding decimals**

Add $47.33 + 12.32$. Then estimate the sum by rounding each addend to one nonzero digit.

SOLUTION STRATEGY

$$\begin{array}{r} 47.33 \\ + \ 12.32 \\ \hline 59.65 \end{array}$$ Add.

$$\begin{array}{rcr} 47.33 & \rightarrow & 50 \\ + \ 12.32 & \rightarrow & + \ 10 \\ \hline & & 60 \end{array}$$ To estimate the sum, round each addend to one nonzero digit. Add the rounded numbers.

Note that the exact answer is close to the estimate.

TRY-IT EXERCISE 4

Add $75.98 + 2.62$. Then estimate the sum by rounding each addend to the nearest whole number.

Check your answer with the solution in Appendix A. ■

EXAMPLE 5   Estimate when subtracting decimals

Subtract 102.19 − 88.4. Then estimate the difference by rounding the minuend and subtrahend to the nearest whole number.

SOLUTION STRATEGY

$$
\begin{array}{r}
102.19 \\
-\ 88.40 \\
\hline
13.79
\end{array}
$$

Subtract.

$$
\begin{array}{rcr}
102.19 & \rightarrow & 102 \\
-\ 88.4 & \rightarrow & -\ 88 \\
\hline
& & 14
\end{array}
$$

To estimate the difference, round the minuend and subtrahend to the nearest whole number. Subtract the rounded numbers.

Note that the exact answer is close to the estimate.

TRY-IT EXERCISE 5

Subtract 8.43 − 1.391. Then estimate the difference by rounding the minuend and subtrahend to the nearest whole number.

Check your answer with the solution in Appendix A. ■

Objective 3.2D   ## Apply your knowledge

KEEPING CHECKBOOK RECORDS

Addition and subtraction of decimals is applied extensively when you do bookkeeping for monetary transactions such as balancing your checkbook.

Making a deposit or earning interest in a checking account requires you to add to your checkbook balance. An addition to a checkbook balance is called a **credit**. Writing a check, making an ATM withdrawal, using a debit card, or incurring a service charge requires you to subtract from your checkbook balance. A subtraction from a checkbook balance is called a **debit**.

Typically, checking account holders use a checkbook register to record transactions. An example of a checkbook register is shown below. The starting balance is located in the upper right corner. The individual transactions are listed by date, check number, description, and amount. The last column keeps a running balance of the amount in the checking account.

credit
An addition to a checkbook balance.

debit
A subtraction from a checkbook balance.

Number or Code	Date	Transaction Description	Payment, Fee, Withdrawal (−)		✓	Deposit, Credit (+)		$ Balance	
	6/1							1450	75
321	6/3	MasterCard	72	30				1378	45
	6/8	Deposit				200	00	1578	45
	6/12	ATM withdrawal	40	00				1538	45

EXAMPLE 6   Keep a checkbook record

On April 1, your checkbook balance was $755.42. On April 10, you wrote check #155 for $132.29 to Macy's. On April 13, you wrote check #156 to the IRS for $260.00. On April 22, you made a deposit of $505.24. Complete the check register for these transactions and find the new balance in your checking account.

SOLUTION STRATEGY

Number or Code	Date	Transaction Description	Payment, Fee, Withdrawal (–)		✓	Deposit, Credit (+)		$ Balance	
	4/1							755	42
155	4/10	Macy's	132	29				623	13
156	4/13	IRS	260	00				363	13
	4/22	deposit				505	24	868	37

TRY-IT EXERCISE 6

On May 1, your checkbook balance was $1264.59. On May 4, you wrote check #183 for $327.68 to Shell Oil. On May 9, you wrote check #184 for $36.50 to Gardner's Market. On May 26, you made a deposit of $116.81. Complete the check register for these transactions and find the new balance in your checking account.

Number or Code	Date	Transaction Description	Payment, Fee, Withdrawal (–)		✓	Deposit, Credit (+)		$ Balance	

Check your answers with the solutions in Appendix A. ■

SECTION 3.2 REVIEW EXERCISES

Concept Check

1. When adding and subtracting decimals, we write the numbers so that the _____ _____ are vertically aligned.

2. When adding and subtracting decimals, it is sometimes necessary to insert extra _____ to the right of the last digit after the decimal point so that each decimal has the same number of decimal places.

3. When adding or subtracting decimals, add or subtract as if working with _____ numbers. When adding, carry if necessary. When subtracting, borrow if necessary.

4. Explain where the decimal point should be placed in the answer of an addition or subtraction problem.

Objective 3.2A   Add decimals

GUIDE PROBLEMS

5. Add 4.6 + 2.09 + 15.48.

    a. Write the decimals so that the decimal points are vertically aligned. If necessary, insert extra zeros to the right of the last digit after the decimal point.

    b. Add as with whole numbers. Place the decimal point in the sum.

6. Add 43.5 + 21.29 + 16.31.

    a. Write the decimals so that the decimal points are vertically aligned. If necessary, insert extra zeros to the right of the last digit after the decimal point.

    b. Add as with whole numbers. Place the decimal point in the sum.

Add.

7.
$$\begin{array}{r} 2.45 \\ + \ 0.24 \\ \hline \end{array}$$

8.
$$\begin{array}{r} 0.251 \\ + \ 5.208 \\ \hline \end{array}$$

9.
$$\begin{array}{r} 30.63 \\ + \ 38.55 \\ \hline \end{array}$$

10.
$$\begin{array}{r} 0.29 \\ + \ 0.82 \\ \hline \end{array}$$

11.
$$\begin{array}{r} 3.189 \\ + \ 0.015 \\ \hline \end{array}$$

12.
$$\begin{array}{r} 6.396 \\ + \ 1.452 \\ \hline \end{array}$$

13.
$$\begin{array}{r} 5.134 \\ + \ 0.635 \\ \hline \end{array}$$

14.
$$\begin{array}{r} 94.08 \\ + \ 94.71 \\ \hline \end{array}$$

15.
$$\begin{array}{r} 52.5805 \\ + \ 26.7890 \\ \hline \end{array}$$

16. 0.05 + 0.63

17. 9.64 + 6.37

18. 2.83 + 0.903

19. 23.485 + 11.24

20. 7.4003 + 3.4833

21. 49.35 + 0.9928

22. 0.396 + 0.452

23. 3.3396 + 9.1726

24. 0.002762 + 1.4945

25.
$$\begin{array}{r} 1.13 \\ 5.70 \\ + \ 3.85 \\ \hline \end{array}$$

26.
$$\begin{array}{r} 0.38 \\ 4.55 \\ + \ 9.12 \\ \hline \end{array}$$

27.
$$\begin{array}{r} 21.390 \\ 3.767 \\ + \ 11.001 \\ \hline \end{array}$$

28.   16.11
      44.10
  + 15.57

29.   3.20
    14.82
    19.00
  + 40.27

30.   42.75
    23.10
    40.87
  + 143.50

31. 1.54 + 4.87 + 0.79 + 6

32. 65.4 + 23.99 + 3 + 23 + 0.003

33. Add twelve and two tenths and thirty-two hundredths.

34. Add twenty-one and thirty-five hundredths and one hundred forty-three and five thousandths.

35. Find the sum of four dollars and fifty-one cents and two dollars and forty cents.

36. Add three and fourteen hundredths and twenty-six thousandths.

Objective 3.2B   **Subtract decimals**

GUIDE PROBLEMS

37. Subtract 16.4 − 2.91.

    a. Write the decimals so that the decimal points are vertically aligned. If necessary, insert extra zeros to the right of the last digit after the decimal point.

    b. Subtract as with whole numbers. Place the decimal point in the difference.

38. Subtract 8.96 − 6.17.

    a. Write the decimals so that the decimal points are vertically aligned. If necessary, insert extra zeros to the right of the last digit after the decimal point.

    b. Subtract as with whole numbers. Place the decimal point in the difference.

Subtract.

39.   9.9
   − 9.5

40.   1.5
   − 1.2

41.   8.44
   − 2.71

42.   6.56
   − 3.42

43.   67.09
   − 13.45

44.   40.79
   − 36.48

45.   89.750
   − 87.893

46.   31.860
   − 23.737

47. 6.4 − 1.2

48. $3.8 - 1.5$

49. $18.3 - 3.8$

50. $44.8 - 3.6$

51. $92.58 - 27.21$

52. $87.38 - 14.44$

53. $95.68 - 6.21$

54. $16.36 - 15.231$

55. $57.92 - 50.823$

56. $42.61 - 23.796$

57.
$$\begin{array}{r} 488.20 \\ -\ \ 87.92 \\ \hline \end{array}$$

58.
$$\begin{array}{r} 512.2 \\ -\ 117.9 \\ \hline \end{array}$$

59.
$$\begin{array}{r} 886.285 \\ -\ 202.774 \\ \hline \end{array}$$

60.
$$\begin{array}{r} 924.814 \\ -\ \ \ \ 7.180 \\ \hline \end{array}$$

61. $81.016 - 37.05$

62. $65.07 - 65.001$

63. Fourteen and two tenths minus eight and twenty-three hundredths.

64. Thirty-seven and eleven hundredths minus twenty-nine and fifteen thousandths.

65. One and five hundredths subtracted from seven.

66. Eleven dollars and sixteen cents subtracted from twenty dollars.

67. What is the difference between eighteen and three and three tenths?

68. What is the difference between ninety-six and seven hundredths and eighty-two and one tenth?

Objective 3.2C   **Estimate when adding or subtracting decimals**

GUIDE PROBLEMS

69. Estimate $199.99 + 19.99$ by rounding each addend to the nearest whole number.

$$\begin{array}{rcr} 199.99 & \rightarrow & 200 \\ +\ \ 19.99 & \rightarrow & +\underline{} \\ & & \underline{} \end{array}$$

70. Estimate $509.96 - 432.48$ by rounding the minuend and subtrahend to the nearest ten.

$$\begin{array}{rcr} 509.96 & \rightarrow & 510 \\ -\ 432.48 & \rightarrow & -\underline{} \\ & & \underline{} \end{array}$$

Estimate each sum by rounding each addend to the specified place. Estimate each difference by rounding the minuend and subtrahend to the specified place value.

71. $5.37 + 1.81$ to the nearest whole number

72. $159.25 + 18.98$ to the nearest ten

73. $28.77 - 0.99$ to the nearest whole number

74. $339.2 - 23.19$ to the nearest ten

75. $42.12 + 12.88$ to the nearest tenth

76. $33.569 + 3.289 + 0.344$ to the nearest hundredth

77. $14.667 - 0.049$ to the nearest hundredth

78. $13.665 - 4.814$ to the nearest tenth

Objective 3.2D   **Apply your knowledge**

79. Fernando wants to build a fence around his property. If the dimensions are 215.4 feet, 143.7 feet, 190.2 feet, and 124.3 feet, what is the total length of the fence?

80. Bob has started a new job as a technical consultant for Pico Energy, Inc. During his first 3 weeks he worked 46.2 hours, 42.8 hours, and 50.9 hours. What is the total number of hours Bob worked during the three weeks?

Find the perimeter of each figure.

81. (cm = centimeters)

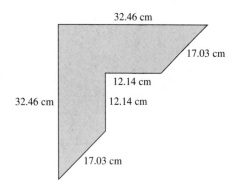

32.46 cm

17.03 cm

12.14 cm

32.46 cm   12.14 cm

17.03 cm

82. (" = inches)

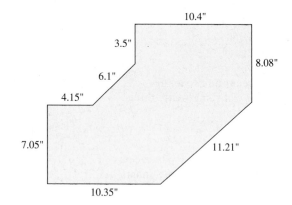

10.4"

3.5"

8.08"

6.1"

4.15"

7.05"

11.21"

10.35"

83. Circuit City has a DVD recorder on sale this week for $184.35. If the original price was $215.25, how much can be saved by purchasing the recorder this week?

84. Miguel sold 43.6 acres of his 127.9-acre property. How many acres does he have left?

85. Yesterday afternoon, the temperature in Lake City was 88.7°F. During the night, it fell 20.9°F. By sunrise it had risen by 11.3°F. What was the temperature at sunrise?

86. Anita and Ken went running this past weekend. Ken ran 12.65 miles and Anita ran 15.77 miles. How many more miles did Anita run?

87. Leonard spent $55.78 on a math book at a Barnes & Noble bookstore. Mandy spent $52.75 on the same book by purchasing it online at books.com. How much less did Mandy pay?

88. Larry traveled to San Francisco last weekend. He traveled 112.5 miles on the first day and 256.8 on the second day. How many total miles did he travel in the 2 days?

89. A laser saw cuts 0.024 inches from a steel plate that is 1.16-inches thick.

   a. What is the new thickness of the steel plate?

   b. If a copper cover that is 0.46 inches thick is then attached to the steel plate, what is the new thickness of the plate?

90. Style-line Furniture sold a wall unit at a sale price of $3422.99.

   a. If this price represents a saving of $590.50, what was the original price of the wall unit?

   b. If the sales tax was $194.39, delivery charges $125.00, and the setup charge $88.25, what was the total amount of the purchase?

91. On November 1, your checkbook balance was $2218.90. On November 12, you wrote check #078 for $451.25 to Castle Decor. On November 19, you made a deposit of $390.55. On November 27, you wrote check #079 to the Winton Realty for $257.80. Complete the check register for these transactions to find the new balance in your checking account.

Number or Code	Date	Transaction Description	Payment, Fee, Withdrawal (–)	✓	Deposit, Credit (+)	$ Balance	

92. On July 1, your checkbook balance was $1438.01. On July 8, you made a deposit of $193.40. On July 15, you wrote check # 260 for $89.22 to Union Oil. On July 25, you made an ATM withdrawal of $300. Complete the check register for these transactions to find the new balance in your checking account.

Number or Code	Date	Transaction Description	Payment, Fee, Withdrawal (–)	✓	Deposit, Credit (+)	$ Balance	

CUMULATIVE SKILLS REVIEW

1. Divide $\frac{3}{28} \div \frac{1}{7}$. Simplify, if possible. (2.5A)

2. Add $\frac{5}{8} + 1\frac{3}{4}$. Simplify, if possible. (2.6C)

3. Multiply $88 \cdot 12$. (1.4B)

4. Simplify $59 \cdot 8 - 12 \cdot 3 \cdot 1$. (1.6C)

5. Write $18\frac{1}{9}$ as an improper fraction. (2.2C)

6. Write $\frac{13}{7}$ as a mixed number. (2.2C)

7. Round 21,448 to the nearest ten. (1.1D)

8. Evaluate 4^3. (1.6B)

9. Write $\frac{13}{24}$ as a fraction with a denominator of 72. (2.3B)

10. How many $1\frac{3}{4}$-pound cheese wedges can be cut from a 35-pound cheese wheel? (2.5C)

3.3   MULTIPLYING DECIMALS

Objective 3.3A   Multiply decimals

To understand how to multiply decimals, let's consider $(0.05)(0.009)$. To multiply these decimals, let's first write each decimal as a fraction and then multiply.

$$0.05 \cdot 0.009 = \frac{5}{100} \cdot \frac{9}{1000} = \frac{45}{100,000} = 0.00045$$

2 decimal places   3 decimal places   5 decimal places

Notice that there are 2 decimal places in the first factor, 3 decimal places in the second factor, and 5 decimal places in the product.

This example suggests that the number of decimal places in the product is equal to the sum of the number of decimal places in the factors. Given this, it is not necessary to write decimals as fractions before we multiply. We can use the following steps instead.

> ### Steps for Multiplying Decimals
> **Step 1.** Multiply without regard to the decimal points. That is, multiply the factors as though they are whole numbers.
>
> **Step 2.** Determine the total number of decimal places in both of the factors.
>
> **Step 3.** Place the decimal point in the product so that the number of places to the right of the decimal point is equal to the total determined in step 2. If necessary, insert zeros as placeholders to get the correct number of decimal places. Any inserted zeros will be on the immediate right of the decimal point.

To demonstrate these steps, let's multiply a number with three decimal places, say 0.111, by a number with one decimal place, say 0.3.

$$
\begin{array}{r}
0.111 \quad \longleftarrow \text{ 3 decimal places} \\
\times \quad 0.3 \quad \longleftarrow \text{ 1 decimal place} \\
\hline
0.0333 \quad \longleftarrow \text{ 4 decimal places}
\end{array}
$$

Insert a zero as a placeholder in the tenths place

Note that the resulting product will have four decimal places. A zero must be written in the tenths place as a placeholder since the product has only three places.

EXAMPLE 1 Multiply decimals

Multiply.

a. (5.47)(0.2)   **b.** (7.83)(3.45)   **c.** (0.00045)(0.9)

SOLUTION STRATEGY

a. 5.47   2 decimal places.
  $\times$ 0.2   1 decimal place.
  1.094   Insert the decimal point so that there are 2 + 1 = 3 places to the right of the decimal point.

b.   7.83   2 decimal places.
    $\times$ 3.45   2 decimal places.
    3915
    31320
    234900   Insert the decimal point so that there are 2 + 2 = 4 places to the
    27.0135   right of point.

c. 0.00045   5 decimal places.
  $\times$ 0.9   1 decimal place.
  0.000405   Insert the decimal point so that there are 5 + 1 = 6 places to the right of the decimal point. Note that we insert three zeros as placeholders to get the correct number of decimal places.

> ### Learning Tip
>
> In the problem 5.47 · 0.2, there are a total of three decimal places. To insert the decimal point correctly, count backward three places from the right.
>
>   5.47
> $\times$ 0.2
>   1.094

TRY-IT EXERCISE 1

Multiply.

a. (76.4)(15.1)   **b.** (1.0012)(0.27)   **c.** (143)(11.28)

Check your answers with the solutions in Appendix A. ■

| Objective 3.3B | **Multiply a decimal by a power of 10** |

When we multiply a decimal by powers of 10, certain patterns emerge. Consider the following products.

45.281	45.281	45.281
$\times$ 10	$\times$ 100	$\times$ 1000
00000	00000	00000
45281	00000	00000
452.810	45281	00000
	4528.100	00000
		45281
		45,281.000

The product is 452.81.   The product is 4528.1.   The product is 45,281.

Notice that in each example above, the product involves the same digits as the factor 45.281. Moreover, note that the decimal point of the factor 45.281 is moved to the right in each successive product shown. In particular, the number of places the decimal moves to the right depends on the power of 10.

$45.281 \times 10 = 452.81$ Move the decimal point 1 place to the right.
1 zero

$45.281 \times 100 = 4528.1$ Move the decimal point 2 places to the right.
2 zeros

$45.281 \times 1000 = 45{,}281$ Move the decimal point 3 places to the right.
3 zeros

These observations suggest the following rule.

Multiplying a Decimal by a Power of 10 such as 10, 100, 1000 . . .

Move the decimal point to the *right* the same number of places as there are zeros in the power of 10. Fill in any missing places with zeros.

The decimals 0.1, 0.01, 0.001, and so on are also powers of 10, but these are less than one. Let's look at some products involving these.

$$
\begin{array}{ccc}
45.281 & 45.281 & 45.281 \\
\underline{\times\ \ 0.1} & \underline{\times\ 0.01} & \underline{\times\ 0.001} \\
4.5281 & 0.45281 & 0.045281
\end{array}
$$

The product is 4.5281.   The product is 0.45281.   The product is 0.045281.

In each example, the product once again involves the same digits as the factor 45.281. This time, however, the decimal point of the factor 45.281 is moved to the left in each product.

$45.281 \times 0.1 = 4.5281$ Move the decimal point 1 place to the left.
1 decimal place

$45.281 \times 0.01 = 0.45281$ Move the decimal point 2 places to the left.
2 decimal places

$45.281 \times 0.001 = 0.045281$ Move the decimal point 3 places to the left.
3 decimal places

The above examples suggest the following rule.

Multiplying a Decimal by a Power of 10 such as 0.1, 0.01, 0.001 . . .

Move the decimal point to the *left* the same number of places as there are place values in the decimal power of 10. Fill in any missing places with zeros.

EXAMPLE 2   **Multiply a decimal by a power of 10**

Multiply.

a. (36.687)(10)   **b.** (0.827)(10,000)   **c.** (2.11)(0.1)   **d.** (0.95)(0.001)

SOLUTION STRATEGY

a. (36.687)(10)   Because 10 has one zero, move the decimal point in 36.387 one place
                        to the *right.*
    366.87

b. (0.827)(10,000) Because 10,000 has four zeros, move the decimal point in 0.827 four
                        places to the *right.*
    8270

c. (2.11)(0.1)   Because 0.1 has one decimal place, move the decimal point in 2.11
                        one place to the *left.*
    0.211

d. (0.95)(0.001)   Because 0.001 has three decimal places, move the decimal point in
                        0.95 three places to the *left.*
    0.00095

> **Learning Tip**
>
> When multiplying a decimal by a power of 10 greater than one, move the decimal point to the right. When multiplying by a power of 10 less than one, move the decimal point to the left.

TRY-IT EXERCISE 2

Multiply.

a. (42.769)(100)

b. (0.0035)(1000)

c. (78.42)(0.01)

d. (0.047)(0.0001)

Check your answers with the solutions in Appendix A. ■

Large numbers are often expressed in words. For example, government statistics might report that 1.4 million vehicles were registered in the state last year. To express 1.4 million in standard notation, multiply 1.4 by one million (1,000,000).

$$\textbf{1.4 million} = \textbf{1.4} \cdot \textbf{1,000,000} = \textbf{1,400,000}$$

EXAMPLE 3   **Multiply a decimal by a power of 10**

Write each number in standard notation.

a. 3.56 billion   **b.** 2.715 trillion

SOLUTION STRATEGY

a. 3.56 billion

    3.56 × 1,000,000,000   1 billion = 1,000,000,000

    3,560,000,000   Multiply.

b. 2.715 trillion

$2.715 \times 1{,}000{,}000{,}000{,}000$ 1 trillion = 1,000,000,000,000

$2{,}715{,}000{,}000{,}000$ Multiply.

TRY-IT EXERCISE 3

Write each number in standard notation.

a. 41.3 million

b. 8.69 billion

c. 1.5 trillion

Check your answers with the solutions in Appendix A. ■

Objective 3.3C   **Estimate when multiplying decimals**

Just as when adding and subtracting decimals, we can estimate when multiplying decimals to see whether an answer is reasonable. We use the following steps.

EXAMPLE 4   **Estimate when multiplying decimals**

Multiply (7.8)(0.62). Then estimate the product by rounding each factor to one nonzero digit.

SOLUTION STRATEGY

$$
\begin{array}{r}
7.8 \\
\times\, 0.62 \\
\hline
156 \\
+\, 4680 \\
\hline
4.836
\end{array}
$$
Multiply.

$$
\begin{array}{r}
7.8 \\
\times\, 0.62
\end{array}
\rightarrow
\begin{array}{r}
8 \\
\times\, 0.6 \\
\hline
4.8
\end{array}
$$
To estimate the product, round each factor to one nonzero digit. Multiply the rounded factors.

Note that the exact answer is close to the estimate.

TRY-IT EXERCISE 4

Multiply (54.3)(0.48) Then estimate the product by rounding each factor to one nonzero digit.

Check your answer with the solution in Appendix A. ■

Objective 3.3D   **Apply your knowledge**

invoice
A business document detailing the sales of goods or services.

EXTEND AND TOTAL AN INVOICE

A common business application of decimal multiplication deals with extending an invoice. An **invoice** is a business document detailing the sales of goods or services.

Let's look at an example. Bright Light Productions sold 450 candle holders at $3.75 each and 260 candles at $1.50 each to a chain of gift shops. They charged $54.75 for shipping and handling and $12.50 for insurance. The incomplete invoice looks like this.

BRIGHT LIGHT PRODUCTIONS

Quantity	Description	Cost per Item	Total
450	Candle Holders	$3.75	
260	Candles	1.50	
	Merchandise total		
	Shipping and handling		54.75
	Insurance		12.50
	Invoice total		

To extend the invoice, multiply the number of items by the cost per item in each row. For example, to extend the first row, multiply $450 \cdot \$3.75$. To find the merchandise total, add entries in the column containing the totals from each row. Other invoice charges might include shipping and handling, insurance, and sales tax. These would be added to the merchandise total to obtain the invoice total. The completed invoice looks like this.

BRIGHT LIGHT PRODUCTIONS

Quantity	Description	Cost per Item	Total
450	Candle Holders	$3.75	$1687.50
260	Candles	1.50	390.00
	Merchandise total		2077.50
	Shipping and handling		54.75
	Insurance		12.50
	Invoice total		$2144.75

EXAMPLE 5   Extend and total an invoice

You are a salesperson for Tango Industries, a distributor of men's shirts and ties. You have just written an order for a men's shop for 130 short-sleeve shirts at $23.15 each; 140 long-sleeve shirts at $28.48 each; and 200 assorted silk ties at $16.25 each. In addition, there is a $121.40 charge for shipping and handling and $41.00 charge for insurance. Complete the invoice for Tango Industries.

SOLUTION STRATEGY

TANGO INDUSTRIES

Quantity	Description	Cost per Item	Total
130	Short-sleeve Shirts	$23.15	$3,009.50
140	Long-sleeve Shirts	28.48	3,987.20
200	Assorted Silk Ties	16.25	3,250.00
	Merchandise total		10,246.70
	Shipping and handling		121.40
	Insurance		41.00
	Invoice total		$10,409.10

TRY-IT EXERCISE 5

You are a salesperson for Sparkwell Electronics, a distributor of audio and video equipment. You have just written an order for your client, BrandsMartUSA. They have ordered 430 MP3 players at $115.20 each; 300 DVD burners at $160 each; and 500 packages of blank DVDs at $7.25 each. In addition, there is a charge of $590.00 for shipping and handling and $345.50 for insurance. Complete the invoice for Sparkwell.

SPARKWELL ELECTRONICS

Quantity	Description	Cost per Item	Total
	Merchandise total		
	Shipping and handling		
	Insurance		
	Invoice total		

Check your answers with the solutions in Appendix A. ■

SECTION 3.3 REVIEW EXERCISES

Concept Check

1. When multiplying decimals, the product has as many decimal places as the total number of decimal places in the two _____.

2. When multiplying decimals, insert _____ as place-holders to get the correct number of decimal places.

3. When multiplying a number by a power of 10 greater than one (such as 10, 100, 1000, and so on), move the decimal point to the _____ the same number of places as there are zeros in the power of 10.

4. When multiplying a number by a power of 10 less than one (such as 0.1, 0.01, 0.001, and so on), move the decimal point to the _____ the same number of places as there are place values in the power of 10.

Objective 3.3A   **Multiply decimals**

GUIDE PROBLEMS

5. Multiply $5.26 \cdot 1.4$.

a. How many decimal places are in the factor 5.26?

b. How many decimal places are in the factor 1.4?

c. How many decimal places will the product have?

d. Determine the product.

$$\begin{array}{r} 5.26 \\ \times 1.4 \\ \hline \end{array}$$

6. Multiply $0.0007 \cdot 4.2$.

a. How many decimal places are in the factor 0.0007?

b. How many decimal places are in the factor 4.2?

c. How many decimal places will the product have?

d. Determine the product.

$$\begin{array}{r} 0.0007 \\ \times\ \ 4.2 \\ \hline \end{array}$$

Multiply.

7. $\begin{array}{r} 0.44 \\ \times\ 0.8 \\ \hline \end{array}$

8. $\begin{array}{r} 3.7 \\ \times\ 0.2 \\ \hline \end{array}$

9. $\begin{array}{r} 19 \\ \times\ 1.9 \\ \hline \end{array}$

10. $\begin{array}{r} 155 \\ \times\ 3.1 \\ \hline \end{array}$

11. $\begin{array}{r} 5.98 \\ \times\ 14.1 \\ \hline \end{array}$

12. $\begin{array}{r} 23.1 \\ \times\ 12.4 \\ \hline \end{array}$

13. $\begin{array}{r} 0.45 \\ \times\ 4.05 \\ \hline \end{array}$

14. $\begin{array}{r} 0.0075 \\ \times\ 5.8 \\ \hline \end{array}$

15. $\begin{array}{r} 4.24 \\ \times\ 7 \\ \hline \end{array}$

16. $\begin{array}{r} 0.374 \\ \times\ 20 \\ \hline \end{array}$

17. $\begin{array}{r} 6.26 \\ \times\ 0.06 \\ \hline \end{array}$

18. $\begin{array}{r} 11.2 \\ \times\ 4.8 \\ \hline \end{array}$

19. $(0.45)(0.22)$

20. $(0.123)(0.84)$

21. $(200.2)(0.08)$

22. $(62.2)(0.005)$

23. (138)(150.25)

24. (216)(89.32)

25. ($8050.20)(1.6)

26. ($9.75)(2.4)

27. (21.089)(9.7)

28. (19.375)(14.2)

29. (3.000041)(5.02)

30. (1.00062)(3.2)

31. How much is $16.88 times 0.75?

32. How much is five and two hundredths times eighteen?

33. What is the product of one and three tenths and four and twelve hundredths?

34. What is the product of 35.25 and 33.78?

Objective 3.3B **Multiply a decimal by a power of 10**

GUIDE PROBLEMS

35. Multiply (3.6)(100).

Because there are _____ zeros in 100, move the decimal point _____ places to the _____.

(3.6)(100) = _____

36. Multiply (5.1)(0.0001).

Because there are _____ place values in 0.0001, move the decimal point _____ places to the _____.

(5.1)(0.0001) = _____

Multiply.

37. (2.75)(1000)

38. (8.93)(10,000)

39. (1.955)(10,000)

40. (0.16)(100,000)

41. (0.75)(10^4)

42. (3.5)(10^3)

43. (5.4)(0.001)

44. (21.3)(0.0001)

45. (0.072)(0.01)

46. (0.006302)(0.1)

47. (32.09)(0.00001)

48. (45.69)(0.00001)

Write each number in standard form.

49. According to the U.S. Census Bureau, in 2006, the population of the United States was 298.99 million.

50. McDonald's has sold over 100 billion hamburgers.

51. According to the National Debt Clock, the national debt in June, 2006 was $8.383 trillion.

52. The U.S. Census Bureau predicts that by 2015 there will be 312.26 million people in the United States.

Objective 3.3C **Estimate when multiplying decimals**

GUIDE PROBLEMS

53. Estimate (10.5)(3.82) by rounding each factor to one nonzero digit.

$$\begin{array}{r} 10.5 \rightarrow 10 \\ \times\, 3.82 \rightarrow \times \underline{} \\ \hline \underline{} \end{array}$$

54. Estimate (24.66)(1.499) by rounding each factor to two nonzero digits.

$$\begin{array}{r} 24.66 \rightarrow 25 \\ \times\, 1.499 \rightarrow \times \underline{} \\ \hline \underline{} \end{array}$$

Estimate each product by rounding each factor to one nonzero digit.

55. (3.1)(0.49)   **56.** (7.9)(0.95)   **57.** (9.4)(0.32)   **58.** (2.5)(0.49)

Estimate each product by rounding each factor to two nonzero digits.

59. (32.78)(2.48)   **60.** (16.99)(10.721)   **61.** (51.523)(10.49)   **62.** (43.218)(21.3)

Objective 3.3D	Apply your knowledge

63. A highway paving crew can complete 0.42 miles of highway per hour. How many miles can they pave in 7 hours?

64. Louie's Alfredo Sauce contains 0.88 grams of protein per ounce. How much protein is in a 2.5-ounce serving?

65. Wild Flour Bakery sliced a loaf of rye bread into 30 pieces. If each piece is 0.375 inches thick, what is the total length of the bread?

66. A set of Great Classics books contains 12 volumes. If each book is 1.6 inches thick, how much shelf space will the books require?

67. Fantasy World had 4319 adults and 5322 children in attendance last weekend. Adult tickets cost $18.65 and children's tickets cost $12.40. How much did the theme park take in?

68. Patrice owes Nationwide Bank $65,000 on her home mortgage. If she makes monthly payments of $725.40 for 3 years, what is the balance remaining on the loan?

69. Ameri-Car Auto Rental charges $35.00 per day plus $0.15 per mile for a Ford Taurus. What would be the total charge for a 6-day trip of 550 miles?

70. A long-distance phone call to London costs $2.27 for the first 3 minutes plus $0.38 for each additional minute. What would be the cost of a 10-minute call?

71. In 2003, the United States Bureau of Engraving and Printing issued a newly designed twenty dollar bill with subtle background colors and enhanced security features. Twenty billion dollars worth of the bills were put into circulation in the first printing.

  a. Write this number in standard notation.

  b. The printing cost for each of the one billion twenty dollar bills was $0.075. What was the total cost for the first print run?

72. An office building cost $2.48 million per floor to construct.

  a. Write this number in standard notation.

  b. If the building is 15-floors tall, what is the total cost of construction?

You are the payroll manager for Rocky Mountain Industries. Complete the payroll data sheet. Round to the nearest cent, that is, round to the nearest hundredth.

	Employee	Hours	Hourly Wage	Total	Deductions	Net Pay
73.	Calder	34.5	$7.80		$53.22	
74.	Martinez	38.12	$9.18		$102.29	
75.	Wong	42.7	$8.25			$261.27
76.	Dinkowitz	25.1	$12.65			$248.01

77. A "two-a-day" multivitamin pill contains 0.05 mg (milligrams) of copper and 0.5 mg of manganese. You take the recommended dosage each day for 30 days.

a. How much copper have you taken?

b. How much manganese have you taken?

78. A doctor's order requires a patient to take 5.8 mg of a particular medication every 6 hours (4 times a day).

a. How many milligrams of the medication will the patient take each day?

b. How many milligrams should be prescribed for a 15-day regimen of the medication?

Use the table *Life Insurance—Monthly Premiums* for exercises 79–82.

Life Insurance—Monthly Premiums

Age	$250,000	$500,000
35 Male	$12.18	$20.01
35 Female	$11.53	$18.71
45 Male	$22.84	$41.33
45 Female	$20.01	$35.67
55 Male	$51.55	$98.75
55 Female	$36.98	$69.60

79. What is the annual premium for $500,000 of life insurance for a 45-year-old female?

80. What is the annual premium for $250,000 of life insurance for a 35-year-old male?

81. How much more is the annual premium for $250,000 of life insurance for a 55-year-old male compared to a 55-year-old female?

82. How much less is the annual premium for $500,000 of life insurance for a 35-year-old female compared to a 35-year-old male?

83. Cuisineart sold 200 toasters at $69.50 each and 130 blenders at $75.80 each to Appliance Depot. Shipping and handling charges totaled $1327.08. Insurance on the order was $644.20. Complete the invoice.

CUISINEART

Quantity	Description	Cost per Item	Total
200	Toasters	$69.50	$13,900.00
130	Blenders	75.80	9854.00
	Merchandise total		23,754.00
	Shipping and handling		1327.08
	Insurance		644.20
	Invoice total		$25,725.28

84. You are the manager of the Trendy Tire Company. Your company has placed the following advertisement in the morning paper. Use the advertisement and the invoice template to write up an order for a set of four Hi-Way King tires, size P205/70R14, and a set of four Road-Hugger tires, size P235/75R15. The sales tax on the two sets of tires is $37.50.

PASSENGER

70000 mile limited warranty

Road-Hugger

$65⁹⁹

P185/65R14

P205/75R15.....66.99
P215/75R15.....67.99
P235/75R15.....74.99

PASSENGER

80000 mile limited warranty

Hi-Way King

$69⁹⁹

P175/70R13

P195/70R14.....86.99
P205/70R14.....89.99
P205/60R15.....96.99

TRENDY TIRE COMPANY

Quantity	Description	Cost per Item	Total
	Merchandise total		
	Sales tax		
	Invoice total		

CUMULATIVE SKILLS REVIEW

1. Divide $0 \div 89$. (1.5A)

2. Write fifty-two and thirty-six hundredths in decimal notation. (3.1C)

3. Add $3.66 + 1.299 + 9$. (3.2A)

4. Find the least common denominator of $\frac{1}{7}, \frac{3}{8}$, and $\frac{5}{14}$. (2.3C)

5. Write 6.852 in word form. (3.1C)

6. Subtract $10{,}552 - 5389$. (1.3A)

7. Write $8\frac{5}{6}$ as an improper fraction. (2.2C)

8. Find the prime factorization of 18. Express your answer in standard and exponential notation. (2.1C)

9. How much is $5\frac{3}{5}$ less $2\frac{1}{2}$? (2.7C)

10. What is the average of 136, 122, 170, and 144? (1.5C)

3.4 DIVIDING DECIMALS

Suppose you and two of your friends go to lunch, and the bill comes to $27.45. If the three of you decide to split the bill equally, then each person will owe $9.15. To figure this out, you could divide the dollar amount by 3 (27 dollars ÷ 3 = 9 dollars) and the cent amount by 3 (45 cents ÷ 3 = 15 cents). Alternatively, you could simply divide the decimal $27.45 by 3.

In this section, we consider division problems involving decimals. Recall from Chapter 1 that the number being divided is called the dividend, the number by which it is divided is called the divisor, and the result of dividing numbers is called the quotient.

$$\text{Dividend} \div \text{Divisor} = \text{Quotient} \qquad \frac{\text{Dividend}}{\text{Divisor}} = \text{Quotient} \qquad \text{Divisor}\overline{)\text{Dividend}}^{\text{Quotient}}$$

Objective 3.4A   Divide a decimal by a whole number

Consider the division problem 39 ÷ 10. We can calculate the quotient using long division.

$$\begin{array}{r} 3 \\ 10\overline{)39} \\ -30 \\ \hline 9 \end{array}$$

We can express the result in the form $\text{quotient}\dfrac{\text{remainder}}{\text{divisor}}$.

We can write the result as $3\dfrac{9}{10}$. But, since we can also write $\dfrac{9}{10}$ as 0.9, we could alternatively write the result as the decimal 3.9. To obtain this decimal result directly from the long division, we write 39 as 39.0 and divide as we would whole numbers, placing the decimal point in the quotient directly above the decimal point in the dividend.

$$\begin{array}{r} 3.9 \\ 10\overline{)39.0} \\ -30\downarrow \\ \hline 90 \\ -90 \\ \hline 0 \end{array}$$

Note the decimal point in the quotient is placed directly above the decimal point in the dividend.

In general, use the following steps to divide a decimal by a whole number.

Steps for Dividing a Decimal by a Whole Number

Step 1. Write the problem in long division form.

Step 2. Divide as if working with whole numbers. Place the decimal point in the quotient directly above the decimal point in the dividend.

Step 3. If necessary, write additional zeros to the right of the last digit following the decimal point in the dividend to allow the division to continue.

EXAMPLE 1   **Divide a decimal by a whole number**

Divide.

a. $6\overline{)13.56}$

b. $102.18 \div 4$

c. $0.27 \div 3$

SOLUTION STRATEGY

a.
$$\begin{array}{r} 2.26 \\ 6\overline{)13.56} \\ \underline{-12} \\ 15 \\ \underline{-12} \\ 36 \\ \underline{-36} \\ 0 \end{array}$$

Divide as if working with whole numbers.

Place the decimal point in the quotient directly above the decimal point in the dividend.

b.
$$\begin{array}{r} 25.54 \\ 4\overline{)102.18} \\ \underline{-8} \\ 22 \\ \underline{-20} \\ 21 \\ \underline{-20} \\ 18 \\ \underline{-16} \\ 2 \end{array}$$

Write the problem in long division form.

Divide as if working with whole numbers.

Place the decimal point in the quotient directly above the decimal point in the dividend.

Note that all of the digits of the dividend have been used, but the remainder is not 0.

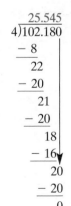
$$\begin{array}{r} 25.545 \\ 4\overline{)102.180} \\ \underline{-8} \\ 22 \\ \underline{-20} \\ 21 \\ \underline{-20} \\ 18 \\ \underline{-16} \\ 20 \\ \underline{-20} \\ 0 \end{array}$$

Write a 0 after the 8 in the dividend to allow the division to continue.

Bring down the 0. Continue to divide.

c.
$$\begin{array}{r} 0.09 \\ 3\overline{)0.27} \\ \underline{-27} \\ 0 \end{array}$$

Write the problem in long division form.
Divide as if working with whole numbers.
Insert a 0 as a placeholder in the tenths place.

TRY-IT EXERCISE 1

Divide.

a. $2\overline{)33.66}$

b. $75.8 \div 10$

c. $0.0916 \div 4$

Check your answers with the solutions in Appendix A. ■

<hr />

| Objective 3.4B | **Divide a decimal by a power of 10** |

In the previous section, we observed some shortcuts for multiplying a decimal by a power of 10. We now state similar shortcuts for dividing a decimal by a power of 10. We leave it to the reader to explain why these rules work. (Refer back to Section 3.3.)

Dividing a Decimal by a Power of 10 such as 10, 100, 1000 . . .

Move the decimal point in the dividend to the *left* the same number of places as there are zeros in the power of 10. Insert zeros, as necessary.

Recall that the decimals 0.1, 0.01, 0.001, and so on are powers of 10 less than one. The following rule is used when we divide a decimal or whole number by one of these powers of 10.

Dividing a Decimal by a Power of 10 such as 0.1, 0.01, 0.001 . . .

Move the decimal point in the dividend to the *right* the same number of places as there are place values in the decimal power of 10. Insert zeros, as necessary.

EXAMPLE 2 **Divide a decimal by a power of 10**

Divide.

a. $100\overline{)13.204}$ **b.** $45.68 \div 1000$ **c.** $\dfrac{3.724}{0.01}$ **d.** $12,000 \div 0.001$

SOLUTION STRATEGY

a. $100\overline{)13.204}$ — The divisor is a power of 10 with two zeros.
Move the decimal point two places to the *left*.

0.13204

b. $45.68 \div 1000 = 0.04568$ — The divisor is a power of 10 with three zeros.
Move the decimal point three places to the *left*.

Insert a 0 in the tenths place as a placeholder to get the correct number of decimal places.

c. $\dfrac{3.724}{0.01} = 372.4$

The divisor is a power of 10 that is less than one. Because 0.01 has two decimal places, move the decimal point of the dividend two places to the *right*.

d. $12{,}000 \div 0.001 = 12{,}000{,}000$

The divisor is a decimal power of 10 that is less than one. Because 0.001 has three decimal places, move the decimal point of the dividend three places to the *right*. Insert a 0 in each of the ones, tens, and hundreds places.

TRY-IT EXERCISE 2

Divide.

a. $48.3 \div 0.001$

b. $\dfrac{15{,}286.61}{10{,}000}$

c. $0.00028 \div 0.00001$

d. $10\overline{)1.357}$

Check your answers with the solutions in Appendix A. ∎

Objective 3.4C **Divide a decimal or a whole number by a decimal**

Consider the problem $5.625 \div 0.45$. In fraction notation, this problem is $\dfrac{5.625}{0.45}$. We can write an equivalent fraction whose denominator is a whole number by multiplying by one in the form of $\dfrac{100}{100}$.

$$5.625 \div 0.45 = \frac{5.625}{0.45} \cdot \frac{100}{100} = \frac{562.5}{45} = 562.5 \div 45$$

From this, we see that the original division problem, $5.625 \div 0.45$, is equivalent to $562.5 \div 45$. We now perform the division.

$$
\begin{array}{r}
12.5 \\
45\overline{)562.5} \\
-45 \\
\hline
112 \\
-90 \\
\hline
225 \\
-225 \\
\hline
0
\end{array}
$$

Note that the decimal point in the quotient is placed directly above the decimal point in the dividend.

Learning Tip

When using a calculator to divide, be sure to enter the dividend first, then the divisor.

For example, $0.45\overline{)5.625}$ would be entered in this way.

$$5.625 \div 0.45 = 12.5$$

Since $562.5 \div 45 = 12.5$, it follows that $5.625 \div 0.45 = 12.5$ as well. To verify this, simply confirm that the product of the quotient and the original divisor is equal to the original dividend.

$$
\begin{array}{r}
12.5 \\
\times\ 0.45 \\
\hline
625 \\
+\ 5000 \\
\hline
5.625
\end{array}
$$

Quotient.
Original divisor.

Original dividend.

When we multiply $\dfrac{5.625}{0.45}$ by one in the form of $\dfrac{100}{100}$, we effectively move the decimal point two places to the right in both the divisor and dividend. In general, to divide a decimal or whole number by a decimal, we write an equivalent division problem with a whole number divisor. To do so, all we have to do is (1) move the decimal point in the divisor as many places to the right as necessary to get a whole number, and (2) move the decimal point in the dividend the same number of places to the right.

The following rules are used to divide a decimal or whole number by a decimal.

Steps for Dividing a Decimal or Whole Number by a Decimal

Step 1. Write the problem in long division format.

Step 2. Write an equivalent division problem with a whole number divisor. In particular, move the decimal point in the divisor to the right as many places as necessary until the divisor is a whole number. Also, move the decimal point in the dividend the same number of places to the right.

Step 3. Divide. Place the decimal point in the quotient directly above the moved decimal point in the dividend. Then divide.

Learning Tip

In a division problem involving decimals, the divisor is the key to any movement of the decimal point. Always move the decimal point in the divisor to the "end" of the divisor. Move the decimal point in the dividend the same number of places to the right.

EXAMPLE 3 Divide a whole number or a decimal by a decimal

Divide.

a. $0.69\overline{)38.226}$ **b.** $1.8\overline{)22.725}$ **c.** $8.4\overline{)45}$ Round to the nearest tenth.

SOLUTION STRATEGY

a. $0.69\overline{)38.226}$

$$
\begin{array}{r}
55.4 \\
69\overline{)3822.6} \\
-\ 345 \\
\hline
372 \\
-\ 345 \\
\hline
276 \\
-\ 276 \\
\hline
0
\end{array}
$$

Write an equivalent division problem by moving the decimal point two places to the right in both the divisor and dividend.

Divide as if working with whole numbers.

Place the decimal point in the quotient directly above the decimal point in the dividend.

b. $22.725 \div 1.8$

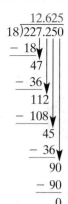

$$
\begin{array}{r}
12.625 \\
18\overline{)227.250} \\
-18 \\
\hline
47 \\
-36 \\
\hline
112 \\
-108 \\
\hline
45 \\
-36 \\
\hline
90 \\
-90 \\
\hline
0
\end{array}
$$

Write an equivalent division problem by moving the decimal point one place to the right in both the divisor and dividend.

Divide as if working with whole numbers. Place a decimal point in the quotient directly above the decimal point in the dividend.

Write a 0 after the 5 in the dividend to allow the division to continue.

c. $8.4\overline{)45}$

$$
\begin{array}{r}
5.35 \\
84\overline{)450.00} \\
-420 \\
\hline
300 \\
-252 \\
\hline
480 \\
-420 \\
\hline
60
\end{array}
$$

$5.35 \approx 5.4$

Write an equivalent division problem by moving the decimal point one place to the right in both the divisor and dividend.

Insert a 0 after the 5 so that the decimal point is correctly placed.

Because we are rounding to the nearest tenth, we divide out to the hundredths place. Write two additional zeros to the right of the decimal point to allow division to continue to the hundredths place.

TRY-IT EXERCISE 3

Divide.

a. $1.88 \div 0.094$

b. $3.735\overline{)62.67330}$

c. $4.2 \div 13.39$. Round to the nearest hundredth.

Check your answers with the solutions in Appendix A. ■

Objective 3.4D   Estimate when dividing decimals

Just as when adding, subtracting, and multiplying decimals, we can estimate when dividing decimals to see whether an answer is reasonable.

EXAMPLE 4   Estimate when dividing decimals

Divide $96.9 \div 9.5$. Then estimate the quotient by rounding the dividend and divisor to one nonzero digit.

SOLUTION STRATEGY

$$9.5 \overline{)96.9} \qquad \text{Divide.}$$

$$\begin{array}{r} 10.2 \\ 95\overline{)969.0} \\ -\underline{95} \\ 190 \\ -\underline{190} \\ 0 \end{array}$$

$$\begin{array}{cc} 96.9 \div 9.5 & \text{To estimate the quotient, round the dividend and di-} \\ \downarrow \qquad \downarrow & \text{visor to one nonzero digit.} \\ 100 \div 10 \end{array}$$

$$\begin{array}{r} 10 \\ 10\overline{)100} \\ -\underline{10} \\ 00 \end{array} \qquad \begin{array}{l} \text{Divide the rounded numbers.} \\ \\ \\ \text{Note that the exact answer is close to the estimate.} \end{array}$$

TRY-IT EXERCISE 4

Divide $61.07 \div 19.7$. Then estimate the quotient by rounding the dividend and divisor to one nonzero digit.

Check your answer with the solution in Appendix A. ■

Real-World Connection

Your GPA (grade point average) is an example of an average. It is calculated by assigning a value to each grade earned (such as A = 4, B = 3, C = 2, and so on). Each value is then multiplied by the number of credits associated with the course in which you earned a particular grade. The sum of these products divided by the total number of credits earned is your GPA.

Objective 3.4E **Apply your knowledge**

In Section 1.5, we learned that an average, or arithmetic mean, is the value obtained by dividing the sum of all the values in a data set by the number of values in the set. We found that an average is a convenient way to describe a large set of numbers with a single value. Here again are the steps for calculating an average.

Steps for Calculating an Average

Step 1. Find the sum of all the values in the data set.

Step 2. Divide the sum in step 1 by the number of values in the set.

$$\text{Average} = \frac{\text{Sum of values}}{\text{Number of values}}$$

EXAMPLE 5 Calculate an average

You are a clerk at The Clothes Horse boutique. This morning you made sales of $234.58, $132.66, and $79.52. What is the average of your morning sales?

SOLUTION STRATEGY

$$\frac{234.58 + 132.66 + 79.52}{3} = \frac{446.76}{3} = \$148.92$$

Add the three sales amounts and divide by the number of sales transactions.

TRY-IT EXERCISE 5

You work in the shipping department of a local warehouse. Today you shipped packages weighing 36.6 pounds, 25.8 pounds, 175 pounds, and 58.5 pounds. What is the average weight of these packages? Round to the nearest pound.

Check your answer with the solution in Appendix A. ■

SECTION 3.4 REVIEW EXERCISES

Concept Check

1. The number being divided is known as the _____.

2. The number by which the dividend is divided is called the _____.

3. The result of dividing numbers is called the _____.

4. When dividing a decimal by a whole number, place the decimal point in the quotient directly _____ the decimal point in the dividend.

5. When dividing a decimal by a whole number, it is some-times necessary to write additional zeros to the right of the _____ digit following the decimal point in the _____.

6. Explain how to write an equivalent division problem when the divisor contains a decimal point.

7. When dividing a decimal by a power of 10 greater than one (such as 10, 100, 1000, and so on), move the decimal point in the dividend to the _____ the same number of places as there are _____ in the power of 10.

8. When dividing a decimal by a power of 10 less than one (such as 0.1, 0.01, 0.001, and so on), move the decimal point in the dividend to the _____ the same number of places as there are _____ _____ in the decimal power of 10.

Objective 3.4A   **Divide a decimal by a whole number**

GUIDE PROBLEMS

9. Divide $6.75 \div 5$.

$$5\overline{)6.75}$$

10. Divide $57.23 \div 2$.

$$2\overline{)57.230}$$
$$\underline{-\ 4}$$
$$17$$

Divide.

11. $4 \overline{)10.8}$

12. $3 \overline{)0.015}$

13. $6 \overline{)33.6}$

14. $7 \overline{)26.95}$

15. $25 \overline{)43.5}$

16. $12 \overline{)198.24}$

17. $93 \overline{)37.2}$

18. $8 \overline{)48.8}$

19. $3 \div 40$

20. $50 \div 8$

21. $68.97 \div 11$

22. $57.5 \div 5$

23. $\dfrac{2.2}{50}$

24. $\dfrac{24.54}{3}$

25. $\dfrac{4.69}{67}$

26. $\dfrac{6.84}{18}$

Objective 3.4B   **Divide a decimal by a power of 10**

GUIDE PROBLEMS

27. Divide $4.7 \div 100$.

Because there are _____ zeros in 100, move the decimal point _____ places to the _____.

$4.7 \div 100 =$ _____

28. Divide $9.2 \div 0.00001$.

Because there are _____ place values in 0.00001, move the decimal point _____ places to the _____.

$9.2 \div 0.00001 =$ _____

Divide.

29. $\dfrac{24.78}{100}$

30. $\dfrac{0.85}{0.0001}$

31. $\dfrac{67}{0.001}$

32. $\dfrac{954.58}{10}$

33. $56.003 \div 0.00001$

34. $13.1 \div 10,000$

35. $76 \div 100,000$

36. $9.04 \div 0.01$

Objective 3.4C   **Divide a decimal or a whole number by a decimal**

GUIDE PROBLEMS

37. Consider $3.5 \overline{)1.96}$

   a. Write an equivalent division problem in which the divisor is a whole number.

   $3.5 \overline{)1.96}$ is equivalent to _____

   b. Divide.

   $35 \overline{)19.60}$

38. Consider $5.23 \overline{)0.039748}$

   a. Write an equivalent division problem in which the divisor is a whole number.

   $5.23 \overline{)0.039748}$ is equivalent to _____

   b. Divide.

   $523 \overline{)3.9748}$

Divide.

39. $0.8\overline{)64}$

40. $0.54\overline{)2.7}$

41. $1.5\overline{)40.2}$

42. $4.9\overline{)102.9}$

43. $2.55\overline{)7.905}$

44. $6.5\overline{)50.7}$

45. $0.81\overline{)3.564}$

46. $63\overline{)0.378}$

47. $6.586 \div 7.4$

48. $15.18 \div 0.69$

49. $37.8 \div 84$

50. $0.7 \div 0.28$

Divide. Round answer to the nearest whole number.

51. $49 \div 2.6$

52. $11.4\overline{)2000}$

53. $12.42 \div 0.39$

54. $\dfrac{66.7}{3.4}$

Divide. Round answer to the nearest tenth.

55. $34.5 \div 12.8$

56. $5.7 \div 18$

57. $2.3\overline{)1.6}$

58. $0.0096 \div 0.0011$

Divide. Round answer to the nearest hundredth.

59. $1 \div 13$

60. $6.55 \div 7$

61. $239 \div 1.1$

62. $148.267 \div 10$

Objective 3.4D	**Estimate when dividing decimals**

GUIDE PROBLEMS

63. Estimate $39.1 \div 7.6$ by rounding the dividend and divisor to one nonzero digit.

   a. Round the dividend and divisor to one nonzero digit.

$$39.1 \; \rightarrow \; \underline{}$$
$$7.6 \; \rightarrow \; 8$$

   b. Divide the rounded numbers.

$$8\overline{)\underline{}}$$

64. Estimate $0.061 \div 0.52$ by rounding the dividend and divisor to one nonzero digit.

   a. Round the dividend and divisor to one nonzero digit.

$$0.061 \; \rightarrow \; \underline{}$$
$$0.52 \; \rightarrow \; 0.5$$

   b. Divide the rounded numbers.

$$0.5\overline{)\underline{}} \; \rightarrow \; 5\overline{)\overline{\underline{}}}$$

Estimate each quotient by rounding the dividend and divisor to one nonzero digit.

65. $29.5 \div 5.9$

66. $5.842 \div 1.91$

67. $0.0212 \div 0.39$

68. $85.7 \div 0.118$

Objective 3.4E   **Apply your knowledge**

69. A case of 24 bottles of water were on sale at Costco for $5.33. What is the cost per bottle? Round to the nearest cent.

70. Ted has $3200 to invest in the Abbot Technology Mutual Fund. If the fund is selling for $12.68 per share, how many shares can he purchase? Round to the nearest tenth of a share.

71. Adult human scalp hair grows 4.89 inches per year. How many inches does it grow per day? Round to the nearest ten-thousandth.

72. Norm bought season tickets to the Drama Playhouse for $167.52. The season has 6 plays. What is the cost per ticket?

73. Bernard worked 32.9 hours last week and earned $411.25. How much does he make per hour?

74. Mickey, a carpenter, spent $22.08 on finishing nails at Ace Hardware. If Ace sells these nails for $0.48 per pound, how many pounds did Mickey purchase?

75. Terry ran a 10K race in 52.7 minutes. The term 10K means 10 kilometers and is equivalent to a distance of 6.2 miles.

    a. How many minutes per mile did Terry run?

    b. At that rate, how long would it take Terry to run a 5K race?

76. A Maserati began an auto race with a full tank of fuel totaling 26.4 gallons. During the two pit stops, the crew added 19.7 gallons and 23.1 gallons of fuel. At the end of the race, the car had 6.4 gallons left in the tank.

    a. How many gallons were used during the race?

    b. If the race was 350 miles, how many miles per gallon did the race car average? Round to the nearest tenth.

77. At Whole Foods, cantaloupes are on sale at 3 for $4.89. How much will you pay for 2 cantaloupes?

78. Azalea plants at Kmart are priced at 5 for $12.45. How much will you pay for 18 azalea plants?

79. Vogue Beauty Salon purchased 4 dozen cans of hair spray for $103.68 from Nathan's Beauty Supply. What was the cost per can?

80. A digital camera has a compact flash memory card with a storage capacity of 512 megabytes. At high resolution, photos average 2.2 megabytes each. How many photos can the memory card hold? Round to the nearest whole photo.

81. Jerry lost 57.6 pounds in 9 months on the North Beach diet. What was his average weight loss per month?

82. Karen is practicing the pole vault for an upcoming track meet. On her first try, she vaulted 12.6 feet. On the second try, Karen vaulted 11.8 feet. On her last try, she vaulted 12.4 feet. What is the average of her three vaults? Round to the nearest tenth.

83. Sunland Shopping Center took in $341,000 in rent from its tenants last month. The center charges $3.10 per square foot per month for rent.

   a. How many square feet is the shopping center?

   b. If maintenance costs last month totaled $3960, what was the cost of maintenance per square foot? Round to the nearest cent.

84. A cargo ship, the Matsumo Maru, has a cargo area of 23,220 cubic feet.

   a. How many 154.8 cubic foot storage containers can the ship hold?

   b. The shipping cost per storage container is $890.10 for a trip from Savannah, Georgia, to Miami, Florida. What is the cost per cubic foot?

CUMULATIVE SKILLS REVIEW

1. Multiply $10.45 \cdot 0.65$. (3.3A)

2. Simplify $(10^2 + 9^2) + 10$. (1.6C)

3. Simplify $\dfrac{18}{30}$. (2.3A)

4. List 0.266, 0.2787, and 0.2345 in ascending order. (3.1D)

5. Subtract 3.6 from 24.11. (3.2B)

6. Add $856 + 45$. (1.2B)

7. Golden Realty owns 532 acres of land in Johnston Canyon. If 178 acres are reserved as "common area" for roads and parks, how many 3-acre home sites can be developed on the remaining acreage? (1.3B, 1.5C)

8. Todd has a triangular-shaped patio with sides that measure $11\frac{1}{2}$ feet, $14\frac{3}{8}$ feet, and $9\frac{7}{12}$ feet. What is the perimeter of the patio? (2.6D)

9. A lasagna recipe requires 24 ounces of cheese. If Marcus wants to make $4\frac{1}{3}$ times as much for a party, how many ounces should he use? (2.4C)

10. Write 4.62 billion in standard notation. (3.3B)

3.5 WORKING WITH FRACTIONS AND DECIMALS

LEARNING OBJECTIVES

A. Convert a fraction to a decimal

B. Simplify an expression containing fractions and decimals using order of operations

C. Apply your knowledge

In this section, we will review how to convert decimals to fractions and learn how to convert fractions to decimals. We will also learn how to perform calculations involving fractions and decimals together.

Objective 3.5A	**Convert a fraction to a decimal**

In Section 3.1, we learned how to convert a decimal to a fraction. We saw that writing a decimal as a fraction follows directly from the definition of a decimal. Recall that a decimal is a number that can be written as a fraction whose denominator is a power of 10. Here are some examples:

$$0.4 = \frac{4}{10} = \frac{2}{5} \qquad 0.31 = \frac{31}{100} \qquad 0.215 = \frac{215}{1000} = \frac{43}{200}$$

Note that the numerator of each fraction consists of the digits to the right of the decimal point. The denominator is the power of 10 that has as many zeros as place values in the decimal number itself.

We now turn our attention to converting fractions to decimals. To do this, recall that in Chapter 2, we learned that the fraction bar can represent the operation of division. Thus, the fraction $\frac{1}{4}$ can be thought of as "1 divided by 4." Therefore, to convert a fraction to a decimal, simply divide as we did in the previous section.

Rule for Converting a Fraction to a Decimal

Divide the numerator by the denominator. If necessary, insert zeros in the dividend after the decimal point to allow the division to continue. Also, if necessary, insert zeros as placeholders in the quotient to get the correct number of decimal places.

As an example, let's convert the fraction $\frac{5}{8}$ to a decimal. To do this, divide the numerator, 5, by the denominator, 8.

$$\begin{array}{r} 0.625 \\ 8\overline{)5.000} \\ -\,48 \\ \hline 20 \\ -\,16 \\ \hline 40 \\ -\,40 \\ \hline 0 \end{array}$$

Write a decimal point followed by zeros after the 5.

The remainder is 2. Bring down the 0.

The remainder is 4. Bring down the 0.

The remainder is 0.

terminating decimal
A decimal whose expansion ends.

In the example above, we eventually end up with a remainder of zero, and so the quotient is an example of a **terminating decimal**, a decimal whose expansion ends.

Not all decimal expansions terminate. Sometimes, a decimal continues indefinitely with one or more repeating digits. Such a decimal is called a **repeating decimal**.

As an example, let's convert the fraction $\frac{1}{3}$ to a decimal. To do this, divide the numerator, 1, by the denominator, 3.

repeating decimal
A decimal that continues indefinitely with one or more repeating digits.

$$
\begin{array}{r}
0.333\ldots \\
3\overline{)1.000} \\
-9 \\
\hline
10 \\
-9 \\
\hline
10 \\
-9 \\
\hline
1
\end{array}
$$

Write a decimal point followed by zeros after the 1.

The remainder is 1. Bring down the 0.

The remainder is 1. Bring down the 0.

The remainder is 1.

Notice that the remainder is always 1. Consequently, the digit 3 will continue to repeat in the quotient. To indicate that the 3 repeats indefinitely, we place a bar above the 3.

$$\frac{1}{3} = 0.333\ldots = 0.\overline{3}$$

EXAMPLE 1   Convert a fraction to a decimal

Convert each fraction to a decimal.

a. $\frac{1}{4}$

b. $\frac{6}{25}$

c. $\frac{7}{8}$

d. $\frac{11}{12}$

e. $\frac{9}{11}$

SOLUTION STRATEGY

a.
$$
\begin{array}{r}
0.25 \\
4\overline{)1.00} \\
-8 \\
\hline
20 \\
-20 \\
\hline
0
\end{array}
$$

Divide the numerator, 1, by the denominator, 4. Insert a decimal point followed by some zeros after the 1.

Divide.

b.
$$
\begin{array}{r}
0.24 \\
25\overline{)6.00} \\
-50 \\
\hline
100 \\
-100 \\
\hline
0
\end{array}
$$

Divide the numerator, 6, by the denominator, 25. Insert a decimal point followed by some zeros after the 6.

Divide.

```
        0.875
c. 8)7.000
   − 64
      60
    − 56
      40
    − 40
       0
```

Divide the numerator, 7, by the denominator, 8. Insert a decimal point followed by some zeros after the 7.

Divide.

```
       0.91666... = 0.91\overline{6}
d. 12)11.00000
    − 108
       20
     − 12
       80
     − 72
       80
     − 72
       80
     − 72
        8
```

Divide the numerator, 11, by the denominator, 12. Insert a decimal point followed by some zeros after the 11.

Divide.

The remainder is always 8, and so the digit 6 repeats indefinitely in the quotient.

```
       0.8181... = 0.\overline{81}
e. 11)9.0000
    − 88
      20
    − 11
      90
    − 88
      20
    − 11
       9
```

Divide the numerator, 9, by the denominator, 11. Insert a decimal point followed by some zeros after the 9.

Divide.

The remainder always alternates between 2 and 9, and so the digits 81 repeat indefinitely in the quotient.

TRY-IT EXERCISE 1

Convert each fraction to a decimal.

a. $\dfrac{3}{40}$

b. $\dfrac{15}{16}$

c. $\dfrac{5}{6}$

d. $\dfrac{1}{6}$

e. $\dfrac{4}{15}$

Check your answers with the solutions in Appendix A. ∎

| Objective 3.5B | **Simplify an expression containing fractions and decimals using order of operations** |

When an expression contains a mix of fractions and decimals, we can either convert the fractions to decimals, or we can convert the decimals to fractions. In general, if all of the decimals have terminating decimal expansions, then we convert the fractions to decimals or vice versa. If, on the other hand, the fractions have a repeating decimal expansion, then we prefer to convert the decimals to fractions in order to avoid rounding error.

As an example, consider $\frac{1}{4} \cdot 0.625$. Since $\frac{1}{4}$ has a terminating decimal expansion $\left(\frac{1}{4} = 0.25\right)$, we can calculate the product by either converting the fraction to a decimal or vice versa. Let's first calculate the product by converting the fraction to a decimal.

$$\frac{1}{4} \cdot 0.625 = 0.25 \cdot 0.625 \qquad \text{Write both factors as decimals.}$$
$$= 0.15625 \qquad \text{Multiply the decimals.}$$

Let's now determine the product by converting the decimal to a fraction.

$$\frac{1}{4} \cdot 0.625 = \frac{1}{4} \cdot \frac{5}{8} \qquad \text{Write both factors as fractions.}$$
$$= \frac{5}{32} \qquad \text{Multiply the fractions.}$$

To verify that we obtained the same result, let's convert $\frac{5}{32}$ to a decimal.

$$\begin{array}{r} 0.15625 \\ 32\overline{)5.00000} \end{array} \qquad \text{Divide the numerator, 5, by the denominator, 32.}$$

Thus, $\frac{5}{32} = 0.15625$.

An alternate way of calculating the product $\frac{1}{4} \cdot 0.625$ is by writing 0.625 in fraction notation as $\frac{0.625}{1}$.

$$\frac{1}{4} \cdot \frac{0.625}{1} = \frac{0.625}{4} \qquad \text{Multiply.}$$
$$= 0.15625 \qquad \text{Divide.}$$

Notice that we get the same answer as we did above.

EXAMPLE 2   **Simplify an expression containing a fraction and a decimal**

Simplify each expression.

a. $\frac{1}{8} \cdot 7.25$ **b.** $3.5 \div \frac{5}{6}$ **c.** $\frac{2}{5} + 0.41$

SOLUTION STRATEGY

a. $\dfrac{1}{8} \cdot 7.25 = 0.125 \cdot 7.25$ Convert $\dfrac{1}{8}$ to a decimal.

$= 0.90625$ Multiply.

b. $3.5 \div \dfrac{5}{6} = 3\dfrac{1}{2} \div \dfrac{5}{6}$ Convert 3.5 to a mixed number.

$= \dfrac{7}{2} \div \dfrac{5}{6}$ Convert the mixed number to an improper fraction.

$= \dfrac{7}{2} \cdot \dfrac{6}{5}$ Multiply $\dfrac{7}{2}$ by the reciprocal of $\dfrac{5}{6}$.

$= \dfrac{21}{5} = 4\dfrac{1}{5}$

c. $\dfrac{2}{5} + 0.41 = 0.4 + 0.41$ Convert $\dfrac{2}{5}$ to a decimal.

$= 0.81$ Add.

TRY-IT EXERCISE 2

Simplify each expression.

a. $\dfrac{7}{8} - 0.6$

b. $0.375 \cdot \dfrac{5}{21}$

c. $\dfrac{2}{3} \div 1.75$

Check your answers with the solutions in Appendix A. ∎

Often, expressions containing fractions and decimals will have more than one operation. When multiple operations are present, we must simplify the expression using order of operations. Once again, here are the rules.

Order of Operations

Step 1. Perform all operations within grouping symbols: parentheses ( ), brackets [ ], and curly braces { }. When grouping symbols occur within grouping symbols, begin with the innermost grouping symbols.

Step 2. Evaluate all exponential expressions.

Step 3. Perform all multiplications and divisions as they appear in reading from left to right.

Step 4. Perform all additions and subtractions as they appear in reading from left to right.

EXAMPLE 3   Simplify an expression containing a fraction and a decimal

Simplify each expression.

a. $13\dfrac{1}{2} + 2.4 \cdot 1.4^2$

b. $9.6 - 25\dfrac{4}{5} \div \left(5\dfrac{9}{10} + 15.6\right)$

c. $\dfrac{142.4 + 20.1}{13} + \left(1\dfrac{1}{5}\right)^3$

SOLUTION STRATEGY

a. $13\dfrac{1}{2} + 2.4 \cdot 1.4^2$

$= 13.5 + 2.4 \cdot (1.4)^2$ Write the fraction as a decimal.

$= 13.5 + 2.4 \cdot 1.96$ Evaluate the exponential expression. $1.4^2 = 1.96$.

$= 13.5 + 4.704$ Multiply. $2.4 \cdot 1.96 = 4.704$.

$= 18.204$ Add. $13.5 + 4.704 = 18.204$

b. $9.6 - 25\dfrac{4}{5} \div \left(5\dfrac{9}{10} + 15.6\right)$

$9.6 - 25.8 \div (5.9 + 15.6)$ Write the fractions as decimals.

$= 9.6 - 25.8 \div 21.5$ Add the numbers in the parentheses. $5.9 + 15.6 = 21.5$.

$= 9.6 - 1.2$ Divide. $25.8 \div 21.5 = 1.2$.

$= 8.4$ Subtract. $9.6 - 1.2 = 8.4$.

c. $\dfrac{142.4 + 20.1}{13} + \left(1\dfrac{1}{5}\right)^3$

$\dfrac{142.4 + 20.1}{13} + (1.2)^3$ Write the fraction as a decimal.

$= \dfrac{162.5}{13} + (1.2)^3$ The fraction bar acts as a grouping symbol. Simplify the numerator. $142.4 + 20.1 = 162.5$.

$= \dfrac{162.5}{13} + 1.728$ Evaluate the exponential expression. $(1.2)^3 = 1.728$.

$= 12.5 + 1.728$ Divide. $162.5 \div 13 = 12.5$.

$= 14.228$ Add. $12.5 + 1.728 = 14.228$.

TRY-IT EXERCISE 3

Simplify each expression.

a. $4(10 - 2.5^2) \div \dfrac{1}{10}$

b. $5^3 + 5\left(4^2 - 2\dfrac{1}{2}\right)$

c. $\dfrac{3^2 - 4\dfrac{1}{10}}{10 - 2^3}$

Check your answers with the solutions in Appendix A. ■

Objective 3.5C   **Apply your knowledge**

EXAMPLE 4   **Solve an application problem containing fractions and decimals**

At Safeway market, a customer purchased $4\dfrac{1}{2}$ pounds of bananas at $1.29 per pound,

$3\dfrac{3}{8}$ pounds of peaches at $2.39 per pound, and $\dfrac{3}{4}$ pounds of cherries at $4.99 per pound.

a. What was the cost of each kind of fruit? Round answers to dollars and cents.

b. What was the total cost of the purchase?

SOLUTION STRATEGY

a. bananas:

$4\dfrac{1}{2} \cdot \$1.29 = 4.5 \cdot \$1.29$ Convert the fraction to a decimal.

$\qquad\qquad = \$5.805 \approx \$5.81$ Multiply and round.

peaches:

$3\dfrac{3}{8} \cdot \$2.39 = 3.375 \cdot \$2.39$ Convert the fraction to a decimal.

$\qquad\qquad = \$8.066 \approx \$8.07$ Multiply and round.

cherries:

$\dfrac{3}{4} \cdot \$4.99 = 0.75 \cdot \$4.99$ Convert the fraction to a decimal.

$\qquad\qquad = \$3.742 \approx \$3.74$ Multiply and round.

b. $\$5.81$
$\ 8.07$
$\underline{+\ 3.74}$ Add the amounts of the three individual purchases.
$\ \$17.62$

TRY-IT EXERCISE 4

You have decided to purchase new carpeting for your living room and bedroom. For the living room, you need $24\frac{1}{2}$ square yards of wool carpeting that costs $34.50 per square yard. For the bedroom, you need $18\frac{1}{4}$ square yards of nylon carpeting that costs $17.00 per square yard. In addition, padding will be required for the total yardage of both rooms at $3.60 per square yard, and installation costs an additional $2.40 per square yard.

a. What is the cost to carpet each room?

b. What is the total cost?

Check your answers with the solutions in Appendix A. ■

EXAMPLE 5   **Solve an application problem containing fractions and decimals**

Melanie purchased $13\frac{3}{4}$ pounds of potatoes. If she used 2.3 pounds to make potato salad, how many pounds did she have left? Express your answer in fraction notation.

SOLUTION STRATEGY

$$13\frac{3}{4} - 2.3 = 13\frac{3}{4} - 2\frac{3}{10} \qquad \text{Convert the decimal to a fraction.}$$

$$13\frac{3}{4} \quad\rightarrow\quad 13\frac{15}{20} \qquad \text{Subtract.}$$

$$\underline{-\;2\frac{3}{10}} \quad\rightarrow\quad \underline{-\;2\frac{6}{20}}$$

$$11\frac{9}{20}$$

She has $11\frac{9}{20}$ pounds of potatoes left.

TRY-IT EXERCISE 5

An electrician cut 6.4 feet of wire from a roll measuring $28\frac{1}{5}$ feet long. How many feet of wire were left on the roll? Express your answer in fraction notation.

Check your answer with the solution in Appendix A. ■

SECTION 3.5 REVIEW EXERCISES

Concept Check

1. To convert a fraction to a decimal, _____ the numerator by the denominator.

2. A decimal whose expansion ends is known as a _____ decimal. A decimal whose expansion continues indefinitely with one or more repeating digits is called a _____ decimal.

3. The repeating decimal 0.14141414 . . . is written as _____.

4. When an expression contains a mix of fractions and decimals, we can either convert all fractions to _____, or alternatively, we can convert all decimals to _____.

Objective 3.5A   **Convert a fraction to a decimal**

GUIDE PROBLEMS

5. Convert $\dfrac{5}{16}$ to a decimal.

$$16\overline{)5.0000}\qquad \dfrac{5}{16} = \text{\_\_\_\_\_}$$

6. Convert $\dfrac{7}{15}$ to a decimal.

$$15\overline{)7.000000}\qquad \dfrac{7}{15} = \text{\_\_\_}$$

Convert each fraction to a decimal.

7. $\dfrac{3}{20}$

8. $\dfrac{1}{4}$

9. $\dfrac{9}{16}$

10. $\dfrac{18}{25}$

11. $\dfrac{19}{50}$

12. $\dfrac{5}{4}$

13. $\dfrac{5}{11}$

14. $\dfrac{1}{3}$

15. $1\dfrac{3}{5}$

16. $12\dfrac{7}{8}$

17. $\dfrac{13}{20}$

18. $\dfrac{11}{16}$

19. $\dfrac{11}{6}$ **20.** $\dfrac{4}{15}$ **21.** $\dfrac{3}{16}$ **22.** $\dfrac{31}{40}$

23. $4\dfrac{7}{18}$ **24.** $2\dfrac{5}{12}$ **25.** $5\dfrac{1}{8}$ **26.** $1\dfrac{3}{32}$

Convert each fraction to a decimal. Round to the nearest tenth.

27. $\dfrac{5}{6}$ **28.** $\dfrac{11}{16}$ **29.** $10\dfrac{3}{8}$ **30.** $5\dfrac{19}{32}$

Convert each fraction to a decimal. Round to the nearest hundredth.

31. $\dfrac{4}{23}$ **32.** $\dfrac{11}{24}$ **33.** $\dfrac{39}{34}$ **34.** $\dfrac{19}{9}$

Objective 3.5B   **Simplify an expression containing fractions and decimals using order of operations**

GUIDE PROBLEMS

35. Calculate $6.27 + 5\dfrac{1}{10} \cdot 8.08$.

    a. Convert the fraction to a decimal.

    $6.27 + 5\dfrac{1}{10} \cdot 8.08 = 6.27 + 5.\underline{\ } \cdot 8.08$

    b. Simplify the expression.

    $6.27 + 5.\underline{\ } \cdot 8.08$

    $6.27 + \underline{\qquad}$

    $\underline{\qquad}$

36. Calculate $\left(2\dfrac{2}{5} + 19\right) \div 1\dfrac{13}{25}$. Round to the nearest tenth.

    a. Convert each fraction to a decimal.

    $\left(2\dfrac{2}{5} + 19\right) \div 1\dfrac{13}{25} = (2.\underline{\ } + 19) \div 1.\underline{\ }$

    b. Simplify the expression. Round to the nearest tenth.

    $(2.\underline{\ } + 19) \div 1.\underline{\ }$

    $\underline{\quad} \div 1.\underline{\ }$

    $\underline{\quad}$

Simplify each expression.

37. $76.3 - 4 \cdot 11$ **38.** $82.7 + 6 \cdot 2.3$ **39.** $10.3 + 4\dfrac{1}{5} \cdot 2\dfrac{1}{10}$

40. $10.7 - 4\dfrac{3}{10} + 3.2$ **41.** $\dfrac{1}{5} + \dfrac{0.25 + 2.77}{10}$ **42.** $\dfrac{2}{5} + \dfrac{3.5^2}{2}$

43. $12.4 - 2\left(3\dfrac{3}{5} + 1.2\right)$

44. $18.3 + 2\dfrac{4}{5}\left(3\dfrac{1}{10}\right)$

45. $4\left(\dfrac{6}{25} + 0.56\right) - 1\dfrac{1}{10} \cdot 2$

46. $2 \cdot 6.2 + 5.2 \div 2.6 - 4\dfrac{3}{4}$

47. $(5.2 \cdot 4.5) - 1\dfrac{1}{2} + 0.2$

48. $3\dfrac{1}{5} \cdot 4 - 5.3(6.8 \div 3.4)$

49. $2\dfrac{5}{8} + 3\dfrac{1}{2}(4.9 - 4.1)$

50. $2.03 + \left(5\dfrac{2}{5} + 7.8\right) + 5^2 - 3\dfrac{4}{5}$

51. $20.73 - 3\left(4\dfrac{1}{10} - 3\right)^2$

52. $3\left(2.5 + 3\dfrac{1}{2}\right) \div 1.5^2$

53. $4\dfrac{1}{2} + 0.08^2 + \dfrac{33.5 - 16}{\dfrac{1}{4}}$

54. $2\dfrac{1}{8} + \dfrac{\left(\dfrac{1}{2}\right)^2}{100} \div 0.1$

Objective 3.5C   Apply your knowledge

55. The Heartland Insurance Company pays half of the total bill for their participant's claims. If a claim amounts to $265.12, how much will the insurance company pay?

56. Jamestown Corp. pays one-third of the health insurance premiums for its employees. If Amanda's premiums amount to $2068.20, how much will the company pay?

The formula for the area of a triangle is $A = \dfrac{1}{2}bh$, where b is the base and h is the height.

Calculate the area for each triangle. Round to the nearest tenth.

57. Round to the nearest tenth.

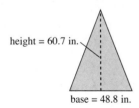

height = 60.7 in.

base = 48.8 in.

58. Round to the nearest hundredth.

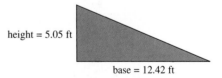

height = 5.05 ft

base = 12.42 ft

59. At Sobey's Market, Fran purchased $2\dfrac{2}{5}$ pounds of almonds at $5.89 per pound, $3\dfrac{7}{8}$ pounds of pears at $3.30 per pound, and $1\dfrac{1}{4}$ pounds of grapes at $2.17 per pound.

   a. What was the cost to purchase each fruit? Round to the nearest cent.

   b. What was the total cost of Fran's purchase?

60. At Home Hardware, Elliott purchased $3\dfrac{1}{2}$ pounds of finishing nails at $3.25 per pound, $8\dfrac{3}{8}$ feet of crown molding at $10.15 per foot, and $2\dfrac{1}{4}$ yards of rope at $2.17 per yard.

   a. What was the cost to purchase each item? Round to the nearest cent.

   b. What was the total cost of Elliott's purchase?

61. A plumber cut 22.8 feet of copper tubing from a roll measuring $68\frac{3}{5}$ feet long. How many feet of tubing were left on the roll? Express your answer in fraction notation.

62. An industrial saw cut 0.5 inches from a piece of aluminum $2\frac{1}{8}$ inches thick. How thick was the aluminum after the cut? Express your answer in decimal notation.

CUMULATIVE SKILLS REVIEW

1. Round 0.58560 to the nearest thousandth. (3.1E)

2. A doctor's order requires a patient to take 8.6 milligrams of a particular medication every 4 hours. How many milligrams of the medication will the patient take each day? (3.3C)

3. Multiply $\frac{3}{4} \cdot \frac{2}{15}$. (2.4A)

4. Write $\frac{5}{7}$ as an equivalent fraction with a denominator of 35. (2.3A)

5. Divide $3.426 \div 1.2$. (3.4B)

6. Simplify $40 \div 2^3 + 3(15 - 6)$. (1.6C)

7. Multiply $14 \cdot 22 \cdot 10{,}000$. (1.4B)

8. Add $2.758 + 1.29 + 3$. (3.2A)

9. Multiply $4 \cdot \frac{1}{3} \cdot 2\frac{5}{6}$. Simplify, if possible. (2.4B)

10. Find the prime factorization of 50. Express your answer in exponential notation. (2.1C)

10-MINUTE CHAPTER REVIEW

3.1 Understanding Decimals

Objective	Important Concepts	Illustrative Examples
A. Identify the place value of a digit in a decimal (page 208)	**decimal fraction** A number that can be written as a fraction whose denominator is a power of 10. **decimal number** or **decimal** A number written in decimal notation.	Identify the place value of the indicated digit. **a.** 2.1659 hundredths **b.** 23.681 tenths **c.** 235.08324 thousandths **d.** 0.835029 ten-thousandths
B. Write a decimal in word form and standard form (page 209)	**Steps for Writing a Decimal in Word Form** **Step 1.** Write the whole number part in words. **Step 2.** Write the word *and* in place of the decimal point. **Step 3.** Write the decimal part in words as though it were a whole number, without any commas, followed by the name of the place value of the last digit.	Write each decimal in word form. **a.** 55.234 fifty-five and two hundred thirty-four thousandths **b.** 184.45 one hundred eighty-four and forty-five hundredths **c.** 0.2456 two thousand four hundred fifty-six ten-thousandths Write each decimal in decimal notation. **a.** nine hundred five and three hundred thirty-six thousandths 905.336 **b.** sixteen and sixty-four hundredths 16.64 **c.** six hundred eighty-eight and five tenths 688.5
C. Convert a decimal to a fraction or mixed number (page 211)	**Rule for Converting a Decimal to a Fraction** To convert a decimal to a fraction, write the whole number formed by the digits to the right of the decimal point as the numerator, and write the power of 10 that has as many zeros as place values in the decimal as the denominator.	Convert each decimal to a fraction or a mixed number. Simplify, if possible. **a.** $0.8 = \dfrac{8}{10} = \dfrac{4}{5}$ **b.** $23.7 = 23\dfrac{7}{10}$ **c.** $7.835 = 7\dfrac{835}{1000} = 7\dfrac{167}{200}$

D. Compare decimals (page 213)	**Steps for Comparing Two Decimal Numbers** **Step 1.** Write the decimals one above another so that their decimal points are vertically aligned. **Step 2.** Compare the whole number parts. If one is greater than the other, then the entire number is greater. If they are equal, continue to the next step. **Step 3.** Compare the digits to the right of the decimal point in corresponding place values from left to right. 　**a.** If the digits are the same, move right one place to the next digit. If necessary, insert zeros after the last digit to the right of the decimal point to continue the comparison. 　**b.** If the digits are not the same, the larger digit corresponds to the larger number.	Insert the symbol $<$, $>$, or $=$ to form a true statement. **a.** 47.709 _____ 47.58 　47.709 $>$ 47.58 **b.** 433.5977 _____ 433.5986 　433.5977 $<$ 433.5986 **c.** 1.305875 _____ 1.312 　1.305875 $<$ 1.312 **d.** 4.2565 _____ 4.256500 　4.2565 $=$ 4.256500
E. Round a decimal to a specified place value (page 214)	**Steps for Rounding Decimals to a Specified Place Value** **Step 1.** Identify the place value after the decimal point to which the decimal is to be rounded. **Step 2.** If the digit to the right of the specified place value is 4 or less, the digit in the specified place value remains the same. If the digit to the right of the specified place value is 5 or more, increase the digit in the specified place value by one. Carry, if necessary. **Step 3.** Delete the digit in each place after the specified place value.	Round each decimal to the specified place value. **a.** 445.7708 to the nearest tenth 　445.8 **b.** 43.5644 to the nearest thousandth 　43.564 **c.** 516.195 to the nearest hundredth 　516.20
F. Apply your knowledge (page 216)	**a.** You are writing a check for $45.65. Write the word form for this amount. 　forty-five and $\frac{65}{100}$ dollars **b.** You are writing a check for one hundred seventeen dollars and twenty-nine cents. Write the decimal notation for this amount. 　$117.29 **c.** A digital memory card is 0.084 inches thick. Round this measurement to the nearest tenth. 　0.1 inches	

3.2 Adding and Subtracting Decimals

Objective	Important Concepts	Illustrative Examples
A. Add decimals (page 223)	**Steps for Adding Decimals** **Step 1.** Write the decimals so that the decimal points are vertically aligned. If necessary, insert extra zeros to the right of the last digit after the decimal point so that each addend has the same number of decimal places. **Step 2.** Add as with whole numbers. Carry, if necessary. **Step 3.** Place the decimal point in the sum so that it is vertically aligned with the decimal points of the addends.	Add. **a.** $30.8708 + 16.164$ $\begin{array}{r} 30.8708 \\ +\ 16.1640 \\ \hline 47.0348 \end{array}$ **b.** $24.378 + 310.389$ $\begin{array}{r} 24.378 \\ +\ 310.389 \\ \hline 334.767 \end{array}$
B. Subtract decimals (page 225)	**Steps for Subtracting Decimals** **Step 1.** Write the decimals so that the decimal points are vertically aligned. If necessary, insert extra zeros to the right of the decimal point where needed so that each addend has the same number of decimal places. **Step 2.** Subtract as with whole numbers. Borrow, if necessary. **Step 3.** Place the decimal point in the difference so that it is vertically aligned with the decimal points of the minuend and subtrahend.	Subtract. **a.** $611.824 - 433.59$ $\begin{array}{r} 611.824 \\ -\ 433.590 \\ \hline 178.234 \end{array}$ **b.** $19.958 - 4.773$ $\begin{array}{r} 19.958 \\ -\ 4.773 \\ \hline 15.185 \end{array}$
C. Estimate when adding or subtracting decimals (page 226)	**Steps for Estimating When Adding or Subtracting Decimals** **Step 1.** Round each decimal factor to the specified place. **Step 2.** Add or subtract.	Estimate $51.31 + 0.853$ by rounding each addend to the nearest whole number. $\begin{array}{rcr} 51.31 & \rightarrow & 51 \\ +\ 0.853 & \rightarrow & +1 \\ \hline & & 52 \end{array}$ Estimate $95.6 - 37.8$ by rounding the minuend and subtrahend to the nearest whole number. $\begin{array}{rcr} 95.6 & \rightarrow & 96 \\ +\ 37.8 & \rightarrow & -\ 38 \\ \hline & & 58 \end{array}$
D. Apply your knowledge (page 227)	On July 3, your beginning checkbook balance was $2905.22. On July 7, you wrote check #055 for $222.21 to City Furniture. On July 12, you made a deposit of $320.65. On July 15, you wrote check #056 for $436.50 to Sports Depot. Complete the check register for these transactions to find the new balance in your checking account.	

Number or Code	Date	Transaction Description	Payment, Fee, Withdrawal (−)		✓	Deposit, Credit (+)		$ Balance	
	7/3							2905	22
055	7/7	City Furniture	222	21				2683	01
	7/12	deposit				320	65	3003	66
056	7/15	Sports Depot	436	50				2567	16

3.3 Multiplying Decimals

Objective	Important Concepts	Illustrative Examples
A. Multiply decimals (page 234)	**Steps for Multiplying Decimals** **Step 1.** Multiply without regard to the decimal points. That is, multiply the factors as though they are whole numbers. **Step 2.** Determine the total number of decimal places in each factor. **Step 3.** Place the decimal point in the product so that the number of places to the right of the decimal point is equal to the total determined in step 2. If necessary, insert zeros as placeholders to get the correct number of decimal places.	Multiply. **a.** $(6.21)(4.5)$ $\begin{array}{r} 6.21 \\ \times\ 4.5 \\ \hline 3105 \\ 2484 \\ \hline 27.945 \end{array}$ **b.** $(63.4)(95.8)$ $\begin{array}{r} 63.4 \\ \times\ 95.8 \\ \hline 5072 \\ 3170 \\ 5706 \\ \hline 6073.72 \end{array}$
B. Multiply a decimal by a power of 10 (page 235)	**Multiplying a Decimal by a Power of 10 such as 10, 100, 1000 . . .** Move the decimal point to the *right* the same number of places as there are zeros in the power of 10. **Multiplying a Decimal by a Power of 10 such as 0.1, 0.01, 0.001 . . .** Move the decimal point to the *left* the same number of places as there are place values in the decimal power of 10.	Multiply. **a.** $(82.2)(100) = 8220$ **b.** $(6558.4)(0.001) = 6.5584$ Write each number in standard notation. **a.** 28.6 million $28.6 \times 1{,}000{,}000 = 28{,}600{,}000$ **b.** 1.24 billion $1.24 \times 1{,}000{,}000{,}000 = 1{,}240{,}000{,}000$
C. Estimate when multiplying decimals (page 238)	We can estimate when multiplying decimals to see whether an answer is reasonable.	Estimate $(5.9)(0.94)$ by rounding each factor to one nonzero digit. $\begin{array}{ccc} 5.9 & \rightarrow & 6 \\ \times\ 0.94 & \rightarrow & \times\ 0.9 \\ \hline & & 5.4 \end{array}$
D. Apply your knowledge (page 238)	Ken's senior class had several fund-raisers this year. For the senior class dance, 154 people attended and paid $53.75 per ticket. The pep rally had 113 participants, each paying $5.25. For the car wash party, 137 students each paid $10.50. **a.** What was the total amount that Ken's senior class raised this year? $154 \cdot \$53.75 = \$8277.50$ $113 \cdot \$5.25 = \$593.25$ $137 \cdot \$10.50 = \$1438.50$ Total raised: $10,309.25 **b.** What was the total amount raised by all the schools in the district, if that total is 10 times the amount that Ken's school raised? $\$10{,}309.25 \cdot 10 = \$103{,}092.50$	

3.4 Dividing Decimals

Objective	Important Concepts	Illustrative Examples
A. Divide a decimal by a whole number (page 246)	**Steps for Dividing a Decimal by a Whole Number** **Step 1.** Write the problem in long division form. **Step 2.** Divide as if working with whole numbers. Place the decimal point in the quotient directly above the decimal point in the dividend. **Step 3.** If necessary, write additional zeros to the right of the last digit following the decimal point in the dividend to allow the division to continue.	Divide. **a.** $425.5 \div 5$ $\begin{array}{r} 85.1 \\ 5\overline{)425.5} \\ -40 \\ \hline 25 \\ -25 \\ \hline 05 \\ -5 \\ \hline 0 \end{array}$ **b.** $85.8 \div 8$ $\begin{array}{r} 10.725 \\ 8\overline{)85.800} \\ -8 \\ \hline 58 \\ -56 \\ \hline 20 \\ -16 \\ \hline 40 \\ -40 \\ \hline 0 \end{array}$
B. Divide a decimal by a power of 10 (page 248)	**Dividing a Decimal by a Power of 10 such as 10, 100, 1000 . . .** Move the decimal point in the dividend to the *left* the same number of places as there are zeros in the power of 10. Insert zeros, as necessary. **Dividing a Decimal by a Power of 10 such as 0.1, 0.01, 0.001 . . .** Move the decimal point in the dividend to the *right* the same number of places as there are place values in the decimal power of 10. Insert zeros, as necessary.	Divide. **a.** $83.8 \div 1000 = 0.0838$ **b.** $1.471 \div 0.01 = 147.1$
C. Divide a decimal or a whole number by a decimal (page 249)	**Steps for Dividing a Decimal or Whole Number by a Decimal** **Step 1.** Write the problem in long division format. **Step 2.** Write an equivalent division problem with a whole number divisor. In particular, move the decimal point in the divisor to the right as many places as necessary until the divisor is a whole number. Also, move the decimal point in the dividend the same number of places to the right. **Step 3.** Divide. Place the decimal point in the quotient directly above the moved decimal point in the dividend.	Divide. **a.** $49.02 \div 11.4$ $\begin{array}{r} 4.3 \\ 114\overline{)490.2} \\ -456 \\ \hline 342 \\ -342 \\ \hline 0 \end{array}$ **b.** $143.1 \div 1.92$ Round to the nearest tenth. $\begin{array}{r} 74.53 \quad \approx 74.5 \\ 192\overline{)14310.00} \\ -1344 \\ \hline 870 \\ -768 \\ \hline 1020 \\ -960 \\ \hline 600 \\ -576 \\ \hline 24 \end{array}$

D. Estimate when dividing decimals (page 251)	We can estimate when dividing decimals to see whether an answer is reasonable.	Estimate $21.3 \div 0.49$ by rounding the dividend and divisor to one nonzero digit. $\begin{array}{ccc} 21.3 & \div & 0.49 \\ \downarrow & & \downarrow \\ 20 & \div & 0.5 \end{array}$ $0.5\overline{)20} \;\rightarrow\; 5\overline{)200}^{\;40}$
E. Apply your knowledge (page 252)	**Steps for Calculating an Average** **Step 1.** Find the sum of all the values in a data set. **Step 2.** Divide the sum in step 1 by the number of values in the set. $\text{Average} = \dfrac{\text{Sum of values}}{\text{Number of values}}$	Todd just started a new job in Paris, France. He worked 7 hours on Monday, 8.5 hours on Tuesday, 6.5 hours on Wednesday, 8 hours on Thursday, and 5.5 hours on Friday. What is the average number of hours Todd worked per day? $\dfrac{7 + 8.5 + 6.5 + 8 + 5.5}{5} = \dfrac{35.5}{5} = 7.1 \text{ hours}$

3.5 Working with Decimals and Fractions

Objective	Important Concepts	Illustrative Examples
A. Convert a fraction to a decimal (page 258)	**terminating decimal** A decimal whose expansion ends. **repeating decimal** A decimal that continues indefinitely with one or more repeating digits. **Rule for Converting a Fraction to a Decimal** Divide the numerator by the denominator. If necessary, insert zeros after the decimal point to allow the division to continue. Also, if necessary, insert zeros as placeholders in the quotient to get the correct number of decimal places.	**Convert each fraction to a decimal.** **a.** $\dfrac{27}{40} = 0.675$ **b.** $\dfrac{5}{16} = 0.3125$ **c.** $\dfrac{4}{11} = 0.3636\ldots$ or $0.\overline{36}$
B. Simplify an expression containing fractions and decimals using order of operations (page 261)	**Order of Operations** **Step 1.** Perform all operations within grouping symbols: parentheses ( ), brackets [ ], and curly braces { }. When grouping symbols occur within grouping symbols, begin with the innermost grouping symbols. **Step 2.** Evaluate all exponential expressions. **Step 3.** Perform all multiplications and divisions as they appear in reading from left to right. **Step 4.** Perform all additions and subtractions as they appear in reading from left to right.	**Simplify each expression.** **a.** $23\frac{3}{4} - 3\frac{1}{2} + 2.2^2 \cdot 10$ $23.75 - 3.5 + 2.2^2 \cdot 10$ $23.75 - 3.5 + 4.84 \cdot 10$ $23.75 - 3.5 + 48.4$ $20.25 + 48.4$ 68.65

b. $\dfrac{96.5 + 100.7}{5} + \left(5\dfrac{1}{5}\right)^2$

$\dfrac{96.5 + 100.7}{5} + 5.2^2$

$\dfrac{197.2}{5} + 5.2^2$

$39.44 + 5.2^2$

$39.44 + 27.04$

66.48

---

c. Apply your knowledge (page 264)

Larry purchased $1\dfrac{3}{4}$ pounds of raisins at \$5.25 per pound and $\dfrac{1}{2}$ pound of peanuts at \$7.35 per pound. How much did Larry spend?

$1\dfrac{3}{4} \cdot 5.25 = 1.75 \cdot 5.25 = 9.1875 = \$9.19$

$\dfrac{1}{2} \cdot 7.35 = 0.5 \cdot 7.35 = 3.675 = \$3.68$

$\$9.19 + \$3.68 = \$12.87$

Larry spent \$12.87 in total.

Numerical Facts of Life

You are a sports reporter for your college newspaper. For an upcoming story about the disparity of major league baseball salaries, your editor has asked you to compile some average payroll statistics for the 2006 season.

**HIGHEST AND LOWEST MAJOR LEAGUE BASEBALL TEAM PAYROLLS:
2006 REGULAR SEASON**

	TEAM	2006 PAYROLL	2006 PAYROLL ROUNDED TO MILLIONS	2006 AVERAGE PAYROLL PER GAME 162-GAME SEASON	2006 AVERAGE SALARY PER PLAYER 30-PLAYER ROSTER
HIGHEST	New York Yankees	$194,663,079			
	Boston Red Sox	$120,099,824			
	Los Angeles Angels	$103,472,000			
LOWEST	Colorado Rockies	$41,233,000			
	Tampa Bay Devil Rays	$35,417,967			
	Florida Marlins	$14,998,500			

1. Calculate the figures for the column "2006 Payroll Rounded to Millions."

2. Using your "rounded to millions" figures, calculate the figures for the column "2006 Average Payroll per Game." There are 162 regular-season games in major league baseball. Round each average payroll per game to dollars and cents.

3. Using your "rounded to millions" figures, calculate the figures for the column "2006 Average Salary per Player." There are 30 players on a major league baseball roster. Round each average salary per player to the nearest dollar.

CHAPTER REVIEW EXERCISES

Identify the place value of the indicated digit. (3.1A)

1. 13.3512

2. 0.1457919

3. 314.09245

4. 89.25901

5. 0.350218

6. 1476.00215962

Write each decimal in word form. (3.1B)

7. 28.355

8. 0.00211

9. 0.158

10. 142.12

11. 59.625

12. 0.39

Write each number in decimal notation. (3.1B)

13. two hundred ninety-eight ten-thousandths

14. twenty-two and three hundred twenty-four thousandths

15. one hundred seventy-eight and thirteen hundredths

16. seven hundred thirty-five ten-thousandths

17. nine hundred twelve and twenty-five hundredths

18. sixteen hundred-thousandths

Convert each decimal to a fraction or a mixed number. Simplify, if possible. (3.1C)

19. 9.57

20. 0.315

21. 5.006

22. 1.19

Insert the symbol <, >, or = to form a true statement. (3.1D)

23. 23.512 _____ 23.519

24. 0.8124 _____ 0.8133

25. 3.45887 _____ 3.45877

26. 125.6127 _____ 124.78

27. 0.02324 _____ 0.02324

28. 55.398 _____ 55.389

Round each decimal to the specified place value. (3.1E)

29. 1.853 to the nearest hundredth

30. 2.1487 to the nearest thousandth

31. 3.396 to the nearest tenth

32. 4.11458 to the nearest ten-thousandth

33. 1.588556 to the nearest hundred-thousandth

34. 7.4512 to the nearest thousandth

Add. (3.2A)

35.
$$\begin{array}{r} 2.135 \\ + \ 3.447 \\ \hline \end{array}$$

36.
$$\begin{array}{r} 6.098 \\ + \ 1.211 \\ \hline \end{array}$$

37.
$$\begin{array}{r} 5.5173 \\ 0.0991 \\ + \ 6.0070 \\ \hline \end{array}$$

38.
$$\begin{array}{r} 1.234 \\ 0.022 \\ + \ 8.455 \\ \hline \end{array}$$

39. 15.445 + 0.3369

40. 12.645 + 0.856

41. 0.089 + 9.652

42. 6.244 + 0.048

43. 22.123 + 9.003 + 0.45

44. 0.033 + 11.92 + 18.2

Subtract. (3.2B)

45.
$$\begin{array}{r} 24.655 \\ - \ 2.362 \\ \hline \end{array}$$

46.
$$\begin{array}{r} 18.329 \\ - \ 6.154 \\ \hline \end{array}$$

47. 12.127
  − 6.015

48. 10.527
  − 8.519

49. 0.0741 − 0.00562

50. 11.155 − 0.0877

51. 0.0864 − 0.0596

52. 6.345 − 2.0089

53. 15.629 − 0.609

54. 0.988 − 0.036

Multiply. (3.3A, B)

55. 5.025
  × 1.25

56. 3.972
  × 0.035

57. 9.041
  × 1.44

58. 7.221
  × 0.009

59. (0.0945)(100)

60. (11.33)(10)

61. (8.1)(1.46)

62. (1.75)(15.66)

63. (0.92)(19.02)

64. (0.005)(21.14)

Write each number in standard notation. (3.3B)

65. 145.9 million

66. 1.25 trillion

67. 455.2 billion

68. $16.78 million

Divide. (3.4A, B)

69. $100\overline{)8.9}$

70. $13\overline{)18.317}$

71. $\dfrac{35.8}{20}$

72. $\dfrac{15.95}{10}$

73. 99.3 ÷ 12

74. 545.28 ÷ 15

Divide. Round to the nearest tenth if necessary. (3.4C)

75. $0.1\overline{)49.88}$

76. $2.6\overline{)32.76}$

77. $\dfrac{21.8}{4.5}$

78. $\dfrac{92.6}{2.3}$

79. $5 \div 0.82$

80. $55 \div 1.6$

Convert each fraction to decimal. (3.5A)

81. $\dfrac{12}{60}$

82. $\dfrac{1}{25}$

83. $\dfrac{11}{12}$

84. $3\dfrac{7}{11}$

Convert each fraction to a decimal. Round to the nearest hundredth if necessary. (3.5A)

85. $\dfrac{6}{7}$

86. $4\dfrac{3}{16}$

Simplify each expression. (3.5B)

87. $25 + (130.99 - 5.3^2)$

88. $1000 \div 125 + 9.2^2$

89. $\dfrac{1.5^3}{5}(96.6 \div 12) \cdot 10^2$

90. $85.3 - 4^3 - \left(1\dfrac{1}{5} \cdot 5\right)$

91. $\dfrac{(45.3 \div 9.06)^2}{10} + 12.1$

92. $30 \div 0.1 \cdot \dfrac{2.6 + 7^2}{10}$

Solve each application problem.

93. Marsha is practicing the long jump for the upcoming Olympic trials. On her first try, she jumps 12.65 feet. On the second try, she jumps 12.18 feet. On her last try, she jumps 12.27 feet. List these distances in ascending order for Marsha's training log.

94. Kelowna Wines is shipping grapes to their winery. They have four cases weighing 126.32 pounds, 155.65 pounds, 114.18 pounds, and 189.44 pounds, respectively. If the cases must be stacked from heaviest to lightest, in what order will they be stacked?

95. Mike and Morley are hiking on Mount Rundle. On Monday they climbed 1265.38 feet and on Tuesday they climbed 1389.12 feet. How many total feet did they climb?

96. Century Cable, Inc. has decided to add a monthly maintenance fee of $5.75. If the cable bill was $46.95 before the extra fee, what is the total of the new bill?

97. Trish received a paycheck in the amount of $4789.25 last month. She paid $1975.12 for rent, $322.45 for food, and $655.24 for her car payment. How much money does Trish have left after she pays these bills?

98. Tree Cutters, Inc. cut two trees yesterday. The first was 145.54 feet tall and the second was 103.92 feet tall. How much taller was the first tree than the second?

99. Cascade Inc. bought 12 reams of fax paper at $5.81 each. What was the total cost of the paper?

100. Greg earns $825.45 dollars per week. How much does he earn in one year?

101. The asteroid 1566 Icarus is 161.27 million kilometers from the sun. Write this distance in standard notation.

102. The asteroid 911 Agamemnon is 778.1 million kilometers from the sun. Write this distance in standard notation.

103. The latest hybrid car model gets 55 miles per gallon of gasoline. How many miles will the car travel on 14.5 gallons of gasoline?

104. Kool-Beanz Gift Shop pays $134.40 for a dozen embroidered caps. If they intend to make $8.75 profit on each cap, what should be the selling price per cap?

105. You are the manager at Twigs Flower Shop. One of your tasks each day is to count the cash for a bank deposit. When you count the cash, you have 54 ones, 18 fives, 11 tens, 27 twenties, and 2 fifties. In addition, there are 28 pennies, 24 nickels, 16 dimes, and 13 quarters.

   a. How much do you have in currency?

   b. How much do you have in coins?

   c. What is the total amount of the deposit?

   d. Write the total deposit in words.

106. You are a teller at the Second National Bank. A customer has come to your window to make a deposit. When you count the cash, there are 26 ones, 15 fives, 19 tens, 32 twenties, and 4 fifties. In addition, there are 16 pennies, 42 nickels, 36 dimes, and 28 quarters.

   a. How much currency is in the deposit?

   b. How much in coins is in the deposit?

   c. What is the total amount of the deposit?

   d. Write the total deposit in words.

107. On July 1, your beginning checkbook balance was $1694.20. On July 12, you wrote check #228 for $183.40 to Wal-Mart. On July 16, you made a deposit of $325.50. On July 24, you made an ATM withdrawal for $200.00. Complete the check register for these transactions to find the new balance in your checking account.

Number or Code	Date	Transaction Description	Payment, Fee, Withdrawal (−)	✓	Deposit, Credit (+)	$ Balance

108. On March 1, your beginning checkbook balance was $2336.40. On March 11, you made a deposit of $1550.35. On March 19, you wrote check #357 for $253.70 to Visa. On March 23, you wrote check #358 for $45.10 to FedEx. Complete the check register for these transactions to find the new balance in your checking account.

Number or Code	Date	Transaction Description	Payment, Fee, Withdrawal (−)	✓	Deposit, Credit (+)	$ Balance

109. Barons Men's Shop is having a sale. If you buy three shirts, the sale price is $56.75 each.

   a. How much will you spend to buy the three shirts at the sale price?

   b. If the regular price of the shirts is $75.00 each, what is your total savings by purchasing the three shirts on sale?

110. Vickie is considering a new job offer. She currently earns $56,000 per year. Her new job would pay $60,000 per year.

   a. How much more will her new job offer pay per week? Round to the nearest cent.

   b. Vickie needs $2307.60 for the down payment on her new car. How many weeks will she have to save her extra income in order to have the down payment?

111. The temperature in Granville has dropped substantially in the last few days. On Monday, the temperature was 52.6°F, Tuesday it dropped to 42.8°F, and on Wednesday it was 40.9°F. What was the average temperature in Granville over the three-day period? Round to the nearest tenth.

112. Ellen earned the following GPAs for each year of high school: 3.56, 3.48, 3.72, and 3.88. What was Ellen's average GPA in high school?

113. Clarissa and George order a large pizza for $18.80. The tax is $1.14, and they tip the delivery boy $3.50. They decide to split the cost according to the amount they eat.

    a. If George eats three-fourths of the pizza, how much is his share of the cost?

    b. How much is Clarissa's share of the cost?

114. A charity fund-raiser netted $158,700 selling raffle tickets last month. The charity received $\frac{7}{8}$ of the money raised and the balance was for administrative expenses and printing costs.

    a. How much did the charity receive?

    b. How much went to administrative expenses and printing costs?

115. Hi-Way Champions Delivery Service has received packages weighing 6.7 pounds, 3.9 pounds, and $4\frac{1}{2}$ pounds. What is the total weight of the three packages? Express your answer in fraction notation.

116. A carpenter purchased 2.1 pounds of roofing nails, $1\frac{4}{5}$ pounds of finishing nails, and $3\frac{3}{4}$ pounds of drywall screws. What is the total weight of the purchase? Express your answer in fraction notation.

117. Toby wants to save a total of $567.68 in one year for a new guitar amplifier. Round this number to two nonzero digits to estimate how much he will have to save each month to reach his goal.

118. Century City's new recycling policy states that each household recycles an average of 653.6 pounds of glass and aluminum per year. Estimate how many pounds each household should recycle per week by rounding this number to two nonzero digits.

ASSESSMENT TEST

Identify the place value of the indicated digit.

    1. 23.0719

    2. 0.360914

Write each decimal in word form.

    3. 42.949

    4. 0.0365

Write each decimal in decimal notation.

    5. twenty one hundred-thousandths

    6. sixty-one and two hundred eleven thousandths

Convert each decimal to a fraction or a mixed number. Simplify, if possible.

    7. 8.85

    8. 0.125

Insert the symbol $<$, $>$, or $=$ to form a true statement.

9. 0.6643 _____ 0.66349

10. 12.118 _____ 12.181

11. 2.14530 _____ 2.145300

Round each number to the specified place value.

12. 1.597 to the nearest tenth

13. 4.11089 to the nearest hundredth

Add.

14.
$$
\begin{array}{r}
3.490 \\
0.006 \\
+ \ 5.800 \\
\hline
\end{array}
$$

15. $13.44 + 10.937 + 0.1009$

Subtract.

16.
$$
\begin{array}{r}
34.029 \\
- \ 6.512 \\
\hline
\end{array}
$$

17. $0.0938 - 0.0045$

Multiply.

18.
$$
\begin{array}{r}
7.228 \\
\times \ 1.3 \\
\hline
\end{array}
$$

19. $(0.008)(15.42)$

Write each number in standard notation.

20. 218.6 million

21. 3.37 billion

22. Divide. $\dfrac{92.8}{1000}$

23. Divide. $1.6\overline{)40.96}$

Simplify each expression.

24. $\dfrac{4.2^2}{8} \cdot (12.5 - 3.6) - 10.6045$

25. $36.3 \div 6.6 + (3.34 - 2.64)^3$

Solve each application problem.

26. Emerson earns $14.00 per hour working in a hospital.

    a. If she worked 19.25 hours last week, how much did she make?

    b. If $20.62 was deducted for social security and Medicare, and $64.20 for income taxes, how much was her take-home pay?

27. Sam buys 3 music CDs at $12.69 each and 2 movies on DVD at $16.50 each. Sales tax amounts to $3.70.

    a. What is the total amount of the purchase?

    b. If he pays with 4 twenty dollar bills, how much change will he receive?

28. On a recent trip you drove $465\frac{6}{10}$ miles on 23.1 gallons of gas. Rounded to the nearest tenth, what was your average miles per gallon?

29. The temperature in Yellowstone Ridge has dropped substantially in the last few days. On Wednesday, the temperature was 62.3°F, Thursday it dropped to 39.6°F, and on Friday it was 43.4°F. What was the average temperature over the three-day period? Round to the nearest tenth.

Use the advertisement for Power Play Advance for exercises 30–32.

30. What is the total cost to purchase the Power Play Advance, the carrying case, and two games?

31. Round each price to the nearest dollar to estimate the cost of purchasing the Slim Magnifier and four games.

32. What would the amount of the monthly payment be if you purchased the Power Play Advance and three games, and paid for the purchase over a one-year period with "interest-free" equal monthly payments?

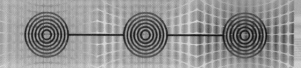
Ratio and Proportion

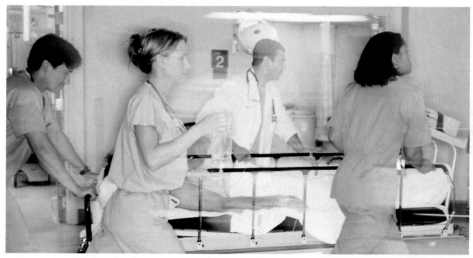

Nursing

As the health care needs of baby boomers swell and as the current nursing population continues to age, the demand for skilled nurses is greater than ever. According to the Bureau of Labor Statistics, employment opportunities for registered nurses are expected to grow by more than 27% through 2014.[1] In May 2004, the median annual income of a registered nurse was $52,330. With the continued demand for skilled nursing care, one can expect the salaries of qualified nurses to increase as well.

While nurses are often thought of as assistants to doctors who merely follow orders, they are medical professionals in their own right with great responsibility. Not only do nurses treat patients and provide advice and emotional support to both patients and family members, they also perform diagnostic tests, analyze results, and administer medications.[2] Nurses generally specialize in a particular field such as pediatrics or cardiology.

In performing tasks such as administering medications, nurses must understand ratio and proportion. If a patient requires 400mg of a medication that comes in 150mg tablets, a nurse must be able to determine the correct number of tablets to administer. If he or she cannot perform this basic calculation, the consequences can be life-threatening. In this chapter, we will see how ratio and proportion are essential to such a calculation.

[1,2] from *U.S. Bureau of Labor Statistics Occupational Outlook Handbook.*

4.1   UNDERSTANDING RATIOS

LEARNING OBJECTIVES

A. Write and simplify a ratio

B. Write a ratio of converted measurement units

C. Apply your knowledge

ratio
A comparison of two quantities by division.

terms of the ratio
The quantities being compared.

It is often said, "You can't compare apples and oranges." Well, with certain ratios, you can!

A **ratio** is a comparison of two quantities by division. Thus, given two numbers a and b, the ratio of a to b can be written as $\frac{a}{b}$. The quantities being compared are known as the **terms of the ratio**. If you had 3 apples and 2 oranges, then the ratio of apples to oranges is $\frac{3}{2}$. If there are 12 females and 13 males in a biology class, then the ratio of females to males is $\frac{12}{13}$.

In this section, we will learn various ways to write ratios, how to simplify them, and how to use ratios to express quantity relationships. Later in the chapter, we will use two ratios in a statement called a proportion to solve some interesting application problems.

Objective 4.1A	**Write and simplify a ratio**

While the ratio of a to b is generally written in fraction notation as $\frac{a}{b}$, we can also denote this ratio as $a{:}b$ or by a to b. Thus, a ratio may be written as a fraction, as two numbers separated by a colon, or as two numbers separated by the word *to*. The ratio of three apples to two oranges, for instance, can be written in any of the following ways.

$$\frac{3}{2} \qquad 3{:}2 \qquad 3 \; to \; 2$$

Our ratio of 12 females to 13 males in a biology class can be written in one of three formats.

$$\frac{12}{13} \qquad 12{:}13 \qquad 12 \; to \; 13$$

In a ratio, the order of the terms is important. The number mentioned first is the numerator of the fraction, the number before the colon, or the number before the word *to*. The number mentioned second is the denominator of the fraction, the number after the colon, or the number after the word *to*.

A ratio may express the relationship of a part to a whole, or it may express the relationship of a part to another part. In our example of 12 females and 13 males in the biology class, our ratio of females to males, 12 to 13, expresses a part to a part ratio. However, because females and males are both parts of the whole class of

25 students (12 females + 13 males = 25 total students), we can also write two ratios expressing the relationship of a part to a whole.

Females → "the ratio of 12 to 25" $\dfrac{12}{25}$ 12:25   12 to 25

Males → "the ratio of 13 to 25" $\dfrac{13}{25}$ 13:25   13 to 25

EXAMPLE 1   Write a ratio in various forms

Write each ratio in three different ways.

a. the ratio of 7 to 11

b. the ratio of 12 to 5

SOLUTION STRATEGY

a. the ratio of 7 to 11

$\dfrac{7}{11}$ 7:11   7 to 11

b. the ratio of 12 to 5

$\dfrac{12}{5}$ 12:5   12 to 5

A ratio can be written
- in fraction notation.
- as two numbers separated by a colon.
- as two numbers separated by the word *to*.

TRY-IT EXERCISE 1

Write each ratio in three different ways.

a. the ratio of 4 to 9   **b.** the ratio of 14 to 5

Check your answers with the solutions in Appendix A. ∎

A ratio can be simplified or reduced to lowest terms. This often allows us to see the comparison more clearly. The procedure for simplifying a ratio is the same as that used for simplifying a fraction. We simply divide out common factors between the first term and the second term.

Let's say, for example, that a new assembly line process makes 88 widgets per hour, whereas the old process made 22 widgets per hour. The ratio of the new process to the old process is 88 to 22. We express this ratio as follows.

$$\frac{88}{22}$$

By simplifying the fraction (dividing out the common factor of 22) we see that the ratio reduces to 4 to 1.

$$\frac{88}{22} = \frac{\overset{4}{88}}{\underset{1}{22}} = \frac{4}{1}$$

From this, we could say that the new process makes 4 widgets for every 1 widget of the old process. Another way to express this information is that the new process is 4 times as fast as the old process.

Steps for Simplifying a Ratio

Step 1. Write the ratio in fraction notation.

Step 2. Simplify, if possible.

EXAMPLE 2 **Simplify ratios**

Simplify each ratio.

a. 6 to 18

b. 14 to 35

c. 30 to 21

SOLUTION STRATEGY

a. 6 to 18

$$\frac{6}{18} = \frac{\overset{1}{\cancel{6}}}{\underset{3}{\cancel{18}}} = \frac{1}{3}$$

Write the ratio in fraction notation.
Simplify by dividing out the common factor, 6.

b. 14 to 35

$$\frac{14}{35} = \frac{\overset{2}{\cancel{14}}}{\underset{5}{\cancel{35}}} = \frac{2}{5}$$

Write the ratio in fraction notation.
Simplify by dividing out the common factor, 7.

c. 30 to 21

$$\frac{30}{21} = \frac{\overset{10}{\cancel{30}}}{\underset{7}{\cancel{21}}} = \frac{10}{7}$$

Write the ratio in fraction notation.
Simplify by dividing out the common factor, 3.

TRY-IT EXERCISE 2

Simplify each ratio.

a. 25 to 40

b. 33 to 72

c. 38 to 4

Check your answers with the solutions in Appendix A. ■

SIMPLIFY A RATIO THAT CONTAINS DECIMALS

For a ratio that contains decimals, write the ratio in fraction notation and then rewrite as a ratio of whole numbers. This is done by multiplying the ratio by 1 in the form $\frac{n}{n}$, where n is a power of 10 large enough to remove any decimals in both the numerator and the denominator. Simplify the ratio, if possible.

For example, the ratio of 2.8 to 5.6 would simplify to 1 to 2.

$$2.8 \text{ to } 5.6 = \frac{2.8}{5.6} = \frac{2.8}{5.6} \cdot \frac{10}{10} = \frac{\overset{1}{28}}{\underset{2}{56}} = \frac{1}{2}$$

Learning Tip

When the decimal is in the tenths place, use $n = 10$; when the decimal is in the hundredths place, use $n = 100$; when the decimal is in the thousandths place, use $n = 1000$; and so on.

Steps for Simplifying a Ratio That Contains Decimals

Step 1. Write the ratio in fraction notation.

Step 2. Rewrite as a ratio of whole numbers. Multiply the ratio by 1 in the form $\frac{n}{n}$, where n is a power of 10 large enough to remove any decimals in both the numerator and the denominator.

Step 3. Simplify, if possible.

EXAMPLE 3   **Simplify a ratio that contains decimals**

Simplify the ratio 2.75 to 0.5.

SOLUTION STRATEGY

2.75 to 0.5

$$\frac{2.75}{0.5}$$ Write the ratio in fraction notation.

$$= \frac{2.75}{0.5} \cdot \frac{100}{100} = \frac{275}{50}$$ Multiply by 1 in the form $\frac{100}{100}$ to remove the decimals.

$$= \frac{\overset{11}{275}}{\underset{2}{50}} = \frac{11}{2}$$ Simplify by dividing out the common factor, 25.

TRY-IT EXERCISE 3

Simplify the ratio 18.5 to 5.5.

Check your answer with the solution in Appendix A. ∎

SIMPLIFY A RATIO THAT CONTAINS FRACTIONS OR MIXED NUMBERS

For a ratio that contains fractions or mixed numbers, convert the mixed numbers to improper fractions and then divide as we did in Section 2.5, Dividing Fractions. Simplify, if possible.

> ● *Learning Tip*
>
> Recall, the procedure for dividing fractions is to invert the divisor and then multiply.

For example, the ratio of 3 feet to $4\frac{1}{2}$ feet would simplify as follows.

$$\frac{3}{4\frac{1}{2}} = \frac{3}{\frac{9}{2}} = \frac{3}{1} \div \frac{9}{2} = \frac{\overset{1}{3}}{1} \cdot \frac{2}{\underset{3}{9}} = \frac{2}{3}$$

Steps for Simplifying a Ratio That Contains Fractions or Mixed Numbers

Step 1. Write the ratio in fraction notation.

Step 2. Convert any mixed numbers to improper fractions.

Step 3. Divide the fractions by multiplying the numerator by the reciprocal of the denominator.

Step 4. Simplify, if possible.

EXAMPLE 4   **Simplify a ratio that contains fractions or mixed numbers**

Simplify the ratio $1\frac{1}{4}$ to $\frac{7}{8}$.

SOLUTION STRATEGY

$1\frac{1}{4}$ to $\frac{7}{8}$

$$\frac{1\frac{1}{4}}{\frac{7}{8}} = \frac{\frac{5}{4}}{\frac{7}{8}} = \frac{5}{4} \div \frac{7}{8}$$

Write the ratio in fraction notation.

Convert the mixed number, $1\frac{1}{4}$, to an improper fraction, $\frac{5}{4}$.

$$= \frac{5}{\underset{1}{4}} \cdot \frac{\overset{2}{8}}{7} = \frac{10}{7}$$

Multiply $\frac{5}{4}$ by $\frac{8}{7}$, the reciprocal of the denominator.

TRY-IT EXERCISE 4

Simplify the ratio $3\frac{1}{8}$ to $2\frac{1}{2}$.

Check your answer with the solution in Appendix A. ■

Objective 4.1B   **Write a ratio of converted measurement units**

Let's say that a speed limit sign is 36 inches high and 24 inches wide. We can write the simplified ratio of the height to the width.

$$\frac{\textbf{height}}{\textbf{width}} = \frac{36}{24} = \frac{3}{2}$$

24 in.

SPEED
LIMIT
45

36 in.

What if the information listed the height of the speed limit sign as 3 *feet* and the width as 24 *inches*? In ratios that compare measurement, the units must be the same. In this case, we are given different units, feet and inches. When this occurs, we must rewrite the terms of the ratio using the same units.

Table 4.1, Measurement Conversion Tables, lists some familiar measurement equivalents for time, volume, length, and weight. Use these values to write a ratio with terms expressed in the same units. These and other tables will be used more extensively in Chapter 6, Measurement.

From the "Length" category in Table 4.1, we find the conversion equivalent.

$$\text{1 foot} = \text{12 inches}$$

With this information, we can write the ratio of the speed limit sign dimensions in either feet or inches. Let's do both.

Ratio in feet: Because 12 inches = 1 foot, 24 inches = 2 feet.

$$\left(24 \text{ inches} \cdot \frac{1 \text{ foot}}{12 \text{ inches}} = 2 \text{ feet} \right)$$

$$\text{ratio} = \frac{\text{height}}{\text{width}} = \frac{3 \text{ feet}}{24 \text{ inches}} \longrightarrow \frac{3 \text{ feet}}{2 \text{ feet}} = \frac{3}{2}$$

Ratio in inches: Because 1 foot = 12 inches, 3 feet = 36 inches.

$$\left(3 \text{ feet} \cdot \frac{12 \text{ inches}}{1 \text{ foot}} = 36 \text{ inches} \right)$$

$$\text{ratio} = \frac{\text{height}}{\text{width}} = \frac{3 \text{ feet}}{24 \text{ inches}} \longrightarrow \frac{36 \text{ inches}}{24 \text{ inches}} = \frac{3}{2}$$

Although the simplified ratio will be the same either way, as a general rule, it is easier to write the ratio with values in terms of the *smaller* measurement units.

TABLE 4.1   MEASUREMENT CONVERSION TABLES

TIME		LIQUID MEASURE (VOLUME)	
UNIT	**EQUIVALENT**	**UNIT**	**EQUIVALENT**
1 minute	60 seconds	1 cup	8 ounces
1 hour	60 minutes	1 pint	2 cups
1 day	24 hours	1 quart	4 cups
1 week	7 days	1 quart	2 pints
1 year	52 weeks	1 gallon	4 quarts
1 year	365 days		

LINEAR MEASURE (LENGTH)		WEIGHT	
UNIT	**EQUIVALENT**	**UNIT**	**EQUIVALENT**
1 foot	12 inches	1 ounce	16 drams
1 yard	3 feet	1 pound	16 ounces
1 yard	36 inches	1 ton	2000 pounds
1 mile	5280 feet		

Learning Tip

Remember that different units in the same measurement category, such as feet and inches, can be converted to either feet or inches to form the ratio.

Note: It is usually easier to use ratio values in terms of the *smaller* measurement units.

EXAMPLE 5 **Write a ratio of converted measurement units**

Simplify each ratio. Use values in terms of the smaller measurement units.

a. 14 hours to 2 days **b.** 5 quarts to 4 pints

SOLUTION STRATEGY

a. 14 hours to 2 days

$$\frac{14 \text{ hours}}{2 \text{ days}} = \frac{14 \text{ hours}}{48 \text{ hours}} = \frac{7}{24}$$

Convert days to the smaller units, hours.

1 day = 24 hours

2 days = 2 · 24 hours = 48 hours

Set up the ratio and simplify.

b. 5 quarts to 4 pints

$$\frac{5 \text{ quarts}}{4 \text{ pints}} = \frac{10 \text{ pints}}{4 \text{ pints}} = \frac{5}{2}$$

Convert quarts to the smaller units, pints.

1 quart = 2 pints

5 quarts = 5 · 2 pints = 10 pints

Set up the ratio and simplify.

TRY-IT EXERCISE 5

Simplify each ratio. Use values in terms of the smaller measurement units.

a. 20 minutes to 300 seconds

b. 15 inches to 2.5 feet

c. 5 cups to 4 pints

Check your answers with the solutions in Appendix A. ■

EXAMPLE 6 **Write a ratio of converted measurement units**

Simplify each ratio. Use values in terms of the smaller measurement units.

a. 4 yards to 10 feet

b. 42 ounces to 3 pounds

SOLUTION STRATEGY

a. 4 yards to 10 feet

$$\frac{4 \text{ yards}}{10 \text{ feet}} = \frac{12 \text{ feet}}{10 \text{ feet}} = \frac{6}{5}$$

Convert yards to the smaller units, feet.

1 yard = 3 feet

4 yards = 4 · 3 feet = 12 feet

Set up the ratio and simplify.

b. 42 ounces to 3 pounds

$$\frac{42 \text{ ounces}}{3 \text{ pounds}} = \frac{42 \text{ ounces}}{48 \text{ ounces}} = \frac{7}{8}$$

Convert pounds to the smaller units, ounces.

1 pound = 16 ounces

3 pounds = 3 · 16 ounces = 48 ounces

Set up the ratio and simplify.

TRY-IT EXERCISE 6

Simplify each ratio. Use values in terms of the smaller measurement units.

a. 26 drams to 2 ounces

b. 2 gallons to 3 quarts

c. 1.5 days to 9 hours

Check your answers with the solutions in Appendix A. ■

| Objective 4.1C | **Apply your knowledge** |

EXAMPLE 7   Work with ratios in an application problem

A small bag of M&Ms has 18 red, 11 blue, 13 yellow, and 9 orange M&Ms. Write each ratio in three different ways. Simplify, if possible.

a. the ratio of red to yellow

b. the ratio of blue to orange

c. the ratio of orange to red

d. the ratio of yellow to the total   .

e. the ratio of the total to blue

SOLUTION STRATEGY

a. the ratio of red to yellow

$$18 \text{ to } 13 \quad 18{:}13 \quad \frac{18}{13}$$

A ratio can be written

- in fraction notation.
- as two numbers separated by a colon.
- as two numbers separated by the word *to*.

b. the ratio of blue to orange

$$11 \text{ to } 9 \quad 11{:}9 \quad \frac{11}{9}$$

c. the ratio of orange to red

$$\frac{9}{18} = \frac{1}{2}$$

Simplify by dividing out the common factor, 9.

$$1 \text{ to } 2 \quad 1{:}2 \quad \frac{1}{2}$$

d. the ratio of yellow to the total

$$13 \text{ to } 51 \quad 13{:}51 \quad \frac{13}{51}$$

In parts d and e, use the total number of M&Ms, $18 + 11 + 13 + 9 = 51$, to write the ratio.

e. the ratio of the total to blue

$$51 \text{ to } 11 \quad 51{:}11 \quad \frac{51}{11}$$

Photo by George Bergeman

TRY-IT EXERCISE 7

At the Round Hill Doggy Olympics there were 32 cocker spaniels, 15 golden retrievers, 25 poodles, and 18 corgis. Write each ratio in three different ways. Simplify, if possible.

a. the ratio of corgis to golden retrievers

b. the ratio of poodles to the total

c. the ratio of golden retrievers to cocker spaniels

d. the ratio of the total to corgis

e. the ratio of corgis and poodles to golden retrievers

Check your answers with the solutions in Appendix A. ■

SECTION 4.1 REVIEW EXERCISES

Concept Check

1. A _____ is a comparison of two quantities by division.

2. The quantitites being compared in a ratio are called the _____ of the ratio.

3. Ratios may be written as two numbers separated by the word _____, as two numbers separated by a _____, or as a _____.

4. Write the ratio of *a* to *b*, where $b \neq 0$, in three different ways.

5. A ratio may express a comparison of a part to a _____ or a part to a _____.

6. A ratio can be simplified by dividing out _____ factors.

7. Explain the procedure to simplify a ratio that contains decimals.

8. To write a ratio containing different units in the same "measurement category," such as feet and inches, it is generally easier to use values in terms of the _____ measurement units.

Objective 4.1A	Write and simplify a ratio.

GUIDE PROBLEMS

9. Write the ratio of 7 to 12.

    a. Use the word *to*.

    b. Use a colon.

    c. Write in fraction notation.

10. Write the ratio of 2.9 to 1.42.

    a. Use the word *to*.

    b. Use a colon.

    c. Write in fraction notation.

Write each ratio in three different ways.

11. the ratio of 5 to 17

12. the ratio of 11 to 7

13. the ratio of 3 to $8\frac{1}{4}$

14. the ratio of $6\frac{1}{2}$ to $9\frac{1}{3}$

15. the ratio of 2.7 to 9

16. the ratio of 5.8 to 2

17. the ratio of 5 to 2

18. the ratio of 1 to 10

19. the ratio of 8 to 15

20. the ratio of 15 to 32

21. the ratio of 44 to 1.2

22. the ratio of 10 to 10.3

GUIDE PROBLEMS

23. Consider the ratio 18 to 27.

    a. Write the ratio in fraction notation.

    b. Simplify.

24. Consider the ratio 40 to 16.

    a. Write the ratio in fraction notation.

    b. Simplify.

25. Consider the ratio 2.6 to 50.

    a. Write the ratio in fraction notation.

    b. Identify 1 in the form $\frac{n}{n}$, where n is a power of 10 large enough to remove any decimals in both the numerator and the denominator.

    c. Multiply the ratio by the fraction from part b.

    d. Simplify.

26. Consider the ratio $1\frac{5}{8}$ to $2\frac{1}{4}$.

    a. Write the ratio in fraction notation.

    b. Convert each mixed number to an improper fraction.

    c. Divide.

Simplify each ratio.

27. 20 to 6

28. 18 to 96

29. 144 to 12

30. 25 to 45

31. 16 to 64

32. 42 to 56

33. 500 to 1000

34. 81 to 18

35. 0.3 to 1.1

36. 2.4 to 4.6

37. 3.2 to 6

38. 5.2 to 5.6

39. 1.25 to 1

40. 0.95 to 0.05

41. 9 to $2\frac{1}{4}$

42. $\frac{3}{8}$ to $\frac{1}{8}$

43. $1\frac{1}{3}$ to $1\frac{2}{3}$

44. $2\frac{4}{9}$ to $3\frac{2}{3}$

45. 9 to $1\frac{1}{3}$

46. $2\frac{3}{7}$ to $\frac{5}{14}$

| **Objective 4.1B** | **Write a ratio of converted measurement units** |

GUIDE PROBLEMS

47. Consider the ratio 6 quarts to 2 gallons.

    a. Identify the smaller units.

    b. Convert gallons to quarts.

    c. Write the ratio.

    d. Simplify.

48. Consider the ratio 18 minutes to 1.5 hours.

    a. Identify the smaller units.

    b. Convert hours to minutes.

    c. Write the ratio.

    d. Simplify.

Simplify each ratio. Use values in terms of the smaller measurement units.

49. 3 feet to 4 yards

50. 2200 pounds to 2 tons

51. 8 cups to 10 pints

52. 5 weeks to 18 days

53. 144 inches to 3.5 feet

54. 15 quarts to 3 pints

55. 10 pounds to 150 ounces

56. 65 seconds to 2 minutes

57. 12 yards to 2 feet

58. 4 gallons to 17 quarts

59. 5 ounces to 20 drams

60. 240 seconds to 5 minutes

| **Objective 4.1C** | **Apply your knowledge** |

61. Mark Kelsch, a professional hockey player, has scored 9 goals in 12 games so far this season.

    a. Write a simplified ratio in three different ways of Mark's goals to games.

    b. Write a simplified ratio in three different ways of Mark's career record of 152 goals in 284 games.

62. A cellular phone requires 5 minutes of charge time for every 45 minutes of talk time used.

    a. Write a simplified ratio in three different ways of charge time to talk time.

    b. Write a simplified ratio in three different ways of talk time to charge time.

63. A cake mix requires 3 cups of milk, 7 cups of flour, and 1 cup of butter.

  a. What is the ratio of the milk to the flour?

  b. What is the ratio of the flour to the butter?

  c. What is the ratio of the butter to the total amount of these ingredients?

64. On its last voyage, a cruise ship had 1850 passengers and 540 crew members.

  a. Write a simplified ratio of passengers to crew members.

  b. If 30 of the crew members are chefs, write a simplified ratio of chefs to the total number of people on board.

65. A certain coffee blend has 12 ounces of Arabica beans for every 3 pounds of Special Blend coffee. Write a simplified ratio of the amount of Arabica beans to Special Blend coffee. Use values in terms of the smaller measurement units.

66. A fenced-in yard measures 25 yards long and 80 feet wide. Write a simplified ratio of the length to the width of the fence. Use values in terms of the smaller measurement units.

67. A window is 3 feet high and 16 inches wide. Write a simplified ratio of the height to the width of the window. Use values in terms of the smaller measurement units.

68. A 2004 movie is 88 minutes long. The 2007 sequel is 2 hours long. Write a simplified ratio of the length of the 2004 movie to the 2007 sequel. Use values in terms of the smaller measurement units.

Use the figures for exercises 69–72.

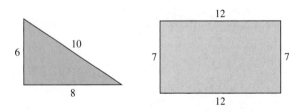

69. Write a simplified ratio in fraction notation of the length of the longest side to the length of the shortest side of the triangle.

70. Write a simplified ratio in fraction notation of the length of the shortest side to the perimeter of the triangle.

71. Write a simplified ratio in fraction notation of the length of the longest side to the length of the shortest side of the rectangle.

72. Write a simplified ratio in fraction notation of the length of the shortest side to the perimeter of the rectangle.

Use the data about KFC's top five markets for exercises 73–76.

KFC's Top Five Markets

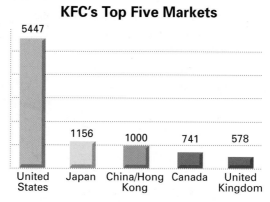

Number of Restaurants

73. Write a ratio in three different ways of the total number of restaurants in Canada to the total number in Japan.

74. Write a ratio in three different ways of the total number of restaurants in Japan, China/Hong Kong, Canada, and the United Kingdom to the total number in the United States.

75. Write a simplified ratio in fraction notation of the total number of restaurants in the United Kingdom to the total number in China/Hong Kong.

76. Write a simplified ratio in fraction notation of the total number of restaurants in China/Hong Kong to the total number of restaurants in KFC's top five markets.

According to company reports, Burger King, Wendy's, and McDonald's had the following number of restaurants at the beginning of 2006. Use this information for exercises 77–80.

Number of Restaurants Worldwide - 2006

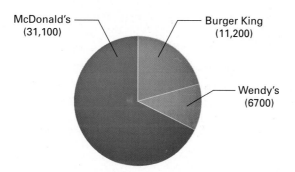

77. Write a simplified ratio in fraction notation of the total number of McDonald's restaurants to Wendy's restaurants.

78. Write a simplified ratio in fraction notation of the total number of Wendy's restaurants to Burger King restaurants.

79. Write a simplified ratio in fraction notation of the total number of Burger King restaurants to the number of McDonald's and Wendy's restaurants combined.

80. Write a simplified ratio in fraction notation of the total number of McDonald's restaurants to the total number of restaurants of the three chains combined.

Use the graph, Online Shopping, for exercises 81–84.

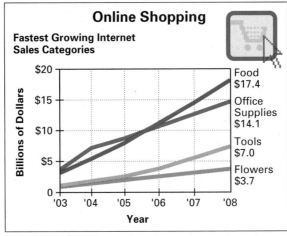

Online Shopping

Fastest Growing Internet Sales Categories

Billions of Dollars

Food $17.4
Office Supplies $14.1
Tools $7.0
Flowers $3.7

Year

Source: Forrester Research

81. Write a simplified ratio in three different ways to represent the estimated online purchases of flowers to the online purchases of tools in 2008.

82. Write a simplified ratio in three different ways to represent the estimated online food purchases to the online purchases of office supplies in 2008.

83. Write a simplified ratio in three different ways to represent the estimated online tool purchases to the overall online purchases in 2008.

84. Write a simplified ratio in three different ways to represent the estimated online purchases of food and flowers to the online purchases of tools and office supplies in 2008.

CUMULATIVE SKILLS REVIEW

1. Simplify. $400 \div 5^2 - 4(2 + 1)$ (1.6C)

2. Chambers Investment Corp. owns $8\frac{1}{4}$ acres of real estate. How much can the company make if it divides the land into $\frac{1}{4}$-acre lots that would sell for $55,000 each? (2.4C)

3. Divide. $65.155 \div 3\frac{2}{5}$. Round to the nearest thousandth. (3.5C)

4. Find the LCD of $\frac{2}{3}, \frac{5}{8}$, and $\frac{8}{9}$. (2.3C)

5. Add. $127 + 5652 + 78 + 10{,}322$. (1.2A)

6. Find the prime factorization of 40. Express your answer in exponential notation. (2.1C)

7. List $\frac{23}{47}, \frac{4}{5}$, and $\frac{8}{15}$ in descending order. (2.3C)

8. Albert is working on a project that requires 50 pounds of modeling clay. If the clay costs $6.25 per pound, how much did Albert pay for the clay? (3.3C)

9. Round 8975.455 to the nearest hundredth. (3.1C)

10. Add. $10{,}879 + 599 + 19 + 5050$. (1.2B)

4.2 WORKING WITH RATES AND UNITS

In this section, we will learn about a special type of ratio known as a rate. A **rate** is a ratio that compares two quantities that have different kinds of units. Two common rates are unit rates and unit prices.

Rates are a common way of comparing two quantities with different kinds of units that relate to each other. Some familiar examples of these are miles per hour, calories per serving, and price per unit. These are examples of comparisons that we see and use every day. As with ratios, rates can be written in fraction notation and then simplified to lowest terms.

Objective 4.2A	**Write and interpret a rate**

Rates are written in fraction notation with the units *included*. We include the units because they are *different* and therefore do not divide out.

For example, last week a freight train in the Rocky Mountains traveled 850 miles in 4 days. In this comparison, we have two quantities with different units, distance (850 miles) and time (4 days). The distance to time rate for the train would be written in fraction notation and simplified by dividing out the common factor, 2.

$$\frac{\text{distance}}{\text{time}} = \frac{\overset{425}{\cancel{850}} \text{ miles}}{\underset{2}{\cancel{4}} \text{ days}} = \frac{425 \text{ miles}}{2 \text{ days}}$$

It is important to keep in mind what "comparative fact" the rate is actually stating. In our train example, we can state the rate as follows.

On this trip, the train averaged 425 miles every 2 days.

Learning Tip

Remember, when the units are the same, they divide out and are not written.

Ratio: $\dfrac{2 \text{ feet}}{6 \text{ feet}} = \dfrac{1}{3}$

When the units are different, they do not divide out and therefore are written.

Rate: $\dfrac{15 \text{ gallons}}{100 \text{ hours}} = \dfrac{3 \text{ gallons}}{20 \text{ hours}}$

EXAMPLE 1   Write and interpret a rate

Write each rate as a simplified fraction. Then write the rate in word form.

a. 180 horses on 8 acres

b. 350 miles on 12 gallons of fuel

c. 390 calories for 9 cookies

SOLUTION STRATEGY

a. 180 horses on 8 acres

$$\frac{180 \text{ horses}}{8 \text{ acres}} = \frac{\overset{45}{\cancel{180}} \text{ horses}}{\underset{2}{\cancel{8}} \text{ acres}} = \frac{45 \text{ horses}}{2 \text{ acres}}$$

45 horses for every 2 acres

Write the rate in fraction notation with the units, horses and acres, included. Simplify by dividing out the common factor, 4.

b. 350 miles on 12 gallons of fuel

$$\frac{350 \text{ miles}}{12 \text{ gallons}} = \frac{\overset{175}{\cancel{350}} \text{ miles}}{\underset{6}{\cancel{12}} \text{ gallons}} = \frac{175 \text{ miles}}{6 \text{ gallons}}$$

175 miles for every 6 gallons of fuel

Write the rate in fraction notation with the units, miles and gallons, included. Simplify by dividing out the common factor, 2.

Photo by Robert Brechner

c. 390 calories for 9 cookies

$$\frac{390 \text{ calories}}{9 \text{ cookies}} = \frac{130 \text{ calories}}{3 \text{ cookies}}$$

130 calories for every 3 cookies

Write the rate in fraction notation with the units, calories and cookies, included.

Simplify by dividing out the common factor, 3.

TRY-IT EXERCISE 1

Write each rate as a simplified fraction. Then write the rate in word form.

a. 6 computers for 15 students

b. 22 inches of snow in 8 hours

c. $35,000 in 14 weeks

Check your answers with the solutions in Appendix A. ■

| Objective 4.2B | **Write a unit rate** |

unit rate
A rate in which the number in the denominator is 1.

A **unit rate** is a rate in which the number in the denominator is 1. A common example would be miles per gallon. Let's say that a car travels 160 miles on 8 gallons of fuel. Our unit rate would be written as a fraction and then simplified by dividing out the common factor, 8.

$$\frac{\overset{20}{\cancel{160}} \text{ miles}}{\underset{1}{\cancel{8}} \text{ gallons}} = \frac{20 \text{ miles}}{1 \text{ gallon}}$$

This unit rate would be expressed as follows.

20 miles per gallon   or   **20 miles/gallon**   or   **20 mpg**

> ### Learning Tip
>
> The word *per* means "for every." Note that "20 miles for every 1 gallon" is written as "20 miles per gallon" and abbreviated as "20 mpg."

Steps for Writing a Unit Rate

Step 1. Write the rate in fraction notation with the units included.

Step 2. Divide the numerator by the denominator.

Step 3. Round as specified, if necessary.

EXAMPLE 2   Write a unit rate

Write each as a unit rate. Round to the nearest tenth, if necessary.

a. 500 people in 4 days   **b.** 145 miles in 3 hours

SOLUTION STRATEGY

a. 500 people in 4 days

$$\frac{500 \text{ people}}{4 \text{ days}} = 125 \text{ people per day}$$

Write the rate in fraction notation with the units, people and days, included.

Divide the numerator, 500, by the denominator, 4. No rounding is necessary.

b. 145 miles in 3 hours

$$\frac{145\text{ miles}}{3\text{ hours}} = 48.3\text{ miles per hour}$$

Write the rate in fraction notation with the units, miles and hours, included.

Divide the numerator, 145, by the denominator, 3. Round to the nearest tenth.

TRY-IT EXERCISE 2

Write each as a unit rate. Round to the nearest tenth, if necessary.

a. $5400 in 6 months

b. 349 gallons every 2.8 hours

Check your answers with the solutions in Appendix A. ■

EXAMPLE 3　　Write a unit rate

Write each as a unit rate. Round to the nearest tenth, if necessary.

a. An English major read 42 books in 12 months.

b. A farm produced 1300 bushels on corn on 22 acres.

SOLUTION STRATEGY

a. 42 books in 12 months

$$\frac{42\text{ books}}{12\text{ months}} = 3.5\text{ books per month}$$

Write the rate in fraction notation with the units, books and months, included.

Divide the numerator, 42, by the denominator, 12. No rounding is necessary.

b. 1300 bushels of corn on 22 acres

$$\frac{1300\text{ bushels}}{22\text{ acres}} = 59.1\text{ bushels per acre}$$

Write the rate in fraction notation with the units, bushels and acres, included.

Divide the numerator, 1300, by the denominator, 22. Round to the nearest tenth.

TRY-IT EXERCISE 3

Write each as a unit rate. Round to the nearest tenth, if necessary.

a. A pitcher threw 98 pitches in 7 innings.

b. A delivery service transported 10,000 pounds of merchandise in 7 trucks.

Check your answers with the solutions in Appendix A. ■

Objective 4.2C　　Write a unit price

A common application of unit rate is unit price. A **unit price** is a rate expressed as price per single item of something. It tells us the "price per item" or "price per measure" of a particular product or service.

unit price
A rate expressed as price per single item of something.

For example, Food Fair sells a 16-ounce package of imported penne pasta for $3.59. What would be the unit price per ounce?

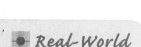
Real-World Connection

Retail Buying Decision
Unit price is an important consideration when comparing merchandise to be carried in a retail store. A few cents difference in unit price can often mean a big difference in company sales revenue and profits.

To calculate the unit price of the pasta, we set up the ratio of the price to the number of ounces. We then divide and round to the nearest cent.

$$\text{Unit price} = \frac{\text{Price}}{\text{Number of units}} = \frac{\$3.59}{16 \text{ ounces}} = \$0.22 \text{ per ounce}$$

Steps for Writing a Unit Price

Step 1. Write the rate in fraction notation with the price as the numerator and the quantity (number of items or units) as the denominator.

Step 2. Divide the numerator by the denominator.

Step 3. Round to the nearest cent, if necessary.

EXAMPLE 4   Write a unit price

Calculate the unit price for each. Round to the nearest cent, if necessary.

a. 3 light bulbs for $4.80

b. a dozen eggs for $1.77

SOLUTION STRATEGY

a. 3 light bulbs for $4.80

$$\frac{\$4.80}{3 \text{ bulbs}} = \$1.60 \text{ per bulb}$$

Write the rate in fraction notation with the price, $4.80, as the numerator, and the quantity, 3 bulbs, as the denominator.

Divide the numerator by the denominator. No rounding is necessary.

b. a dozen eggs for $1.77

$$\frac{\$1.77}{12} = \$0.1475 \approx \$0.15 \text{ per egg}$$

Write the rate in fraction notation with the price, $1.77, as the numerator, and the quantity, 12 eggs, as the denominator.

Divide the numerator by the denominator. Round to the nearest cent.

TRY-IT EXERCISE 4

Calculate the unit price for each. Round to the nearest cent, if necessary.

a. a 5-day Mississippi River cruise for $1350

b. a 2.48-carat diamond ring for $3300

Check your answers with the solutions in Appendix A. ■

Real-World Connection

Carat
A *carat* (ct.) is a standard measure of weight used for gemstones or pure gold. One carat weighs 0.2 gram (1/5 of a gram or 0.0007 ounce). A hundredth of a carat is called a *point*.

Objective 4.2D   **Apply your knowledge**

In consumer economics, unit pricing helps us determine the "best buy" when comparing various shopping choices. Everything else being equal, the best buy is the choice with the *lowest* price per unit. Note that in some cases we must round to the nearest *thousandth* in order to see a difference between unit prices.

EXAMPLE 5   Determine the "best buy"

A local grocer sells a 12-ounce can of soda for $0.75 and a 16-ounce bottle of the same type of soda for $1.25.

a. What is the unit price for each product? Round to the nearest cent.

b. Based on unit price, which size is the best buy?

SOLUTION STRATEGY

a. unit price (can): $\dfrac{\$0.75}{12 \text{ ounces}} =$ Find the unit price for each.

$0.06 per ounce

unit price (bottle): $\dfrac{\$1.25}{16 \text{ ounces}} =$

$0.08 per ounce

b. The best buy is the 12-ounce can.   The best buy is the product with the lower unit price, the 12-ounce can.

TRY-IT EXERCISE 5

Consider packages of varying sizes of Uncle Bernie's French Vanilla Rice Pudding.

a. Calculate the unit price for each size. Round to the nearest cent.

SIZE	PRICE	UNIT PRICE
16 ounces	$3.29	
24 ounces	$4.50	
31 ounces	$5.39	

b. Based on unit price, which size is the best buy?

Check your answers with the solutions in Appendix A. ■

SECTION 4.2 REVIEW EXERCISES

Concept Check

1. A _____ is a ratio that compares two quantities that have different units.

2. Rates are written in fraction notation with the _____ included.

3. In rates, we include the units because they are *different* and therefore do not _____ out.

4. A _____ rate is a special type of rate in which the number in the denominator is _____.

5. A unit rate is written in fraction notation. We then _____ the numerator by the denominator.

6. A common application of unit rate is unit _____.

7. To write a unit price, we write the rate in fraction notation with the _____ as the numerator and the _____ as the denominator. We then divide and round to the nearest cent.

8. When comparing shopping choices, everything else being equal, the best buy is the choice with the _____ price per unit.

| Objective 4.2A | Write and interpret a rate |

GUIDE PROBLEMS

9. a. Write the rate 8 pages in 12 minutes in fraction notation.

b. Simplify.

c. Write the rate in word form.

10. a. Write the rate $55 for 80 pounds of fertilizer in fraction notation.

b. Simplify.

c. Write the rate in word form.

Write each rate as a simplified fraction. Then write the rate in word form.

11. 85 fence panels for 1350 feet

12. $58 for 6 tickets

13. 9 vans for 78 people

14. 500 gifts for 200 children

15. 32 bags for 24 passengers

16. 4 pizzas for 18 children

17. 2500 revolutions for 8 minutes

18. 1798 pounds for 12 packages

19. 75 patients for 9 doctors

20. $26 for 500 photos

21. 182 gallons of milk for 34 cows

22. 22,568 pixels for 30 square inches

23. 562 students for 28 teachers

24. 65 swing sets for 15 playgrounds

25. 6284 square feet for 14 gallons of paint

26. 49 aces for 14 tennis matches

27. 55 hits for 180 at bats

28. 90 flowers for 8 bouquets

| Objective 4.2B | Write a unit rate |

GUIDE PROBLEMS

29. a. Write the rate 280 miles on 20 gallons of fuel in fraction notation.

    b. Divide the numerator by the denominator and write the unit rate as a fraction.

    c. Write the unit rate in word form.

30. a. Write the rate 15 pounds in 3 months in fraction notation.

    b. Divide the numerator by the denominator and write the unit rate as a fraction.

    c. Write the unit rate in word form.

Write each as a unit rate. Round to the nearest tenth, if necessary.

31. $3600 in 12 months

32. 72 interns in 18 summers

33. 16 touchdowns in 3 games

34. 55 calories for 4 ounces

35. 30 parking spaces for 30 apartments

36. 60 gallons in 10 hours

37. 325 yards of material for 85 shirts

38. 14 events in 6 years

39. 28 servings for 7 pizzas

40. 25 bushels for 5 acres

41. 176 roses in 8 vases

42. 180 cinemas in 12 cities

43. 19 kilowatts in 6 hours

44. 65 golf shots in 16 holes

45. 8835 branches per 95 trees

46. 395 miles in 5 hours

47. 5040 words on 12 pages

48. 18 children for 9 families

| Objective 4.2C | Write a unit price |

GUIDE PROBLEMS

49. a. Set up the rate, $22.50 for 12 golf balls, in fraction notation with price as the numerator and the quantity (number of items or units) as the denominator.

    b. Divide the numerator by the denominator and write the unit price in fraction notation.

    c. Write the unit price in word form. Round to the nearest cent.

50. a. Set up the ratio, a 16-ounce can of corn for $2.79, as a rate in fraction notation. Use the price as the numerator and the quantity (number of items or units) as the denominator.

    b. Divide the numerator by the denominator and write the unit price in fraction notation.

    c. Write the unit price in word form. Round to the nearest cent.

Calculate the unit price for each. Round to the nearest cent, if necessary.

51. $24 for 300 minutes of long distance

52. $675 for 18 passengers

53. 55 ounces of detergent for $7.15

54. 18 hours of work for $522

55. 45 oranges for $12.60

56. 19 dresses for $910.10

57. $9.30 for 6 milkshakes

58. $17.60 for 55 party invitations

59. 4 batteries for $4.64

60. 25 plants for $15.95

61. $23.20 for a 16-pound turkey

62. $18.75 for 75 jukebox songs

63. 16 pies for $143.20

64. 5 shirts laundered for $22.65

65. $5.50 for 24 bottles of spring water

66. $17.25 for 30 candy bars

Objective 4.2D   Apply your knowledge

67. Doctor's Hospital has 14 patients for 6 nurses on the midnight shift. Write the simplified rate in fraction notation and in word form.

68. A kitchen display case has 75 plates on 10 shelves. Write the simplified rate in fraction notation and in word form.

69. This morning the deli counter of Supreme Foods sold 28 pounds of cheese in 21 orders. Write the simplified rate as a fraction and in word form.

70. Norm gives 27 tennis lessons every 12 days. Write the simplified rate as a fraction and in word form.

71. Todd and Kimberly each ran a race for charity. Todd ran 29 miles in 4.3 hours and Kimberly ran 25 miles in 4 hours.

   a. Find the unit rate for Todd. Round to the nearest tenth.

   b. Find the unit rate for Kimberly. Round to the nearest tenth.

   c. Who ran faster, Todd or Kimberly?

72. Ben and Mal walk to Starbucks each Saturday to meet for coffee. Ben walks the 2 miles from his house in 30 minutes and Mal walks the 3 miles from her house in 36 minutes.

   a. Find the unit rate in minutes per mile for Ben.

   b. Find the unit rate in minutes per mile for Mal.

   c. Who walks faster, Ben or Mal?

73. You are in the market to buy a new sewing machine. You have found that one model, X400, can sew 15 inches of fabric in 9 seconds. An older model, T300, can sew 13 inches of fabric in 8 seconds.

   a. Find the unit rate for the X400. Round to the nearest tenth.

   b. Find the unit rate for the T300. Round to the nearest tenth.

   c. Which model is faster?

74. Ed and Jim are floor tile installers. Ed can install 1500 square feet of tile in 12 hours. Jim can install 1200 square feet of tile in 10 hours.

   a. Find the unit rate for Ed.

   b. Find the unit rate for Jim.

   c. Who works more quickly, Ed or Jim?

Use the aviation statistics for exercises 75–78.

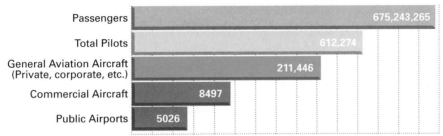

Aviation Statistics

Passengers	675,243,265
Total Pilots	612,274
General Aviation Aircraft (Private, corporate, etc.)	211,446
Commercial Aircraft	8497
Public Airports	5026

75. Write the ratio of total pilots to general aviation aircraft as a simplified fraction and in word form.

76. Write the ratio of total pilots to public airports as a simplified fraction and in word form.

77. Write the unit rate of passengers to public airports in fraction notation and in word form. Round to the nearest whole number.

78. Write the unit rate of general aviation aircraft to commercial aircraft in fraction notation and in word form. Round to the nearest whole number.

79. An importer has two special offers on name brand purses, $610 for 12 purses or $916 for 20 purses. As the buyer for Fancy Fashions Department Store, determine which offer is the best buy.

80. Dr. Arrandt, a chiropractor, offers 10 visits for $350 or 16 visits for $540. Which is the best buy?

81. Pharmacy World is having a special on Tea Tree Toothpaste. The 12-ounce tube is $3.65 and the 16-ounce tube is $5.28. Which is the best buy? Round to the nearest cent.

82. Organic Roots sells canned button mushrooms in two sizes, 12-ounce and 16-ounce. The 12-ounce can sells for $2.65 and the 16-ounce can sells for $3.20. Which is the best buy? Round to the nearest cent.

83. Clarissa is comparing dog food brands for her dog Anny. If Anny's favorite, Tiny Bits, comes in the three sizes as listed below, which size is the best buy? (Hint: Determine the unit price for each size.)

SIZE	PRICE	UNIT PRICE
25 pounds	$41.25	
30 pounds	$51.90	
45 pounds	$67.50	

84. Dana is going on vacation and needs to buy some 35 mm film. If Camera World sells various sizes, as listed below, which size is the best buy? (Hint: Determine the unit price for each size.)

SIZE	PRICE	UNIT PRICE
24 exposures	$6.00	
36 exposures	$9.36	
48 exposures	$11.04	

85. Fred is painting his house this weekend and is looking for a good deal on paint. Painter's Paradise offers three paint can sizes as listed below. Determine which size is the best buy.

SIZE	PRICE	UNIT PRICE
4 gallons	$65.00	
5 gallons	$79.10	
6 gallons	$100.50	

86. Sam is shopping for fishing line. Outdoor Sportsman offers three sizes of fishing line as listed below. Determine which size is the best buy.

SIZE	PRICE	UNIT PRICE
200 yards	$8.00	
370 yards	$11.10	
450 yards	$18.00	

Sun Bright **99¢**

Dishwashing 14.7-oz.
Liquid

Dishwasher
Gel or Powder 45 to 50-oz.

$2.99

87. a. What is the unit price for the 14.7-ounce size of Sun Bright dishwashing liquid? Round to the nearest cent.

b. What is the unit price for the 50-ounce size of Sun Bright dishwasher powder? Round to the nearest cent.

c. If the 45-ounce size of Sun Bright dishwasher gel went on sale for $2.25, which would be the best buy, the 45-ounce gel for $2.25 or the 50-ounce powder for $2.99?

88. a. What is the unit price for the Hearty Twist Tie bags? Round to the nearest cent.

b. What is unit price of the Hearty Cinch Sak bags? Round to the nearest cent.

c. If a larger package of Hearty Cinch Sak bags contains 65 bags and costs $7.50, which would be the best buy for Cinch Sak bags? Round to the nearest cent.

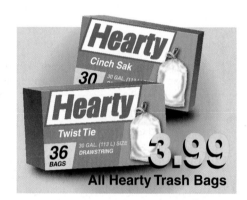

CUMULATIVE SKILLS REVIEW

1. Evaluate. $41 \div 0$ (1.5A)

2. Evaluate. $3.95 \cdot 8.3$ (3.3A)

3. Evaluate. $15\frac{5}{12} - 6\frac{1}{6}$ (2.7C)

4. Determine whether 83 is prime, composite, or neither. (2.1B)

5. Evaluate. $45 - 5.999$ (3.2B)

6. Evaluate. $23{,}695 - 12{,}014$ (1.3A)

7. Write a simplified ratio with values in terms of the smaller measurement units for each. (1 yard = 3 feet) (4.1C)

a. 8 yards to 14 feet

b. 3 yards to 7 feet

8. A batch of cookies requires $\frac{1}{2}$ pound of chocolate morsels. How many batches of cookies can you make from $3\frac{3}{4}$ pounds of chocolate morsels? (2.5C)

9. Nick purchased $6\frac{1}{2}$ pounds of spareribs, $5\frac{3}{8}$ pounds of coleslaw, and $4\frac{3}{4}$ pounds of potato salad for a picnic. What is the total weight of his purchases? (2.6D)

10. A packet of multicolored paper contains 12 yellow pages, 10 red pages, 15 blue pages, 8 orange pages, and 45 white pages. Write each ratio in three different ways. (4.1D)

    a. What is the ratio of yellow to blue paper?

    b. What is the ratio of red to white paper?

    c. What is the ratio of orange paper to the total?

4.3 UNDERSTANDING AND SOLVING PROPORTIONS

In this section, we will add to our knowledge of ratios the concept of proportion. A proportion is used to show the "equality" relationship between two ratios. When two ratios are equal, we say that they are "proportional," or "in proportion" to each other.

For example, at Cookies Galore, 2 cookies cost $0.25. This rate is written as follows.

$$\frac{\$0.25}{2 \text{ cookies}}$$

At this rate, we can readily see that 4 cookies would cost $0.50. That rate is written as follows.

$$\frac{\$0.50}{4 \text{ cookies}}$$

Because these rates are equal (they are just written with a different set of numbers), we can write them as a mathematical statement known as a proportion.

$$\frac{\$0.25}{2 \text{ cookies}} = \frac{\$0.50}{4 \text{ cookies}}$$

The proportion is read as follows.

      $0.25 is to 2 cookies as $0.50 is to 4 cookies

LEARNING OBJECTIVES

A. Write a proportion

B. Determine whether two ratios are proportional

C. Solve a proportion

D. Apply your knowledge

> **Learning Tip**
>
> Your work in this chapter will include "solving" some simple algebraic equations. This concept will be covered in more detail in Chapter 10, Introduction to Algebra.

| Objective 4.3A | Write a proportion |

A **proportion** is a mathematical statement showing that two ratios are equal. A proportion is written as an equation with a ratio on each side of the equal sign.

proportion
A mathematical statement showing that two ratios are equal.

Remember to include the units when writing a rate. Also, keep in mind that the order of the units is important. Be sure that like units for each rate are in the same position. In our example above, note that in each ratio, the price was in the numerator and the number of cookies was in the denominator.

EXAMPLE 1   Write a proportion

Write each sentence as a proportion.

a. 3 is to 8 as 6 is to 16

b. 12 eggs is to 4 chickens as 3 eggs is to 1 chicken

SOLUTION STRATEGY

a. 3 is to 8 as 6 is to 16

$$\frac{3}{8} = \frac{6}{16}$$

Write a ratio on each side of an equal sign.

b. 12 eggs is to 4 chickens as 3 eggs is to 1 chicken

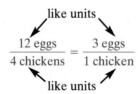

like units

$$\frac{12 \text{ eggs}}{4 \text{ chickens}} = \frac{3 \text{ eggs}}{1 \text{ chicken}}$$

like units

Each ratio is a rate, because the units, eggs and chickens, are different. Be sure to include units as you write the proportion.

The order of the units must be consistent on each side of the proportion. Note that eggs are in the *numerator* and chickens are in the *denominator.*

TRY-IT EXERCISE 1

Write each sentence as a proportion.

a. 5 is to 12 as 15 is to 36

b. 14 grams is to 6 ounces as 7 grams is to 3 ounces

Check your answers with the solutions in Appendix A. ■

EXAMPLE 2   Write a proportion

Write each proportion as a sentence.

a. $\dfrac{9}{18} = \dfrac{1}{2}$

b. $\dfrac{8 \text{ batteries}}{4 \text{ flashlights}} = \dfrac{2 \text{ batteries}}{1 \text{ flashlight}}$

SOLUTION STRATEGY

a. $\dfrac{9}{18} = \dfrac{1}{2}$ When writing a proportion in sentence form, we separate the numerator and denominator of each ratio by the phrase *is to*. The equal sign is represented by the word *as*.

9 is to 18 as 1 is to 2.

b. $\dfrac{8 \text{ batteries}}{4 \text{ flashlights}} = \dfrac{2 \text{ batteries}}{1 \text{ flashlight}}$ Because this ratio is a rate, include the units in the sentence.

8 batteries is to 4 flashlights as
2 batteries is to 1 flashlight

TRY-IT EXERCISE 2

Write each proportion as a sentence.

a. $\dfrac{3}{40} = \dfrac{6}{80}$

b. $\dfrac{22 \text{ pounds}}{6 \text{ weeks}} = \dfrac{11 \text{ pounds}}{3 \text{ weeks}}$

Check your answers with the solutions in Appendix A. ■

| Objective 4.3B | **Determine whether two ratios are proportional** |

By definition, a proportion is a mathematical statement showing that two ratios are equal. For example, we can readily see that 5 to 10 and 10 to 20 are "proportional" ratios, that is, they are equal.

$$\frac{5}{10} = \frac{10}{20}$$

Sometimes the equality of two ratios is not so obvious. Consider the ratios 8 to 12 and 14 to 21. Are these two ratios proportional?

$$\frac{8}{12} \stackrel{?}{=} \frac{14}{21}$$

A way of verifying whether these two ratios are proportional is by determining whether their *cross products* are equal. To compute the cross products, multiply the denominator of the first ratio, 12, by the numerator of the second ratio, 14; then multiply the numerator of the first ratio, 8, by the denominator of the second ratio, 21.

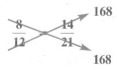

Because the cross products are equal, 168 = 168, the two ratios are proportional.

In general, if $\dfrac{a}{b} = \dfrac{c}{d}$ where $b \neq 0$ and $d \neq 0$, then $bc = ad$.

> **Learning Tip**
>
> Another way to verify that two ratios are equal is to reduce them both to lowest terms. In our example, both ratios simplify to the same fraction.
>
>
>
> $\dfrac{8}{12} = \dfrac{2}{3}$
>
> $\dfrac{14}{21} = \dfrac{2}{3}$ Equal fractions

Steps for Determining Whether Two Ratios Are Proportional

Step 1. Multiply the denominator of the first ratio by the numerator of the second ratio.

Step 2. Multiply the numerator of the first ratio by the denominator of the second ratio.

Step 3. Determine whether or not the cross products are equal.

- If the cross products are *equal*, the *ratios are proportional*, and we can write a proportion.

- If the cross products are *not equal*, the *ratios are not proportional*, and we cannot write a proportion.

EXAMPLE 3   **Determine whether two ratios are proportional**

Determine whether the ratios are proportional. If they are, write a corresponding proportion.

$$\frac{24}{6} \overset{?}{=} \frac{16}{4}$$

SOLUTION STRATEGY

$$\frac{24}{6} \overset{?}{=} \frac{16}{4}$$

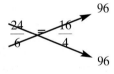
96

96

To determine whether these ratios are proportional, begin by multiplying the denominator of the first ratio, 6, by the numerator of the second ratio, 16.

Next, multiply the numerator of the first ratio, 24, by the denominator of the second ratio, 4.

The cross products are equal (96 = 96). Therefore, the ratios are proportional, and we can write a proportion.

The ratios are proportional.

$$\frac{24}{6} = \frac{16}{4}$$

TRY-IT EXERCISE 3

Determine whether the ratios are proportional. If they are, write a corresponding proportion.

$$\frac{30}{15} \overset{?}{=} \frac{40}{20}$$

Check your answer with the solution in Appendix A. ■

EXAMPLE 4 **Determine whether two ratios are proportional**

Determine whether the ratios are proportional. If they are, write a corresponding proportion.

$$\frac{5}{9} \overset{?}{=} \frac{6}{11}$$

SOLUTION STRATEGY

$$\frac{5}{9} \overset{?}{=} \frac{6}{11}$$

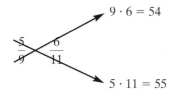

$9 \cdot 6 = 54$

$5 \cdot 11 = 55$

In this example, the cross products are not equal, $54 \neq 55$. Therefore, the ratios are not proportional and we cannot write a proportion.

The ratios are not proportional.

TRY-IT EXERCISE 4

Determine whether the ratios are proportional. If they are, write a corresponding proportion.

$$\frac{52}{4} \overset{?}{=} \frac{140}{10}$$

Check your answer with the solution in Appendix A. ■

Objective 4.3C **Solve a proportion**

When one of the terms of a proportion is unknown, we can "solve" the proportion for that term. The solution is the value of the unknown that makes the proportion true. Proportions can be solved using cross multiplication.

Consider this proportion.

4 is to 12 as an unknown number **is to 60**

$$\frac{4}{12} = \frac{x}{60}$$

Note that the numerator of the second ratio is unknown. We represent this unknown quantity with a letter of the alphabet, x. To solve the proportion means to find the value of x that makes the proportion true. We begin by finding the cross products.

$$\frac{4}{12} \qquad \frac{x}{60}$$

$12 \cdot x = 12x$

$4 \cdot 60 = 240$

In a proportion, the cross products are equal, so we can write the following.

$$12x = 240$$

To isolate the unknown, x, on one side of the equation, we divide both sides of the equation by 12, the number on the side with the unknown. We then simplify.

$$\frac{12x}{12} = \frac{240}{12}$$

$$\frac{\overset{1}{\cancel{12}}x}{\underset{1}{\cancel{12}}} = \frac{\overset{20}{\cancel{240}}}{\underset{1}{\cancel{12}}}$$

$$x = 20$$

To verify the answer, replace the unknown in the original proportion with the answer, 20, and check whether the cross products are equal.

$$12 \cdot 20 = 240$$

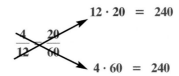

$$4 \cdot 60 = 240$$

The cross products are equal. Solution is verified.

Steps for Solving a Proportion

Step 1. Assign a letter to represent the *unknown* quantity.

Step 2. Cross multiply to find the cross products.

Step 3. Separate the cross products by an equal sign to form an equation.

Step 4. Divide both sides of the equation by the *number* on the side with the *unknown*.

Step 5. Simplify, if possible.

Step 6. Verify the answer by replacing the unknown in the original proportion with the answer, and check that the cross products are equal.

EXAMPLE 5   **Solve a proportion**

Solve for the unknown quantity. Verify your answer.

$$\frac{x}{18} = \frac{2}{3}$$

SOLUTION STRATEGY

$$\frac{x}{18} = \frac{2}{3}$$

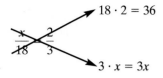

18 · 2 = 36

Find the cross products.

3 · x = 3x

$$36 = 3x$$

Separate the cross products by an equal sign to form an equation.

$$\frac{36}{3} = \frac{3x}{3}$$

Divide both sides of the equation by 3, the number on the side with the unknown.

$$12 = x$$

Simplify. The answer is 12.

Verify:

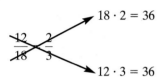

18 · 2 = 36

12 · 3 = 36

Verify the solution. Replace the unknown in the original proportion with the answer, 12, and check that the cross products are equal.

The cross products are equal (36 = 36). Therefore, the answer, 12, is correct.

TRY-IT EXERCISE 5

Solve for the unknown quantity. Verify your answer.

$$\frac{w}{12} = \frac{1}{3}$$

Check your answer with the solution in Appendix A. ∎

EXAMPLE 6   Solve a proportion

Solve for the unknown quantity. Verify your answer.

$$\frac{4.5}{m} = \frac{2}{5}$$

SOLUTION STRATEGY

$$\frac{4.5}{m} = \frac{2}{5}$$

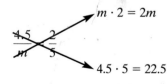

m · 2 = 2m

Find the cross products.

4.5 · 5 = 22.5

$$2m = 22.5$$

Separate the cross products by an equal sign to form an equation.

$$\frac{2m}{2} = \frac{22.5}{2}$$

Divide both sides of the equation by the number on the side with the unknown, 2.

$$m = 11.25$$

Simplify. The answer is 11.25.

Verify:

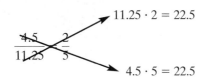

$11.25 \cdot 2 = 22.5$

$4.5 \cdot 5 = 22.5$

Verify the solution. Replace the unknown in the original proportion with the answer, 11.25, and check that the cross products are equal.

The cross products are equal (22.5 = 22.5).

Therefore, the answer, 11.25, is correct.

TRY-IT EXERCISE 6

Solve for the unknown quantity. Verify your answer.

$$\frac{12}{x} = \frac{15}{2.5}$$

Check your answer with the solution in Appendix A. ■

| Objective 4.3D | **Apply your knowledge** |

Proportions are a useful tool for solving problems in a variety of disciplines, including the sciences, engineering, medicine, and business. Proportions are also used in many of our everyday activities, such as shopping and traveling.

The following steps may be used to solve an application problem using a proportion. Keep in mind that *like units* must be in their respective numerators and denominators of the ratios when setting up the proportion.

Steps for Solving an Application Problem Using a Proportion

Step 1. Read and understand the problem. Assign a letter to represent the unknown quantity.

Step 2. Set up a proportion. Keep like units in their respective numerators and denominators.

Step 3. Solve and verify the proportion.

Step 4. State the answer.

EXAMPLE 7 **Solve an application problem using proportion**

A cake recipe requires 4 eggs for every 3 cups of flour. If a large cake requires 9 cups of flour, how many eggs should be used?

SOLUTION STRATEGY

x = number of eggs for the large cake

This problem compares number of eggs to cups of flour for a large cake. Let x represent the unknown number of eggs.

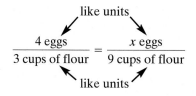

Set up the proportion, keeping like units in their respective places, eggs in the numerators and cups of flour in the denominators.

$3 \cdot x = 4 \cdot 9$

$3x = 36$

$\dfrac{3x}{3} = \dfrac{36}{3}$

$x = 12$

Solve the proportion.

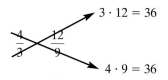

$3 \cdot 12 = 36$

$4 \cdot 9 = 36$

Verify the answer, 12. The cross products are equal (36 = 36).

The large cake requires 12 eggs.

State the answer.

TRY-IT EXERCISE 7

On a recent trip in your car, you traveled 180 miles on 12 gallons of gasoline. At that rate, how many gallons of gasoline would be required for a trip of 330 miles?

Check your answer with the solution in Appendix A. ■

EXAMPLE 8   Solve an application problem using proportion

A patient was administered 46 mg of a certain medication over an 8-hour period. At that rate, how much medication will the patient receive in a 14-hour period?

SOLUTION STRATEGY

m = amount of medication

This problem compares amount of medication to number of hours.

Let m represent the unknown amount of medication.

$$\frac{46 \text{ mg of medication}}{8 \text{ hours}} = \frac{m \text{ mg of medication}}{14 \text{ hours}}$$

Set up the proportion, keeping like units in their respective places, mg of medication in the numerators and hours in the denominators.

$8 \cdot m = 46 \cdot 14$

$8m = 644$

$\dfrac{8m}{8} = \dfrac{644}{8}$

$m = 80.5$

Solve the proportion.

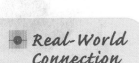

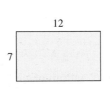

$$8 \cdot 80.5 = 644$$

$$46 \cdot 14 = 644$$

Verify the answer, 80.5. The cross products are equal ($644 = 644$).

The patient will receive 80.5 mg of medication in 14 hours.

State the answer.

TRY-IT EXERCISE 8

A factory used 24 square yards of leather material to make 6 chairs. At that rate, how many yards of material would be required to make 11 chairs?

Check your answer with the solution in Appendix A. ■

One common application of proportions is solving problems involving *similar* geometric figures. **Similar geometric figures** are geometric figures with the same shape in which the ratios of the lengths of their corresponding sides are equal. Because these ratios are equal, they are proportional.

Consider the similar rectangles below.

similar geometric figures
Geometric figures with the same shape in which the ratios of the lengths of their corresponding sides are equal.

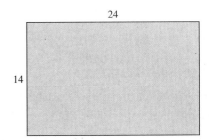

The similar rectangles yield this proportion.

$$\frac{7}{14} = \frac{12}{24}$$

The similar triangles below yield these proportions.

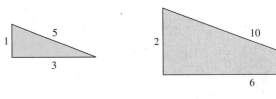

$$\frac{1}{2} = \frac{3}{6} \qquad \frac{1}{2} = \frac{5}{10} \qquad \frac{3}{6} = \frac{5}{10}$$

To find the measure of an unknown length of a similar geometric figure, we substitute a letter in the proportion and solve for that unknown, as we did in Section 4.3C.

Congruent vs similar

EXAMPLE 9   Find the value of the unknown length in similar geometric figures

Melanie has a photograph of the Grand Canyon that measures 4 inches high and 6 inches wide. If she has it enlarged proportionally to 24 inches wide, what is the height of the new photograph?

4 in.

6 in.

h in.

24 in.

Photos by Robert Brechner

SOLUTION STRATEGY

h = height of the new photo

Let h represent the height of the new photo.

$$\frac{4}{h} = \frac{6}{24}$$

Set up a proportion. Use the ratio of the heights of each photo to the ratio of the widths of each photo.

4 is to h as 6 is to 24

$$h \cdot 6 = 4 \cdot 24$$

Separate the cross products with an equal sign to form an equation.

$$6h = 96$$

Solve the proportion.

$$\frac{6h}{6} = \frac{96}{6}$$

$$h = 16$$

$16 \cdot 6 = 96$

$$\frac{4}{16} \quad \frac{6}{24}$$

$4 \cdot 24 = 96$

Verify the answer, 16. The cross products are equal (96 = 96).

The height of the new photograph is 16 inches.

State the answer.

TRY-IT EXERCISE 9

A photograph that measures 5.25 inches high and 7 inches wide is being enlarged proportionally to 20 inches wide. What is the height of the new photo?

5.25 in.

7 in.

x in.

20 in.

Photos by Robert Brechner

Check your answer with the solution in Appendix A. ■

We can use the concept of similar triangles to measure objects without actually having to physically measure them. This procedure is used to find dimensions of things that would otherwise be difficult to obtain, such as the height of a building, a tree, or even a mountain.

EXAMPLE 10 Using shadow proportions to find "difficult to measure" lengths

Kyle is 5.8 feet tall. Late one afternoon while visiting the Grove Isle Lighthouse, he noticed that his shadow was 9 feet long. At the same time, the lighthouse cast a shadow 108 feet long. What is the height of the lighthouse?

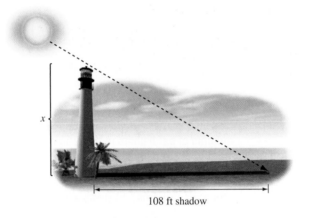
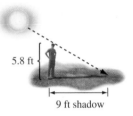

108 ft shadow   9 ft shadow

SOLUTION STRATEGY

x = height of the lighthouse

Let *x* represent the height of the lighthouse.

$$\frac{x}{5.8} = \frac{108}{9}$$

Set up a proportion. Use the ratio of the heights of each object to the ratio of the lengths of the shadows cast.

x is to 5.8 as 108 is to 9

$$5.8 \cdot 108 = x \cdot 9$$

Separate the cross products with an equal sign to form an equation.

$$626.4 = 9x$$

$$\frac{626.4}{9} = \frac{9x}{9}$$

Solve the proportion.

$$69.6 = x$$

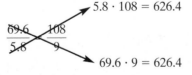

Verify the answer, 69.6. The cross products are equal (626.4 = 626.4).

The height of the lighthouse is 69.6 feet.   State the answer.

TRY-IT EXERCISE 10

Marissa is 5 feet tall. While standing near a tree in her yard one afternoon, she casts a shadow 4 feet long. At the same time, the tree casts a shadow 13 feet long. How tall is the tree?

Check your answer with the solution in Appendix A. ∎

SECTION 4.3 REVIEW EXERCISES

Concept Check

1. A proportion is a mathematical statement showing that two ratios are _____.

2. Because they express an "equality" relationship, proportions are written with one ratio on each side of an _____.

3. If $\dfrac{a}{b}$ and $\dfrac{c}{d}$ are equal ratios, their proportion is written as _____.

4. The proportion $\dfrac{a}{b} = \dfrac{c}{d}$ is read as _____.

5. To verify whether two ratios are proportional, use _____ _____ to be sure that the cross products are _____.

6. As a general rule for proportions, for $b \neq 0$ and $d \neq 0$, if $\dfrac{a}{b} = \dfrac{c}{d}$, then _____ = _____.

7. When one of the terms of a proportion is unknown, we can _____ the proportion for that term.

8. List the steps to solve a proportion.

9. To verify the answer after solving a proportion, we replace the unknown in the original proportion with the answer, and check to see that the _____ _____ are equal.

10. Similar geometric figures have the same shape and the ratios of the lengths of their corresponding sides are _____.

Objective 4.3A   Write a proportion

GUIDE PROBLEMS

11. Write 5 is to 10 as 9 is to 18 as a proportion.

    a. Write 5 to 10 as a ratio.

    b. Write 9 to 18 as a ratio.

    c. Write a proportion by separating the two ratios with an equal sign.

12. Write 25 miles is to 5 hours as 15 miles is to 3 hours as a proportion.

    a. Write 25 miles to 5 hours as a rate.

    b. Write 15 miles to 3 hours as a rate.

    c. Write a proportion by separating the two rates with an equal sign.

Write each sentence as a proportion.

13. 22 is to 44 as 7 is to 14.

14. 4 is to 7 as 60 is to 105.

15. 8 suits is to 3 weeks as 32 suits is to 12 weeks.

16. 3 ice cream cones is to 2 children as 60 ice cream cones is to 40 children.

17. 3.6 is to 5.8 as 14.4 is to 23.2.

18. 9.9 is to 1.2 as 19.8 is to 2.4.

19. 5 cans is to $8 as 15 cans is to $24.

20. 13 employees is to 5 departments as 52 employees is to 20 departments.

21. 12 is to 7 as 3.6 is to 2.1.

22. 1.5 is to 4.7 as 7.5 is to 23.5.

23. 150 calories is to 7 ounces as 300 calories is to 14 ounces.

24. 5 gallons is to 2 square feet as 25 gallons is to 10 square feet.

Write each proportion as a sentence.

25. $\dfrac{6}{3} = \dfrac{30}{15}$

26. $\dfrac{25}{4} = \dfrac{100}{16}$

27. $\dfrac{15 \text{ pages}}{2 \text{ minutes}} = \dfrac{75 \text{ pages}}{10 \text{ minutes}}$

28. $\dfrac{2 \text{ showrooms}}{9 \text{ cars}} = \dfrac{6 \text{ showrooms}}{27 \text{ cars}}$

29. $\dfrac{3 \text{ strikeouts}}{2 \text{ hits}} = \dfrac{27 \text{ strikeouts}}{18 \text{ hits}}$

30. $\dfrac{4 \text{ fish}}{60 \text{ gallons}} = \dfrac{20 \text{ fish}}{300 \text{ gallons}}$

31. $\dfrac{16}{5} = \dfrac{80}{25}$

32. $\dfrac{14}{33} = \dfrac{56}{132}$

33. $\dfrac{22.2}{65.3} = \dfrac{44.4}{130.6}$

34. $\dfrac{13.2}{17.7} = \dfrac{52.8}{70.8}$

35. $\dfrac{25 \text{ songs}}{2 \text{ CDs}} = \dfrac{125 \text{ songs}}{10 \text{ CDs}}$

36. $\dfrac{19 \text{ nurses}}{2 \text{ doctors}} = \dfrac{57 \text{ nurses}}{6 \text{ doctors}}$

| Objective 4.3B | Determine whether two ratios are proportional |

GUIDE PROBLEMS

37. Determine whether the ratios $\dfrac{55}{11}$ and $\dfrac{80}{16}$ are proportional.

  a. Multiply the denominator of the first ratio by the numerator of the second ratio.

  b. Multiply the numerator of the first ratio by the denominator of the second ratio.

  c. Are the cross products equal?

  d. Are the ratios proportional?

  e. If the ratios are proportional, write a proportion.

38. Determine whether the ratios $\dfrac{2}{18}$ and $\dfrac{8}{74}$ are proportional.

  a. Multiply the denominator of the first ratio by the numerator of the second ratio.

  b. Multiply the numerator of the first ratio by the denominator of the second ratio.

  c. Are the cross products equal?

  d. Are the ratios proportional?

  e. If the ratios are proportional, write a proportion.

Determine whether the ratios are proportional. If they are, write a corresponding proportion.

39. $\dfrac{45}{15} \overset{?}{=} \dfrac{33}{12}$

40. $\dfrac{24}{3} \overset{?}{=} \dfrac{56}{7}$

41. $\dfrac{16}{23} \overset{?}{=} \dfrac{48}{79}$

42. $\dfrac{65}{12} \overset{?}{=} \dfrac{100}{28}$

43. $\dfrac{80}{5} \overset{?}{=} \dfrac{400}{25}$

44. $\dfrac{18}{93} \overset{?}{=} \dfrac{25}{129}$

45. $\dfrac{5}{17} \overset{?}{=} \dfrac{35}{119}$

46. $\dfrac{6}{45} \overset{?}{=} \dfrac{12}{90}$

47. $\dfrac{63}{7} \overset{?}{=} \dfrac{26}{3}$

48. $\dfrac{93}{39} \overset{?}{=} \dfrac{31}{12}$

49. $\dfrac{25}{39} \overset{?}{=} \dfrac{75}{117}$

50. $\dfrac{100}{36} \overset{?}{=} \dfrac{50}{18}$

51. $\dfrac{54}{13} \overset{?}{=} \dfrac{108}{26}$

52. $\dfrac{76}{22} \overset{?}{=} \dfrac{38}{11}$

| Objective 4.3C | Solve a proportion |

GUIDE PROBLEMS

53. Solve for the unknown quantity in the proportion $\dfrac{c}{20} = \dfrac{14}{56}$.

  a. Cross multiply to find the cross products.

  b. Separate the cross products by an equal sign to form an equation.

  c. Divide both sides of the equation by the number on the side with the unknown.

  d. Simplify.

  e. To verify, replace the unknown in the original proportion with the answer, and check that the cross products are equal.

54. Solve for the unknown quantity in the proportion $\dfrac{7}{49} = \dfrac{b}{91}$.

  a. Cross multiply to find the cross products.

  b. Separate the cross products by an equal sign to form an equation.

  c. Divide both sides of the equation by the number on the side with the unknown.

  d. Simplify

  e. To verify, replace the unknown in the original proportion with the answer, and check that the cross products are equal.

Solve for the unknown quantity. Verify your answer.

55. $\dfrac{8}{5} = \dfrac{w}{90}$

56. $\dfrac{11}{12} = \dfrac{r}{84}$

57. $\dfrac{c}{35} = \dfrac{48}{70}$

58. $\dfrac{24}{5} = \dfrac{48}{s}$

59. $\dfrac{4.4}{22} = \dfrac{6}{m}$

60. $\dfrac{3.5}{k} = \dfrac{1.5}{21}$

61. $\dfrac{v}{30} = \dfrac{30}{9}$

62. $\dfrac{13}{15} = \dfrac{u}{75}$

63. $\dfrac{5}{\frac{1}{4}} = \dfrac{60}{j}$

64. $\dfrac{4}{2} = \dfrac{z}{5\frac{1}{2}}$

65. $\dfrac{2.8}{1.2} = \dfrac{8.4}{h}$

66. $\dfrac{1.6}{p} = \dfrac{3.2}{0.8}$

67. $\dfrac{16}{b} = \dfrac{64}{120}$

68. $\dfrac{5}{8} = \dfrac{v}{40}$

69. $\dfrac{6}{42} = \dfrac{8}{q}$

70. $\dfrac{t}{40} = \dfrac{12}{60}$

71. $\dfrac{y}{1.5} = \dfrac{20}{6}$

72. $\dfrac{0.75}{2} = \dfrac{x}{40}$

Objective 4.3D   Apply your knowledge

73. Last semester in an English class, 18 students out of 40 earned a grade of B. In an economics class, 54 students out of 120 earned a grade of B. Did students earn a grade of B at proportional rates in these two classes?

74. A sports car traveled 280 miles in 6 hours. A truck traveled 160 miles in 4 hours. Did these two vehicles travel at proportional rates?

75. John pays $250 per year for $10,000 of life insurance coverage. Sam pays $400 per year for $18,000 of life insurance coverage. Are John and Sam paying proportional rates for their life insurance?

76. A toy assembly line makes 25 model cars every 1.5 hours. A competitive company makes 125 model cars every 7.5 hours. Do these companies make model cars at proportional rates?

77. At an airport, 4 cargo flights arrive for every 3 passenger flights. If 32 cargo flights arrived this morning, how many passenger flights came in?

78. A patient received 438 cc of medication in 32 hours. At that rate, how many cc of medication will the patient receive in 80 hours?

79. A school field trip requires 3 buses for every 126 students. How many buses would be required for 588 students?

80. You are interested in purchasing one of the new widescreen television sets. On this type of TV, the ratio of the height of the screen to the width of the screen is 9 to 16. If a certain model you are considering has a screen height of 27 inches, what would be the width of this screen?

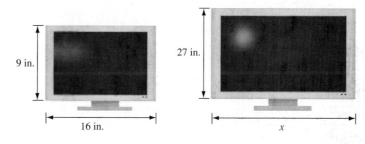

9 in.   16 in.   27 in.   x

81. A recipe calls for $1\dfrac{3}{4}$ ounces of whipped cream for every 2 cups of strawberries. If a dessert platter requires 8 cups of strawberries, how many ounces of whipped cream should be used?

82. An architect uses a scale of $\dfrac{1}{4}$ inch to represent 1 foot on a blueprint for an office building. If the west wall of the building is 60 feet long, what is the length of the line on the blueprint?

83. A savings account at the Regal Bank earns $34.50 interest for every $2000 of savings. How much interest would be earned on savings of $5400?

84. If the sales tax on $350 is $28, what would be the tax on $1500?

85. A circus is visited by people in the ratio of 8 children for every 5 adults. A total of 1500 adults attended last Tuesday.

   a. How many children attended?

   b. On the average, 1.75 bags of popcorn were sold for each child in attendance. Use your answer from part a to determine how many bags of popcorn were sold that day.

   c. If each bag of popcorn sold for $4.50, how much revenue did the popcorn concession generate last Tuesday?

86. 90 ounces of Weed Eater fertilizer cover 2400 square feet of lawn.

   a. How many ounces would be required to cover a 5300 square foot lawn?

   b. How many 25-ounce bags of fertilizer will be needed for the job? Round to the nearest whole number.

   c. If Weed Eater costs $3.25 for each 25-ounce bag, what is the total cost to fertilize the lawn?

Use the "Falling U.S. Birth Rate" graph for exercises 87–92.

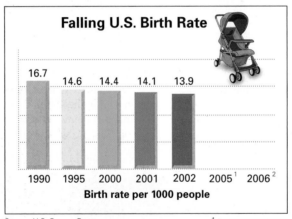

Source: U.S. Census Bureau

[1] Refer to exercise 91
[2] Refer to exercise 92

87. If a city had a population of 150,000 people in 2002, how many births would there have been. (Note: The chart lists the birth rates per 1000 people.)

88. If a city had a population of 740,000 people in 1995, how many births would there have been?

89. If a city had 5845 births in 1990, what was the population?

90. If a city had 1833 births in 2001, what was the population?

91. You have been asked to update the chart "Falling U.S. Birth Rate." The U.S. Census Bureau reported that the U.S. population at the end of 2005 was 298 million people. They also reported that there were 3,942,000 births in 2005. What was the birth rate per 1000 people for 2005? Round to the nearest tenth, if necessary.

92. Once again, you have been asked to update the chart "Falling U.S. Birth Rate." The U.S. Census Bureau reported that the U.S. population at the end of 2006 was 302 million people. They also reported that there were 3,926,000 births in 2006. What was the birth rate per 1000 people for 2006? Round to the nearest tenth, if necessary.

93. An engineer is using the concept of similar geometric figures and a small prototype model to build a triangular cover plate for an electrical circuit. What is the length of the unknown side, b, for the new cover?

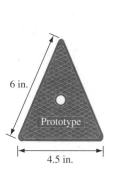
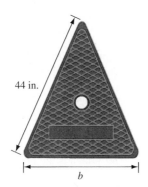

6 in.

Prototype

4.5 in.

44 in.

b

94. A rectangular corral that measures 18 feet long and 12 feet wide is being enlarged proportionately to 24 feet long. What is the width of the new corral?

Photo by Robert Brechner

95. At 1 P.M. yesterday, a palm tree with a height of 28 feet cast a shadow of 8 feet. How high is a sailboat mast next to the tree, if the mast cast a shadow of 4 feet?

28 ft

x

4 ft

8 ft

96. A power line pole 18 feet high casts a shadow 27 feet long in the bright morning sun. At the same time, the shadow of a nearby building measures 78 feet long. How tall is the building?

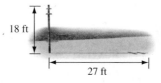

18 ft

27 ft

x

78 ft

CUMULATIVE SKILLS REVIEW

1. Divide. $2.85\overline{)9.2625}$ (3.4B)

2. Simplify the ratio of 65 to 85. (4.1B)

3. Evaluate. Simplify if necessary.

  a. $1\dfrac{1}{2} + \dfrac{2}{3}$ (2.6C)

  b. $1\dfrac{1}{2} - \dfrac{2}{3}$ (2.7C)

  c. $1\dfrac{1}{2} \cdot \dfrac{2}{3}$ (2.4B)

  d. $1\dfrac{1}{2} \div \dfrac{2}{3}$ (2.5B)

4. A local grocer sells a 12-ounce container of spinach dip for $4.80 and a 16-ounce container for $5.44. (4.2D)

  a. What is the unit price for each product?

  b. Which is the best buy?

5. Write 62.0399 in word form. (3.1B)

6. What is the least common denominator (LCD) for $\dfrac{1}{6}$ and $\dfrac{3}{7}$? (2.3C)

7. What is the cost of $3\dfrac{2}{3}$ pounds of imported Swiss cheese at $9.00 per pound? (2.4C)

8. Replace the "?" with the number that makes the statement true. (1.2A)
$(3 + 12) + 80 = \text{?} + (12 + 80)$

9. Write the ratio of 18 to 25 in three different ways. (4.1A)

10. What is the unit price of 2 chocolate cakes for $13.50? (4.2C)

10-MINUTE CHAPTER REVIEW

4.1 Understanding Ratios

Objective	Important Concepts	Illustrative Examples

A. Write and simplify a ratio	**ratio**
	A comparison of two quantities by division.
	
	terms of a ratio
	The quantities being compared.
	
	As a general rule, the ratio of a and b, where $b \neq 0$, may be written
	  • in fraction notation.
	$$\frac{a}{b}$$
	  • as two numbers separated by a *colon*.
	$$a : b$$
	  • as two numbers separated by the word *to*.
	$$a \text{ to } b$$
		Write the ratio of 9 to 26 in three different ways.
		
		9 to 26 9:26 $\dfrac{9}{26}$
		
		A box of crayons contains 4 red, 3 blue, 5 black, and 2 orange crayons. Write each ratio in three different ways.
		
		a. the ratio of orange to black crayons
		
		2 to 5 2:5 $\dfrac{2}{5}$
		
		b. the ratio of blue to the total number of crayons
		
		3 to 14 3:14 $\dfrac{3}{14}$

	Simplifying a Ratio **Step 1.** Write the ratio in fraction notation. **Step 2.** Simplify, if possible.	Simplify the ratio 12 to 27. $$\frac{12}{27} = \frac{12 \div 3}{27 \div 3} = \frac{4}{9}$$
	Simplifying a Ratio That Contains Decimals **Step 1.** Write the ratio in fraction notation. **Step 2.** Rewrite as a ratio of whole numbers. Multiply the ratio by 1 in the form $\dfrac{n}{n}$, where n is a power of 10 large enough to remove any decimals in both the numerator and the denominator. **Step 3.** Simplify, if possible.	Simplify the ratio 21.5 to 12. $$\frac{21.5}{12} = \frac{21.5}{12} \cdot \frac{10}{10} = \frac{215}{120}$$ $$\frac{215}{120} = \frac{215 \div 5}{120 \div 5} = \frac{43}{24}$$
	Simplifying a Ratio That Contains Fractions or Mixed Numbers **Step 1.** Write the ratio in fraction notation. **Step 2.** Convert any mixed numbers to improper fractions. **Step 3.** Multiply the numerator by the reciprocal of the denominator. **Step 4.** Simplify, if possible.	Simplify the ratio $4\dfrac{5}{8}$ to $2\dfrac{1}{2}$. $$\frac{4\frac{5}{8}}{2\frac{1}{2}} = \frac{\frac{37}{8}}{\frac{5}{2}}$$ $$\frac{\frac{37}{8}}{\frac{5}{2}} = \frac{37}{8} \div \frac{5}{2} = \frac{37}{8} \cdot \frac{2}{5}$$ $$\frac{37}{8} \cdot \frac{\overset{1}{2}}{5} = \frac{37}{20}$$ $\;\;\;\;{}_{4}$

| **B.** Write a ratio of converted measurement units (page 292) | Different units in the same measurement category, such as feet and inches, can be converted to either feet or inches to form the ratio.

Note: As a general rule, it is easier to write the ratio with values in terms of the *smaller* measurement units. | Simplify each ratio. Use values in terms of the smaller measurement units.

a. 62 drams to 3 ounces
$$\frac{62 \text{ drams}}{3 \text{ ounces}} = \frac{62 \text{ drams}}{48 \text{ drams}} = \frac{31}{24}$$

b. 6 yards to 27 feet
$$\frac{6 \text{ yards}}{27 \text{ feet}} = \frac{18 \text{ feet}}{27 \text{ feet}} = \frac{2}{3}$$

c. 15 minutes to 600 seconds
$$\frac{15 \text{ minutes}}{600 \text{ seconds}} = \frac{900 \text{ seconds}}{600 \text{ seconds}} = \frac{3}{2}$$

d. 12 cups to 8 pints
$$\frac{12 \text{ cups}}{8 \text{ pints}} = \frac{12 \text{ cups}}{16 \text{ cups}} = \frac{3}{4}$$ |
| **C.** Apply your knowledge (page 295) | | On a recent Royal Airways flight, 16 passengers sat in first class, 22 sat in business class, and 125 sat in coach.

a. Write a simplified ratio of the number of first class passengers to the number of business class passengers.
$$\frac{16}{22} = \frac{8}{11}$$

b. Write a ratio of the number of coach passengers to the total number of passengers.
$$\frac{125}{163}$$ |

4.2 Working with Rates and Units

Objective	Important Concepts	Illustrative Examples
A. Write and interpret a rate (page 303)	**rate** A ratio that compares two quantities that have different kinds of units. Rates are written in fraction notation with the units *included*. We include the units because they are *different* and therefore do not divide out.	Write each rate as a simplified fraction. Then write the rate in word form. **a.** 230 cows on 15 farms $$\frac{230 \text{ cows}}{15 \text{ farms}} = \frac{230 \text{ cows} \div 5}{15 \text{ farms} \div 5} = \frac{46 \text{ cows}}{3 \text{ farms}}$$ 46 cows for every 3 farms **b.** 36 boxes on 16 shelves $$\frac{36 \text{ boxes}}{16 \text{ shelves}} = \frac{36 \text{ boxes} \div 4}{16 \text{ shelves} \div 4} = \frac{9 \text{ boxes}}{4 \text{ shelves}}$$ 9 boxes for every 4 shelves

B. Write a unit rate (page 304)	**unit rate** A rate in which the number in the denominator is 1. *Writing a Unit Rate* **Step 1.** Write the rate in fraction notation with the units included. **Step 2.** Divide the numerator by the denominator. **Step 3.** Round as specified, if necessary.	Write each as a unit rate. **a.** 125 pencils in 5 containers $$\frac{125 \text{ pencils}}{5 \text{ containers}} = 25 \text{ pencils per container}$$ **b.** 45 sick days for 12 employees $$\frac{45 \text{ sick days}}{12 \text{ employees}} = 3.75 \text{ sick days per employee}$$
C. Write a unit price (page 309)	**unit price** A rate expressed as price per single item of something. Unit price is the "price per item" or "price per measure" of a particular product or service. *Writing a Unit Price* **Step 1.** Write the rate in fraction notation with the price as the numerator and the quantity (number of items or units) as the denominator. **Step 2.** Divide the numerator by the denominator. **Step 3.** Round to the nearest cent, if necessary.	Calculate the unit price for each. Round to the nearest cent, when necessary. **a.** 15 shirts ironed for $48.75 $$\frac{\$48.75}{15 \text{ shirts ironed}} = \$3.25 \text{ per ironed shirt}$$ **b.** $102 for 8 tools $$\frac{\$102}{8 \text{ tools}} = \$12.75 \text{ per tool}$$
D. Apply your knowledge (page 310)	By calculating the unit price of two or more competitive products, we can determine which choice is the best buy. Note: The best buy is the choice with the *lowest* unit price.	The Nautilus College band is selling tickets to the annual homecoming concert. Students can purchase single tickets for $30 each, 2 tickets for $57, or 4 tickets for $100. What is the unit price per ticket for each offer and which is the best buy? 1 ticket = $30.00 per ticket $$\frac{\$57}{2 \text{ tickets}} = \$28.50 \text{ per ticket}$$ $$\frac{\$100}{4 \text{ tickets}} = \$25.00 \text{ per ticket}$$ Best buy is 4 tickets for $100 Calculate the unit price for each size sack of flour, and determine which choice is the best buy. Round to the nearest cent.

SIZE	PRICE	UNIT PRICE
12 lbs.	$3.25	$0.27
14 lbs.	$3.70	$0.26
18 lbs.	$4.85	$0.27

Best buy is 14 lbs. for $3.70

4.3 Understanding and Solving Proportions

Objective	Important Concepts	Illustrative Examples
A. Write a proportion (page 313)	**proportion** A mathematical statement showing that two ratios are equal. If $\dfrac{a}{b}$ and $\dfrac{c}{d}$ are equal ratios, their proportion is written as $\dfrac{a}{b} = \dfrac{c}{d}$. It is read as "$a$ is to b as c is to d."	Write each sentence as a proportion. **a.** 12 is to 23 as 48 is to 92. $$\frac{12}{23} = \frac{48}{92}$$ **b.** 58 roses is to 3 bouquets as 174 roses is to 9 bouquets. $$\frac{58 \text{ roses}}{3 \text{ bouquets}} = \frac{174 \text{ roses}}{9 \text{ bouquets}}$$ Write each proportion as a sentence. **a.** $\dfrac{17}{9} = \dfrac{34}{18}$ 17 is to 9 as 34 is to 18. **b.** $\dfrac{2 \text{ hot air balloons}}{7 \text{ passengers}} = \dfrac{10 \text{ hot air balloons}}{35 \text{ passengers}}$ 2 hot air balloons is to 7 passengers as 10 hot air balloons is to 35 passengers.
B. Determine whether two ratios are proportional (page 315)	To verify whether two ratios are proportional, use the cross multiplication procedure learned in Section 2.6. **Determining Whether Two Ratios Are Proportional** **Step 1.** Multiply the denominator of the first ratio by the numerator of the second ratio. **Step 2.** Multiply the numerator of the first ratio by the denominator of the second ratio. **Step 3.** Determine whether or not the cross products are equal. • If the cross products are *equal*, the *ratios are proportional*, and we can write a proportion. • If the cross products are *not equal*, the *ratios are not proportional*, and we cannot write a proportion. As a general rule for proportions, for $b \neq 0$ and $d \neq 0$, if $\dfrac{a}{b} = \dfrac{c}{d}$ then $bc = ad$.	Determine whether the ratios are proportional. If they are, write a corresponding proportion. **a.** $\dfrac{13}{25} \overset{?}{=} \dfrac{2.6}{5}$ $25 \cdot 2.6 = 65$ $13 \cdot 5 = 65$ The cross products are equal ($65 = 65$). Therefore, the ratios are proportional and we can write a proportion. $$\frac{13}{25} = \frac{2.6}{5}$$ **b.** $\dfrac{15}{18} \overset{?}{=} \dfrac{45}{60}$ $18 \cdot 45 = 810$ $15 \cdot 60 = 900$ The cross products are not equal ($810 \neq 900$). Therefore, the ratios are not proportional, and we cannot write a proportion.

C. Solve a proportion (page 317)

When one of the terms of a proportion is unknown, we can *solve* the proportion for that term.

The solution is the value of the unknown that makes the proportion true.

Solving a Proportion

Step 1. Assign a letter to represent the *unknown* quantity.

Step 2. Cross multiply to find the cross products.

Step 3. Separate the cross products by an equal sign to form an equation.

Step 4. Divide both sides of the equation by the *number* on the side with the *unknown*.

Step 5. Simplify, if possible.

Step 6. Verify the answer by replacing the unknown in the original proportion with the answer, and check that the cross products are equal.

Solve for the unknown quantity and verify your answer.

$$\frac{5}{4} = \frac{r}{16}$$

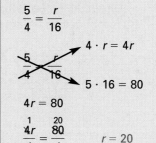

$4 \cdot r = 4r$

$5 \cdot 16 = 80$

$4r = 80$

$$\frac{\overset{1}{\cancel{4}}r}{\cancel{4}_1} = \frac{\overset{20}{\cancel{80}}}{\cancel{4}_1} \qquad r = 20$$

Verify:

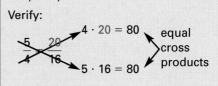

$4 \cdot 20 = 80$

$5 \cdot 16 = 80$

equal cross products

D. Apply your knowledge (page 320)

When setting up a proportion, keep in mind that *like units* must be in their respective numerators and denominators of the ratios.

Solving an Application Problem Using a Proportion

Step 1. Read and understand the problem. Assign a letter to represent the unknown quantity.

Step 2. Set up a proportion. Keep like units in their respective numerators and denominators.

Step 3. Solve and verify the proportion.

Step 4. State the answer.

A certain medication is administered to patients using the ratio of 24 milliliters for every 50 pounds of body weight. How much medication should be given to a patient who weighs 130 pounds?

Let m = the amount of medication

$$\frac{24 \text{ milliliters}}{50 \text{ pounds}} = \frac{m \text{ milliliters}}{130 \text{ pounds}}$$

$50 \cdot m = 24 \cdot 130$

$50m = 3120$

$$\frac{50m}{50} = \frac{3120}{50} \qquad m = 62.4$$

Verify:

$50 \cdot 62.4 = 3120$

$24 \cdot 130 = 3120$

equal cross products

The patient should be given 62.4 milliliters of medication.

similar geometric figures
Geometric figures with the same shape in which the ratios of the lengths of their corresponding sides are equal.

Find the value of the unknown side, h, in the similar rectangles. Verify your answer.

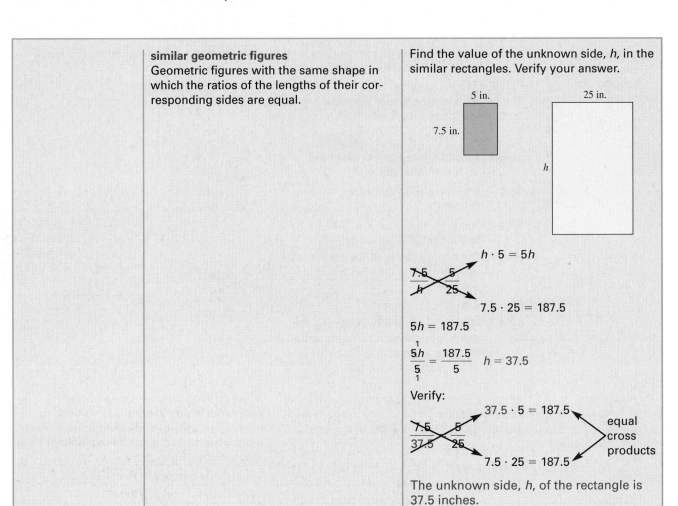

$$h \cdot 5 = 5h$$

$$\frac{7.5}{h} \times \frac{5}{25}$$

$$7.5 \cdot 25 = 187.5$$

$$5h = 187.5$$

$$\frac{\overset{1}{5}h}{\underset{1}{5}} = \frac{187.5}{5} \qquad h = 37.5$$

Verify:

$$\frac{7.5}{37.5} \times \frac{5}{25}$$

$$37.5 \cdot 5 = 187.5$$

$$7.5 \cdot 25 = 187.5$$

equal cross products

The unknown side, h, of the rectangle is 37.5 inches.

Numerical Facts of Life

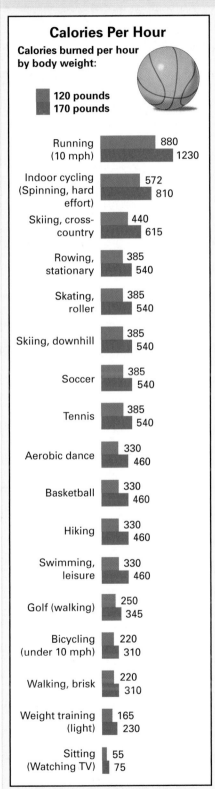

Calories Per Hour

Calories burned per hour by body weight:

- █ 120 pounds
- █ 170 pounds

Activity	120	170
Running (10 mph)	880	1230
Indoor cycling (Spinning, hard effort)	572	810
Skiing, cross-country	440	615
Rowing, stationary	385	540
Skating, roller	385	540
Skiing, downhill	385	540
Soccer	385	540
Tennis	385	540
Aerobic dance	330	460
Basketball	330	460
Hiking	330	460
Swimming, leisure	330	460
Golf (walking)	250	345
Bicycling (under 10 mph)	220	310
Walking, brisk	220	310
Weight training (light)	165	230
Sitting (Watching TV)	55	75

Source: The American Dietetic Association's Complete Food & Nutrition Guide and Medicine and Science in Sports and Exercise

Calories to Burn

Mike, your athletic friend, has asked for your help with some exercise calculations. He plays tennis, runs, and weighs 185 pounds.

1. If a 170 pound person burns 1230 calories per hour while running, how many calories per hour does Mike burn while running? Round to the nearest whole number.

2. If a 170 pound person burns 540 calories per hour playing tennis, how many calories per hour does Mike burn playing tennis? Round to the nearest whole number.

3. How many calories per hour does he burn running for each calorie burned playing tennis? Round to the nearest tenth.

4. Research tells us that each pound of body fat contains 3500 calories. Theoretically, how many pounds will Mike lose by running 4 hours per week for 6 weeks? Round to the nearest tenth.

CHAPTER REVIEW EXERCISES

Write each ratio in three different ways. (4.1A)

1. the ratio of 3 to 8

2. the ratio of 62 to 7

3. the ratio of 12 to 5.2

4. the ratio of 9 to 14.3

5. the ratio of 3 to $\frac{5}{9}$

6. the ratio of $2\frac{1}{2}$ to $\frac{1}{16}$

Simplify each ratio. (4.1B)

7. 10 to 16

8. 58 to 6

9. 16 to 52

10. 24 to 21

11. 5 to 12.5

12. 1.1 to 15

13. 2 to $\frac{7}{8}$

14. $\frac{9}{17}$ to 7

Write a simplified ratio. Use values in terms of the smaller measurement units. (4.1C)

15. 110 feet to 16 yards

16. 3 pounds to 20 ounces

17. 12 minutes to 220 seconds

18. 10,000 feet to 4 miles

19. 8500 pounds to 5 tons

20. 12 quarts to 50 pints

21. 280 days to 16 weeks

22. 5.5 gallons to 12 quarts

Write each rate as a simplified fraction. Then write the rate in word form. (4.2A)

23. 75 sprinklers for 6 acres

24. 392 avocados for 40 trees

25. 38 kittens for 3 pet stores

26. $98 for 4 tires

27. 30 ponies for 12 trainers

28. 120 cheeseburgers for $200

Write each as a unit rate. Round to the nearest tenth, if necessary. (4.2B)

29. 60 miles in 5 days

30. 1588 pounds in 2 trucks

31. 18 yards in 7 minutes

32. 9615 jellybeans in 12 bags

33. 168 cars in 6 lanes

34. 13,005 bees in 9 beehives

35. 47 tons of fuel in 3 cruises

36. 25 pounds in 8 weeks

Calculate the unit price for each. Round to the nearest cent, if necessary. (4.2C)

37. 5 tickets for $90

38. 15 T-shirts for $187.50

39. $14 for 2 car washes

40. $695 for 4 days

41. 6 flight lessons for $510

42. 125 sugar cookies for $81.25

43. $4.75 for 3 tennis balls

44. $12,900 for 3 sales events

Write each sentence as a proportion. (4.3A)

45. 9 is to 11 as 36 is to 44.

46. 124 graduates is to 3 schools as 248 graduates is to 6 schools.

47. 3 is to 5 as 300 is to 500.

48. 2 days is to 95 mail orders as 6 days is to 285 mail orders.

49. 2.1 is to 6.5 as 16.8 is to 52.

50. 5 concerts is to 7 days as 15 concerts is to 21 days.

Write each proportion as a sentence. (4.3A)

51. $\dfrac{30 \text{ violins}}{5 \text{ orchestras}} = \dfrac{90 \text{ violins}}{15 \text{ orchestras}}$

52. $\dfrac{9}{13} = \dfrac{81}{117}$

53. $\dfrac{3 \text{ tours}}{450 \text{ bicycles}} = \dfrac{6 \text{ tours}}{900 \text{ bicycles}}$

54. $\dfrac{12}{33} = \dfrac{36}{99}$

55. $\dfrac{8 \text{ swings}}{3 \text{ playgrounds}} = \dfrac{16 \text{ swings}}{6 \text{ playgrounds}}$

56. $\dfrac{3.7}{1.2} = \dfrac{37}{12}$

Determine whether the ratios are proportional. If they are, write a corresponding proportion. (4.3B)

57. $\dfrac{18}{17} \overset{?}{=} \dfrac{54}{51}$

58. $\dfrac{6}{1.9} \overset{?}{=} \dfrac{18}{5.4}$

59. $\dfrac{39}{28} \overset{?}{=} \dfrac{13}{9}$

60. $\dfrac{35}{21} \overset{?}{=} \dfrac{70}{42}$

61. $\dfrac{7.5}{11} \overset{?}{=} \dfrac{60}{88}$

62. $\dfrac{2.3}{5.5} \overset{?}{=} \dfrac{9.2}{22}$

Solve for the unknown quantity. Verify your answer. (4.3C)

63. $\dfrac{2}{5} = \dfrac{14}{g}$

64. $\dfrac{28}{100} = \dfrac{y}{25}$

65. $\dfrac{m}{3} = \dfrac{46}{2}$

66. $\dfrac{t}{3} = \dfrac{44}{6}$

67. $\dfrac{18}{0.5} = \dfrac{a}{3}$

68. $\dfrac{1.6}{f} = \dfrac{4}{40}$

69. $\dfrac{4}{u} = \dfrac{24}{18}$

70. $\dfrac{b}{2} = \dfrac{30}{12}$

71. $\dfrac{q}{7} = \dfrac{20}{3.5}$

72. $\dfrac{2.5}{10} = \dfrac{r}{12}$

73. $\dfrac{2\frac{1}{4}}{h} = \dfrac{9}{12}$

74. $\dfrac{3\frac{1}{4}}{6\frac{1}{2}} = \dfrac{4}{x}$

Solve each application problem. (4.1D, 4.2D, 4.3D)

75. There are 14 girls and 27 boys in a middle school mathematics class.

   a. Write a ratio in three different ways that represents the number of girls to the number of boys in the class.

   b. Write a ratio in three different ways that represents the number of boys to the total number of students in the class.

76. Starpointe Homes is developing 33 townhomes and 125 condominium units at the Wispy Willow Resort.

   a. Write a ratio in three different ways that represents the number of condominiums to the number of townhomes.

   b. Write a ratio in three different ways that represents the total number of homes to the number of condominiums.

77. Randy's job required him to travel 65 miles on Monday, 40 miles on Tuesday, 25 miles on Wednesday, and 50 miles on Thursday.

   a. Write a simplified ratio of the miles Randy traveled on Monday to the number of miles he traveled on Wednesday.

   b. Write a simplified ratio of the number of miles Randy traveled on Tuesday to the miles he traveled on Thursday.

   c. Write a simplified ratio of the number of miles Randy traveled on Monday to the total number of miles he traveled.

78. At Bayview Community College last semester, 150 students earned associate in arts degrees, 225 students earned associate in science degrees, and 60 students earned various bachelor degrees.

   a. Write a simplified ratio of the number of associate in science degrees to the number of bachelor degrees awarded.

   b. Write a simplified ratio of the number of associate in arts degrees to the number of associate in science degrees awarded.

   c. Write a simplified ratio of the number of bachelor degrees to the total number of degrees awarded.

79. An industrial coffeemaker can brew 4 cups of coffee in 3 minutes.

   a. Write a rate for the coffee machine's brewing time.

   b. Write a unit rate for the coffee machine's brewing time.

   c. If the coffee beans needed to brew 4 cups of coffee cost $1.80, what is the unit price per cup of coffee?

80. Gardiner's Market offers freshly squeezed orange juice daily. The market uses a machine that requires 27 oranges for every 5 pints of orange juice.

   a. Write a rate that represents the performance of the juice machine.

   b. Write a unit rate that represents the performance for the juice machine.

   c. If the average cost of 27 oranges is $11.50, what is the unit price per pint of orange juice?

For exercises 81–84, determine which choice is the best buy, based on the lowest unit price.

81. A 10-ounce bag of popcorn for $1.20 or a 13-ounce bag of popcorn for $1.69

82. 12 ferry rides for $34.80, 6 ferry rides for $18, or 3 ferry rides for $9.75

83. 2 dozen bagels for $5.95 or 3 dozen bagels for $8.75

84. 9 yoga classes for $50, 12 yoga classes for $64.20, or 15 yoga classes for $84.75

85. Josh bought a 1600 square foot condominium for $152,000. His friend Todd bought a 1950 square foot condominium for $185,250. Are their rates of cost per square foot proportional? If they are, write a corresponding proportion.

86. An inkjet printer can produce five 8 × 10 color prints every 7 minutes. A competitive printer produces seven 8 × 10 color prints every 9 minutes. Are their printing rates proportional? If they are, write a corresponding proportion.

87. The Green Thumb Gardening Service can cut 15 acres of grass every 3 hours. A competitor, Majestic Lawn Service, can cut 19 acres of grass every 4 hours. Are their grass-cutting rates proportional? If they are, write a corresponding proportion.

88. Harold spends $52 on fuel every 8 days. Jenna spends $32.50 every 5 days. Are their fuel consumption rates proportional? If they are, write a corresponding proportion.

89. The Canine College offers training classes for puppies. The ratio is 5 puppies for every 3 instructors. How many puppies can attend a class with 9 instructors?

90. Jim is building a new horse corral at his ranch. The current corral occupies 1500 square feet and accommodates 5 horses. If he plans to increase the size of the corral proportionately to accommodate 12 horses, how many square feet of corral will be needed?

91. A teacher is given 45 notebooks for each 20 students. How many notebooks are needed for a class of 60 students?

92. Zona's Restaurant offers a 20-ounce soda for $2.50. At this rate, how much should they charge for the new 26-ounce size?

93. Shaun's new job requires that he work 50 minutes for every 5-minute break. If he wants to take a 30-minute break, how many hours will he have to work?

94. Alicia has taken 10 classes in 3 semesters. At that rate, how many classes will she take in 12 semesters?

95. The Magnum nail gun uses 65 nails every $1\frac{1}{2}$ minutes. How many nails will be used in 20 minutes? Round to the nearest whole number.

96. A recipe for peach pie requires $\frac{3}{4}$ cup of sugar for every 3 pounds of peaches. How many pounds of peaches are needed for a mix that contains 2 cups of sugar?

97. Brad, a construction worker, buys 3 pairs of work boots every 6 months. How many pairs will he buy in 2 years?

98. Claudia's car gets 28 miles per gallon. How many gallons of gasoline will she need for a 1498 mile trip? Round to the nearest tenth.

99. A new reality TV show expects to have 3,000,000 viewers over a 4-night period. How many viewers are expected in a 7-night period?

100. A new water-saving lawn sprinkler uses 20 gallons of water every 5 minutes. How many gallons of water will be used in 1 hour?

101. Galaxy Ceramics makes flower pots in various sizes for sale to nurseries and garden shops. The company uses the concept of similar geometric figures to size the pots in their product line. Calculate the value of the unknown height, x, of a smaller flower pot being added to the Galaxy product line.

102. The Atlas Pool Company built the L-shaped pool pictured on the left for a residential client. Now, they are building a larger, geometrically similar, version of the pool for a local hotel. Calculate the unknown side, z, of the new pool.

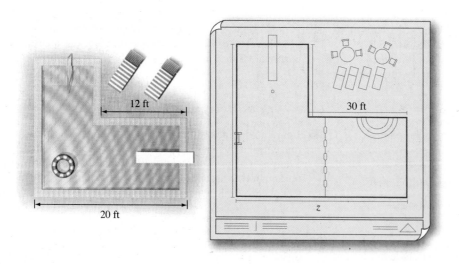

103. A dock piling 10 feet high casts a shadow 14 feet long in the bright morning sun. At the same time, the shadow of a nearby sailboat mast measures 56 feet long. How tall is the mast?

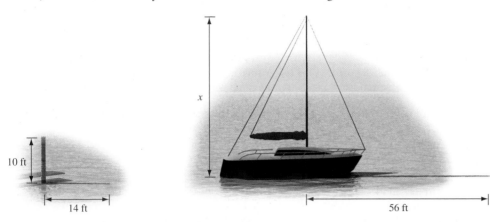

10 ft

14 ft

x

56 ft

104. On a construction site, a crane 80 feet high casts a shadow 25 feet long. At the same time, the shadow of the building under construction is 60 feet long. How tall is the building?

80 ft

x

25 ft

60 ft

Use the information about the Boeing 787 compared to the 767 and the Airbus A330 for exercises 105–110.

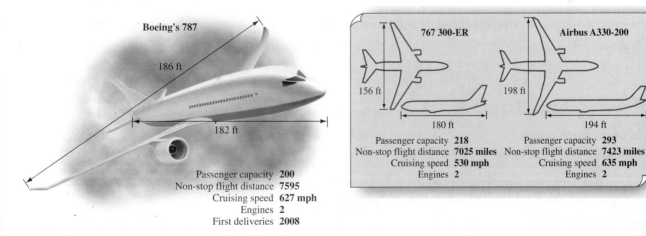

Boeing's 787

186 ft

182 ft

Passenger capacity	**200**
Non-stop flight distance	**7595**
Cruising speed	**627 mph**
Engines	**2**
First deliveries	**2008**

767 300-ER

156 ft

180 ft

Passenger capacity	**218**
Non-stop flight distance	**7025 miles**
Cruising speed	**530 mph**
Engines	**2**

Airbus A330-200

198 ft

194 ft

Passenger capacity	**293**
Non-stop flight distance	**7423 miles**
Cruising speed	**635 mph**
Engines	**2**

105. Write a simplified ratio in three different ways to represent the wingspan of the Boeing 787 to the wingspan of the Airbus A330.

106. Write a simplified ratio in three different ways to represent the length of the Boeing 787 to the length of the Boeing 767.

107. Write a simplified ratio in word form for the cruising speed of the Airbus A330 to the cruising speed of the Boeing 767.

108. Write a simplified ratio in word form for the passenger capacity of the Boeing 787 to the passenger capacity of the Boeing 767.

109. Boeing is considering a "stretch" model of the 787 with the same wingspan-to-length ratio as the base model.

    a. What is the wingspan-to-length ratio of the base model?

    b. If the proposed length of the "stretch" model is 198 feet, what would be the wingspan of the new aircraft? Round to the nearest foot.

110. Airbus is considering a "short" model of the A330 with the same wingspan-to-length ratio as the base model.

    a. What is the wingspan-to-length ratio of the base model?

    b. If the proposed wingspan of the "short" model is 180 feet, what would be the length of the new aircraft? Round to the nearest foot.

ASSESSMENT TEST

Write each ratio in three different ways.

1. the ratio of 28 to 65

2. the ratio of 5.8 to 2.1

Simplify each ratio.

3. 16 to 24

4. 15 to 6

5. 68 to 36

6. 2.5 to 75

Write a simplified ratio. Use values in terms of the smaller measurement units.

7. 2 days to 15 hours

8. 5 quarts to 3 pints

Write each rate as a simplified fraction. Then write the rate in word form.

9. 56 apples for 10 baskets

10. 12 cabinets for 88 files

Write each as a unit rate. Round to the nearest tenth, if necessary.

11. 385 miles for 12 gallons

12. 12 birds in 4 cages

Calculate the unit price for each.

13. $675 for 4 dining room chairs

14. $5.76 for 12 tropical fish

Write each sentence as a proportion.

15. 3 is to 45 as 18 is to 270.

16. 9 labels is to 4 folders as 45 labels is to 20 folders.

Write each proportion as a sentence.

17. $\dfrac{2}{17} = \dfrac{6}{51}$

18. $\dfrac{12 \text{ photos}}{5 \text{ hours}} = \dfrac{24 \text{ photos}}{10 \text{ hours}}$

Determine whether the ratios are proportional. If they are, write a corresponding proportion.

19. $\dfrac{7}{16} \overset{?}{=} \dfrac{35}{80}$

20. $\dfrac{22}{18} \overset{?}{=} \dfrac{14}{12}$

Solve for the unknown quantity. Verify your answer.

21. $\dfrac{5}{p} = \dfrac{125}{150}$

22. $\dfrac{8}{13} = \dfrac{c}{52}$

23. $\dfrac{22}{19} = \dfrac{55}{m}$

24. $\dfrac{t}{3.5} = \dfrac{27}{10.5}$

Solve each application problem.

25. During a football game, a fullback ran for 160 yards in 12 carries.

   a. Write a simplified ratio in three different ways to illustrate the player's performance.

   b. Write a unit rate of his performance. Round to the nearest tenth.

For questions 26 and 27, determine which choice is the best buy, based on the lowest unit price.

26. 5 pounds of bananas for $7.25 or 3 pounds of bananas for $4.20

27. 18 ounces of sugar for $3.60, 24 ounces of sugar for $4.08, or 32 ounces of sugar for $5.76

28. An automated assembly line can make 45 stuffed animals every 4 minutes. A competitive company can make 78 stuffed animals every 7 minutes. Are these assembly lines operating at proportional rates?

29. On a map, the scale is 4 inches equals 35 miles. If two cities are 2.6 inches apart on the map, how far apart are they in reality?

30. A lamppost 12 feet high casts a shadow 20 feet long in the afternoon sun. At the same time, the shadow of a nearby building is 130 feet long. How tall is the building?

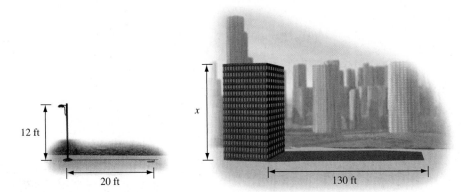

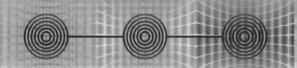

Percents

Atmospheric Scientists

According to the United States Bureau of Labor Statistics, atmospheric scientists, also known as meteorologists, study the atmosphere's physical characteristics, motions, and processes.[1] Using sophisticated mathematical models and computers, atmospheric scientists study the connections between the atmosphere and our environment. In recent years, they have paid particular attention to climate trends, particularly global warming. Effects of global warming include increased risk of drought and wildfire, more intense storms and hurricanes, and glacial melting.

In analyzing the consequences of global warming, atmospheric scientists often use percents. For example, they note that an Antarctic ice shelf larger than the state of Rhode Island has shrunk by nearly 40% since 1995.[2] They also have observed that annual precipitation has increased by up to 10% across the United States since the beginning of the 20th century. Perhaps atmospheric scientists are best known for local, short-term weather prediction. You have almost certainly heard a meteorologist say something like, "There is a 30% chance of rain tonight," or "The humidity stands at 81%."

In this chapter, we will learn about percents. We will also focus on solving practical application problems that involve percents.

[1]from *U.S. Bureau of Labor Statistics Occupational Outlook Handbook*
[2]from *Natural Resources Defense Council* (*www.nrdc.org*)

5.1   INTRODUCTION TO PERCENTS

Percents are used frequently in our everyday lives. Here are some examples.

- The Centers for Disease Control anticipates a 12% increase in flu cases this season.
- Apple, Inc. stock jumps 5% on news that the company will produce a new type of iPod.
- The polar ice caps are shrinking at a rate of 9% each decade.
- Oil and gas production fell by 8.2% in the fourth quarter last year.

It takes only a glance at a newspaper to see that percents are used to describe many situations. In this section, we investigate percents and discuss various ways of representing them.

| Objective 5.1A | **Convert a percent to a fraction or a decimal** |

The word *percent* comes from the Latin phrase *per centum,* which translates as *per hundred.* Thus, a **percent** is a part per 100. The % symbol is called the **percent sign.** As an example, 41% represents the fraction $\frac{41}{100}$. We say that 41% of the figure below is shaded.

percent
A part per 100.

percent sign
The % symbol.

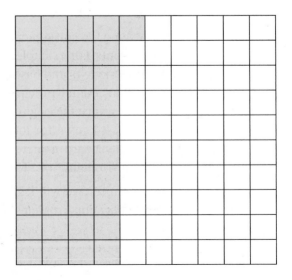

To convert a percent to a fraction, we use the following rule.

Rule for Converting a Percent to a Fraction

Write the number preceding the percent sign over 100. Simplify, if possible.

EXAMPLE 1   Convert a percent to a fraction

Convert each percent to a fraction. Simplify, if possible.

a. 7%   **b.** 100%   **c.** 145%   **d.** 7.8%   **e.** $\dfrac{3}{4}$%

SOLUTION STRATEGY

a. $7\% = \dfrac{7}{100}$

Write 7 over 100.

b. $100\% = \dfrac{100}{100} = 1$

Write 100 over 100. Simplify.

c. $145\% = \dfrac{145}{100} = \dfrac{29}{20} = 1\dfrac{9}{20}$

Write 145 over 100. Simplify. Express as a mixed number.

d. $7.8\% = \dfrac{7.8}{100} = \dfrac{7.8}{100} \cdot \dfrac{10}{10} = \dfrac{78}{1000} = \dfrac{39}{500}$

Write 7.8 over 100. Multiply by 1 in the form of $\dfrac{10}{10}$ to obtain a whole number in the numerator. Simplify.

e. $\dfrac{3}{4}\% = \dfrac{\frac{3}{4}}{100} = \dfrac{3}{4} \div \dfrac{100}{1} = \dfrac{3}{4} \cdot \dfrac{1}{100} = \dfrac{3}{400}$

Write $\dfrac{3}{4}$ over 100. Divide $\dfrac{3}{4}$ by 100. To do so, multiply $\dfrac{3}{4}$ by $\dfrac{1}{100}$.

TRY-IT EXERCISE 1

Convert each percent to a fraction. Simplify, if possible.

a. 19%   **b.** 38%   **c.** 266%   **d.** 18.4%   **e.** $\dfrac{9}{16}$%

Check your answers with the solutions in Appendix A. ■

In the part e of Example 1, we wrote $\dfrac{3}{4}$% as $\dfrac{\frac{3}{4}}{100}$. To simplify this complex fraction, we must divide the numerator by the denominator. In this example, we divide $\dfrac{3}{4}$ by

---

● Learning Tip

Calculators with a % key can be used to convert percents to decimals. Enter the number preceding the percent sign and press the % key. If the % key on your calculator is the second operation of a particular key, you will first have to press 2nd or SHIFT.

For example, to convert 5.4% to a decimal, enter the following.

or

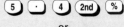

or

5 · 4 SHIFT %

The display will read 0.054.

100. To perform this division problem, we *multiply* $\frac{3}{4}$ by the *reciprocal of 100*, namely, $\frac{1}{100}$. When we do this we obtain the fraction $\frac{3}{400}$.

This example points to an important fact: dividing by 100 is the same as multiplying by $\frac{1}{100}$. Therefore, $n\% = n \cdot \frac{1}{100}$. As an example, consider 27%.

$$27\% = 27 \cdot \frac{1}{100} = \frac{27}{100}$$

To convert a percent to a decimal, we use the fact that $\frac{1}{100} = 0.01$.

$$27\% = 27 \cdot \frac{1}{100} = 27 \cdot 0.01 = 0.27$$

Recall that when we multiply a number by 0.01, we ultimately move the decimal point two places to the left.

Rule for Converting a Percent to a Decimal

Multiply the number preceding the percent sign by 0.01. Alternatively, drop the percent sign and move the decimal two places to the *left*.

EXAMPLE 2   Convert a percent to a decimal

Convert each percent to a decimal.

a. 18%   **b.** 100%   **c.** 230%   **d.** 41.3%   **e.** 0.05%   **f.** $\frac{3}{8}\%$

SOLUTION STRATEGY

a. $18\% = 18 \cdot 0.01 = 0.18$ Multiply the number preceding the percent sign by 0.01.

b. $100\% = 100 \cdot 0.01 = 1.00 = 1$ Or, alternatively, drop the percent sign and move the decimal point two places to the left.

c. $230\% = 230 \cdot 0.01 = 2.30 = 2.3$

d. $41.3\% = 41.3 \cdot 0.01 = 0.413$

e. $0.05\% = 0.05 \cdot 0.01 = 0.0005$

f. $\frac{3}{8}\% = 0.375\% = 0.375 \cdot 0.01 = 0.00375$

TRY-IT EXERCISE 2

Convert each percent to a decimal.

a. 89%   **b.** 7%   **c.** 420%   **d.** 32.6%   **e.** 0.008%   **f.** $3\frac{7}{8}\%$

Check your answers with the solutions in Appendix A. ∎

Objective 5.1B	**Convert a decimal, a fraction, or a whole number to a percent**

Consider the decimal 0.53. We can write 0.53 as a fraction and then convert the fraction to a percent.

$$0.53 = \frac{53}{100} = 53\%$$

Alternatively, we can use the fact that 100% = 1.

$$0.53 = 0.53 \cdot 1 = 0.53 \cdot 100\% = 53\%$$

In either case, we see that 0.53 = 53%. Notice that we ultimately move the decimal point two places to the right and append a percent sign.

Rule for Converting a Decimal to a Percent

Multiply the decimal by 100%. Alternatively, move the decimal point two places to the *right* and append a percent sign.

EXAMPLE 3   Convert a decimal or a whole number to a percent

Convert each decimal or whole number to a percent.

a. 0.75   **b.** 0.2   **c.** 0.049   **d.** 0.006   **e.** 8

SOLUTION STRATEGY

a. $0.75 = 0.75 \cdot 100\% = 75\%$ Multiply the decimal number by 100%.

b. $0.2 = 0.2 \cdot 100\% = 20\%$ Or, alternatively, move the decimal point two places to the right and append a percent sign.

c. $0.049 = 0.049 \cdot 100\% = 4.9\%$

d. $0.006 = 0.006 \cdot 100\% = 0.6\%$

e. $8 = 8.0 = 8.0 \cdot 100\% = 800\%$

TRY-IT EXERCISE 3

Convert each decimal or whole number to a percent.

a. 0.91   **b.** 7.2   **c.** 0.009   **d.** 3   **e.** 1.84

Check your answers with the solutions in Appendix A. ■

In Section 3.5, we learned how to convert a fraction to a decimal. To convert a fraction to a percent, first write the fraction as a decimal and then convert the decimal to a percent.

Steps for Converting a Fraction to a Percent

Step 1. Convert the fraction to a decimal.

Step 2. Convert the decimal to a percent.

EXAMPLE 4   Convert a fraction or mixed number to a percent

Convert each fraction, mixed number, or whole number to a percent.

a. $\dfrac{5}{8}$ **b.** $\dfrac{18}{25}$ **c.** $1\dfrac{4}{5}$ **d.** $\dfrac{17}{4}$ **e.** $\dfrac{2}{3}$

SOLUTION STRATEGY

a. $\dfrac{5}{8}$

$$8)\overline{5.000} \quad 0.625$$

$$0.625 = 0.625 \cdot 100\% = 62.5\%$$

Convert each fraction to a decimal, and multiply by 100%.

Or, alternatively, convert each fraction to a decimal, move the decimal point two places to the right, and append a percent sign.

b. $\dfrac{18}{25}$

$$25)\overline{18.00} \quad 0.72$$

$$0.72 = 0.72 \cdot 100\% = 72\%$$

c. $1\dfrac{4}{5}$

$$5)\overline{4.0} \quad 0.8$$

$$1\dfrac{4}{5} = 1 + \dfrac{4}{5} = 1 + 0.8 = 1.8$$

$$1.8 = 1.8 \cdot 100\% = 180\%$$

d. $\dfrac{17}{4}$

$$\begin{array}{r} 4.25 \\ 4{\overline{)17.00}} \end{array}$$

$4.25 = 4.25 \cdot 100\% = 425\%$

e. $\dfrac{2}{3}$

$$\begin{array}{r} 0.\overline{6} \\ 3{\overline{)2.0}} \end{array}$$

$0.\overline{6} = 0.66\overline{6} = 0.66\overline{6} \cdot 100\% = 66.\overline{6}\% = 66\dfrac{2}{3}\%$

Learning Tip

A percent with a repeating decimal may be rounded or written as a fraction.

$$66.\overline{6}\% \approx 66.7\%$$

or

$$66.\overline{6}\% = 66\dfrac{2}{3}\%$$

TRY-IT EXERCISE 4

Convert each fraction, mixed number, or whole number to a percent.

a. $\dfrac{3}{8}$ **b.** $\dfrac{49}{100}$ **c.** $2\dfrac{1}{4}$ **d.** $\dfrac{22}{5}$ **e.** $\dfrac{1}{3}$

Check your answers with the solutions in Appendix A. ∎

For reference, some of the most commonly used fraction, decimal, and percent equivalents are listed in Table 5.1. Although you now know how to mathematically convert between these, it may be helpful to memorize them for your future use.

TABLE 5.1   FRACTION, DECIMAL, AND PERCENT EQUIVALENTS

FRACTION	DECIMAL	PERCENT	FRACTION	DECIMAL	PERCENT
$\dfrac{1}{100}$	0.01	1%	$\dfrac{2}{5}$	0.4	40%
$\dfrac{1}{25}$	0.04	4%	$\dfrac{1}{2}$	0.5	50%
$\dfrac{1}{20}$	0.05	5%	$\dfrac{3}{5}$	0.6	60%
$\dfrac{1}{10}$	0.1	10%	$\dfrac{5}{8}$	0.625	62.5%
$\dfrac{1}{8}$	0.125	12.5%	$\dfrac{2}{3}$	0.66$\overline{6}$	$66\dfrac{2}{3}\%$
$\dfrac{1}{6}$	0.16$\overline{6}$	$16\dfrac{2}{3}\%$	$\dfrac{3}{4}$	0.75	75%
$\dfrac{1}{5}$	0.2	20%	$\dfrac{4}{5}$	0.8	80%
$\dfrac{1}{4}$	0.25	25%	$\dfrac{5}{6}$	0.833$\overline{3}$	$83\dfrac{1}{3}\%$
$\dfrac{1}{3}$	0.33$\overline{3}$	$33\dfrac{1}{3}\%$	$\dfrac{7}{8}$	0.875	87.5%
$\dfrac{3}{8}$	0.375	37.5%	$\dfrac{1}{1}$	1	100%

| Objective 5.1C | Apply your knowledge |

EXAMPLE 5 **Convert a decimal to a percent**

a. In a biology class, 0.425 of the students are women. Convert this decimal to a percent.

b. The property tax rate in Canmore County is 0.0372. Convert this decimal to a percent.

SOLUTION STRATEGY

a. $0.425 = 0.425 \cdot 100\% = 42.5\%$ Multiply each decimal number by 100%.

b. $0.0372 = 0.0372 \cdot 100\% = 3.72\%$ Or, alternatively, move the decimal point two places to the right and append a percent sign.

TRY-IT EXERCISE 5

a. According to a recent survey, 0.263 of newspapers sold each day are home delivered. Convert this decimal to a percent.

b. It is estimated that 0.014 of DVD players on the market currently have the progressive scan feature. Convert this decimal to a percent.

Check your answers with the solution in Appendix A. ■

EXAMPLE 6 **Convert a percent to a decimal**

Use the bar graph *Pizza Chain Preferences* to answer the following questions.

Pizza Chain Preferences

In a recent survey, college students were asked to identify their favorite pizza chain.

Pizza Hut	Domino's	Little Caesars	Papa John's	Other
13.4%	8.4%	5.3%	4.6%	68.3%

a. Convert the preference percent for Domino's to a decimal.

b. Convert the preference percent for Papa John's to a decimal.

SOLUTION STRATEGY

a. $8.4\% = 8.4 \cdot 0.01 = 0.084$ Multiply the number preceding the percent sign by 0.01.

b. $4.6\% = 4.6 \cdot 0.01 = 0.046$ Or, alternatively, move the decimal point two places to the left.

TRY-IT EXERCISE 6

Use the bar graph *Pizza Chain Preferences* to answer the following questions.

a. Convert the preference percent for Other to a decimal.

b. Convert the preference percent for Pizza Hut to a decimal.

c. Convert the preference percent for Little Caesars to a decimal.

Check your answers with the solutions in Appendix A. ■

EXAMPLE 7   Convert a decimal to a percent

Use the bar graph *AFC Teams Post-Season Winnings* to answer the following questions.

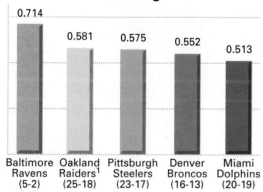

AFC Teams Post-Season Winnings

0.714 Baltimore Ravens (5-2)
0.581 Oakland Raiders[1] (25-18)
0.575 Pittsburgh Steelers (23-17)
0.552 Denver Broncos (16-13)
0.513 Miami Dolphins (20-19)

[1] Includes 12 games played when franchise was in Los Angeles

a. Convert the decimal for the Baltimore Ravens to a percent.

b. Convert the decimal for the Miami Dolphins to a percent.

SOLUTION STRATEGY

a. $0.714 = 0.714 \cdot 100\% = 71.4\%$ Multiply each decimal number by 100%.

b. $0.513 = 0.513 \cdot 100\% = 51.3\%$ Or, alternatively, move the decimal point two places to the right and append a percent sign.

TRY-IT EXERCISE 7

Use the bar graph *AFC Teams Post-Season Winnings* to answer the following questions.

a. Convert the decimal for the Denver Broncos to a percent.

b. Convert the decimal for the Oakland Raiders to a percent.

c. Convert the decimal for the Pittsburgh Steelers to a percent.

Check your answers with the solutions in Appendix A. ∎

EXAMPLE 8   Convert a fraction to a percent

Use the graph *Sodium Intake* to answer the following questions.

Sodium Intake

The average person intakes much more sodium than what's needed, which is slightly more than half a teaspoon of table salt each day. The actual numbers in milligrams are given below.

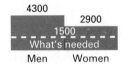

Where Americans get their sodium

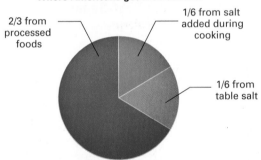

a. What percent of sodium do Americans get from table salt? Round to the nearest hundredth of a percent.

b. The ratio of "sodium intake to what's needed" for men is $\dfrac{4300}{1500}$. Convert this to the nearest whole percent.

SOLUTION STRATEGY

a. $\dfrac{1}{6} = 0.166\overline{6} \approx 0.1667 = 16.67\%$ Convert the fraction to a decimal. Convert the decimal to a percent.

b. $\dfrac{4300}{1500} = 2.86\overline{6} \approx 2.87 = 287\%$ Convert the fraction to a decimal. Convert the decimal to a percent.

TRY-IT EXERCISE 8

Use the graph *Sodium Intake* to answer the following questions.

a. What percent of sodium do Americans get from processed foods? Round to the nearest tenth of a percent.

b. The ratio of "sodium intake to what's needed" for women is $\dfrac{2900}{1500}$. Convert this to the nearest whole percent.

Check your answers with the solutions in Appendix A. ∎

EXAMPLE 9   Convert percents to decimals and fractions

Use the graph *More Adults Than Children* to answer the following questions.

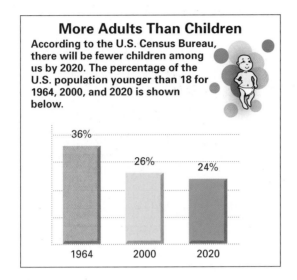

a. What decimal of the population were children in 1964?

b. What fraction of the population were children in 1964?

SOLUTION STRATEGY

a. $36\% = 0.36$ Convert the percent to a decimal.

b. $0.36 = \dfrac{36}{100} = \dfrac{9}{25}$ Convert the decimal to a fraction. Simplify.

TRY-IT EXERCISE 9

Use the graph *More Adults Than Children* to answer the following questions.

a. What decimal and what fraction of the population were children in 2000?

b. What decimal and what fraction of the population are estimated to be children in 2020?

Check your answers with the solutions in Appendix A. ■

SECTION 5.1 REVIEW EXERCISES

Concept Check

1. A _____ is a part per 100.

2. The % symbol is called the _____ _____.

3. To convert a percent to a fraction, write the number preceding the percent sign over _____. Simplify, if possible.

4. To convert a percent to a decimal, multiply the number preceding the percent sign by _____. Alternatively, drop the percent sign and move the decimal point two places to the _____.

5. To convert a decimal to a percent, multiply the decimal by _____. Alternatively, move the decimal point two places to the _____ and append a percent sign.

6. To convert a fraction to a percent, first convert the fraction to a _____.

7. Consider the following figure.

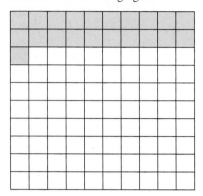

   a. What percent is represented by the shaded area?

   b. What percent is represented by the unshaded area?

8. Consider the following figure.

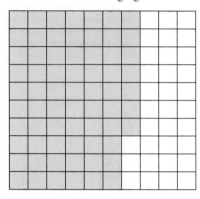

   a. What percent is represented by the shaded area?

   b. What percent is represented by the unshaded area?

Objective 5.1A	Convert a percent to a fraction or a decimal

GUIDE PROBLEMS

9. Consider 32%.

   a. Convert 32% to a fraction.

$$32\% = \frac{\overline{\quad\quad}}{100}$$

   b. Simplify the fraction in part a.

$$\frac{\overline{\quad\quad}}{100} = \frac{\overline{\quad\quad}}{\underline{\quad\quad}}$$

11. Convert 29% to a decimal.

$$29\% = 29 \cdot 0.01 = \underline{\quad\quad}$$

10. Consider 19.5%.

   a. Convert 19.5% to a fraction.

$$19.5\% = \frac{\overline{\quad\quad}}{100} \cdot \frac{\overline{\quad\quad}}{\underline{\quad\quad}} = \frac{\overline{\quad\quad}}{\underline{\quad\quad}}$$

   b. Simplify the fraction in part a.

$$\frac{\overline{\quad\quad}}{\underline{\quad\quad}} = \frac{\overline{\quad\quad}}{\underline{\quad\quad}}$$

12. Convert 29.3% to a decimal.

$$29.3\% = 29 \cdot 0.01 = \underline{\quad\quad}$$

Convert each percent to a fraction. Simplify, if possible.

13. 60%

14. 40%

15. 10%

16. 80%

17. 25%

18. 22%

19. 42%

20. 56%

21. $14\frac{3}{4}\%$ **22.** $18\frac{1}{2}\%$ **23.** $13\frac{1}{2}\%$ **24.** $11\frac{1}{4}\%$

25. $4\frac{1}{4}\%$ **26.** $18\frac{3}{4}\%$ **27.** 14.5% **28.** 4.5%

29. 10.5% **30.** 11.5% **31.** 18.5% **32.** 13.25%

33. 3.75% **34.** 17.6% **35.** 110% **36.** 140%

37. 165% **38.** 125% **39.** 260% **40.** 118%

Convert each percent to a decimal.

41. 45% **42.** 69% **43.** 98% **44.** 86%

45. 150% **46.** 186% **47.** 115% **48.** 371%

49. $98\frac{1}{5}\%$ **50.** $71\frac{1}{2}\%$ **51.** $76\frac{1}{5}\%$ **52.** $6\frac{3}{5}\%$

53. $57\frac{2}{5}\%$ **54.** $32\frac{1}{2}\%$ **55.** $64\frac{4}{5}\%$ **56.** $43\frac{1}{5}\%$

57. 87.8% **58.** 47.1% **59.** 35.74% **60.** 66.24%

61. 4.2% **62.** 93.6% **63.** 0.37% **64.** 0.53%

65. 0.72% **66.** 0.75% **67.** 0.883% **68.** 0.572%

Objective 5.1B   **Convert a decimal or a fraction to a percent**

GUIDE PROBLEMS

69. Convert 0.81 to a percent.

$0.81 \cdot 100\% = $ _____

70. Convert 0.247 to a percent.

$0.247 \cdot 100\% = $ _____

71. Consider $\dfrac{7}{16}$.

  a. Convert the fraction to a decimal.

  $\dfrac{7}{16} = $ _____

  b. Convert the decimal in part a to a percent.

  _____ · 100% = _____

72. Consider $3\dfrac{1}{5}$.

  a. Convert the mixed number to a decimal.

  $3\dfrac{1}{5} = $ ____

  b. Convert the decimal in part a to a percent.

  ____ · 100% = _____

Convert each decimal or a whole number to a percent.

73. 0.45

74. 0.35

75. 0.3

76. 0.6

77. 0.01

78. 0.09

79. 0.769

80. 0.832

81. 0.6675

82. 0.981

83. 0.072

84. 0.0312

85. 0.00048

86. 0.0074

87. 10

88. 5

89. 16

90. 23

91. 3.76

92. 2.278

93. 2.268

94. 5.34

95. 6.92

96. 8.3

97. 1.99

98. 14.3

99. 2.35

100. 17.2

Convert each fraction to a percent.

101. $\dfrac{1}{10}$

102. $\dfrac{7}{10}$

103. $\dfrac{1}{5}$

104. $\dfrac{1}{4}$

105. $\dfrac{23}{100}$

106. $\dfrac{19}{100}$

107. $\dfrac{21}{100}$

108. $\dfrac{43}{100}$

109. $\dfrac{3}{25}$

110. $\dfrac{17}{50}$

111. $\dfrac{13}{20}$

112. $\dfrac{3}{50}$

113. $\dfrac{9}{8}$

114. $\dfrac{11}{8}$

115. $\dfrac{19}{8}$

116. $\dfrac{19}{16}$

117. $\dfrac{33}{16}$

118. $\dfrac{23}{8}$

119. $\dfrac{45}{16}$

120. $1\dfrac{3}{10}$

121. $1\dfrac{4}{5}$ **122.** $1\dfrac{33}{50}$ **123.** $1\dfrac{22}{25}$ **124.** $1\dfrac{13}{25}$

125. $2\dfrac{3}{5}$ **126.** $2\dfrac{1}{4}$ **127.** $2\dfrac{3}{4}$ **128.** $1\dfrac{18}{25}$

Objective 5.1C   Apply your knowledge

129. At Lake Minnewonka, 0.46 of the campers are from out of state. What percent are from out of state?

130. Justin has completed 18% of his college credits. Convert this percent to a decimal.

131. It's the first day of school and only 89% of the class has arrived. Convert this percent to a decimal.

132. New "Techron" gasoline claims to be 0.788 cleaner than the competition. What percent does this represent?

133. Tangiers Corporation sold 38.4% of its merchandise over the Internet last year. What decimal does this represent?

134. Last month the unemployment rate in Jasper County was 3.2%. Express this in decimal form.

135. According to statistics, people who brush their teeth regularly have 37.5% fewer dental problems. Express this in decimal form.

136. According to a recent survey, 57% of auto accidents are due to careless driving. What decimal does this represent?

137. A charity dinner raised 1.22 times its goal. What percent of the goal was reached?

138. A particular recipe for cookies requires 22% sugar. Express the part that is sugar in decimal form.

139. Because of lower interest rates, real estate sales are up 231.4% from two years ago. Express this in decimal form.

140. At Sobey's Market, 0.427 of sodas sold are diet. What percent are diet?

CUMULATIVE SKILLS REVIEW

1. Write $9 \cdot 9 \cdot 9 \cdot 9$ in exponential notation and in words. (1.6A)

2. Write 8.625 in word form. (3.1B)

3. Determine whether the ratios $\dfrac{12}{39}$ and $\dfrac{4}{13}$ are proportional. If they are, write a corresponding proportion. (4.3B)

4. Divide $\dfrac{9}{16} \div \dfrac{1}{4}$. (2.5A)

5. Convert 0.386 to a simplified fraction. (3.1C)

6. Calculate the unit price for the ratio "20 ribbons for $18.00." (4.2C)

7. Subtract $\dfrac{8}{6} - \dfrac{1}{3}$. Simplify, if possible. (2.7B)   **8.** Multiply $68 \cdot 4$. (1.4B)

9. Write the ratio of 22 to 17 in three different ways. (4.1A)   **10.** Simplify $\dfrac{15}{36}$. (2.3A)

5.2 SOLVE PERCENT PROBLEMS USING EQUATIONS

LEARNING OBJECTIVES

A. Write a percent problem as an equation

B. Solve a percent equation

C. Apply your knowledge

Problems involving percents can be solved by two different methods. In this section, we will use equations to solve percent problems. In Section 5.3, we will use proportions.

| Objective 5.2A | **Write a percent problem as an equation** |

To solve a percent problem, we can write the percent statement as an equation and then use the equation to find the unknown number. Recall from Chapter 4 that an equation is a mathematical statement containing an equal sign. The following key words and phrases are used to write a percent problem as an equation.

WORD	MEANING	MATH SYMBOL
is, are, was, will be, results in, yields	equals	$=$
of	multiply	$\times$ or $\cdot$ or $(\ )$
what what number what percent	unknown	any letter of the alphabet, such as x or n

As an example, consider the problem, "What is 25% of 40?" Using the key words and phrases, we can write this statement as an equation.

$$
\begin{array}{ccccc}
\text{What} & \text{is} & 25\% & \text{of} & 40 \\
\downarrow & \downarrow & \downarrow & \downarrow & \downarrow \\
x & = & 25\% & \cdot & 40
\end{array}
$$

In our example, we let the letter x represent the unknown number.

EXAMPLE 1   Write a percent problem as an equation

Write each percent problem as an equation.

a. What number is 6% of 200?   **b.** 42% of 16 is what number?

SOLUTION STRATEGY

a. What number is 6% of 200?

$$
\begin{array}{ccccc}
\cdot & x & = & 6\% & \cdot & 200
\end{array}
$$

Write an equation by substituting the key words with the corresponding math symbols. Note that we can use any letter to represent the unknown.

b. 42% of 16 is what number?

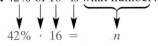

$42\% \cdot 16 = n$

TRY-IT EXERCISE 1

Write each percent problem as an equation.

a. What number is 34% of 80?

b. 130% of 68 is what number?

Check your answers with the solutions in Appendix A. ■

EXAMPLE 2   Write a percent problem as an equation

Write each percent problem as an equation.

a. 85 is what percent of 350?

b. What percent of 18 is 9?

SOLUTION STRATEGY

a. 85 is what percent of 350?

$85 = p \cdot 350$

Write an equation by substituting the key words with the corresponding math symbols. Note that we can use any letter to represent the unknown.

b. What percent of 18 is 9?

$q \cdot 18 = 9$

TRY-IT EXERCISE 2

Write each percent problem as an equation.

a. 57 is what percent of 239?

b. What percent of 96 is 33?

Check your answers with the solutions in Appendix A. ■

EXAMPLE 3   Write a percent problem as an equation

Write each percent problem as an equation.

a. What is 56% of 280?

b. 0.8% of what is 15?

SOLUTION STRATEGY

a. What is 56% of 280?

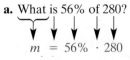

$m = 56\% \cdot 280$

Write an equation by substituting the key words with the corresponding math symbols. Note that we can use any letter to represent the unknown.

b. 0.8% of what is 15?

$0.8\% \cdot a = 15$

TRY-IT EXERCISE 3

Write each percent problem as an equation.

a. What is 135% of 90?   **b.** 0.55% of what is 104?

Check your answers with the solution in Appendix A. ■

Objective 5.2B   **Solve a percent equation**

Now that we have learned how to write percent problems as equations, let's see how to solve them. Notice that each equation has three numbers. In each example above, two of the numbers are known and one is unknown. Each number is given a special name. In the following example, we show the names associated with each number.

amount
In a percent problem, the number that represents part of a whole.

20 is 50% of 40

$$20 \quad = \quad 50\% \quad \cdot \quad 40$$

Amount   Percent   Base

percent
In a percent problem, the number that defines what part the amount is of the whole.

In a percent problem, the **amount** is the number that represents part of a whole. The **percent** is the number that defines what part the amount is of the whole. The **base** is the number that represents the whole or 100%.

Sometimes, the amount is less than the base, and other times it is more than the base. The base is always preceded by the word "of." An equation of the following form is called a **percent equation**.

base
In a percent problem, the number that represents the whole or 100%.

$$\text{Amount} = \text{Percent} \cdot \text{Base}$$

Once a percent problem has been written as a percent equation, we use the equation to find the unknown number. This is called solving the equation. In solving a percent equation, we always write the percent as a decimal. The next example demonstrates this.

percent equation
An equation of the form Amount = Percent · Base.

Learning Tip

When using the percent equation to solve for the base or amount, the percent must be converted to a decimal.

When using the percent equation to solve for the percent, the answer will be a decimal or a fraction and must be converted to a percent.

EXAMPLE 4   Solve a percent equation for the amount

What number is 58% of 300?

SOLUTION STRATEGY

What number is 58% of 300?   Note that 300 follows the word *of*. Therefore, the base
                                     is 300. The percent is 58%. The amount is unknown.

$$a \quad = 58\% \cdot 300$$ Write as a percent equation.

$$a = 0.58 \cdot 300$$ Convert the percent, 58%, to a decimal, 0.58

$$a = 174$$ Multiply.

174 is 58% of 300.

TRY-IT EXERCISE 4

What number is 36% of 150?

Check your answer with the solution in Appendix A. ■

EXAMPLE 5 Solve a percent equation for the amount

90% of 135 is what number?

SOLUTION STRATEGY

90% of 135 is what number?

90% · 135 = a

Note that 135 follows the word *of*. Therefore, the base is 135. The percent is 90%. The amount is unknown.

Write as a percent equation.

$0.9 \cdot 135 = a$

Convert the percent, 90%, to a decimal, 0.9.

$121.5 = a$

Multiply.

90% of 135 is 121.5.

TRY-IT EXERCISE 5

115% of 38 is what number?

Check your answer with the solution in Appendix A. ■

When solving a percent equation for the base, the amount and percent will be given. Remember, the base is the number that follows the word "of."

As an example, consider the following problem.

25% of what number is 30?

$25\% \cdot b = 30$

Converting the percent to a decimal, the equation is written as follows.

$$0.25 \cdot b = 30$$

Notice that b is multiplied by 0.25. To solve for b, we must divide both sides of the equation by 0.25.

$$\frac{0.25b}{0.25} = \frac{30}{0.25}$$
$$b = 120$$

Divide both sides of the equation by 0.25.

$\dfrac{\cancel{0.25}b}{\cancel{0.25}} = b; \dfrac{30}{0.25} = 120$

Thus, 25% of 120 is 30.

In general, to solve a percent equation for the base, divide both sides of the equation by the percent.

> **Learning Tip**
>
> $0.25 \cdot b$ is the same as $0.25b$.

> **Learning Tip**
>
> When solving for the base, we may also use a variation of the percent equation.
>
> $$\text{Base} = \frac{\text{Amount}}{\text{Percent}}$$

EXAMPLE 6   Solve a percent equation for the base

75% of what number is 60?

SOLUTION STRATEGY

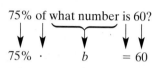

	The base is unknown. The percent is 75%. The amount is 60.
$75\% \cdot b = 60$	Write as a percent equation. Use the letter b to represent the base.
$0.75 \cdot b = 60$	Convert the percent, 75%, to a decimal, 0.75.
$\dfrac{0.75b}{0.75} = \dfrac{60}{0.75}$	Divide both sides by 0.75.
$b = \dfrac{60}{0.75}$	
$b = 80$	

75% of 80 is 60.

TRY-IT EXERCISE 6

45% of what number is 216?

Check your answer with the solutions in Appendix A. ■

EXAMPLE 7   Solve a percent equation for the base

28.8 is 12% of what?

SOLUTION STRATEGY

28.8 is 12% of what?

	The base is unknown. The percent is 12%. The amount is 28.8.
$28.8 = 12\% \cdot b$	Write as a percent equation. Use the letter b to represent the base.
$28.8 = 0.12 \cdot b$	Convert the percent, 12%, to a decimal, 0.12.
$\dfrac{28.8}{0.12} = \dfrac{0.12b}{0.12}$	Divide both sides by 0.12.
$\dfrac{28.8}{0.12} = b$	
$240 = b$	

28.9 is 12% of 240.

TRY-IT EXERCISE 7

55 is 22% of what?

Check your answer with the solution in Appendix A. ■

Learning Tip

When solving for the percent, we may also use a variation of the percent equation.

$$Percent = \frac{Amount}{Base}$$

When solving a percent equation for the percent, the amount and the base will be given. Also, the answer will be in decimal notation. Because the problem asks, "what percent," we must convert the decimal to a percent for the final answer.

EXAMPLE 8   Solve a percent equation for the percent

30 is what percent of 80?

SOLUTION STRATEGY

30 is what percent of 80?   The percent is unknown. The base is 80. The amount is 30.

30 = p ·   80   Write as a percent equation. Use the letter p to represent the percent.

$30 = 80 \cdot p$

$\dfrac{30}{80} = \dfrac{80p}{80}$ Divide both sides by 80.

$\dfrac{30}{80} = p$

$0.375 = p$

$37.5\% = p$ Convert the decimal to a percent.

30 is 37.5% of 80.

TRY-IT EXERCISE 8

300 is what percent of 500?

Check your answer with the solution in Appendix A. ■

EXAMPLE 9   Solve a percent equation for the percent

What percent of 18 is 27?

SOLUTION STRATEGY

What percent of 18 is 27?   The percent is unknown. The base is 18. The amount is 27.

p · 18 = 27   Write as a percent equation. Use the letter p to represent the percent.

$18 \cdot p = 27$

$\dfrac{18p}{18} = \dfrac{27}{18}$ Divide both sides by 18.

$p = \dfrac{27}{18}$

$p = 1.5$

$p = 150\%$ Convert the decimal to a percent.

150% of 18 is 27.

TRY-IT EXERCISE 9

What percent of 56 is 123.2?

Check your answer with the solution in Appendix A. ■

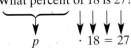
Learning Tip

Remember, the percent expresses "what part" the amount is of the base.

- When the amount is *less* than the base, the percent is *less* than 100%.
- When the amount *equals* the base, the percent *is* 100%.
- When amount is *more* than the base, the percent is *more* than 100%.

Objective 5.2C   Apply your knowledge

Now, let's solve some applied percent problems using percent equations.

EXAMPLE 10   Solve an applied percent problem using an equation

At La Mirage Boutique, 30% of sales are charged on credit cards. If the store had $23,500 in total sales last week, how many sales were charged on credit cards?

SOLUTION STRATEGY

What number is 30% of 23,500?

$$a = 30\% \cdot 23{,}500$$

$$a = 0.3 \cdot 23{,}500$$

$$a = 7050$$

Credit card charges are $7050.

In this problem, we want to find the number of sales charged on credit cards. Therefore, the amount is unknown. The rate is 30%. The base (total sales) is $23,500.

Write as a percent equation. Use the letter a to represent the amount.

TRY-IT EXERCISE 10

a. Office Masters sold 180 calculators last week. If 40% were scientific calculators, how many of this type were sold?

b. Claudia is driving to North Carolina, a distance of 1850 miles from her home. If the first day she drove 14% of the distance, how many miles did she drive?

Check your answers with the solutions in Appendix A. ∎

EXAMPLE 11   Solve an applied percent problem using an equation

A parking garage had 80 spaces occupied at noon. If that represents 62% of the spaces, how many total spaces are in the garage? Round your answer to the nearest whole parking space.

SOLUTION STRATEGY

62% of what number is 80?

$$62\% \cdot b = 80$$

$$0.62 \cdot b = 80$$

$$\frac{0.62b}{0.62} = \frac{80}{0.62}$$

$$b = \frac{80}{0.62} \approx 129.03 \approx 129$$

There are 129 total spaces.

In this problem, we want to find the total number of parking places. Therefore, the base is unknown. The percent is 62%. The amount (the number of occupied parking spaces) is 80.

Write as a percent equation. Use the letter b to represent the base.

Divide both sides by 0.62.

Round to the nearest whole parking space.

TRY-IT EXERCISE 11

a. Maven's Department Store has 15,400 square feet devoted to women's clothing. If that represents 38% of the total floor space, how many total square feet comprise the store? Round to the nearest whole square foot.

b. A baker at Butterflake Bakery is preheating his oven to bake a batch of pies. The oven is currently at 245 degrees. If this is 61.3% of the desired temperature, at what temperature will the pies be baked? Round to the nearest whole degree.

Check your answers with the solutions in Appendix A. ■

EXAMPLE 12 Solve an applied percent problem using an equation

National Warehouse Clubs has a total of 425 stores and 34 of the stores are located in Texas.

a. What percent of the stores are located in Texas?

b. What percent of the store are not located in Texas?

SOLUTION STRATEGY

a. What percent of 425 is 34?

$$p \cdot 425 = 34$$

$$425 \cdot p = 34$$

$$\frac{425p}{425} = \frac{34}{425}$$

$$p = \frac{34}{425} = 0.08 = 8\%$$

8% of the stores are in Texas.

b. $100\% - 8\% = 92\%$

In this problem, we want to find the percent of stores in Texas. The base (the total number of stores) is 425. The amount (the number of stores in Texas) is 34.

Write as a percent equation. Use the letter p to represent the percent.

Divide both sides by 425.

Convert the decimal to a percent.

Subtract 8% (the percent representing the number of stores in Texas) from 100% (the percent representing the total number of stores).

TRY-IT EXERCISE 12

a. In this morning's *City Herald* newspaper, 158 of a total of 382 pages contained advertising. What percent of the pages contained advertising? Round to the nearest tenth of a percent.

b. At the end of this semester, Skip will have earned 42 credits. If he needs a total of 112 credits to graduate, what percent of the total credits will he have completed?

Check your answers with the solutions in Appendix A. ■

Use the graphic *Median Starting Salaries for MBAs*, for Example 13 and Try-It Exercise 13.

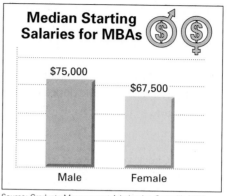

Source: Graduate Management Admisssion Council's MBA Alumni Perspectives Survey conducted in August

EXAMPLE 13   Solve an applied percent problem using an equation

Peter, an MBA graduate, was offered a starting salary of $62,400 at a major corporation. What percent of the male median salary was he offered?

SOLUTION STRATEGY

What percent of 75,000 is 62,400?

$$p \cdot 75{,}000 = 62{,}400$$

$$75{,}000 \cdot p = 62{,}400$$

$$\frac{75{,}000p}{75{,}000} = \frac{62{,}400}{75{,}000}$$

$$p = \frac{62{,}400}{75{,}000} = 0.832 = 83.2\%$$

In this problem, we want to find the percent of the male median salary Peter was offered. The base (the median male salary) is $75,000. The amount (the salary Peter was offered) is $62,400.

Write as a percent equation. Use the letter p to represent the percent.

Divide both sides by 75,000.

Convert the decimal to a percent.

He was offered 83.2% of the MBA median salary.

TRY-IT EXERCISE 13

a. A female MBA graduate is offered a starting salary of $72,300. What percent of the female median was she offered? Round to the nearest whole percent.

b. What percent of the male median salary is the female median?

c. What percent of the female median is the male median? Round to the nearest tenth of a percent.

d. The median starting salary for all bachelor's degrees is 60% of the average of the male and female MBA medians. How much is the bachelor's degree median?

Check your answers with the solutions in Appendix A. ■

SECTION 5.2 REVIEW EXERCISES

Concept Check

1. Percent problems can be solved using either _____ or _____.

2. An equation is a mathematical statement containing an _____ sign.

3. When writing a percent problem as an equation, the word *of* indicates _____ and the word *is* indicates _____.

4. When writing an equation, the words *what*, *what number*, and *what percent* represent the _____ quantity.

5. In a percent problem, the _____ is the number that represents part of a whole.

6. In a percent problem, the _____ is the number that defines what part the amount is of the whole.

7. In a percent problem, the _____ is the number that represents the whole. In a percent problem, it is preceded by the word *of*.

8. The percent equation is written as _____.

9. When solving for the base, we can use the formula _____ as a variation of the percent equation.

10. When solving for the percent, we can use the formula _____ as a variation of the percent equation.

11. When solving the percent equation for the amount or the base, the percent is converted to a _____.

12. When solving the percent equation for the percent, the answer is converted from a _____ to a _____.

Objective 5.2A   Write percent problems as equations

GUIDE PROBLEMS

13. Fill in the following to complete the percent equation.

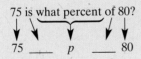

75 is what percent of 80?

75 ___ *p* ___ 80

14. Fill in the following to complete the percent equation.

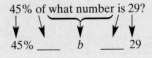

45% of what number is 29?

45% ___ *b* ___ 29

Write each percent problem as an equation.

15. 195.3 is 30% of what number?

16. 57 is 80% of what number?

17. 10 is 3% of what number?

18. 336 is 15% of what number?

19. 736 is 86% of what number?

20. 10% of what number is 64?

21. 38% of what number is 406?

22. What number is 25% of 924?

23. Find 25% of 500.

24. What number is 62.5% of 720?

25. 87% of 4350 is what number?

26. What percent of 5000 is 250?

Objective 5.2B   **Solve percent equations**

GUIDE PROBLEMS

27. What number is 20% of 70?

   a. Identify the parts of the percent problem.
     amount: _____
     percent: _____
     base: _____

   b. Write the problem as a percent equation.

   c. Convert the percent to a decimal.

   d. Solve the equation.

28. 40% of what number is 48?

   a. Identify the parts of the percent problem.
     amount: _____
     percent: _____
     base: _____

   b. Write the problem as a percent equation.

   c. Convert the percent to a decimal.

   d. Solve the equation

29. What percent of 500 is 25?

   a. Identify the parts of the percent problem.
     amount: _____
     percent: _____
     base: _____

   b. Write the problem as a percent equation.

   c. Solve the equation.

   d. Convert the answer to a percent.

Write each percent problem as an equation and solve.

30. What percent of 1400 is 1050?

31. 1050 is 10% of what number?

32. 52 is 80% of what number?

33. 2350 is 25% of what number?

34. What number is 1% of 8700?

35. What is 2% of 1500?

36. 1180 is 20% of what number?

37. 2088 is 36% of what number?

38. 6380 is what percent of 11,000?

39. What number is 32% of 4900?

40. What is 15% of 540?

41. 6120 is what percent of 12,000?

42. What percent is 117 of 900?

43. 2700 is 30% of what number?

44. What percent is 170 of 1700?

45. What is 3% of 3900?

46. 1328 is what percent of 1600?

47. 13,248 is 69% of what number?

48. 5680 is 40% of what?

49. What percent of 13,000 is 2210?

50. 270 is 36% of what number?

51. What number is 82% of 122?

52. What is 81% of 599?

53. What is 12% of 365?

54. 338.4 is 72% of what number?

55. What number is 44% of 699?

56. What number is 12% of 623?

57. What percent of 751 is 518.19?

58. What percent of 394 is 39.4?

59. 326.65 is 47% of what number?

Objective 5.2C	Apply your knowledge

60. Herbert bought a new car at Regal Motors. The navigation system was a $1200 option.

    a. If the cost of the navigation system represents 4% of the total cost of the car, what is the total cost of the car? Round to dollars and cents.

    b. If Regal adds on a 1% dealer preparation charge, how much is that charge?

61. Martine is graduating from Mountainview High School this week. Of 500 students, 400 will graduate on time. What percent of the class is graduating on time?

62. Greg purchased a new pair of shoes, a hat, and a pair of jeans for $160. If he had $400 to spend that day, what percent of his money did he spend on the clothes?

63. Nancy is walking for charity next Sunday. She was able to raise $55 in donations, so far. If $55 is 20% of her goal, how much money does Nancy hope to raise?

64. A new government highway safety test for car bumpers allows only 2% of each car brand tested to have major damage from bumper accidents. If 450 Fords were tested, how many were allowed to have major damage from bumper accidents?

65. The latest election results show the favored candidate has won 60% of the states visited. If the candidates have visited 25 states, how many did the favored candidate win?

66. At 5 PM last night, 88 of 352 seats were occupied at Zona's Restaurant.

    a. What percent of the seats were occupied?

    b. What percent of the seats were not occupied?

67. Selma purchased a new MP3 music player that holds a total of 500 songs. She has already loaded 30% of the capacity of the player.

    a. How many songs has she loaded?

    b. How many songs does she have left to load?

    c. This morning Selma loaded another 47 songs. What percent of the total capacity has she loaded to date? Round to the nearest whole percent.

68. In a recent taste test survey, 4 out of every 7 people preferred regular coffee to decaffeinated coffee. What percent preferred regular? Round to the nearest tenth percent.

69. Kool Air, Inc., is an air conditioner manufacturer. Last week a routine inspection found 46 defective units. If this represents 4% of the total units made, how many total air conditioners were made?

70. Workers for Ace Flooring Company installed 1400 square feet of tile on Monday. If this represents 20% of the total, how many square feet of tile were laid?

71. John earns $3250 per month. If he spends 5% each month on entertainment, how much does he spend on entertainment?

72. Jim is hoping to sell some of the land he purchased for investment. He currently owns 8 acres and wants to sell 5 acres. What percent of the land does he want to sell?

73. The Lamp Factory has produced 90 lamp shades for an order totaling 600 shades. What percent of the order is complete?

74. One day during the flu season, 58 of 160 workers were absent from Continental Industries. What percent of the employees were absent that day?

75. Mark's Automated Car Wash has washed 67 cars so far this week. The business averages 280 cars per week.

   a. What percent of the total expected cars have already been washed? Round to the nearest whole percent.

   b. If 15% of the cars also get a wax job, how many wax jobs are done each week?

76. The campus bookstore sold 71 of 300 algebra textbooks in stock on the first day of class.

   a. What percent of the books were sold the first day? Round to the nearest tenth of a percent.

   b. If the store had 250 English textbooks and sold 18% of them the first day, how many English textbooks were left?

77. At Nathan's Beauty Salon, 60% of the customers get manicures as well as haircuts. If 33 customers got manicures and haircuts on Wednesday, how many total customers did Nathan's have that day?

78. All That Glitters, a jewelry store, purchased 160 ounces of raw sterling silver to make custom jewelry. If 22 ounces were used to make a batch of fraternity and sorority pins, what percent of the silver is left?

79. Frank delivers newspapers as a part-time job. If he delivered 146 papers so far this morning and that represents 40% of his route, how many total papers does he deliver?

80. The property tax in Midvale is 1.6% of the value of the property. If a condominium had property tax last year of $2820.80, what is the value of the condo?

81. Miguel made 12.5% profit on a mutual fund investment of $5600. How much profit did he make?

82. A can of chickpeas contains 20 grams of carbohydrates. If that represents 7% of the recommended daily value (DV) of a 2000 calorie diet, how many grams of carbohydrates are recommended? Round to the nearest whole gram.

Use the graph *America's Most Played Sports* **for exercises 83–88.**

83. If the 65.1 million people who play basketball represent 23.25% of the total population, what was the total population of the United States (in millions) at the time the analysis was done?

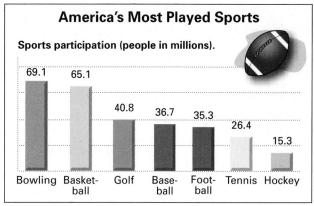

America's Most Played Sports

Sports participation (people in millions).

69.1 65.1 40.8 36.7 35.3 26.4 15.3

Bowling Basket-ball Golf Base-ball Foot-ball Tennis Hockey

Note: Includes all people age 5 and up.
Source: Simmons National Consumer Study, Fall 2003

Use the total U.S. population figure you found in exercise 83 to answer exercises 84–88.

84. What percent of the population bowls? Round to the nearest tenth of a percent.

85. What percent of the population plays tennis? Round to the nearest hundredth percent.

86. If 30% of the total U.S. population plays no sports at all, how many people play no sports?

87. If $\frac{1}{2}$% of the bowlers average over 200 points per game, how many bowlers is that?

88. If 0.02% of the golfers have scored a hole-in-one in the past 12 months, how many have scored a hole-in-one?

CUMULATIVE SKILLS REVIEW

1. Divide $72 \div 8$. (1.5B)

2. Larry the weatherman is predicting 0.6 chance of rain for this weekend. What percent is this? (5.1B)

3. What fraction of the figure is shaded? (2.2B)

4. If 1 minute $= 60$ seconds, what is the ratio of 1.5 minutes to 120 seconds? (4.1C)

5. Add $5354 + 777$. (1.2B)

6. Convert 78% to a decimal. (5.1A)

7. Add $\frac{6}{15} + \frac{7}{15}$. (2.6A)

8. Multiply $(9.25)(0.33)$. (3.3A)

9. Solve the proportion $\frac{3}{9} = \frac{y}{36}$. (4.3C)

10. If 12 of 30 people like to watch reality TV shows, what simplified fraction represents the people who like reality TV shows? (2.3D)

5.3   SOLVE PERCENT PROBLEMS USING PROPORTIONS

In Section 5.2, we learned to solve a percent problem by writing and solving a percent equation. In this section, we will solve a percent problem using a proportion.

> **Objective 5.3A**   **Write a percent problem as a proportion**

In Section 5.1, we learned that 44% represents the fraction $\frac{44}{100}$. Because this fraction simplifies to $\frac{11}{25}$, we can set up the proportion "11 is to 25 as 44 is to 100." We write this as follows.

$$\overset{\text{Amount}}{\underset{\text{Base}}{\frac{11}{25}}} = \overset{\text{Part}}{\underset{100}{\frac{44}{100}}}$$

As in a percent equation, the amount is the number that represents part of a whole and the base is the number that represents the whole or 100%. The fraction on the right side of the equation represents 44%. Since a percent is a part per 100, we refer to the number in the numerator as the *part*.

A proportion of the following form is called a **percent proportion**.

percent proportion
A proportion of the form
$\dfrac{\text{Amount}}{\text{Base}} = \dfrac{\text{Part}}{100}$.

$$\frac{\text{Amount}}{\text{Base}} = \frac{\text{Part}}{100}$$

Given a percent problem, we can write and solve a percent proportion by following these steps.

Steps to Write and Solve a Percent Problem as a Proportion

Step 1. Identify the amount, base, and part.

Step 2. Assign a letter to the unknown number. Substitute the known numbers and letter in the percent proportion.

Step 3. Simplify the fractions in the percent proportion, if possible.

Step 4. Cross multiply to find the cross products. Set the cross products equal.

Step 5. Divide both sides of the equation by the number on the side with the unknown.

We now consider some examples of writing a percent proportion.

EXAMPLE 1   Write a percent problem as a proportion

Write each percent problem as a proportion.

a. 16 is what percent of 48?   **b.** What is 24% of 300?

SOLUTION STRATEGY

a. 16 is what percent of 48?

amount   percent   base

$$\frac{16}{48} = \frac{p}{100}$$ Substitute into the formula $\dfrac{\text{Amount}}{\text{Base}} = \dfrac{\text{Part}}{100}$.

$$\frac{1}{3} = \frac{p}{100}$$ Simplify $\dfrac{16}{48}$.

amount = 16
part = p (percent = $p\%$)
base = 48

b. What is 24% of 300?

amount   percent   base

$$\frac{a}{300} = \frac{24}{100}$$ Substitute into the formula $\dfrac{\text{Amount}}{\text{Base}} = \dfrac{\text{Part}}{100}$.

$$\frac{a}{300} = \frac{6}{25}$$ Simplify $\dfrac{24}{100}$.

amount = a
part = 24 (percent = 24%)
base = 300

TRY-IT EXERCISE 1

Write each percent problem as a proportion.

a. 64 is what percent of 262?   **b.** What is 89% of 120?

Check your answers with the solutions in Appendix A. ■

EXAMPLE 2   Write a percent problem as a proportion

Write each percent problem as a proportion.

a. 19 is 10% of what number?   **b.** 67.4% of 42 is what?

SOLUTION STRATEGY

a. 19 is 10% of what number?

amount   percent   base

$$\frac{19}{b} = \frac{10}{100}$$ Substitute into the formula $\dfrac{\text{Amount}}{\text{Base}} = \dfrac{\text{Part}}{100}$.

$$\frac{19}{b} = \frac{1}{10}$$ Simplify $\dfrac{10}{100}$.

amount = 19
part = 10 (percent = 10%)
base = b

b. 67.4% of 42 is what?

percent   base   amount

part = 67.4 (percent = 67.4%)
base = 42
amount = a

$$\frac{a}{42} = \frac{67.4}{100}$$

Substitute into the formula $\dfrac{\text{Amount}}{\text{Base}} = \dfrac{\text{Part}}{100}$

TRY-IT EXERCISE 2

Write each percent problem as a proportion.

a. 85 is 28% of what number?   **b.** 7% of 90 is what?

Check your answers with the solutions in Appendix A. ■

EXAMPLE 3   Write a percent problem as a proportion

Write each percent problem as a proportion.

a. 175% of what is 48?   **b.** What percent of 70 is 51?

SOLUTION STRATEGY

a. 175% of what is 48?

percent   base   amount

part = 175 (percent = 175%)
base = b
amount = 48

$$\frac{48}{b} = \frac{175}{100}$$

Substitute into the formula $\dfrac{\text{Amount}}{\text{Base}} = \dfrac{\text{Part}}{100}$.

$$\frac{48}{b} = \frac{7}{4}$$

Simplify $\dfrac{175}{100}$.

b. What percent of 70 is 51?

percent   base   amount

part = p (percent = p%)
base = 70
amount = 51

$$\frac{51}{70} = \frac{p}{100}$$

Substitute into the formula $\dfrac{\text{Amount}}{\text{Base}} = \dfrac{\text{Part}}{100}$.

TRY-IT EXERCISE 3

Write each percent problem as a proportion.

a. 8.37% of what is 620?   **b.** What percent of 13.9 is 10.5?

Check your answers with the solutions in Appendix A. ■

Objective 5.3B	Solve a percent proportion

Once we have written a percent problem as a proportion, we can solve the proportion. Note that we solve a percent proportion in the same way that we solved a proportion in Section 4.3.

EXAMPLE 4   Solve a percent proportion for the amount

What is 88% of 300? Write a proportion and solve.

SOLUTION STRATEGY

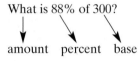

amount = a
part = 88 (percent = 88%)
base = 300

$$\frac{a}{300} = \frac{88}{100}$$

Substitute into the formula $\dfrac{\text{Amount}}{\text{Base}} = \dfrac{\text{Part}}{100}$.

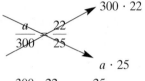

$300 \cdot 22$

$a \cdot 25$

Simplify $\dfrac{88}{100}$.
Find the cross products.

$300 \cdot 22 = a \cdot 25$

$6600 = 25a$ Set the cross products equal.

$\dfrac{6600}{25} = \dfrac{25a}{25}$ Divide both sides of the equation by 25.

$264 = a$ Solve for a.

Thus, 264 is 88% of 300.

TRY-IT EXERCISE 4

Write each percent problem as a proportion and solve.

a. What is 35% of 220?   **b.** 67% of 1800 is what number?

Check your answers with the solutions in Appendix A. ■

EXAMPLE 5   Solve a percent proportion for the base

27 is 13.5% of what number? Write a proportion and solve.

SOLUTION STRATEGY

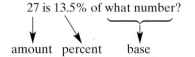

amount = 27
part = 13.5 (percent = 13.5%)
base = b

$$13.5 \cdot b$$

Substitute into the formula $\dfrac{\text{Amount}}{\text{Base}} = \dfrac{\text{Part}}{100}$.

$$\dfrac{27}{b} \diagup\!\!\!\!\diagup\!\!\!\!\diagup \dfrac{13.5}{100}$$

Find the cross products.

$$27 \cdot 100$$

$b \cdot 13.5 = 27 \cdot 100$ Set the cross products equal.

$13.5b = 2700$

$\dfrac{13.5b}{13.5} = \dfrac{2700}{13.5}$ Divide both sides of the equation by 13.5.

$b = 200$ Solve for b.

27 is 13.5% of 200.

TRY-IT EXERCISE 5

Write each percent problem as a proportion and solve.

a. 45 is 30% of what number?   **b.** 140% of what number is 196?

Check your answers with the solutions in Appendix A. ■

EXAMPLE 6   Solve a percent proportion for the percent

196 is what percent of 700? Write a proportion and solve.

SOLUTION STRATEGY

196 is what percent of 700?

↓   ↓   ↓

amount   percent   base

amount = 196
part = p (percent = p%)
base = 700

$\dfrac{196}{700} = \dfrac{p}{100}$ Substitute into the formula $\dfrac{\text{Amount}}{\text{Base}} = \dfrac{\text{Part}}{100}$.

$$25 \cdot p$$
$$7 \cdot 100$$

Simplify $\dfrac{196}{700}$.

Find the cross products.

$25 \cdot p = 7 \cdot 100$ Set the cross products equal.

$25p = 700$

$\dfrac{25p}{25} = \dfrac{700}{25}$ Divide both sides of the equation by 25.

$p = 28$ Solve for p.

Thus, 196 is 28% of 700.

TRY-IT EXERCISE 6

Write each percent problem as a proportion and solve.

a. 21 is what percent of 300?   **b.** What percent of 165 is 66?

Check your answers with the solutions in Appendix A. ■

Objective 5.3C   **Apply your knowledge**

Once again, let's take a look at some additional application problems involving percents. This time, we'll solve each using a proportion.

EXAMPLE 7   **Solve an applied percent problem using a proportion**

The label on a bottle of Fruity Beauty Juice Drink reads "18.5% Real Juice." If the bottle contains 48 ounces of liquid, how many ounces are real juice? Round to the nearest whole ounce.

SOLUTION STRATEGY

What is 18.5% of 48?

↓   ↓   ↓

amount   percent   base

$$\frac{a}{48} \diagup\!\!\!\!\diagup \frac{18.5}{100}$$

$48 \cdot 18.5$

$a \cdot 100$

amount (part that is real juice) $= a$
part $= 18.5$ (percent $= 18.5\%$)
base (total volume of the bottle) $= 48$

Substitute into the formula $\dfrac{\text{Amount}}{\text{Base}} = \dfrac{\text{Part}}{100}$.
Find the cross products.

$48 \cdot 18.5 = a \cdot 100$ Set the cross products equal.

$888 = 100a$

$\dfrac{888}{100} = \dfrac{100a}{100}$ Divide both sides of the equation by 100.

$a = 8.88 \approx 9$ Solve for a. Round to the nearest whole ounce.

Fruity Beauty contains approximately 9 ounces of real juice.

TRY-IT EXERCISE 7

a. A baseball player had 68 at bats and got hits 25% of the time. How many hits did he get?

b. In a shipment of pottery, it was found that 6% of the pieces were broken. If the shipment had a total of 2400 pieces, how many were broken?

Check your answers with the solutions in Appendix A. ■

EXAMPLE 8 **Solve an applied percent problem using a proportion**

The Williams family purchased a home with a down payment of $20,625. If that represents 15% of the price of the house, how much was the house?

SOLUTION STRATEGY

20,625 is 15% of what number?

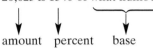

amount   percent   base

$$\frac{20,625}{b} = \frac{15}{100}$$

amount (down payment) = 20,625
part = 15 (percent = 15%)
base (price of the house) = b

Substitute into the formula $\dfrac{\text{Amount}}{\text{Base}} = \dfrac{\text{Part}}{100}$.

$$\frac{20,625}{b} \begin{matrix} b \cdot 3 \\ \nearrow \\ \searrow \end{matrix} \frac{3}{20}$$

$$20,625 \cdot 20$$

Simplify $\dfrac{15}{100}$.

Find the cross products.

$b \cdot 3 = 20,625 \cdot 20$

Set the cross products equal.

$3b = 412,500$

$$\frac{3b}{3} = \frac{412,500}{3}$$

Divide both sides of the equation by 3.

$b = 137,500$

Solve for b.

The price of the house is $137,500.

TRY-IT EXERCISE 8

a. Jason answered 40 questions correctly on a test and got a grade of 80%. How many questions were on the test?

b. During a recent census, it was found that 3550 people in Williamsport were over the age of 65. If this represents 19.7% of the total population, how many people live in that city? Round to the nearest whole person.

Check your answers with the solutions in Appendix A. ■

EXAMPLE 9 **Solve an applied percent problem using a proportion**

Your digital camera has a memory card that holds 256 megabytes of photographs. If you have already used 39 megabytes of memory, what percent of the memory has been used? Round to the nearest whole percent.

SOLUTION STRATEGY

39 is what percent of 256?

amount   percent   base

amount (part of memory card used) = 39
part = p (percent = p%)
base (total memory card) = 256

$$\begin{array}{c} 256 \cdot p \\ \diagup \\ \dfrac{39}{256} \times \dfrac{r}{100} \\ \diagdown \\ 39 \cdot 100 \end{array}$$

Substitute into the formula $\dfrac{\text{Amount}}{\text{Base}} = \dfrac{\text{Part}}{100}$.

Find the cross products.

$256 \cdot p = 39 \cdot 100$ Set the cross products equal.

$256p = 3900$

$\dfrac{256p}{256} = \dfrac{3900}{256}$ Divide both sides of the equation by 256.

$p = 15.2 \approx 15$ Solve for p.

Approximately 15% of the memory has been used.

TRY-IT EXERCISE 9

a. A pot roast takes 2.5 hours to cook. If the roast has been in the oven for 1 hour, what percent of the cooking process is complete?

b. Chocolate chip cookies contain 160 calories each. If 47 calories are from fat, what percent of the total calories are from fat? Round to the nearest whole percent.

Check your answers with the solutions in Appendix A. ■

Use the graphic *U.S. Citizens Born Abroad* for Example 10 and Try-It Exercise 10.

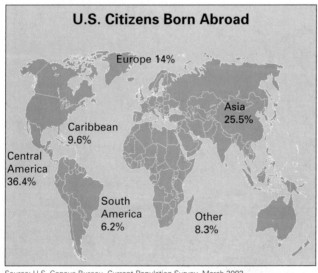

Source: U.S. Census Bureau, Current Population Survey, March 2002

EXAMPLE 10   Solve an applied percent problem using a proportion

According to the U.S. Census Bureau, 32 million people living in the United States were born in other countries.

a. If 32 million represented 11.5% of the U.S. population in the year of the census, what was the total U.S. population? Round to the nearest million.

b. Of the 32 million born outside of the United States, 6.2% came from South America. How many were born in South America?

SOLUTION STRATEGY

a. 32 is 11.5% of what number?

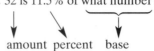

amount percent base

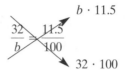

$b \cdot 11.5$

$32 \cdot 100$

$b \cdot 11.5 = 32 \cdot 100$

$11.5b = 3200$

$$\frac{11.5b}{11.5} = \frac{3200}{11.5}$$

$b \approx 278.3 \approx 278$

The U.S. population was 278 million.

amount (part of U.S. population born in other countries) = 32

part = 11.5 (percent = 11.5%)

base (total U.S. population) = b

Substitute into the formula $\dfrac{\text{Amount}}{\text{Base}} = \dfrac{\text{Part}}{100}$.

Find the cross products.

Set the cross products equal.

Divide both sides of the equation by 11.5.

Solve for b.

b. What is 6.2% of 32?

portion rate base

$32 \cdot 6.2$

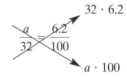

$a \cdot 100$

$32 \cdot 6.2 = a \cdot 100$

$198.4 = 100a$

$$\frac{100a}{100} = \frac{198.4}{100}$$

$a = 1.984$

$1.984 \cdot 1,000,000 = 1,984,000$

1,984,000 people were born in South America.

amount (part of U.S. population born in South America) = a

part = 6.2 (percent = 6.2%)

base (total foreign-born population) = 32

Substitute into the formula $\dfrac{\text{Amount}}{\text{Base}} = \dfrac{\text{Part}}{100}$.

Find the cross products.

Set the cross products equal.

Divide both sides of the equation by 100.

Solve for a.

Multiply 1.984 by 1,000,000 to find how many million people living in the United States were born in South America.

TRY-IT EXERCISE 10

a. According to the graphic *U.S. Citizens Born Abroad* on page 385, 25.5% of the 32 million born outside of the United States were born in Asia. What number represents the people that were born in Asia?

b. What number represents the people that were born in Europe?

c. What number represents the people that were born in Central America?

Check your answers with the solutions in Appendix A. ∎

SECTION 5.3 REVIEW EXERCISES

Concept Check

1. Label the parts of a percent proportion.

$$\frac{\rule{1.5cm}{0.4pt}}{\rule{1.5cm}{0.4pt}} = \frac{\rule{1cm}{0.4pt}}{100}$$

2. List the steps to write and solve a percent proportion.

Objective 5.3A **Write a percent problem as a proportion**

GUIDE PROBLEMS

3. What number is 85% of 358?

  a. Identify the parts of the percent problem.

  amount: _____

  part: _____

  base: _____

  b. Write the percent proportion formula.

  c. Substitute the values of the amount, base, and part into the proportion.

4. What percent of 200 is 60?

  a. Identify the parts of the percent problem.

  amount: _____

  part: _____

  base: _____

  b. Write the percent proportion formula.

  c. Substitute the values of the amount, base, and part into the proportion.

5. 28% of what number is 16?

  a. Identify the parts of the percent problem.

  amount: _____

  part: _____

  base: _____

  b. Write the percent proportion formula.

  c. Substitute the values of amount, base, and part into the proportion.

Write each percent problem as a proportion.

6. What percent of 370 is 74?

7. What is 12% of 279?

8. 1700 is 34% of what number?

9. What number is 88.5% of 190?

10. 432.25 is 45.5% of what number?

11. 200 is what percent of 1000?

| Objective 5.3B | Solve a percent proportion |

GUIDE PROBLEMS

12. What number is 40% of 180?

    a. Identify the parts of the percent problem.

        amount: _____

        part: _____

        base: _____

    b. Substitute the values of amount, base, and part into the proportion.

    c. Simplify the fractions in the percent proportion, if possible.

    d. Cross multiply and set the cross products equal.

    e. Divide both sides of the equation by the number on the side with the unknown.

    ___ is 40% of 180.

13. What percent of 128 is 96?

    a. Identify the parts of the percent problem.

        amount: _____

        part: _____

        base: _____

    b. Substitute the values of amount, base, and part into the proportion.

    c. Simplify the fractions in the percent proportion, if possible.

    d. Cross multiply and set the cross products equal.

    e. Divide both sides of the equation by the number on the side with the unknown.

    ___% of 128 is 96.

14. 8% of what number is 50?

    a. Identify the parts of the percent problem.

        amount: _____

        part: _____

        base: _____

    b. Substitute the values of amount, base, and part into the proportion.

    c. Simplify the fractions in the percent proportion, if possible.

    d. Cross multiply and set the cross products equal.

    e. Divide both sides of the equation by the number on the side with the unknown.

    8% of ___ is 50.

Write each percent problem as a proportion and solve.

15. What number is 25% of 700?

16. What is 20% of 2740?

17. 330 is what percent of 1100?

18. 546 is what percent of 1400?

19. 1440 is what percent of 900?

20. What percent of 370 is 148?

21. 150% of 622 is what number?

22. 650 is 40% of what number?

23. 6975 is 31% of what number?

24. 13,014 is 54% of what number?

25. 270 is 60% of what number?

26. 6501 is 33% of what number?

27. What is 2.5% of 2000?

28. 1% of 4200 is what number?

29. 288 is what percent of 1200?

30. What percent of 1100 is 121?

31. 300 is 16% of what number?

32. What percent of 570 is 285?

33. 25% of 528 is what number?

34. 80% of what number is 7200?

35. 390 is what percent of 300?

36. What number is 28.5% of 460?

37. What number is 10% of 3525?

38. 1.5% of 600 is what number?

39. 1950 is what percent of 6000?

40. What number is 28% of 799?

41. What is 2% of 263?

Objective 5.3C   Apply your knowledge

42. Auto Parts Depot sold 330 car and truck batteries last month. This represents 37% of the total batteries they had in stock at the beginning of the month.

  a. How many batteries were in stock at the beginning of the month? Round to the nearest whole battery.

  b. If 20% of the battery sales included a set of new cables, how many sets of cables were sold?

43. New Castle Community College offers housing for 20% of the total student body. If 1350 students receive housing, what is the total number of students who attend the school?

44. Ian is keeping track of his cell phone minutes for the month. His plan currently offers 750 minutes per month of which he has already used 40%. How many minutes has Ian already used?

45. A 6-ounce container of yogurt lists 7 grams of protein among its ingredients.

  a. If this represents 14% of the recommended daily allowance (RDA) of protein for a 2000 calorie diet, what is the total number of grams of protein recommended per day?

  b. If the container lists the dietary fiber content as 2 grams and 8% of the daily value, what is the total number of dietary fiber grams recommended per day?

46. A real estate office sent out invitations to an open house to entice prospective buyers to see one of their properties.

    a. Before noon, 45 people attended the open house. If this represents 25% of the total invitations sent out, how many invitations were sent?

    b. By the end of the day, 18 of the 60 condos had down payments made on them. What percent of the condos were sold?

48. Renee has a health insurance policy that pays 75% of medical expenses for any accidents. If she was injured while skiing and had expenses of $1242, how much was covered by insurance?

50. Every year Paul pays about 35% of his total earnings in taxes. If he expects to make $78,000 this year, how much tax will he pay?

52. Total Workout, a new fitness center, is offering a 20% discount on membership fees for the first 25 customers that sign up. If the regular membership fee is $450, what is the cost of the membership after the discount?

54. By law, companies whose stock is owned by the general public must report operating results quarterly (4 times per year). Melville Corporation reported profits of $2,400,000 last quarter.

    a. If this represents 4% of the company's sales, how much were the sales?

    b. If the company has offices in 42 out of the 50 states, in what percent of the states do they have offices?

56. Of a total of 200 dinners served last night at Franco's Italian Restaurant, 120 were pasta dinners. What percent of the dinners were non-pasta dinners?

58. At the Floorbright Tile Distributors, 64.2% of sales are from customers in the Northeast part of the country. If those sales amounted to $513,600 last year, what were the total sales for the company?

47. You own 40% of a decorating service. If the total worth of the business is $58,000, how much is your share?

49. Denton Motors advertised a down payment of $1450 on a car they sell for $15,500. What percent of the cost of the car is the down payment? Round to the nearest tenth of a percent.

51. The Pine Wood Hospital delivers 67 babies each month. If this represents 2% of all the deliveries for the county, how many deliveries are made each month in the county?

53. Colin is brewing coffee and wants to serve 10 of the 12 cups available in the coffee pot. What percent of the coffee pot does he want to use? Round to the nearest whole percent.

55. A large swimming pool holds 40,000 gallons of water. After draining the pool for patching and painting, 7000 gallons were filled to check for leaks.

    a. What percent of the pool was filled for the leak check?

    b. What percent remained to be filled?

57. A baby elephant was born at the zoo with a birth weight of 54 pounds. Her mother weighed 880 pounds. What percent of the mother's weight is the baby's weight? Round to the nearest tenth of a percent.

59. Five out of every six packages sent via Continental Express arrive on time. What percent of the packages do *not* arrive on time? Round to the nearest tenth of a percent.

60. A container of hydrochloric acid and water is marked 40% hydrochloric acid. How much hydrochloric acid is in a 12-liter container of this solution?

61. If Matt's new job gives him 5% of the total days he works as vacation time, how many vacation days will he have after working 280 days?

62. According to industry sources, Nextel had 12,344,000 subscribers in 2004.

   a. If this represents 8% of the total market, how many total subscribers were there?

   b. If T-Mobile had 8.51% of that same market, how many subscribers did they have?

   c. When Cingular and AT&T Wireless merged, together they accounted for 29.8% of the market. How many subscribers is that?

Use the graphic, *Elvis Tops the Solo List,* for exercises 63–66.

Elvis Tops the Solo List
With 166.5 million albums, the Beatles have outsold all other recording artists. But among soloists, Elvis still tops the list. The following are the number of albums sold by artists in millions.[1]

Elvis Presley	Garth Brooks	Billy Joel	Barbra Streisand	Elton John
117.5	105	78.5	71.5	67.5

[1] Jan. 2004 catalog audit
Source: Recording Industry Association of America

63. What percent of the Beatles' album sales is Elvis Presley's? Round to the nearest whole percent.

64. What percent of Elvis Presley's album sales is Elton John's? Round to the nearest whole percent.

65. If 8.5% of Garth Brook's album sales have been from the Internet, how many albums were ordered that way? Round to the nearest million.

66. If Billy Joel sold 15 million of his albums overseas, what percent does that represent of his total album sales? Round to the nearest tenth of a percent.

CUMULATIVE SKILLS REVIEW

1. Convert 85% to a simplified fraction and a decimal. (5.1A)

2. Round 896,155 to the nearest hundred. (1.1D)

3. Use $>$, $<$, or $=$ to write a true statement. (3.1D)

51.2523 ___ 51.252478

4. Albert's band wants to win the next Battle of the Bands competition. They will need to practice $\frac{1}{4}$ more than they did before. How much more practice time does this translate to in percent form? (5.1C)

5. Convert 22.5% to a decimal. (5.1A)

6. A new economy car can travel 855 miles using only 15 gallons of gasoline. What is the unit rate? (4.2D)

7. Determine whether the ratios $\frac{3}{13}$ and $\frac{21}{45}$ are proportional. If they are, write them as a proportion. (4.3B)

8. Subtract $552 - 129$. (1.3A)

9. Brian is making a spaghetti sauce. The recipe requires that for every cup of tomato sauce, $\frac{1}{4}$ cup of mushrooms should be added. How many cups of mushrooms will be added for 4 cups of tomato sauce? (2.4C)

10. If 6 songs downloaded from iTunes costs $9.90, what is the unit cost? (4.2C)

5.4   SOLVE PERCENT APPLICATION PROBLEMS

LEARNING OBJECTIVES

A. Calculate percent change

B. Calculate sales tax, tip, commission, and discount

C. Calculate the amount or base in a percent change situation

D. Apply your knowledge

In Section 5.1, we noted that percents are used frequently in our daily lives. In this section, we will consider some common applications of percents.

Objective 5.4A   **Calculate percent change**

Percents are often used to express how much a quantity changes. When a quantity increases, the percent change is referred to as a *percent increase*. When a quantity decreases, the percent change is referred to as a *percent decrease*.

Suppose that a clothing boutique had sales of $8000 on Monday. On Tuesday, sales were $10,000. Since Tuesday's sales were greater than Monday's, we can calculate the percent increase. To do this, we find the change by subtracting Monday's sales, $8000, from Tuesday's, $10,000.

$$\$10,000 - \$8000 = \$2000$$

The base is the number of dollars we are changing from ($8000), the amount is the change ($2000), and the percent is unknown.

Learning Tip

In a percent change problem, the base is always the amount we are changing *from* and the amount is always the change (either an increase or a decrease).

There are two ways to solve for the percent. On one hand, we can write and solve a percent equation.

$$2000 = 8000p$$ Use the equation Amount = Base · Percent
Use p to represent the percent.

$$\frac{2000}{8000} = \frac{8000p}{8000}$$ Divide both sides by 8000.

$$0.25 = p$$
$$25\% = p$$ Convert the decimal to a percent.

Alternatively, we can write and solve a percent proportion.

$$\frac{2000}{8000} = \frac{p}{100}$$ Substitute into the formula $\frac{\text{Amount}}{\text{Base}} = \frac{\text{Part}}{100}$.
Use p to represent the part.

$$\frac{1}{4} = \frac{p}{100}$$ Simplify $\frac{2000}{8000}$. Cross multiply.

$$4 \cdot p$$
$$100$$

$$4p = 100$$ Set the cross products equal.

$$\frac{4p}{4} = \frac{100}{4}$$ Divide both sides by 4.

$$p = 25$$ Solve for p. Since p represents the part per 100, the percent change is 25%.

In either case, we find that boutique sales increased by 25% from Monday to Tuesday.

In calculating the percent change, we ultimately divide the change amount by the original amount (that is, the amount we are changing from).

$$\begin{array}{l}\text{change amount} \rightarrow \\ \text{original amount} \rightarrow\end{array} \frac{2000}{8000} = 0.25 = 25\%$$

Continuing with the boutique example, suppose that sales were $7000 on Wednesday. Since Wednesday's sales were less than Tuesday's, we can calculate the *percent decrease*. To do so, we find the change by subtracting Wednesday's sales, $7000, from Tuesday's, $10,000.

$$\$10,000 - \$7000 = \$3000$$

Once again, the base is the number of dollars that we are changing from ($10,000), the amount is the change ($3000), and the percent is unknown.

To solve for the percent, we can either write an equation or a percent proportion. But, as noted above, we can find the percent change by simply dividing the change amount by the original amount.

$$\begin{array}{l}\text{change amount} \rightarrow \\ \text{original amount} \rightarrow\end{array} \frac{3000}{10,000} = 0.3 = 30\%$$

Thus, the boutique sales decreased by 30% from Tuesday to Wednesday.

In general, to calculate the percent change, use the following steps.

Steps for Finding the Percent Change

Step 1. Find the change amount.

    a. If a quantity increases, subtract the original quantity from the new quantity.

    b. If a quantity decreases, subtract the new quantity from the original quantity.

Step 2. Divide the change amount from Step 1 by the original quantity. Convert the result to a percent.

In general, use the following formula and convert the quotient to a percent.

$$\text{Percent change} = \frac{\text{Change amount}}{\text{Original amount}}$$

EXAMPLE 1   Calculate percent change

a. If a quantity changes from 40 to 46, what is the percent change?

b. If a quantity changes from 78 to 35, what is the percent change? Round to the nearest tenth of a percent.

SOLUTION STRATEGY

a. $46 - 40 = 6$

A smaller quantity changes to a larger quantity, and so the change is an increase.
Subtract the original quantity from the new quantity.

$\frac{6}{40} = 0.15 = 15\%$

$\text{Percent change} = \frac{\text{Change amount}}{\text{Original amount}}$

b. $78 - 35 = 43$

A larger quantity changes to a smaller quantity, and so the change is a decrease.
Subtract the new quantity from the original quantity.

$\frac{43}{78} \approx 0.551 = 55.1\%$

$\text{Percent change} = \frac{\text{Change amount}}{\text{Original amount}}$

TRY-IT EXERCISE 1

a. If a quantity changes from 260 to 312, what is the percent change?

b. If a quantity changes from 4250 to 1820, what is the percent change? Round to the nearest tenth of a percent.

Check your answers with the solutions in Appendix A. ■

Objective 5.4B   Calculate sales tax, tip, commission, and discount

How much is an iPhone with sales tax? How much is a dinner tab including tip? How much is a shirt after a discount? These common situations require us to find a new amount when an original amount and a percent change are known.

As an example, suppose that your dinner bill at a restaurant is $54.00. If you want to give your server an 18% tip, how much money do you leave? To determine this, you must first answer the question, "What is 18% of $54.00?"

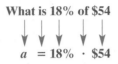

$$a = 18\% \cdot \$54$$

Now, we solve for a.

$$a = 0.18 \cdot \$54 \qquad \text{Write 18\% as a decimal.}$$
$$a = \$9.72 \qquad \text{Multiply.}$$

Alternatively, we can write a percent proportion. In this problem, the amount is the tip, the part is 18, and the base is $54.

$$\frac{a}{\$54} = \frac{18}{100} \qquad \text{Substitute into the formula } \frac{\text{Amount}}{\text{Base}} = \frac{\text{Part}}{100}.$$

$$\frac{a}{\$54} \diagdown\!\!\!\!\diagup \frac{9}{50} \qquad \text{Simplify } \frac{18}{100}. \text{ Find the cross products.}$$

$$50a = \$486 \qquad \text{Set the cross products equal.}$$
$$\frac{50a}{50} = \frac{\$486}{50} \qquad \text{Divide both sides by 50.}$$
$$a = \$9.72 \qquad \text{Solve for } a.$$

In either case, the tip is $9.72. To figure out how much to leave, add the dinner bill and the tip.

$$\text{Total} = \$54 + \$9.72 = \$63.72$$

As another example, suppose that you want to buy a coat that is 20% off. If the coat normally costs $200, how much would you pay with the discount? To determine the new price, you must first figure out the discount by answering the question, "What is 20% of $200?".

What is 20% of 200

$$a = 20\% \cdot 200$$

Now, we solve for a.

$$a = 0.2 \cdot \$200 \qquad \text{Write 20\% as a decimal.}$$
$$a = \$40 \qquad \text{Multiply.}$$

Alternatively, we can write a percent proportion. In this problem, the amount is the discount, the part is 20, and the base is $200.

$$\frac{a}{\$200} = \frac{20}{100}$$ Substitute into the formula $\frac{\text{Amount}}{\text{Base}} = \frac{\text{Part}}{100}$.

$$\frac{a}{\$200} = \frac{1}{5}$$ Simplify $\frac{20}{100}$. Find the cross products.

$$5a = \$200$$ Set the cross products equal.

$$\frac{5a}{5} = \frac{\$200}{5}$$ Divide both sides by 5.

$$a = \$40$$ Solve for a.

In either case, the discount is $40. To find the sale price of the coat, subtract the discount from the original cost.

Sale price = $200 − $40 = $160

In addition to tip and discount, we also consider two other percent applications: sales tax and commission. **Sales tax** is a state tax based on the retail price or rental cost of certain items. **Commission** is a form of compensation based on a percent of sales.

The table below provides equations for solving these four types of application problems.

sales tax
A state tax based on the retail price or rental cost of certain items.

commission
A form of compensation based on a percent of sales.

PERCENT APPLICATIONS

APPLICATION	AMOUNT	PERCENT	BASE	EQUATION
Sales tax	Sales tax	Sales tax rate	Item cost	Sales tax = Sales tax rate · Item cost
Tip	Tip	Tip rate	Bill amount	Tip = Tip rate · Bill amount
Commission	Commission	Commission rate	Sales amount	Commission = Commission rate · Sales amount
Discount	Discount	Discount rate	Original cost	Discount = Discount rate · Original cost

EXAMPLE 2   **Calculate sales tax and total purchase price**

David purchased a mountain bike for $875. The sales tax rate in his state is 5%.

a. What is the sales tax on the bike?

b. What is the total purchase price of the bike?

SOLUTION STRATEGY

a. Sales tax = Sales tax rate · Item cost   Use the sales tax equation.

$$t = 5\% \cdot \$875$$ Let t represent sales tax. Substitute values for sales tax rate and item cost in the sales tax equation.

$$t = 0.05 \cdot \$875$$ Substitute values for the item cost and sales tax.

$$t = \$43.75$$

The sales tax amount is $43.75.

b. Item cost + Sales tax = Total purchase price

$875.00 + $43.75 = $918.75

The total purchase price is $918.75.

TRY-IT EXERCISE 2

Charlotte purchased books at Barnes and Noble amounting to $54.25. The sales tax rate is 7.5%.

a. What is the amount of sales tax on the books? Round to the nearest cent.

b. What is the total purchase price of the books?

Check your answers with the solutions in Appendix A. ■

EXAMPLE 3   Calculate tip and total bill

Michelle's lunch bill at Dave's Tavern was $13.42. She wants to give her server a 20% tip.

a. What is the tip?

b. What is the total including tip?

SOLUTION STRATEGY

a. Tip = Tip rate · Bill amount

$$t = 20\% \cdot \$13.42$$

Use the tip equation.

Let t represent tip.
Substitute values for tip rate and bill amount in the tip equation.

$t = 0.2 \cdot \$13.42$

$t = \$2.684 \approx \$2.68$

The tip amount is $2.68.

b. Bill amount + Tip amount = Total

Substitute values for the bill amount and tip.

$13.42 + $2.68 = $16.10

The total including tip is $16.10.

TRY-IT EXERCISE 3

After an afternoon at the beach, Ivan and Michael headed to Roscoe's Grille for an early dinner. Their total bill was $35.70. They want to give their server a 22% tip.

a. What is the tip?

b. What is the total including tip?

Check your answer with the solutions in Appendix A. ■

EXAMPLE 4   Calculate commission

Christine works at a boutique shop as a salesperson. She makes 7% commission on all of her clothing sales. If she sold $5148 in merchandise last week, what is the amount of her commission?

SOLUTION STRATEGY

Commission = Commission rate · Sales amount   Use the commission equation.

$$c \qquad = \qquad 7\% \qquad \cdot \qquad \$5148$$

Let c represent commission. Substitute values for the commission rate and sales amount in the commission equation.

$$c = 0.07 \cdot \$5148$$

$$c = \$360.36$$

Christine made $360.36 commission.

TRY-IT EXERCISE 4

Coastal Realty makes 6% commission on real estate sales. If a house was sold for $158,000, how much commission did Coastal make?

Check your answer with the solutions in Appendix A. ∎

EXAMPLE 5   Calculate discount rate

Anita purchased $1600 of outdoor patio furniture and was given a $200 discount. What was the discount rate on her purchase?

SOLUTION STRATEGY

Discount = Discount rate · Original cost   Use the discount equation.

$$\$200 \qquad = \qquad r \qquad \cdot \qquad \$1600$$

Let r represent the discount rate. Substitute values for the discount amount and original cost.

$$\$200 = r \cdot \$1600$$

$$\frac{\$200}{\$1600} = \frac{\$1600r}{\$1600}$$

$$0.125 = r$$

$$12.5\% = r$$

The discount rate is 12.5%.

TRY-IT EXERCISE 5

Adam purchased a $990 desktop computer at Computer Corner, and was given a $178.20 discount. What was the discount rate on his purchase?

Check your answer with the solutions in Appendix A. ∎

Objective 5.4C	**Calculate the amount or base in a percent change situation**

Calculating tip, sales tax, commission, and discount are particular examples of problems that require us to find a new amount when an original amount and a percent change are known. We now consider an alternate, more general approach to such problems.

As an example, suppose that a town of 40,000 people is expected to experience a 6% increase in population next year. The new population will be the total of the current population (which represents 100% of the people) and the amount of increase (6%). Thus, the new population will be 106% (100% + 6%) of the current population. To determine this new population, we must answer the question, "What is 106% of 40,000?"

$$\text{What is } 106\% \text{ of } 40{,}000?$$
$$a = 106\% \cdot 40{,}000$$

Next, we solve for a.

$$a = (1.06)(40{,}000) \qquad \text{Write 106\% as 1.06.}$$
$$a = 42{,}400 \qquad \text{Multiply.}$$

Alternatively, we can write and solve a percent proportion.

$$\frac{a}{40{,}000} = \frac{106}{100} \qquad \text{Substitute into the formula } \frac{\text{Amount}}{\text{Base}} = \frac{\text{Part}}{100}.$$

$$\frac{a}{40{,}000} \overset{40{,}000 \cdot 53}{\underset{p \cdot 50}{\diagdown}} \frac{53}{50} \qquad \text{Simplify } \frac{106}{100}. \text{ Find the cross products.}$$

$$50a = 40{,}000 \cdot 53 \qquad \text{Set the cross products equal.}$$
$$\frac{50a}{50} = \frac{2{,}120{,}000}{50} \qquad \text{Divide both sides by 50.}$$
$$a = 42{,}400 \qquad \text{Solve for } a.$$

Thus, the population of the town is expected to be 42,400.

Let's now suppose that a town of 40,000 is expected to experience a 6% decrease in population next year. The new population will be the difference between the current population (which represents 100% of the people) and the amount of decrease (6%). Thus, the new population will be 94% (100% − 6%) of the current population. To determine this new population, we must answer the question, "What is 94% of 40,000?"

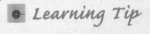

Learning Tip

If the rate of change is an *increase*, then *add* the percent change to 100%. If the rate of change is a *decrease*, then *subtract* the percent change from 100%.

$$\text{What is } 94\% \text{ of } 40{,}000?$$
$$a = 94\% \cdot 40{,}000$$

Next, we solve for a.

$$a = (0.94)(40{,}000) \qquad \text{Write 94\% as 0.94.}$$
$$a = 37{,}600 \qquad \text{Multiply.}$$

Alternatively, we can write and solve a percent proportion. In either case, the population of the town is expected to be 37,600.

In general, we use these steps to calculate a new amount after a percent change.

Steps for Calculating the New Amount After a Percent Change

Step 1. If the quantity increases, add the percent increase to 100%. If the quantity decreases, subtract the percent decrease from 100%.

Step 2. Solve for the new amount by solving either a percent equation or a percent proportion containing the percent from step 1 and the original amount.

EXAMPLE 6 **Calculate a new amount after a percent change**

a. What is 600 increased by 22%? **b.** What is 80 decreased by 40%?

SOLUTION STRATEGY

a. $100\% + 22\% = 122\%$ Since 600 is increased by 22%, add 22% to 100%.

What is 122% of 600?   State the problem in words.
$$a = 1.22 \cdot 600$$
Write as a percent equation. Convert the percent, 122%, to a decimal, 1.22.

$$a = 732$$

600 increased by 22% is 732.

b. $100\% - 40\% = 60\%$ Since 80 is decreased by 40%, subtract 40% from 100%.

What is 60% of 80?   State the problem in words.
$$a = 0.6 \cdot 80$$
Write as a percent equation. Convert the percent, 60%, to a decimal, 0.6.

$$a = 48$$

80 decreased by 40% is 48.

TRY-IT EXERCISE 6

a. What is 260 increased by 120%? **b.** What is 1400 decreased by 15%?

Check your answers with the solutions in Appendix A. ■

Another common situation involving percent change is when the new amount is known but the original amount is unknown.

As an example, suppose that after a 25% load increase, a truck weighed 25,000 pounds. What was the original weight of the truck before the load increase?

Because the load increased 25%, the new load is 125% (100% + 25%) of the original load. To determine the original load, we must answer the question, "25,000 is 125% of what?"

$$25{,}000 \text{ is } 125\% \text{ of what?}$$

$$25{,}000 = 125\% \cdot b$$

Next, we solve for b.

$25{,}000 = 1.25 \cdot b$	Write 125% as 1.25.
$\dfrac{25{,}000}{1.25} = \dfrac{1.25b}{1.25}$	Divide both sides by 1.25.
$20{,}000 = b$	

Thus, the weight of the truck before the load increase was 20,000 pounds. Alternatively, we can write and solve a percent proportion. In either case, we get the same result.

In general, we use these steps to calculate the original amount before a percent change.

Steps for Calculating the Original Amount Before a Percent Change

Step 1. If the quantity increases, add the percent increase to 100%.
If the quantity decreases, subtract the percent decrease from 100%.

Step 2. Solve for the original amount (the base) by solving either a percent equation or a percent proportion containing the percent from step 1 and the new amount.

Learning Tip

In percent change problems, the original amount is always the base.

EXAMPLE 7   **Calculate the original amount before a percent change**

a. A number decreased 25% to 37,500. What was the original number?

b. A number increased 8% to 270. What was the original number?

SOLUTION STRATEGY

a. $100\% - 25\% = 75\%$ Since a number *decreased* 25%, subtract 25% from 100%.

37,500 is 75% of what number?   State the problem in words.

$37{,}500 = 0.75 \cdot b$ Write as a percent equation. Convert the percent, 75%, to a decimal, 0.75.

$37{,}500 = 0.75 \cdot b$

$\dfrac{37{,}500}{0.75} = \dfrac{0.75b}{0.75}$ Divide both sides by 0.75.

$50{,}000 = b$

37,500 is 75% of 50,000.

b. $100\% + 8\% = 108\%$ Since a number *increased* 8%, add 8% to 100%.

270 is 108% of what number?   State the problem in words.

$$270 = 1.08 \cdot b$$

Write as a percent equation. Convert the percent, 108%, to a decimal, 1.08.

$$270 = 1.08 \cdot b$$

Divide both sides by 1.08.

$$\frac{270}{1.08} = \frac{1.08b}{1.08}$$

$$250 = b$$

270 is 108% of 250.

TRY-IT EXERCISE 7

a. A number decreased 30% to 714. What was the original amount?

b. A number increased 40% to 1764. What was the original amount?

Check your answers with the solutions in Appendix A. ■

Objective 5.4D   **Apply your knowledge**

Next, let's take a look at some common business and consumer applications involving percent change and amounts in percent change situations.

EXAMPLE 8   Calculate percent change

Answer the following, rounding to a tenth of a percent when necessary.

a. A house that sold for $120,000 last year is now priced to sell at $165,000. What is the percent change of the price of the house?

b. A company had 350 employees last year and 275 employees this year. What is the percent change in the number of employees? Round to the nearest tenth of a percent.

SOLUTION STRATEGY

a. $165,000 - 120,000 = 45,000$

A smaller quantity changes to a larger quantity, and so the change is an increase.
Subtract the original quantity from the new quantity.

$$\frac{45,000}{120,000} = 0.375 = 37.5\% \text{ increase}$$

Percent change $= \dfrac{\text{Change amount}}{\text{Original amount}}$

b. $350 - 275 = 75$

A larger quantity changes to a smaller quantity, and so the change is a decrease.
Subtract the new quantity from the original quantity.

$$\frac{75}{350} = 0.214286 \approx 21.4\% \text{ decrease}$$

Percent change $= \dfrac{\text{Change amount}}{\text{Original amount}}$

TRY-IT EXERCISE 8

Answer the following, rounding to a tenth of a percent when necessary.

a. A puppy weighed 3.5 pounds at birth, and now weighs 5.2 pounds. What is the percent change of the puppy's weight? Round to the nearest tenth of a percent.

b. Enrollment in an economics course went from 58 students last semester to 42 students this semester. What is the percent change in enrollment? Round to the nearest whole percent.

Check your answers with the solutions in Appendix A. ■

EXAMPLE 9   Calculate a new amount after a percent change

a. By changing construction material from fiberglass to Kevlar, the weight of a boat's hull was reduced by 18%. If the fiberglass hull weighed 5650 pounds, what is the weight of the Kevlar hull?

b. Last year, Sigma Computers offered a particular model with a 30-gigabyte hard drive. This year the company is offering a hard drive option with 30% more capacity. How many gigabytes are in the new hard drive?

SOLUTION STRATEGY

a. $100\% - 18\% = 82\%$ Since the weight of the hull decreased 18%, subtract 18% from 100%.

What is 82% of 5650?   State the problem in words.

$$a \;=\; 0.82 \cdot 5650$$

Write as a percent equation. Convert the percent, 82%, to a decimal, 0.82.

$$a = 4633$$

The Kevlar hull weighs 4633 pounds.

b. $100\% + 30\% = 130\%$ Since the capacity increased 30%, add 30% to 100%.

What is 130% of 30?   State the problem in words.

$$a \;=\; 1.3 \cdot 30$$

Write as a percent equation. Convert the percent, 130%, to a decimal, 1.3.

$$a = 39$$

The new hard drive will have 39 gigabytes.

TRY-IT EXERCISE 9

a. A local Jiffy Lube franchise serviced 180 cars last week and estimates that they will service 20% more cars this week because of a "$19.95 oil change" special. How many cars do they expect to service this week?

b. An airport averages 260 baggage handlers working each shift during the December holiday season. For the rest of the year, 10% fewer handlers are needed for the decreased baggage load. How many handlers work each shift during the normal months?

Check your answers with the solutions in Appendix A. ■

EXAMPLE 10   Calculate an original amount before a percent change

a. The amount of milk in a large holding tank decreased to 12,000 gallons. If it is down 40% from last week, how many gallons were in the tank last week?

b. Superstar Video has 4431 DVDs in stocks this month. If this represents an increase of 5.5% from last month, how many DVDs were in stock last month?

SOLUTION STRATEGY

a. $100\% - 40\% = 60\%$

Since the amount of milk decreased 40%, subtract 40% from 100%.

12,000 is 60% of what number?

State the problem in words.

$12,000 = 0.6 \cdot b$

Write as a percent equation. Convert the percent, 60%, to a decimal, 0.6.

$12,000 = 0.6 \cdot b$

$\dfrac{12,000}{0.6} = \dfrac{0.6b}{0.6}$

Divide both sides by 0.6.

$20,000 = b$

There were 20,000 gallons of milk in the tank last week.

b. rate $= 100\% + 5.5\% = 105.5\%$

Since the number of DVDs increased 5.5%, add 5.5% to 100%.

4431 is 105.5% of what number?

State the problem in words.

$4431 = 1.055 \cdot b$

Write as a percent equation. Convert the percent, 105.5%, to a decimal, 1.055.

$4431 = 1.055 \cdot b$

$\dfrac{4431}{1.055} = \dfrac{1.055b}{1.055}$

Divide both sides by 1.055.

$4200 = b$

There were 4200 DVDs at Superstar Video last month.

TRY-IT EXERCISE 10

a. Dr. Mager, a dentist, currently has 1353 patients. If this represents a 10% increase from last year, how many patients did he have last year?

b. A two-year old automobile is appraised at $28,500. If this represents a decrease of 25% from the original new car selling price, what was the original price? Round to the nearest whole dollar.

Check your answers with the solutions in Appendix A ∎

EXAMPLE 11   Calculate percent change

Use the graph *Marriage Age Rising in the United States* to answer the following questions.

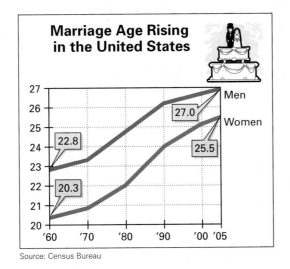

Marriage Age Rising in the United States

22.8

20.3

27.0

25.5

Men

Women

Source: Census Bureau

a. What is the percent change in men's marrying age from 1960 to 2005? Round to the nearest whole percent.

b. If the men's marrying age decreased to 25 years in 2007, what is the percent change from 2005? Round to the nearest tenth of a percent.

SOLUTION STRATEGY

a. $27.0 - 22.8 = 4.2$ years

A smaller number changes to a larger number, and so the change is an increase.
Subtract the original quantity from the new quantity.

$\dfrac{4.2}{22.8} \approx 0.184 \approx 18\%$ increase

$\text{Percent change} = \dfrac{\text{Change amount}}{\text{Original amount}}$

b. $27.0 - 25 = 2$ years

A larger quantity changes to a smaller quantity, and so the change is a decrease.
Subtract the new quantity from the original quantity.

$\dfrac{2}{27} \approx 0.074 \approx 7.4\%$ decrease

$\text{Percent change} = \dfrac{\text{Change amount}}{\text{Original amount}}$

TRY-IT EXERCISE 11

Use the graph *Marriage Age Rising in the United States* to answer the following questions.

a. What is the percent change in women's marrying age from 1960 to 2005? Round to the nearest whole percent.

b. If the men's age decreased to 26.1 years in 2007, what is the percent change from 2005? Round to the nearest tenth of a percent.

Check your answers with the solutions in Appendix A. ■

SECTION 5.4 REVIEW EXERCISES

Concept Check

1. A common application of percents is expressing how much a particular quantity has _____.

2. When numbers go up, the percent change is referred to as a percent _____.

3. When numbers go down, the percent change is referred to as a percent _____.

4. Write the formula for percent change.

5. _____ _____ is a state tax based on the retail price or rental cost of certain items.

6. Write the sales tax equation.

7. Write the tip equation.

8. A form of compensation based on a percent of sales is called _____.

9. Write the commission equation.

10. Write the discount equation.

Objective 5.4A   Calculate percent change

GUIDE PROBLEMS

11. If a number changes from 100 to 123, what is the percent change?

    a. What is the change amount?

    b. Set up the percent change formula.

    c. Determine the percent change.

12. If a number changes from 565 to 300, what is the percentage change?

    a. What is the change amount?

    b. Set up the percent change formula.

    c. Determine the percent change. Round to the nearest tenth of a percent.

Complete the table. Round to the nearest whole percent when necessary.

	ORIGINAL AMOUNT	NEW AMOUNT	AMOUNT OF CHANGE	PERCENT CHANGE
13.	50	65		
14.	15	12.75		
15.	18	22		
16.	$65	$50		
17.	1000	1260		
18.	875	900		
19.	$150	$70		
20.	$10	$50		
21.	68	12		
22.	48.2	60		

| Objective 5.4B | **Calculate sales tax, tip, commission, and discount** |

GUIDE PROBLEMS

23. A toaster sells for $55. If the sales tax rate is 5%, determine the sales tax and the total purchase price.

    a. Write the sales tax formula.

    b. Substitute the values in the formula.

    c. Calculate the sales tax.

    d. Determine the total purchase price.

24. Mary Lou's dinner tab was $23.25. She wants to leave a 20% tip.

    a. Write the tip formula.

    b. Substitute the values in the formula.

    c. Calculate the tip.

    d. Determine the total.

25. Bernie earned a 20% commission on $600 in magazine sales. How much commission will he receive?

    a. Write the commission formula.

    b. Substitute the values in the formula.

    c. Calculate the commission.

26. At Harrison's Department Store, leather handbags are on sale. If the original price is $150 and the discount is 50%, what is the amount of the discount and the sale price?

    a. Write the discount formula.

    b. Substitute the values in the formula.

    c. Calculate the discount.

    d. Determine the sale price.

27. A $65.40 wool sweater is subject to a 6% sales tax. What is the amount of the sales tax?

28. A $12.95 DVD is subject to a 5.4% sales tax. What is the amount of the sales tax?

29. A laser printer with a price of $327.19 is subject to a sales tax of 4.3%.

    a. What is the amount of the sales tax?

    b. What is the total purchase price of the printer?

30. Bob purchased a new boat for $250,000. He must pay a sales tax of 7%.

    a. What is the amount of the sales tax on the boat?

    b. What is the total purchase price of the boat?

31. Eric's lunch at Moody's Pub was $13.00. He wants to leave 15% tip. What is the tip amount? What is the total including tip? Round to the nearest cent.

32. Azizia and her friends had dinner at Joe's Crab Shack. Their bill was $55.20. They want to leave a 22% tip. What is the tip amount? What is the total including tip? Round to the nearest cent.

33. Jason just served a group of people whose total bill was $120. If they left $150, how much was the tip? What was the tip rate?

34. Daryl's served a group of 10 people whose total bill was $780. If they left $1000, how much was the tip? What was the tip rate? Round to the nearest whole percent.

35. Ramsey earns 2.5% commission on all sales of groceries to various food markets. If he sold $500,000 last month, how much commission did he earn?

36. Mardell earns 6% commission on all computers she sells at Computer City. How much commission would she make on a sale of $3575?

37. Francis earned commission of $139.50 on a sale of $900. What is the commission rate on this sale?

38. Landmark Realty earned $50,000 commission on a sale of $800,000 in property. What is the commission rate on this sale?

39. Taylor's department store had a "30% off" sale on sporting goods.. You found a tennis racket with an original price of $90.

   a. What is the discount amount?

   b. What is the sale price of the racket?

40. Every year toy stores must display the most popular items and sell the older models. A particular store has a policy of selling older model toys at a 60% discount rate. A remote control car originally priced at $50 is being phased out.

   a. What is the amount of the discount?

   b. What is the sale price?

41. Antoine purchased a $350 stereo and was given a discount of $44 because it was on sale. What was the discount rate on his stereo? Round to the nearest tenth of a percent.

42. A refurbished computer was on sale for $790. If the original price was $1250, what is the discount rate?

43. In the summer time heavy winter coats can often be found at discounted prices. A black leather jacket that sells for $500 in the winter can be purchased for $300. What is the discount rate on the leather jacket in the summer time?

44. Trevor purchased some additional software for his computer. The price of the software was listed at $90 with a discount rate of 20%. What was the discounted sale price on the software?

Objective 5.4C   **Calculate the amount or base in percent change situations**

GUIDE PROBLEMS

45. A refrigerator weighed 400 pounds empty. After putting in food, the weight increased by 20%. How much does the refrigerator weigh after the increase?

   a. Because the weight increased, add the percent change to 100%.

   _____ + 100% = _____

46. The number of employees at Armstrong Corporation declined 15% to 306. How many employees did the company have before the decrease?

   a. Because the number of employees decreased, subtract the percent change from 100%.

   100% − _____ = _____

b. Substitute the original weight and the percent from part a. into the percent equation.

b. Substitute the new number of employees and the percent from part a. into the percent equation.

d. Determine the new weight.

d. Determine the original number of employees.

Complete the table. Round to the nearest whole number, when necessary.

	ORIGINAL AMOUNT	PERCENT CHANGE	INCREASE OR DECREASE	NEW AMOUNT
47.	$290	57%	increase	
48.		78%	increase	$80
49.		35%	decrease	4000
50.	1850	84%	increase	
51.	$13,882	15%	decrease	
52.	500	262%	increase	
53.	$20,000	19%	increase	
54.	57	47%	decrease	30
55.	90	9%	decrease	
56.		50%	increase	$450
57.	$100	4%	decrease	
58.		15%	decrease	26
59.	16	6%	decrease	
60.		133%	increase	105

Objective 5.4D   Apply your knowledge

61. During a sale, the price of a motor home decreased to $43,500. If that represents a 20% decrease, what was the original price?

62. A 6 foot piece of wire was cut from a 15 foot roll. What percent of the roll remains?

63. Last month the Shop-Rite Market had 10,000 customers and this month 8500 customers visited the store.

  a. What is the percent change in customers?

  b. Next month, Shop-Rite will be having a number of special sales and expects to increase customer traffic by 10% over the previous month. How many customers do they expect next month?

64. Last year, Dandy Dry Cleaning Service operated from 200 franchise locations nationwide. This year the company has added 10 new stores.

  a. What is the percent change in service locations?

  b. If the weekly revenue, $4000 per store, increases by 22%, what will be the new weekly revenue per store?

65. In June, the wedding business increases by about 40% over the rest of the year. If a wedding planner normally does 5 weddings per month, how many weddings can be expected in June?

66. The propane level in a 170-gallon liquid propane (LP) tank decreased by 26% after a day of filling LP tanks for barbeque grills. How many gallons of LP remain in the tank? Round to the nearest whole gallon.

67. On the first day at sea, the cruise ship *Neptune of the Seas* covered 500 miles of the 1850-mile trip. What percent of the trip was completed? Round to the nearest whole percent.

68. An ink jet printer's black cartridge can print about 750 pages of material. If the company now offers a "super-size" cartridge that prints 40% more pages, how many pages can the larger cartridge print?

69. According to Photo Marketing Association International, in 2000, 948 million rolls of film were sold in the United States. By 2004, that figure had decreased by 19.1%. How many rolls were sold in 2004? Round to the nearest million rolls.

70. Greg switched from one Internet service provider to another that offered better rates. If Greg used to pay $23 per month and now pays $16 per month for Internet service, what is the percentage change in Greg's Internet service cost? Round to nearest whole percent.

71. A 6-inch rubber band can stretch to 18 inches.

  a. What is the percent increase in size?

  b. If the rubber band is designed to break at 300% of its unstretched length, at how many inches will the rubber band break?

72. A local foundation helps in the building of new homes for families in need. Ten years ago the volunteers available numbered 180. Currently there are 500 volunteers on any given day.

  a. What is the percent change in volunteers over the last 10 years? Round to the nearest whole percent.

  b. This year the group built 5 homes; next year they expect to build 7 homes. What is the percent change in houses built?

73. According to the White House Office of Management and Budget, the gross domestic product (GDP), the broadest measure of goods and services produced in the United States, will increase from $9.4 trillion in 2002 to $12 trillion in 2009. Calculate the percent increase. Round to the nearest tenth of a percent.

74. According to the Office of Management and Budget, spending by the Department of Education will increase from $31 billion in 1993 to $64 billion in 2009. Calculate the percent increase. Round to the nearest whole percent.

75. According to the Office of Management and Budget, the spending for NASA will increase from $14.3 billion in 1993 to $18 billion in 2009. Calculate the percent increase. Round to the nearest hundredth percent.

76. In 2005, the cost of a 30-second commercial during the Super Bowl was $2.3 million. If that represents a 91.7% increase over 1995, how much was a Super Bowl commercial in 1995? Round to the nearest tenth of a million.

77. Before a trip, the tires on John's car had 27 pounds of pressure per square inch (psi). After a drive on the highway, the tire pressure increased by 17%. How much pressure was in the tires after the trip? Round to the nearest whole psi.

78. Albert is responsible for leasing computers for his office. Last year he leased 12 laptops and this year plans to lease 22 laptops. What is the percentage change in laptop orders? Round to the nearest percent.

79. A water-saver toilet uses one gallon per flush instead of the normal 2.4 gallons. What percent of water is saved on each flush? Round to the nearest whole percent.

80. According to the Census Bureau, in 1996 there were 52.9 million dogs in the United States. By 2006 that number increased to 73.9 million. What is the percent increase in dogs? Round to the nearest tenth of a percent.

81. According to the Census Bureau, in 1996 there were 59.1 million cats in the United States. By 2006 that number increased to 90.5 million. What is the percent increase in cats? Round to the nearest tenth of a percent.

82. In 1996, $11.1 billion was spent on pet care. In 2006, $26.6 billion was spent. What is the percent increase in spending for pet care? Round to the nearest tenth of a percent.

Use the graph *Mobile Phone Users in the United States* for exercises 83–86.

83. What was the percent change in millions of mobile phone users from 2003 to 2004? Round to the nearest tenth of a percent.

84. What was the percent change in millions of mobile phone users from 2004 to 2006? Round to the nearest tenth of a percent.

85. If the number of mobile phone users increased 8% from 2002 to 2003, how many mobile phone users were there in 2002? Round to the nearest tenth.

86. If the number of mobile phone users in 2008 was 2% higher than the number of users in 2007, how many mobile phone users were there in 2008?

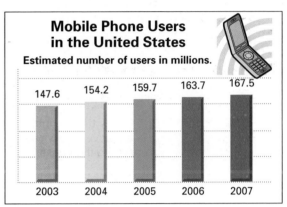

Mobile Phone Users in the United States
Estimated number of users in millions.

| 147.6 | 154.2 | 159.7 | 163.7 | 167.5 |
| 2003 | 2004 | 2005 | 2006 | 2007 |

Source: Yankee Group

CUMULATIVE SKILLS REVIEW

1. Write "25 is what percent of 500?" as a proportion. (5.3A)

2. Write "8 is to 13" as a ratio in fraction notation. (4.1A)

3. Evaluate $22.8 + 3.95 \times 2.1^3$. (3.5B)

4. Convert 5.2% to a decimal. (5.1A)

5. Are $\frac{25}{7}$ and $\frac{75}{21}$ proportional? (4.3B)

6. Write "what percent of 65 is 3" as an equation. (5.2A)

7. Multiply $0.895 \cdot 0.322$. (3.3A)

8. Write the ratio "4 to 7" in 3 different ways. (4.1A)

9. Convert 92% to a simplified fraction and to a decimal. (5.1A)

10. What is 65% of 1000? (5.2B, 5.3B)

10-MINUTE CHAPTER REVIEW

5.1 Introduction to Percents

Objective	Important Concepts	Illustrative Examples
A. Convert a percent to a fraction or a decimal (page 350)	**percent** A part per 100. **percent sign** The % symbol. **Rule for Converting a Percent to a Fraction** Write the number preceding the percent sign over 100. Simplify, if possible. **Rule for Converting a Percent to a Decimal** Multiply the number preceding the percent sign by 0.01. Alternatively, drop the percent sign and move the decimal two places to the *left*.	Convert 12% to a fraction. Simplify, if possible. $12\% = \dfrac{12}{100} = \dfrac{3}{25}$ Convert $\dfrac{2}{5}\%$ to a decimal. $\dfrac{2}{5}\% = 0.4\% = 0.4 \cdot 0.01 = 0.004$
B. Convert a decimal, a fraction, or a whole number to a percent (page 353)	**Rule for Converting a Decimal to a Percent** Multiply the decimal by 100%. Alternatively, move the decimal point two places to the *right* and append a percent sign. **Steps for Converting a Fraction to a Percent** **Step 1.** Convert the fraction to a decimal. **Step 2.** Convert the decimal to a percent.	Convert 0.65 to a percent. $0.65 \cdot 100\% = 65\%$ Convert $1\dfrac{3}{4}$ to a percent. $1\dfrac{3}{4} = 1.75$ $1.75 \cdot 100\% = 175\%$
C. Apply your knowledge (page 356)	Gasoline prices have increased by 35% this year alone. Write the percent increase of gasoline as a fraction and as a decimal. $35\% = \dfrac{35}{100} = 0.35$	

5.2 Solve Percent Problems Using Equations

Objective	Important Concepts	Illustrative Examples
A. Write a percent problem as an equation (page 364)	Refer to these key words and phrases when writing percent problems as equations. 	WORD	MEANING	MATH SYMBOL	 |---|---|---| | is, are, was, will be, results in, yields	equals	$=$	 | of	multiply	$\times$ $\cdot$ $(\ )$	 | what, what number, what percent	unknown	any letter of the alphabet, such as x or n		Write each percent problem as an equation. **a.** What number is 3% of 150? $k = 3\% \cdot 150$ **b.** 500 is what percent of 6000? $500 = s \cdot 6000$ **c.** 62 is 5% of what number? $62 = 5\% \cdot z$

B. Solve a percent equation (page 366)	**amount** In a percent problem, the number that represents a part of a whole. **percent** In a percent problem, the number that defines what part the amount is of the whole. **base** Ina a percent problem the number that represents the whole or 100%. **percent equation** An equation of the form Amount = Percent · Base.	Solve. **a.** What number is 80% of 1500? $a = 80\% \cdot 1500$ $a = 0.80 \cdot 1500 = 1200$ **b.** 15 is what percent of 125? $15 = p \cdot 125$ $15 = p \cdot 125$ $\dfrac{15}{125} = \dfrac{125p}{125}$ $p = \dfrac{15}{125}$ $p = 0.12 = 12\%$ **c.** 70 is 35% of what number? $70 = 35\% \cdot b$ $70 = 0.35 \cdot b$ $\dfrac{70}{0.35} = \dfrac{0.35b}{0.35}$ $b = \dfrac{70}{0.35} = 200$
C. Apply your knowledge (page 370)	Nestor wants to sell a portion of his business. The business is valued at $25,000 and he wants to sell a 20% share to an investor. How much will the investor pay? What number is 20% of $25,000? $a = 20\% \cdot \$25,000$ $a = 20\% \cdot 25,000$ $a = \$5000$ The investor will pay $5000.	

5.3 Solve Percent Problems Using Proportions

Objective	Important Concepts	Illustrative Examples
A. Write a percent problem as a proportion (page 378)	**Steps to Write and Solve a Percent Problem as a Proportion** **Step 1.** Identify the amount, base, and part. **Step 2.** Assign a letter to the unknown number. Substitute the known numbers and letter in the percent proportion. **Step 3.** Simplify the fractions in the percent proportion, if possible. **Step 4.** Cross multiply to find the cross products. Set the cross-products equal. **Step 5.** Divide both sides of the equation by the number on the side with the unknown.	Write each percent problem as a proportion. **a.** 48 is 25% of what number? amount percent base $\dfrac{\text{Amount}}{\text{Base}} = \dfrac{\text{Part}}{100} \longrightarrow \dfrac{48}{b} = \dfrac{25}{100}$ **b.** What number is 60% of 440? amount = percent · base $\dfrac{\text{Amount}}{\text{Base}} = \dfrac{\text{Part}}{100} \longrightarrow \dfrac{a}{440} = \dfrac{60}{100}$ **c.** 75 is what percent of 25? amount = percent · base $\dfrac{\text{Amount}}{\text{Base}} = \dfrac{\text{Part}}{100} \longrightarrow \dfrac{75}{25} = \dfrac{p}{100}$
B. Solve a percent proportion (page 381)	Solve a percent proportion in the same way that we solved a proportion in Section 4.3.	Write each percent problem as a proportion and solve. **a.** What percent of 850 is 510? percent base amount $\dfrac{\text{Amount}}{\text{Base}} = \dfrac{\text{Part}}{100} \longrightarrow \dfrac{510}{850} = \dfrac{p}{100}$ $850 \cdot p = 510 \cdot 100$ $850p = 51{,}000$ $\dfrac{850p}{850} = \dfrac{51{,}000}{850} \quad p = 60$ 60% of 850 is 510 **b.** 200 is 40% of what number? amount percent base $\dfrac{\text{Amount}}{\text{Base}} = \dfrac{\text{Part}}{100} \longrightarrow \dfrac{200}{b} = \dfrac{40}{100}$ $b \cdot 40 = 200 \cdot 100$ $40b = 20{,}000$ $\dfrac{40b}{40} = \dfrac{20{,}000}{40} \quad b = 500$ 200 is 40% of 500

C. Apply your knowledge (page 383)	At the Alison Company, 3 out of every 25 applicants for clerical positions do not pass the word processing skills test. What percent of applicants don't pass the test?

What percent of 25 is 3?

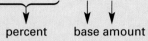

$$\underbrace{\text{percent}} \qquad \downarrow \qquad \downarrow$$
$$\text{percent} \qquad \text{base} \quad \text{amount}$$

$$\frac{\text{Amount}}{\text{Base}} = \frac{\text{Part}}{100} \rightarrow \frac{3}{25} = \frac{p}{100}$$

$$25 \cdot p = 3 \cdot 100$$

$$25p = 300$$

$$\frac{25p}{25} = \frac{300}{25} \quad p = 12$$

12% of the applicants do not pass the test.

5.4 Solve Percent Application Problems

Objective	Important Concepts	Illustrative Examples

A. Calculate percent change (page 392)	**Steps for Finding the Percent Change**
	Step 1. Find the change amount.
	   a. If a quantity increases, subtract the original quantity from the new quantity.
	   b. If a quantity decreases, subtract the new quantity from the original quantity.
	Step 2. Divide the change amount from Step 1 by the original quantity. Convert the result to a percent.
	In general, use the following formula and convert the quotient to a percent.
	
	$$\text{Percent change} = \frac{\text{Change amount}}{\text{Original amount}}$$
		If a number changes from 500 to 760, what is the percent increase?
		$$760 - 500 = 260$$
		$$\text{Percent change} = \frac{260}{500} = 0.52 = 52\%$$
		The number increases 52%.
		If a number changes from 400 to 350, what is the percent change?
		$$400 - 350 = 50$$
		$$\text{Percent change} = \frac{50}{400} = 0.125 = 12.5\%$$
		The number decreases 12.5%.

B. Calculate sales tax, tip, commission, and discount (page 395)	**sales tax**
	A state tax based on the retail price or rental cost of certain items.
	commission
	A form of compensation based on a percent of sales.
	Sales tax = Sales tax rate · Item cost
	Tip = Tip rate · Bill amount
	Commission = Commission rate · Sales amount
	Discount = Discount rate · Original cost
		Vicki purchased a coat for $125. The sales tax rate in her state is 7%.
		a. What is the sales tax on the coat?
		  Sales tax = Sales tax rate · Item cost
		     $\downarrow$ $\downarrow$ $\downarrow$
		      t = 7% · $125
		  $t = 0.07 \cdot \$125$
		  $t = \$8.75$
		b. What is the total purchase price?
		  Item cost + Sales tax = Total price
		  $\$125.00 + 8.75 = \$133.75$

C. Calculate the amount or base in a percent change situation (page 399)

Steps for Calculating the New Amount After a Percent Change

Step 1. If the quantity increases, add the percent increase to 100%.

If the quantity decreases, subtract the percent decrease from 100%.

Step 2. Solve for the new amount by solving either a percent equation or a percent proportion containing the percent from step 1 and the new amount.

Steps for Calculating the Original Amount Before a Percent Change

Step 1. If the quantity increases, add the percent increase to 100%.

If the quantity decreases, subtract the percent decrease from 100%.

Step 2. Solve for the original amount (the base) by solving either a percent equation or a percent proportion containing the percent from step 1 and the new amount.

What is 722 decreased by 50%?

$100\% - 50\% = 50\%$

What is 50% of 722?

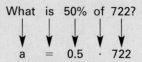

$a = 0.5 \cdot 722$

$a = 361$

722 decreased by 50% is 361.

A number increased 25% to 1875. What was the original number?

$100\% + 25\% = 125\%$

1875 is 125% of what number?

$1875 = 1.25 \cdot b$

$1875 = 1.25b$

$\dfrac{1875}{1.25} = \dfrac{1.25b}{1.25}$

$1500 = b$

1500 increased 25% is 1875.

D. Apply your knowledge (page 402)

Nancy purchased a home for $150,000 five years ago. Presently, the home is valued at 35% more than she paid. What is the current value of the home?

$100\% + 35\% = 135\%$

What is 135% of $150,000?

$a = 1.35 \cdot \$150{,}000$

$a = \$202{,}500$

The home is currently worth $202,500.

Patty's new exercise routine has resulted in a 20% decrease in her bodyweight. If Patty's current weight is 120 lb, what was her weight before starting the routine?

$100\% - 20\% = 80\%$

120 is 80% of what?

$120 = 0.8 \cdot b$

$120 = 0.8b$

$\dfrac{120}{0.8} = \dfrac{0.8b}{0.8}$

$150 = b$

Patty's original weight was 150 pounds.

Numerical Facts of Life

Qualifying for a Mortgage

A **mortgage** is a loan in which real estate is used as security for a debt. Mortgages are the most popular method of financing real estate purchases. Mortgages today fall into one of three categories: FHA insured, VA guaranteed, and conventional.

- The **Federal Housing Administration (FHA)** is a government agency within the U.S. Department of Housing and Urban Development (HUD) that sets construction standards and insures residential mortgage loans.

- **VA mortgages** are long-term, low down payment home loans made to eligible veterans and guaranteed by the Veterans Administration in the event of a default.

- **Conventional mortgage loans** are real estate loans made by private lenders that are not FHA insured or VA guaranteed.

Mortgage lenders use **lending ratios** to determine whether borrowers have the economic ability to repay the loan. FHA, VA, and conventional lenders all use monthly gross income as the "base" for calculating these ratios. Two important ratios used for this purpose are the **housing expense ratio** and the **total obligations ratio**. These ratios are expressed as percents. In each formula below, the ratio represents the percent, the monthly housing expense and total obligations represent the amount, and the monthly gross income represents the base.

$$\text{Housing expense ratio} = \frac{\text{Monthly housing expense}}{\text{Monthly gross income}}$$

$$\text{Total obligations ratio} = \frac{\text{Total monthly financial obligations}}{\text{Monthly gross income}}$$

The following lending ratio guidelines are used by mortgage lenders as benchmarks that should not be exceeded.

MORTGAGE TYPE	HOUSING EXPENSE RATIO	TOTAL OBLIGATIONS RATIO
FHA	29%	41%
Conventional	28%	36%

You are a lending officer with Canmore Bank. Toby Kaluzny, one of your clients, earns a gross income of $4650.00 per month. He has made application for a mortgage with a monthly housing expense of $1230.00. Toby has other financial obligations totaling $615.00 per month.

a. What is Toby's housing expense ratio? Round to the nearest tenth of a percent.

b. What is Toby's total obligations ratio? Round to the nearest tenth of a percent.

c. According to the lending ratio guidelines, what types of mortgage would Toby qualify for, if any?

CHAPTER REVIEW EXERCISES

Convert each percent to a fraction. Simplify, if possible. (5.1A)

1. 4.5%

2. 284%

3. 8%

4. 75%

5. 32.5%

6. 0.25%

Convert each percent to a decimal. (5.1A)

7. 37.5%

8. $56\frac{4}{5}\%$

9. 95%

10. 40.01%

11. 88%

12. $77\frac{1}{2}\%$

Convert each decimal to a percent. (5.1B)

13. 1.65

14. 0.2

15. 9.0

16. 0.45

17. 0.0028

18. 0.31

Convert each fraction or mixed number to a percent. (5.1B)

19. $2\frac{1}{5}$

20. $1\frac{1}{2}$

21. $\frac{21}{25}$

22. $\frac{17}{50}$

23. $\frac{7}{8}$

24. $3\frac{2}{5}$

Complete the following table. (5.1A, 5.1B)

	FRACTION	DECIMAL	PERCENT
25.			60%
26.	$1\frac{5}{8}$		
27.		0.81	
28.	$\frac{2}{5}$		

	FRACTION	DECIMAL	PERCENT
29.			68%
30.		0.14	
31.	$\frac{17}{400}$		
32.			79%

Write each percent problem as an equation and solve. (5.2A, 5.2B)

33. What number is 22% of 1980?

34. 120 is 80% of what number?

35. What percent of 50 is 7.5?

36. 245 is 49% of what number?

37. 2200 is what percent of 4400?

38. 70% of 690 is what number?

39. 392 is 28% of what number?

40. What is 60% of 300?

41. What percent of 400 is 64?

42. What is 30% of 802?

43. 13 is what percent of 65?

44. 64.08 is 72% of what number?

Write each percent problem as a proportion and solve. (5.3A, 5.3B)

45. What number is 7% of 2000?

46. 261 is what percent of 450?

47. 30 is 20% of what number?

48. 50 is what percent of 50?

49. What is 15% of 8000?

50. 136 is 34% of what number?

51. What number is 9% of 540?

52. 136 is 40% of what number?

53. 516 is what percent of 645?

54. 210 is 56% of what number?

55. 245 is what percent of 100?

56. What number is 70% of 833?

Solve each percent application problem. (5.4A, 5.4B, 5.4C, 5.4D)

57. Porsche Enterprises is doing very well in its third year of operations. The owner expects $3,000,000 in sales this year compared to $2,500,000 in sales last year. What is the percent increase in sales expected this year?

58. Last year a company spent $11,000 per month on long distance. After signing up with a new provider offering a nationwide long distance contract, the monthly charges are now $8400. What is the percent change in long distance charges? Round to the nearest tenth of a percent.

59. Trendy Shops is experiencing a tough year in sales. Consequently, the owner had to reduce the staff from 600 employees to 550. What is the percent change in employees at Trendy? Round to nearest whole percent.

60. Waldo's Surf Store is seasonal in nature and is usually very busy during the summer months. Waldo typically sells 40 surfboards in a regular month and about 120 during the summer months. What is the percent change in sales for Waldo's from the regular season to the busy summer months?

61. Ken and Ashley's dinner bill at the Davis Street Fishmarket was $79.50. They want to give their server a 20% tip.

   a. What is the tip?

   b. What is the total including tip?

62. John is in charge of purchasing three new cars for his company's sales team. Each car has a purchase price of $12,500 and the tax rate is 5.8%.

   a. What is the total sales tax paid for the purchase of the three vehicles?

   b. What is the total purchase price of the cars?

63. Housing sales rates are at an all time high and Clay is taking full advantage of his excellent sales techniques. Clay earns 7.5% commission on all sales of kitchen cabinets to housing developers. If Clay sold $1,500,000 in kitchen cabinets last year, how much commission did he earn for the year?

64. A new hit single CD sold for $16 last month and is currently on sale at 10% off.

   a. What is the amount of the discount?

   b. What is the sale price?

65. This month, new jobs increased 15% to 144,900. What was last month's figure?

66. Tourism has slowed down in various areas. To increase sales, car rental rates have gone down 16% to $42 per day. What was the daily rate before the promotion?

67. Gina and Danny decided to purchase a condo instead of renting an apartment. Their rent was $900 per month for the apartment and their mortgage payment will be 22% less. What is the amount of the mortgage payment?

68. Tracy has changed her work schedule to avoid rush-hour traffic when visiting her clients. In the past, Tracy spent $36 a week on gasoline and now spends $26 per week. What is the percent change in Tracy's gasoline cost due to her schedule change? Round to nearest whole percent.

Use the chart *U.S. Snack Food Revenue* **for exercises 69–72.**

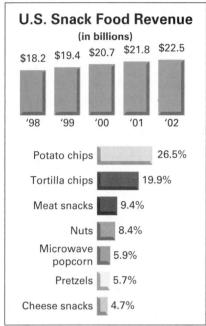

Source: Snack Food Association

69. What is the percent increase in snack food sales from 2001 to 2002? Round to the nearest tenth percent.

70. If sales in 2007 represent a 10% increase from sales in 2002, what were the snack food sales in 2007? Round to the nearest tenth of a billion.

71. If snack foods sales totaled $20.7 billion in 2000, how much was from nut sales? Express your answer in dollars.

72. If snack foods sales totaled $21.8 billion in 2001, how much was from tortilla chips? Express your answer in dollars.

ASSESSMENT TEST

Convert each percent to a fraction. Simplify, if possible.

1. 76%

2. 3%

Convert each percent to a decimal.

3. 13.5%

4. 68.8%

Convert each decimal to a percent.

5. 0.57

6. 6.45

Convert each fraction or mixed number to a percent.

7. $\dfrac{11}{8}$

8. $10\dfrac{1}{2}$

Write each percent problem as an equation and solve.

9. What percent of 610 is 106.75?

10. 186 is 62% of what number?

11. What is 47% of 450?

12. 367 is 20% of what number?

13. What number is 80% of 4560?

14. 77 is what percent of 280?

Write each percent problem as a proportion and solve.

15. 560 is 14% of what number?

16. 95 is what percent of 380?

17. What is 83% of 180?

18. What percent of 490 is 196?

19. What number is 29% of 158?

20. 245 is 35% of what number?

Solve each percent application problem.

21. Last year, Pizza Pete Restaurants sold 5600 small pizza pies compared to this year's 3500 small pies. What is the percent change in small pies sold this year compared to last?

22. Gilbert teaches several summer courses in diving to earn extra money during the summer break. Last year his average rate per student for a week long course was $500. This year Gilbert has decided to increase his rates to $575. What is the percent change in price for the diving course?

23. Randy and her husband have to pay about $13,600 in taxes this year for their business. Last year, tax rates were higher and their taxes totaled $16,800. What is the percent change in tax payments for Randy and her husband? Round to nearest whole percent.

24. Andrew has accepted a new position in New York City and will move from Florida. One major difference is the cost of living. In Florida, Andrew paid $800 for an apartment and will pay $1500 for a similar apartment in New York. What is the percent change in rent from one location to the other? Round to nearest whole percent.

25. Ivan purchased a pair of swimming goggles for $20. If the sales tax rate is 7%, what is the total purchase price of the goggles?

26. Gary brings lunch for his office staff every Friday. If the lunch total was $52.50 and the sales tax was $3.10, what is the sales tax rate in that area? Round to the nearest tenth of a percent.

27. Before going on a diet, Sylvan weighed 190 pounds. On the diet he lost 8% of his total weight. How much does he weigh now? Round to the nearest pound.

28. A truck driver delivered 54 packages yesterday and 30% more today. How many packages did he deliver today? Round to the nearest whole package.

29. A high-pressure pump lost 40% of its pressure because of a leaky valve. If the pressure now is 168 pounds per square inch, what was the pressure before the leak?

30. After a 22% increase, the temperature hit 90°F. What was the temperature before the increase? Round to the nearest whole degree.

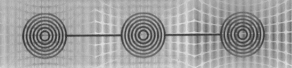

Signed Numbers

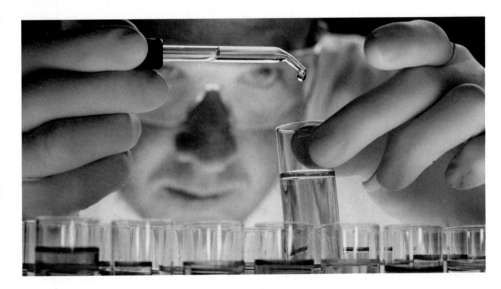

Chemist

Everything in our environment, whether natural or synthetic, is made up of chemicals. Chemists study the chemical composition of matter. They use their knowledge of chemicals to develop drugs, adhesives, cosmetics, and a wide variety of other products.[1] Through their research, chemists contribute to advances in medicine, agriculture, biotechnology, and many other fields.

Chemists and chemistry students alike must have a strong mathematics background. In particular, they must have an understanding of signed numbers. In the analysis of chemical reactions, for example, chemists must know about the oxidation states of atoms. The oxidation state of an atom is the sum of the positive and negative charges in the atom.[2] When an atom is not involved in a chemical reaction, its oxidation state is zero. But, when involved in certain chemical reactions, the oxidation state of some atoms is a positive number while the oxidation state of other atoms is a negative number. To understand such chemical reaction, chemists must be able to manipulate the oxidation states of the atoms involved in the process. This requires the ability to work with signed numbers.

[1]from *U.S. Bureau of Labor Statistics Occupational Outlook Handbook.*
[2]from http://library.kcc.hawaii.edu/external/chemistry/.

In this chapter, we investigate signed numbers. We will learn how to add, subtract, multiply, and divide them. We will also see how signed numbers apply to real-world situations.

9.1 INTRODUCTION TO SIGNED NUMBERS

LEARNING OBJECTIVES

A. Find the opposite of a number

B. Graph a signed number on a number line

C. Find the absolute value of a number

D. Compare signed numbers

E. Apply your knowledge

positive number
A number that is greater than 0.

negative number
A number that is less than 0.

origin
The number 0 on a number line.

signed number
A number that is either positive or negative.

So far, all numbers encountered in this book have been either 0 or greater than 0. A number that is greater than 0 is called a **positive number**. Examples involving positive numbers include a building whose height is 1451 feet and a summertime high temperature of 86°F.

Not all numbers are positive. Indeed, some numbers are less than 0. A number that is less than 0 is called a **negative number**. You certainly know something about negative numbers if you live in a city such as Chicago or Minneapolis. There, during a typical winter, you may experience a temperature such as 5 degrees below zero. Numerically, you would express this temperature as -5 degrees, or $-5°$.

Note that a negative number is written with a $(-)$ sign, known also as a negative sign. Some other examples of negative numbers are -109, $-\dfrac{3}{4}$, and -17.3.

In Chapter 2, we graphed 0 and positive numbers on a number line. Negative numbers can be graphed on a number line, too. Simply extend the number line to the left of 0. The number 0 is neither positive nor negative. It separates the positive numbers from the negative numbers. For this reason, the number 0 on the number line is often referred to as the **origin**.

Below is a number line that shows negative numbers, 0, and positive numbers.

A **signed number** is a number that is either positive or negative. Therefore, we refer to the positive and negative numbers collectively as the signed numbers.

In this section, we introduce basic features associated with signed numbers. In the subsequent sections of this chapter, we learn how to add, subtract, multiply, and divide signed numbers.

opposites
Two numbers that lie the same distance from the origin on opposite sides of the origin.

Objective 9.1A   Find the opposite of a number

Two numbers that lie the same distance from the origin on opposite sides of the origin are called **opposites**. For example, -3 and 3 are opposites. Notice that -3 and 3 are the same distance from the origin but are on opposite sides of the origin.

To determine the opposite of a number, simply change the sign of the number. Thus, the opposite of a positive number is negative, and the opposite of a negative number is positive. As an example, the opposite of 9 is -9. Also, the opposite of $-\frac{1}{2}$ is $\frac{1}{2}$. Since 0 is neither positive nor negative, it is its own opposite.

EXAMPLE 1   Find the opposite of a number

Find the opposite of each number.

a. 15   **b.** $-\frac{2}{3}$ **c.** 5.32

SOLUTION STRATEGY

a. The opposite of 15 is -15.   15 is a positive number and so its opposite is negative.

b. The opposite of $-\frac{2}{3}$ is $\frac{2}{3}$. $-\frac{2}{3}$ is a negative number and so its opposite is positive.

c. The opposite of 5.32 is -5.32.   5.32 is a positive number and so its opposite is negative.

TRY-IT EXERCISE 1

Find the opposite of each number.

a. -12 **b.** $8\frac{3}{5}$ **c.** -2.25

Check your answers with the solutions in Appendix A. ■

| **Objective 9.1B** | **Graph a signed number on a number line** |

The **integers** are the whole numbers together with the opposites of the positive whole numbers. That is, the integers are the numbers $\ldots -3, -2, -1, 0, 1, 2, 3, \ldots$. The ellipses before -3 and after 3 indicate that the integers continue indefinitely in either direction.

Typically when drawing a number line, we show only the integers. We can, however, show other numbers, such as fractions, decimals, and their opposites. Fractions, decimals, and their opposites are rational numbers. More formally, a **rational number** is a number that can be written in the form $\frac{a}{b}$, where a and b are integers and $b \neq 0$. Here are some examples of rational numbers.

$$-\frac{1}{5} \qquad \frac{2}{3} \qquad \frac{13}{8} \qquad -\frac{4}{9}$$

integers
The whole numbers together with the opposites of the positive whole numbers, that is, the numbers $\ldots -3, -2, -1, 0, 1, 2, 3, \ldots$.

rational number
A number that can be written in the form $\frac{a}{b}$, where a and b are integers and $b \neq 0$.

The number $-\frac{1}{5}$, which is read as "negative one-fifth," can also be written as $\frac{-1}{5}$ or $\frac{1}{-5}$. In general, we have the following.

$$-\frac{a}{b} = \frac{-a}{b} = \frac{a}{-b}$$

Other examples of rational numbers include the following.

$$-5 \quad 10 \quad -0.7 \quad 3.25$$

Each of these numbers is a rational number since each one can be written in the form $\frac{a}{b}$, where a and b are integers and $b \neq 0$. For example, -5 can be written as $\frac{-5}{1}$ or as $\frac{10}{-2}$. Also, -0.7 can be written as $-\frac{7}{10}$.

To graph a number is to draw a dot on the number line at the point corresponding to that number. For example, let's graph 0.5. Since 0.5 is halfway between 0 and 1 on the number line, we draw a dot halfway from 0 to 1.

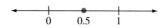

Let's now consider -0.5. Since -0.5 is halfway between 0 and -1 on the number line, draw a dot halfway from 0 to -1.

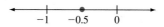

To graph an improper fraction, first convert it to a mixed number. For example, to graph $\frac{5}{3}$, first covert it to $1\frac{2}{3}$. Note that $1\frac{2}{3}$ is between 1 and 2. Draw a dot two-thirds of the way from 1 to 2. That is, start at 1 and draw a dot two-thirds of a unit to the right of 1.

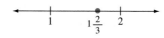

Next, let's consider $-\frac{5}{3}$. Since $\frac{5}{3} = 1\frac{2}{3}$, it follows that $-\frac{5}{3} = -1\frac{2}{3}$. Note that $-1\frac{2}{3}$ is between -1 and -2. Draw a dot two-thirds of the way from -1 to -2. That is, start at -1 and draw a dot two-thirds of a unit to the left of -1.

EXAMPLE 2   Graph a rational number

Graph each number on a number line.

a. 0.25   **b.** $\dfrac{15}{4}$ **c.** $-\dfrac{7}{3}$

SOLUTION STRATEGY

a. [number line with 0, 0.25, 1]   Draw a dot one-quarter of the way from 0 and 1.

b. [number line with 3, $3\frac{3}{4}$, 4] $\dfrac{15}{4} = 3\dfrac{3}{4}$

Draw a dot three-fourths of the way from 3 to 4.

c. [number line with -3, $-2\frac{1}{3}$, -2] $-\dfrac{7}{3} = -2\dfrac{1}{3}$

Draw a dot one-third of the way from -2 to -3. That is, draw a dot one third of a unit to the left of -2.

TRY-IT EXERCISE 2

Graph each rational number on a number line.

a. $\dfrac{3}{4}$ **b.** $\dfrac{13}{3}$ **c.** $-\dfrac{24}{5}$

Check your answers with the solutions in Appendix A. ■

| **Objective 9.1C** | **Find the absolute value of a number** |

The **absolute value of a number** is the distance between the number and 0 on the number line. Since distance is always non-negative, the absolute value of a number is either 0 or positive. The absolute value of a real number a is denoted by $|a|$.

As an example, consider $|3|$.

absolute value of a number
The distance between the number and 0 on the number line.

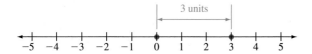

Since 3 lies 3 units away from 0, $|3| = 3$.

As another example, consider $|-5|$.

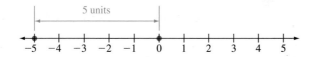

Since -5 lies 5 units away from 0, $|-5| = 5$.

The following properties of absolute value follow directly from the definition.

> **Properties of the Absolute Value of a Number**
>
> The absolute value of a positive number is the number itself.
>
> The absolute value of a negative number is the opposite of the number.
>
> The absolute value of 0 is 0.

EXAMPLE 3   **Find the absolute value of a number**

Evaluate.

a. $|7.43|$ **b.** $\left| -10\frac{1}{2} \right|$ **c.** $|0|$

SOLUTION STRATEGY

a. $|7.43| = 7.43$

7.43 lies 7.43 units from zero. Also, since 7.43 is positive, the absolute value of 7.43 is 7.43 itself.

b. $\left| -10\frac{1}{2} \right| = 10\frac{1}{2}$

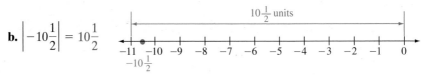

$-10\frac{1}{2}$ is $10\frac{1}{2}$ units from zero. Also, since $-10\frac{1}{2}$ is negative, the absolute

value is the opposite of $-10\frac{1}{2}$, which is $10\frac{1}{2}$.

c. $|0| = 0$

0 is 0 units from zero. The absolute value of 0 is always 0.

TRY-IT EXERCISE 3

Evaluate.

a. $|-13.46|$ **b.** $\left| \frac{3}{8} \right|$ **c.** $|18|$

Check your answers with the solutions in Appendix A. ∎

Objective 9.1D   **Compare signed numbers**

On the number line, numbers increase from left to right. We say that the number to the left is *less than* the number to the right, and the number to the right is *greater than* the number to the left. The less than symbol ($<$) represents "less than," and the greater than symbol ($>$) represents "greater than." Collectively, $<$ and $>$ are referred to as inequality symbols.

As an example, let's compare the numbers -3 and 5. The graph of these numbers is shown below.

Notice that -3 is to the left of 5 on the number line. Thus, -3 is less than 5, and symbolically we can write the following.

$$-3 < 5$$

Also, since 5 is to the right of -3 on the number line, we know that 5 is greater than -3. Symbolically, we can write the following.

$$5 > -3$$

The above example shows that any statement involving the $<$ symbol can be expressed as a statement involving the $>$ symbol. We do this by reversing the order of the numbers and the direction of the symbol.

In general, a negative number is always less than a positive number. For example, when comparing $\frac{1}{3}$ and $-\frac{2}{9}$, we can immediately write the following.

$$-\frac{2}{9} < \frac{1}{3} \quad \text{or} \quad \frac{1}{3} > -\frac{2}{9}$$

When two rational numbers have the same sign, the smaller of the two numbers may not be obvious. To compare rational numbers, we can find a common denominator as we did in Section 2.3, and then compare numerators. Alternatively, we can write each rational number as a decimal and then compare the decimals as we did in Section 3.1. The following examples demonstrate how to do this.

EXAMPLE 4   **Compare signed numbers**

Compare the signed numbers.

a. -2 and 5   **b.** -2.56 and -1.23 **c.** $-\frac{1}{5}$ and $-\frac{2}{7}$

SOLUTION STRATEGY

a. -2 and 5

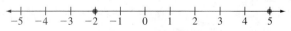

$-2 < 5$ or $5 > -2$ -2 is to the left of 5, and so $-2 < 5$. Also, 5 is to the right of -2 on the number line, and so $5 > -2$.

b. -2.56 and -1.23

$-2.56 < -1.23$ or
$-1.23 > -2.56$

-2.56 is to the left of -1.23, and so $-2.56 < -1.23$. Also, -1.23 is to the right of -2.56 on the number line, and so $-1.23 > -2.56$.

c. $-\dfrac{1}{5}$ and $-\dfrac{2}{7}$

$\text{LCD} = 35$ Find the LCD.

$$-\frac{1}{5} = -\frac{1 \cdot 7}{5 \cdot 7} = -\frac{7}{35}$$

$$-\frac{2}{7} = -\frac{2 \cdot 5}{7 \cdot 5} = -\frac{10}{35}$$

Write each fraction as an equivalent fraction with a denominator of 35.

$$-\frac{2}{7} < -\frac{1}{5} \text{ or } -\frac{1}{5} > -\frac{2}{7}$$

Because $-10 < -7$, $-\dfrac{10}{35} < -\dfrac{7}{35}$. Thus, $-\dfrac{2}{7} < -\dfrac{1}{5}$.

TRY-IT EXERCISE 4

Compare the signed numbers.

a. 6 and 11   **b.** -4 and 7   **c.** -3.18 and -2.57 **d.** $\dfrac{1}{4}$ and $\dfrac{2}{5}$

Check your answers with the solutions in Appendix A. ∎

Objective 9.1E   Apply your knowledge

Certain key words and phrases can help us determine whether we are dealing with positive or negative numbers.

Positive numbers: up, above, increase, gain

Negative numbers: down, below, decrease, loss

The following examples illustrate how to write signed numbers in problems involving these key words.

EXAMPLE 5   Apply your knowledge

The Dow Jones Industrial Average (DJIA), often referred to as the Dow, is an indicator of U.S. stock market performance. In general, if the Dow is up, then the stock market is viewed as doing well (or, at least, improving). If the Dow is down, the stock market is viewed as faltering.

The greatest DJIA daily point loss occurred on September 17, 2001, the first day the market reopened following the events of September 11th. On that day, the Dow closed down 684 points from the last day that the market was open. Express this quantity as a signed number. (See www.djindexes.com for more information.)

SOLUTION STRATEGY

−684 points   Because the Dow closed *down*, the quantity is negative.

TRY-IT EXERCISE 5

According to the South Florida Water Management District during the summer drought of 2007, Lake Okeechobee, the second largest freshwater lake entirely contained within the United States, decreased 4.03 feet below its average water level. Express this quantity as a signed number.

Check your answer with the solution in Appendix A. ■

●━●━● SECTION 9.1 REVIEW EXERCISES

Concept Check

1. A _____ number is a number that is greater than 0.

2. A _____ number is a number that is less than 0.

3. The number 0 on the number line is known as the _____.

4. A number that is either positive or negative is called a _____ _____.

5. Two numbers that lie the same distance from the origin on opposite sides of the origin are called _____.

6. The numbers . . . −3, −2, −1, 0, 1, 2, 3, . . . are known as the _____.

7. A number that can be written in the form $\frac{a}{b}$, where a and b are integers and $b \neq 0$ is a _____ number.

8. The _____ _____ of a number is the distance between the number and zero on the number line.

Objective 9.1A   **Find the opposite of a number**

GUIDE PROBLEMS

9. Find the opposite of 8.

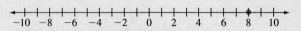

The opposite of 8 is _____.

10. Find the opposite of −3.

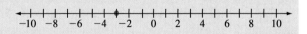

The opposite of −3 is _____.

Find the opposite of each number.

11. 14   **12.** 69   **13.** -23.5 **14.** -67.25

15. $\dfrac{2}{9}$ **16.** $\dfrac{3}{4}$ **17.** $-\dfrac{5}{2}$ **18.** $-7\dfrac{4}{13}$

Objective 9.1B   **Graph a signed number on a number line**

GUIDE PROBLEMS

19. Graph the signed numbers $-2, 5, 7,$ and 0.

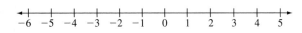

20. Graph the signed numbers $-8.5, 2.25, -3\dfrac{1}{2},$ and $\dfrac{3}{4}$.

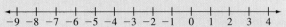

Graph each signed number.

21. $-5, -3, 1, 4$

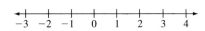

22. $1.5, -2.25, -1\dfrac{1}{3}, 4\dfrac{1}{2}$

23. $-0.25, 2.4, -2\dfrac{1}{5}, 3\dfrac{1}{10}$

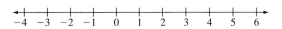

24. $2.3, -0.75, -3\dfrac{3}{4}, 5\dfrac{2}{5}$

Objective 9.1C   **Find the absolute value of a number**

GUIDE PROBLEMS

25. Evaluate $|15|$.

     $|15| = $ _____

26. Evaluate $|-12.3|$.

     $|-12.3| = $ _____

Evaluate.

27. $|43|$ **28.** $|59|$ **29.** $|-31|$ **30.** $|-70|$

31. $|-2.7|$ **32.** $|-58.3|$ **33.** $\left|7\dfrac{2}{9}\right|$ **34.** $\left|-13\dfrac{5}{11}\right|$

Objective 9.1D	Compare signed numbers

GUIDE PROBLEMS

35. Compare -3.2 and 8.5.

$$
\begin{array}{c}
\begin{array}{|c|c|c|c|c|c|c|c|c|c|c|c|c|c|}
-4 & -3 & -2 & -1 & 0 & 1 & 2 & 3 & 4 & 5 & 6 & 7 & 8 & 9
\end{array}
\end{array}
$$

-3.2 ____ 8.5 or 8.5 ____ -3.2

36. Compare $-\dfrac{2}{9}$ and $-\dfrac{4}{15}$.

The LCD of $-\dfrac{2}{9}$ and $-\dfrac{4}{15}$ is _____.

$$-\dfrac{2}{9} = -\dfrac{2 \cdot \_\_}{9 \cdot \_\_} = -\dfrac{\_\_}{\_\_}$$

$$-\dfrac{4}{15} = -\dfrac{4 \cdot \_\_}{15 \cdot \_\_} = -\dfrac{\_\_}{\_\_}$$

$-\dfrac{2}{9}$ ____ $-\dfrac{4}{15}$ or $-\dfrac{4}{15}$ ____ $-\dfrac{2}{9}$

Compare each pair of signed numbers.

37. 2 and 7

38. 3 and 16

39. -24.8 and -24.0

40. -32.75 and -32.0

41. -15 and 21

42. 83 and -11

43. -11.0 and -11.5

44. -40.0 and -40.3

45. $-\dfrac{7}{9}$ and $-\dfrac{2}{3}$

46. $\dfrac{1}{3}$ and $\dfrac{3}{8}$

47. $-\dfrac{6}{5}$ and $-\dfrac{13}{12}$

48. $-\dfrac{3}{7}$ and $-\dfrac{7}{16}$

Objective 9.1E	Apply your knowledge

49. Your most recent blood pressure reading was two points above normal. Express this quantity as a signed number.

50. Absolute zero is two hundred seventy-three degrees below zero on the Celsius scale. Express this quantity as a signed number.

51. In a NASCAR race, Tony Stewart was 6.5 seconds behind Kyle Swiatek after 200 laps. After 300 laps, Stewart was ahead of Swiatek by 2.4 seconds. At the end of the race, Stewart came in 4.1 seconds behind Swiatek. Express each time quantity as a signed number.

52. Normal body temperature is 37 degrees on the Celsius scale and 98.6 degrees on the Fahrenheit scale. Express these quantities as signed numbers.

53. The sun's outermost region has a temperature of approximately 6000°K (Kelvin). Express this quantity as a signed number.

54. A submarine descends one hundred sixty feet. Express this quantity as a signed number.

CUMULATIVE SKILLS REVIEW

1. Add $2\frac{1}{3} + 3\frac{2}{5}$. (2.6C)

2. Subtract $5\frac{1}{3} - 3\frac{3}{4}$. (2.7C)

3. Round 1822.433 to the nearest tenth. (3.1F)

4. Convert 0.38 to a percent. (5.1B)

5. Write a simplified ratio for 60 minutes to 1200 seconds. (4.1C)

6. Find the circumference of the circle. Use 3.14 for π. (7.3B)

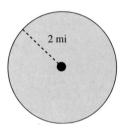

2 mi

7. Convert 12 hg to g. (6.3B)

8. What is the mean of 59, 88, 21, 63, 33? Round to the nearest tenth. (8.2A)

9. Find the mode, if any, of 15, 18, 28, 15, 17, 65. (8.2C)

10. Use the Pythagorean theorem to determine the measure of the missing side of the right triangle. Round to the nearest hundredth. (7.5C)

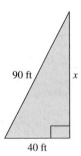

90 ft x

40 ft

9.2 ADDING SIGNED NUMBERS

When we add two signed numbers, the addends either have the same sign or different signs. For example, $2 + 3$ and $-2 + (-3)$ are addition problems in which the addends have the same sign, while $-2 + 3$ and $2 + (-3)$ are addition problems in which the addends have different signs. In this section, we begin by exploring addition of signed numbers with the same sign and then consider addition of signed numbers with different signs.

LEARNING OBJECTIVES

A. Add numbers with the same sign

B. Add numbers with different signs

C. Apply your knowledge

Objective 9.2A   **Add numbers with the same sign**

Consider $2 + 3$. Note that both addends have the same sign. To compute this sum, we start at 0 and move to 2. Then, because we are adding 3, we move 3 more units *to the right.*

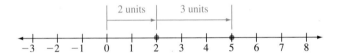

We see that the result is 5. Thus, $2 + 3 = 5$.

Now let's consider $-2 + (-3)$. Notice that we are once again adding two numbers with the same sign. To calculate this sum, we start at 0 and move to -2 on the number line. Then, because we are adding -3 to this number, we move 3 more units *to the left.* Indeed, any time we add a negative number to a number, we move to the left, or backward, on the number line.

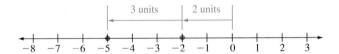

We see that the result is -5. Thus, $-2 + (-3) = -5$.

Notice that in both examples, the result has the same sign as the numbers being added. This observation leads us to the following.

Steps for Adding Numbers with the Same Sign

Step 1. Determine the absolute values of each addend.

Step 2. Add the absolute values of the addends.

Step 3. Attach the common sign of the addends to the sum of step 2.

Adding numbers using a number line is nice for its visual appeal; however, it is not practical for adding large numbers, fractions, or decimals. Therefore, we shall use the aforementioned rule when adding numbers with the same sign.

Since we are already very familiar with adding positive numbers, we'll look at several examples in which we add negative numbers. We begin by adding negative integers.

EXAMPLE 1 **Add two negative integers**

Add.

a. $-15 + (-21)$ **b.** $-6 + (-39)$ **c.** $-13 + (-44)$

SOLUTION STRATEGY

a. $-15 + (-21)$

$|-15| = 15, |-21| = 21$ Determine the absolute value of each addend.

$15 + 21 = 36$ Add the absolute values.

$-15 + (-21) = -36$ Since both addends are negative, the sum is negative.

b. $-6 + (-39)$

$|-6| = 6, |-39| = 39$ Determine the absolute value of each addend.

$6 + 39 = 45$ Add the absolute values.

$-6 + (-39) = -45$ Since both addends are negative, the sum is negative.

c. $-13 + (-44)$

$|-13| = 13, |-44| = 44$ Determine the absolute value of each addend.

$13 + 44 = 57$ Add the absolute values.

$-13 + (-44) = -57$ Since both addends are negative, the sum is negative.

TRY-IT EXERCISE 1

Add.

a. $-30 + (-12)$ **b.** $-19 + (-33)$ **c.** $-59 + (-7)$

Check your answers with the solutions in Appendix A. ∎

Let's now look at some problems in which we add two negative rational numbers. In doing these problems, we will ultimately have to add fractions, mixed numbers, or decimals. For a review of fraction and mixed number addition, refer to Section 2.6, Adding Fractions and Mixed Numbers. For a review of decimal addition, refer to Section 3.2, Adding and Subtracting Decimals.

EXAMPLE 2 **Add two negative rational numbers**

Add. Simplify, if possible.

a. $-\dfrac{1}{5} + \left(-\dfrac{2}{5}\right)$ **b.** $-\dfrac{1}{4} + \left(-\dfrac{2}{3}\right)$ **c.** $-2\dfrac{3}{4} + \left(-5\dfrac{1}{2}\right)$ **d.** $-3.04 + (-7.2)$

SOLUTION STRATEGY

a. $-\dfrac{1}{5} + \left(-\dfrac{2}{5}\right)$

$\left|-\dfrac{1}{5}\right| = \dfrac{1}{5}, \left|-\dfrac{2}{5}\right| = \dfrac{2}{5}$ Determine the absolute value of each addend.

$\dfrac{1}{5} + \dfrac{2}{5} = \dfrac{3}{5}$ Add the absolute values.

$-\dfrac{1}{5} + \left(-\dfrac{2}{5}\right) = -\dfrac{3}{5}$ Since both addends are negative, the sum is negative.

b. $-\dfrac{1}{4} + \left(-\dfrac{2}{3}\right)$

$\left|-\dfrac{1}{4}\right| = \dfrac{1}{4}, \left|-\dfrac{2}{3}\right| = \dfrac{2}{3}$ Determine the absolute value of each addend.

$\text{LCD} = 12$ Find the LCD.

$\dfrac{1}{4} = \dfrac{1 \cdot 3}{4 \cdot 3} = \dfrac{3}{12}$ Write each fraction as an equivalent fraction with denominator 12.

$\dfrac{2}{3} = \dfrac{2 \cdot 4}{3 \cdot 4} = \dfrac{8}{12}$

$\dfrac{3}{12} + \dfrac{8}{12} = \dfrac{11}{12}$ Add the absolute values.

$-\dfrac{1}{4} + \left(-\dfrac{2}{3}\right) = -\dfrac{11}{12}$ Since both addends are negative, the sum is negative.

c. $-2\dfrac{3}{4} + \left(-5\dfrac{1}{2}\right)$

$\left|-2\dfrac{3}{4}\right| = 2\dfrac{3}{4}, \left|-5\dfrac{1}{2}\right| = 5\dfrac{1}{2}$ Determine the absolute value of each addend.

$\text{LCD} = 4$ Find the LCD.

$5\dfrac{1 \cdot 2}{2 \cdot 2} \rightarrow 5\dfrac{2}{4}$ Write each fraction as an equivalent fraction with denominator 4.

$$\begin{array}{r} 2\dfrac{3}{4} \\ + 5\dfrac{2}{4} \\ \hline 7\dfrac{5}{4} \end{array}$$

Add the absolute values by first adding the fraction parts and then the whole numbers.

$$7\frac{5}{4} = 7 + \frac{5}{4}$$ — Write the mixed number as the sum of the whole number and the fraction part.

$$= 7 + 1\frac{1}{4}$$ — Write the fraction part as a mixed number.

$$= 8\frac{1}{4}$$ — Add the whole number and the mixed number.

$$-2\frac{3}{4} + \left(-5\frac{1}{2}\right) = -8\frac{1}{4}$$ — Since both addends are negative, the sum is negative.

d. $-3.04 + (-7.2)$

$$|-3.04| = 3.04, \ |-7.2| = 7.2$$ — Determine the absolute value of each addend.

$$\begin{array}{r} 3.04 \\ +\ 7.20 \\ \hline 10.24 \end{array}$$ — Add the absolute values.

$$-3.04 + (-7.2) = -10.24$$ — Since both addends are negative, the sum is negative.

TRY-IT EXERCISE 2

Add. Simplify, if possible.

a. $-\frac{3}{8} + \left(-\frac{1}{8}\right)$ **b.** $-\frac{5}{7} + \left(-\frac{10}{21}\right)$ **c.** $-3\frac{1}{4} + \left(-6\frac{2}{3}\right)$ **d.** $-12.2 + (-6.814)$

Check your answers with the solutions in Appendix A. ■

Objective 9.2B Add numbers with different signs

Now let's consider adding signed numbers with different signs. For example, consider the sum $3 + (-2)$. To compute this sum, start at 0 and move to 3 on the number line. Then, because we are adding -2, we move two units *to the left* of 3.

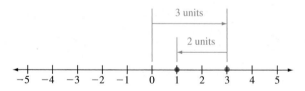

We see that the result is 1. Thus, $3 + (-2) = 1$.

Now let's consider the sum $-3 + 2$. Start at 0 and move to -3 on the number line. Then, because we are adding 2 to -3, we move 2 units *to the right* of -3.

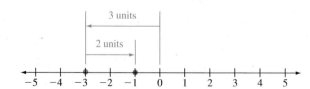

We see that the result is -1. Thus, $-3 + 2 = -1$.

Note that when the addends have different signs, the sum may be positive or negative.

Steps for Adding Signed Numbers with Different Signs

Step 1. Determine the absolute values of each addend.

Step 2. Subtract the smaller absolute value from the larger.

Step 3. Attach the sign of the addend having the larger absolute value to the difference of step 2. If the absolute values are equal, then the sum is 0.

We'll begin by adding integers with different signs.

EXAMPLE 3   **Add integers with different signs**

Add.

a. $5 + (-2)$ **b.** $2 + (-5)$ **c.** $23 + (-23)$

SOLUTION STRATEGY

a. $5 + (-2)$

$\|5\| = 5, \|-2\| = 2$	Determine the absolute value of each addend.
$5 - 2 = 3$	Subtract the smaller absolute value from the larger.
$5 + (-2) = 3$	Attach the sign of the addend having the larger absolute value. Since the positive number is larger in absolute value, the answer is positive.

b. $2 + (-5)$

$\|2\| = 2, \|-5\| = 5$	Determine the absolute value of each addend.
$5 - 2 = 3$	Subtract the smaller absolute value from the larger.
$2 + (-5) = -3$	Attach the sign of the addend having the larger absolute value. Since the negative number is larger in absolute value, the answer is negative.

c. $23 + (-23)$

$\|23\| = 23, \|-23\| = 23$	Determine the absolute value of each addend.
$23 - 23 = 0$	Subtract.
$23 + (-23) = 0$	Because the absolute values are equal, the sum is 0.

TRY-IT EXERCISE 3

Add.

a. $7 + (-4)$ **b.** $4 + (-7)$ **c.** $-16 + 16$

Check your answers with the solutions in Appendix A. ■

Let's now look at some problems in which we add rational numbers with different signs. In doing these problems, we will ultimately have to subtract fractions, mixed numbers, or decimals. For a review of fraction and mixed number subtraction, refer to Section 2.7, Subtracting Fractions and Mixed Numbers. For a review of decimal subtraction, refer to Section 3.2, Adding and Subtracting Decimals.

EXAMPLE 4 **Add rational numbers with different signs**

Add. Simplify, if possible.

a. $\dfrac{2}{7} + \left(-\dfrac{5}{7}\right)$ **b.** $\dfrac{2}{3} + \left(-\dfrac{1}{5}\right)$ **c.** $-5\dfrac{2}{3} + 3\dfrac{1}{4}$ **d.** $-5.03 + 7.3$

SOLUTION STRATEGY

a. $\dfrac{2}{7} + \left(-\dfrac{5}{7}\right)$

$\left|\dfrac{2}{7}\right| = \dfrac{2}{7}, \left|-\dfrac{5}{7}\right| = \dfrac{5}{7}$ Determine the absolute value of each addend.

$\dfrac{5}{7} - \dfrac{2}{7} = \dfrac{3}{7}$ Subtract the smaller absolute value from the larger.

$\dfrac{2}{7} + \left(-\dfrac{5}{7}\right) = -\dfrac{3}{7}$ Since the negative addend is larger in absolute value, the answer is negative.

b. $\dfrac{2}{3} + \left(-\dfrac{1}{5}\right)$

$\left|\dfrac{2}{3}\right| = \dfrac{2}{3}, \left|-\dfrac{1}{5}\right| = \dfrac{1}{5}$ Determine the absolute value of each addend.

$LCD = 15$ Find the LCD.

$\dfrac{2}{3} = \dfrac{2 \cdot 5}{3 \cdot 5} = \dfrac{10}{15}$

$\dfrac{1}{5} = \dfrac{1 \cdot 3}{5 \cdot 3} = \dfrac{3}{15}$ Write each fraction as an equivalent fraction with denominator 15.

$\dfrac{10}{15} - \dfrac{3}{15} = \dfrac{7}{15}$ Subtract the smaller absolute value from the larger.

$\dfrac{2}{3} + \left(-\dfrac{1}{5}\right) = \dfrac{7}{15}$ Since the positive addend is larger in absolute value, the answer is positive.

c. $-5\dfrac{2}{3} + 3\dfrac{1}{4}$

$\left|-5\dfrac{2}{3}\right| = 5\dfrac{2}{3}, \left|3\dfrac{1}{4}\right| = 3\dfrac{1}{4}$ Determine the absolute value of each addend.

$LCD = 12$ Find the LCD.

$$5\frac{2 \cdot 4}{3 \cdot 4} \rightarrow 5\frac{8}{12}$$

$$3\frac{1 \cdot 3}{4 \cdot 3} \rightarrow 3\frac{3}{12}$$

Write each fraction as an equivalent fraction with denominator 12.

$$5\frac{8}{12}$$
$$-3\frac{3}{12}$$
$$\overline{2\frac{5}{12}}$$

Subtract the smaller absolute value from the larger.

$$-5\frac{2}{3} + 3\frac{1}{4} = -2\frac{5}{12}$$

Since the negative addend is larger in absolute value, the answer is negative.

d. $-5.03 + 7.3$

$$|-5.03| = 5.03$$
$$|7.3| = 7.3$$

Determine the absolute value of each addend.

$$7.30$$
$$-5.03$$
$$\overline{2.27}$$

Subtract the smaller absolute value from the larger.

$$-5.03 + 7.3 = 2.27$$

Since the positive addend is larger in absolute value, the answer is positive.

TRY-IT EXERCISE 4

Add.

a. $-\dfrac{7}{9} + \dfrac{4}{9}$ **b.** $-\dfrac{3}{8} + \dfrac{7}{16}$ **c.** $4.381 + (-6.29)$

Check your answers with the solutions in Appendix A. ∎

Objective 9.2C   **Apply your knowledge**

EXAMPLE 5   Apply your knowledge

Octavian Augustus Caesar was the emperor of Rome during an era of great peace and prosperity. He was born in 63 BC and died within days of his 77th birthday. In what year did Octavian Augustus Caesar die?

SOLUTION STRATEGY

B.C.   A.D.

⟵————|————⟶
       0

A number line in which points represent time is called a *time line*. The positive numbers represent years AD and the negative numbers represent years BC.

The year 63 BC is represented by -63.

$-63 + 77$	To find out the year Octavian Augustus Caesar died, add $-63 + 77$.
$|-63| = 63$	Determine the absolute value of each addend.
$|77| = 77$	
$77 - 63 = 14$	Subtract the smaller absolute value from the larger.
$-63 + 77 = 14$	Since the positive number is larger in absolute value, the answer is positive.
Octavian Augustus Caesar died in 14 AD.	On the time line, 14 represents 14 AD.

TRY-IT EXERCISE 5

Cleopatra, the famous queen of Egypt, was born in 69 BC and died at the age of 39. In what year did she die?

Check your answer with the solution in Appendix A. ■

 SECTION 9.2 REVIEW EXERCISES

Concept Check

1. When adding two positive numbers, the sum will be _____.

2. When adding two negative numbers, the sum will be _____.

3. To add signed numbers with different signs, determine the absolute value of each addend. _____ the smaller absolute value from the larger. Then, attach the sign of the addend having the larger absolute value to this difference.

4. When adding two numbers with different signs, the sum will have the same sign as the addend that is _____ in absolute value.

Objective 9.2A   **Add numbers with the same sign**

GUIDE PROBLEMS

5. Add $-12.3 + (-31.5)$.

   a. Determine the absolute value of each addend.

   $|-12.3| =$ ___

   $|-31.5| =$ ___

6. Add $-\dfrac{5}{6} + \left(-\dfrac{3}{8}\right)$.

   a. Determine the absolute value of each addend.

   $\left|-\dfrac{5}{6}\right| =$ __ , $\left|-\dfrac{3}{8}\right| =$ __

b. Add the absolute values of the addends.

$$
\begin{array}{r}
12.3 \\
+ \underline{} \\
\hline
\underline{}
\end{array}
$$

c. Attach the common sign of the addends to the sum of part b.

$-12.3 + (-31.5) = \underline{}$

b. Write each fraction as an equivalent fraction with the LCD.

LCD = $\underline{}$

$\dfrac{5}{6} = \dfrac{5 \cdot }{6 \cdot } = \dfrac{}{} =$

$\dfrac{3}{8} = \dfrac{3 \cdot }{8 \cdot } = \dfrac{}{} =$

c. Add the absolute values of the addends.

$\dfrac{}{} + \dfrac{}{} = \dfrac{}{} = \underline{}$

d. Attach the common sign of the addends to the sum of part c.

$-\dfrac{5}{6} + \left(-\dfrac{3}{8}\right) = \underline{}$

Add. Simplify, if possible.

7. $6 + 3$

8. $8 + 7$

9. $-9 + (-1)$

10. $-6 + (-11)$

11. $-7 + (-8)$

12. $-17 + (-9)$

13. $-43 + (-25)$

14. $-18 + (-28)$

15. $-56 + (-89)$

16. $-30 + (-90)$

17. $-512 + (-106)$

18. $-162 + (-247)$

19. $-518 + (-31)$

20. $-1042 + (-139)$

21. $-126 + (-339)$

22. $-182 + (-80)$

23. $2.51 + 3.54$

24. $6.81 + 18.02$

25. $-6.1 + (-31.2)$

26. $-1.09 + (-9.21)$

27. $-3.21 + (-14.5)$

28. $-42.1 + (-9.07)$

29. $-83.31 + (-14.031)$

30. $-17.43 + (-15.012)$

31. $-\dfrac{1}{4} + \left(-\dfrac{3}{4}\right)$

32. $-\dfrac{2}{9} + \left(-\dfrac{4}{9}\right)$

33. $-\dfrac{3}{7} + \left(-\dfrac{1}{3}\right)$

34. $-\dfrac{1}{2} + \left(-\dfrac{5}{9}\right)$

35. $-\dfrac{1}{8} + \left(-\dfrac{5}{6}\right)$

36. $-\dfrac{3}{8} + \left(-\dfrac{3}{12}\right)$

37. $-\dfrac{3}{10} + \left(-\dfrac{4}{5}\right)$

38. $-\dfrac{1}{6} + \left(-\dfrac{7}{12}\right)$

39. $-1\frac{1}{3} + \left(-4\frac{5}{12}\right)$ **40.** $-2\frac{3}{5} + \left(-4\frac{2}{15}\right)$ **41.** $-21\frac{5}{9} + \left(-33\frac{5}{12}\right)$ **42.** $-18\frac{7}{12} + \left(-29\frac{5}{18}\right)$

43. $-12\frac{2}{3} + \left(-17\frac{5}{6}\right)$ **44.** $-21\frac{1}{3} + \left(-49\frac{11}{12}\right)$ **45.** $-39\frac{8}{9} + \left(-29\frac{7}{12}\right)$ **46.** $-58\frac{5}{8} + \left(-29\frac{7}{12}\right)$

Objective 9.2B   **Add numbers with different signs**

GUIDE PROBLEMS

47. Add $15.2 + (-42.9)$.

   a. Determine the absolute value of each addend.

    $|15.2| = $ ____

    $|-42.9| = $ ____

   b. Subtract the smaller absolute value from the larger.

    $\begin{array}{r} 42.9 \\ - \underline{} \\ \hline \underline{} \end{array}$

   c. Attach the sign of the addend having the larger absolute value to the difference of part b.

    $15.2 + (-42.9) = $ _____

48. Add $\frac{3}{8} + \left(-\frac{1}{12}\right)$.

   a. Determine the absolute value of each addend.

    $\left|\frac{3}{8}\right| = $ __ , $\left|-\frac{1}{12}\right| = $ __

   b. Write each fraction as an equivalent fraction with the LCD.

    $LCD = $ _____

    $\frac{3}{8} = \frac{3 \cdot }{8 \cdot } = \frac{}{}$

    $\frac{1}{12} = \frac{1 \cdot }{12 \cdot } = \frac{}{}$

   c. Subtract the smaller absolute value from the larger.

    $\frac{}{} - \frac{}{} = \frac{}{}$

   d. Attach the sign of the addend having the larger absolute value to the difference of part c.

    $\frac{3}{8} + \left(-\frac{1}{12}\right) = $ __

Add. Simplify, if possible.

49. $6 + (-3)$ **50.** $5 + (-4)$ **51.** $15 + (-8)$ **52.** $21 + (-12)$

53. $-10 + 14$ **54.** $-6 + 13$ **55.** $-8 + 8$ **56.** $-7 + 22$

57. $16 + (-27)$

58. $15 + (-29)$

59. $81 + (-45)$

60. $103 + (-62)$

61. $-139 + 76$

62. $-162 + (200)$

63. $170 + (-530)$

64. $284 + (-181)$

65. $-1216 + (3105)$

66. $2794 + (-4215)$

67. $-13,245 + 2178$

68. $28,093 + (-16,520)$

69. $-2.41 + (3.51)$

70. $10.25 + (-9.41)$

71. $-1.01 + 1.34$

72. $-5.03 + (2.37)$

73. $11.3 + (-3.7)$

74. $14.21 + (-19.02)$

75. $-13.43 + 18.5$

76. $-19.01 + 8.73$

77. $198.3 + (-213.6)$

78. $315.34 + (-149.38)$

79. $-147.23 + 211.9$

80. $-529.76 + 672.83$

81. $-\dfrac{2}{5} + \dfrac{1}{5}$

82. $-\dfrac{5}{7} + \dfrac{4}{7}$

83. $-\dfrac{2}{3} + \dfrac{5}{6}$

84. $-\dfrac{3}{8} + \dfrac{1}{2}$

85. $\dfrac{1}{8} + \left(-\dfrac{5}{6}\right)$

86. $\dfrac{1}{12} + \left(-\dfrac{7}{18}\right)$

87. $\dfrac{5}{9} + \left(-\dfrac{1}{6}\right)$

88. $\dfrac{3}{7} + \left(-\dfrac{4}{21}\right)$

89. $-7\dfrac{1}{3} + 2\dfrac{1}{8}$

90. $-6\dfrac{2}{9} + 8\dfrac{1}{3}$

91. $8\dfrac{2}{3} + \left(-15\dfrac{11}{12}\right)$

92. $17\dfrac{1}{6} + \left(-21\dfrac{2}{3}\right)$

93. $-25 + 17\dfrac{3}{5}$

94. $-19 + 10\dfrac{2}{3}$

95. $41\dfrac{8}{9} + \left(-53\dfrac{1}{6}\right)$

96. $86\dfrac{7}{8} + \left(-101\dfrac{1}{3}\right)$

Objective 9.2C	**Apply your knowledge**

97. Julius Caesar, the great-uncle of Octavian Augustus Caesar and ruler of Rome, was born in 100 BC. He was famously assassinated on the Ides of March (March 15) at the age of 56. In what year was Julius Caesar killed?

98. Early on a cold winter day, the temperature in Butte, Montana, was 6°F below zero. If the temperature rose by 15°F by noon, what was the noontime temperature?

99. The lowest point in California is Death Valley at 282 feet below sea level. Mount Whitney, the highest point in California, is 14,777 feet higher than Death Valley. How tall is Mount Whitney?

100. The Caspian Sea is approximately 92 feet below sea level. The summit of Mount Kilimanjaro is 19,432 feet higher than the Caspian Sea. How tall is Kilimanjaro?

CUMULATIVE SKILLS REVIEW

1. Subtract $\frac{5}{8} - \frac{1}{6}$. (2.7B)

2. Subtract $53 - 14\frac{2}{5}$. (2.7C)

3. Add $881.42 + 78.4$. (3.2A)

4. Write the ratio of 16 to 48 in fraction notation and simplify. (4.1A)

5. The official world's record low temperature, recorded in Antarctica, is $128.5\,°F$ below zero. Express this temperature as a signed number. (9.1E)

6. Convert 13,396 meters to kilometers. (6.2A)

7. The number of visits to the HotTunes website for each of four consecutive days was 3052, 2545, 2800, and 2750. Find the range of daily visits. (8.2D)

8. Calculate the median for the set of numbers 28, 13, 96, 46, 2. (8.2B)

9. Graph $-5, 3, -1$, and 0. (9.1B)

10. Evaluate $|55|$. (9.1C)

9.3 SUBTRACTING SIGNED NUMBERS

LEARNING OBJECTIVES

A. Subtract signed numbers

B. Apply your knowledge

Objective 9.3A   Subtract signed numbers

In order to subtract signed numbers, we rely on two ideas presented in this chapter, namely, finding the opposite of a number and adding signed numbers. To see why these concepts are central to subtracting signed numbers, consider the following example. Suppose that you lose $20 in a bet. If you have $100 in your wallet, $80 will remain after you pay the debt.

$$\$100 - \$20 = \$80$$

There is another way of thinking about this scenario. In Section 9.1, we learned that we can numerically represent a loss of $20 as $-\$20$. If you represent the amount you lost as a negative number, then you must add the two amounts together to determine how much money remains.

$$\$100 + (-\$20) = \$80$$

Notice that the amount remaining is the same no matter how we think about it. This example demonstrates that subtracting a number is the same as adding the opposite of that number. Thus, for any two numbers a and b, we have the following.

$$a - b = a + (-b)$$

The following steps can be used to subtract signed numbers.

Steps for Subtracting Signed Numbers

Step 1. Write the subtraction problem as an addition problem by adding the first number to the opposite of the second number.

Step 2. Add using the steps in Section 9.2, Adding Signed Numbers.

According to these steps, $7 - 3$ can be rewritten as $7 + (-3)$. Note that both problems have the same answer.

$$7 - 3 = 4 \quad \text{and} \quad 7 + (-3) = 4$$

But, why even bother writing such a simple subtraction problem as an addition problem? After all, $7 - 3$ is easy enough to compute. Indeed, when subtracting a smaller positive number from a larger positive number, there is no reason to rewrite the subtraction problem.

It is often useful to rewrite a subtraction problem as an addition problem when we (1) subtract a positive number from a smaller positive number, (2) subtract a positive number from a negative number, and (3) subtract a negative number from either a positive or a negative number.

Let's begin by looking at some examples involving integers.

EXAMPLE 1   **Subtract a positive integer from a smaller positive integer**

Subtract.

a. $4 - 9$ **b.** $17 - 32$

SOLUTION STRATEGY

a. $4 - 9$

A larger positive number is subtracted from a smaller positive number.

$4 + (-9)$

Write the subtraction problem as an addition problem by adding 4 and the opposite of 9. The opposite of 9 is -9.

$|4| = 4, |-9| = 9$

Determine the absolute value of each addend.

$9 - 4 = 5$

Since the addends have different signs, subtract the smaller absolute value from the larger.

$4 - 9 = 4 + (-9) = -5$

Since the negative addend is larger in absolute value, the answer is negative.

b. $17 - 32$

A larger positive number is subtracted from a smaller positive number.

$17 + (-32)$

Write the subtraction problem as an addition problem by adding 17 and the opposite of 32. The opposite of 32 is -32.

Learning Tip

When we subtract a positive integer from a smaller positive integer, the result is always negative.

In general, we have the following.

bigger − smaller = positive
smaller − bigger = negative

$|17| = 17, |-32| = 32$ Determine the absolute value of each addend.

$32 - 17 = 15$ Since the addends have different signs, subtract the smaller absolute value from the larger.

$17 - 32 = 17 + (-32) = -15$ Since the negative addend is larger in absolute value, the answer is negative.

TRY-IT EXERCISE 1

Subtract.

a. $7 - 12$ **b.** $25 - 49$

Check your answers with the solutions in Appendix A. ■

EXAMPLE 2   **Subtract a positive integer from a negative integer**

Subtract.

a. $-41 - 18$ **b.** $-27 - 43$

SOLUTION STRATEGY

a. $-41 - 18$ A positive number is subtracted from a negative number.

$-41 + (-18)$ Write the subtraction problem as an addition problem by adding -41 and the opposite of 18. The opposite of 18 is -18.

$|-41| = 41, |-18| = 18$ Determine the absolute value of each addend.

$41 + 18 = 59$ Since the addends have the same sign, add the absolute values.

$-41 - 18 = -41 + (-18) = -59$ Since both addends are negative, the answer is negative.

b. $-27 - 43$ A positive number is subtracted from a negative number.

$-27 + (-43)$ Write the subtraction problem as an addition problem by adding -27 and the opposite of 43. The opposite of 43 is -43.

$|-27| = 27, |-43| = 43$ Determine the absolute value of each addend.

$27 + 43 = 70$ Since the addends have the same sign, add the absolute values.

$-27 - 43 = -27 + (-43) = -70$ Since both addends are negative, the answer is negative.

> **● Learning Tip**
>
> When we subtract a positive integer from a negative integer, the result is always negative.
>
> Also, since a negative number is less than a positive number, we are using the same idea presented in the previous learning tip.
>
> smaller − bigger = negative

TRY-IT EXERCISE 2

Subtract.

a. $-24 - 19$ **b.** $-39 - 52$

Check your answers with the solutions in Appendix A. ■

EXAMPLE 3   **Subtract a negative integer from an integer**

Subtract.

a. $23 - (-4)$ **b.** $-45 - (-63)$

SOLUTION STRATEGY

a. $23 - (-4)$ A negative number is subtracted from a positive number.

    $23 + 4$ Write the subtraction problem as an addition problem by adding 23 and the opposite of -4. The opposite of -4 is 4.

    $23 + 4 = 27$ Since the addends are both positive, simply add.

    $23 - (-4) = 23 + 4 = 27$

b. $-45 - (-63)$ A negative number is subtracted from a negative number.

    $-45 + 63$ Write the subtraction problem as an addition problem by adding -45 and the opposite of -63. The opposite of -63 is 63.

    $|-45| = 45, |63| = 63$ Determine the absolute value of each addend.

    $63 - 45 = 18$ Since the addends have different signs, subtract the smaller absolute value from the larger.

    $-45 - (-63) = -45 + 63 = 18$ Since the positive addend is larger in absolute value, the answer is positive.

> **Learning Tip**
>
> When we subtract a negative number from a number, we ultimately add a positive number to the first number.

TRY-IT EXERCISE 3

Subtract.

a. $14 - (-12)$ **b.** $-48 - (-51)$

Check your answers with the solutions in Appendix A. ■

    We'll now look at some examples of subtraction problems involving rational numbers. In these problems, we will ultimately add or subtract fractions, decimals, or mixed numbers. For a review of fraction and mixed number addition and subtraction, refer to Section 2.6, Adding Fractions and Mixed Numbers, and Section 2.7, Subtracting Fractions and Mixed Numbers. For a review of decimal addition and subtraction, refer to Section 3.2, Adding and Subtracting Decimals.

EXAMPLE 4   Subtract rational numbers

Subtract. Simplify, if possible.

a. $\dfrac{1}{3} - \dfrac{2}{3}$

b. $-\dfrac{3}{4} - \dfrac{5}{6}$

c. $-9 - \left(-2\dfrac{1}{4}\right)$

d. $1\dfrac{3}{4} - 3\dfrac{1}{5}$

e. $-8.21 - 4.2$

f. $6.32 - (-17.1)$

SOLUTION STRATEGY

Learning Tip

When we subtract a negative number from a number, we ultimately add a positive number to the first number.

a. $\dfrac{1}{3} - \dfrac{2}{3}$

A larger positive number is subtracted from a smaller positive number.

$\dfrac{1}{3} + \left(-\dfrac{2}{3}\right)$

Write the subtraction problem as an addition problem by adding $\dfrac{1}{3}$ and the opposite of $\dfrac{2}{3}$. The opposite of $\dfrac{2}{3}$ is $-\dfrac{2}{3}$.

$\left|\dfrac{1}{3}\right| = \dfrac{1}{3}, \left|-\dfrac{2}{3}\right| = \dfrac{2}{3}$

Determine the absolute value of each addend.

$\dfrac{2}{3} - \dfrac{1}{3} = \dfrac{1}{3}$

Since the addends have different signs, subtract the smaller absolute value from the larger.

$\dfrac{1}{3} - \dfrac{2}{3} = \dfrac{1}{3} + \left(-\dfrac{2}{3}\right) = -\dfrac{1}{3}$

Since the negative addend is larger in absolute value, the answer is negative.

b. $-\dfrac{3}{4} - \dfrac{5}{6}$

A positive number is subtracted from a negative number.

$-\dfrac{3}{4} + \left(-\dfrac{5}{6}\right)$

Write the subtraction problem as an addition problem by adding $-\dfrac{3}{4}$ and the opposite of $\dfrac{5}{6}$. The opposite of $\dfrac{5}{6}$ is $-\dfrac{5}{6}$.

$\left|-\dfrac{3}{4}\right| = \dfrac{3}{4}, \left|-\dfrac{5}{6}\right| = \dfrac{5}{6}$

Determine the absolute value of each addend.

$\text{LCD} = 12$

Find the LCD.

$\dfrac{3}{4} = \dfrac{3 \cdot 3}{4 \cdot 3} = \dfrac{9}{12}$

$\dfrac{5}{6} = \dfrac{5 \cdot 2}{6 \cdot 2} = \dfrac{10}{12}$

Write each fraction as an equivalent fraction with the denominator 12.

$\dfrac{10}{12} + \dfrac{9}{12} = \dfrac{19}{12}$

Since the addends have the same sign, add the absolute values.

$-\dfrac{3}{4} - \dfrac{5}{6} = -\dfrac{3}{4} + \left(-\dfrac{5}{6}\right) = -\dfrac{19}{12}$

Since both addends are negative, the answer is negative.

c. $-9 - \left(-2\frac{1}{4}\right)$

A negative number is subtracted from a negative number.

$-9 + 2\frac{1}{4}$

Write the subtraction problem as an addition problem by adding 9 and the opposite of $-2\frac{1}{4}$. The opposite of $-2\frac{1}{4}$ is $2\frac{1}{4}$.

$|-9| = 9, \left|2\frac{1}{4}\right| = 2\frac{1}{4}$

Determine the absolute value of each addend.

$$\begin{array}{r} 9 \;\rightarrow\; 8\frac{4}{4} \\ -2\frac{1}{4} \;\rightarrow\; -2\frac{1}{4} \\ \hline 6\frac{3}{4} \end{array}$$

Since the addends have different signs, subtract the smaller absolute value from the larger.

$-9 - \left(-2\frac{1}{4}\right) = -9 + 2\frac{1}{4}$

Since the negative addend is larger in absolute value, the answer is negative.

$$= -6\frac{3}{4}$$

d. $1\frac{3}{4} - 3\frac{1}{5}$

A larger positive number is subtracted from a smaller negative number.

$1\frac{3}{4} + \left(-3\frac{1}{5}\right)$

Write the subtraction problem as an addition problem by adding $1\frac{3}{4}$ and the opposite of $3\frac{1}{5}$. The opposite of $3\frac{1}{5}$ is $-3\frac{1}{5}$.

$\left|1\frac{3}{4}\right| = 1\frac{3}{4}, \left|-3\frac{1}{5}\right| = 3\frac{1}{5}$

Determine the absolute value of each addend.

LCD = 20

Find the LCD.

$1\frac{3}{4} = 1\frac{3 \cdot 5}{5 \cdot 5} = 1\frac{15}{20}$

$3\frac{1}{5} = 3\frac{1 \cdot 4}{5 \cdot 4} = 3\frac{4}{20}$

Write each fraction as an equivalent fraction with the denominator 20.

$$\begin{array}{r} 3\frac{4}{20} \;\rightarrow\; 2\frac{24}{20} \\ -1\frac{12}{20} \;\rightarrow\; -1\frac{15}{20} \\ \hline 1\frac{9}{20} \end{array}$$

Since the addends have different signs, subtract the smaller absolute value from the larger.

$1\frac{3}{4} - 3\frac{1}{5} = 1\frac{3}{4} + \left(-3\frac{1}{5}\right)$

Since the negative addend is larger in absolute value, the answer is negative.

$$= -1\frac{9}{20}$$

e. $-8.21 - 4.2$

A positive number is subtracted from a negative number.

$-8.21 + (-4.2)$

Write the subtraction problem as an addition problem by adding -8.21 and the opposite of 4.2. The opposite of 4.2 is -4.2.

$|-8.21| = 8.21, |-4.2| = 4.2$

Determine the absolute value of each addend.

$$\begin{array}{r} 8.21 \\ + \ 4.20 \\ \hline 12.41 \end{array}$$

Since the addends have the same sign, add the absolute values.

$-8.21 - 4.2 = -8.21 + (-4.2)$
$\qquad\qquad\quad = -12.41$

Since both addends are negative, the answer is negative.

f. $6.32 - (-17.1)$

A negative number is subtracted from a positive number.

$6.32 + 17.1$

Write the subtraction problem as an addition problem by adding 6.32 and the opposite of -17.1. The opposite of -17.1 is 17.1.

$6.32 + 17.1 = 23.42$

Add the addends. Since the addends are both positive, simply add.

$6.32 - (-17.1) = 6.32 + 17.1$
$\qquad\qquad\qquad = 23.42$

TRY-IT EXERCISE 4

Subtract. Simplify, if possible.

a. $\dfrac{1}{8} - \dfrac{5}{12}$

b. $-\dfrac{1}{4} - \dfrac{5}{9}$

c. $1\dfrac{1}{5} - \left(-2\dfrac{2}{3}\right)$

d. $-2\dfrac{2}{5} - 4\dfrac{1}{4}$

e. $0.31 - (-0.28)$

f. $-6.7 - 4.15$

Check your answers with the solutions in Appendix A. ■

Objective 9.3B   **Apply your knowledge**

EXAMPLE 5   **Apply your knowledge**

Elements, the most successful textbooks of all time, served as the basic texts for subjects such as geometry for over 2000 years. The great mathematician Euclid wrote *Elements* prior to his death in 283 BC. The textbook you are presently reading was first published in 2008. How many years separate this textbook and Euclid's textbooks?

SOLUTION STRATEGY

a. $2008 - (-283)$

We want to find the difference between the publication dates of this textbook and those of Euclid. Represent the year of Euclid's death as -283.

To find how many years separate the two, subtract -283 from 2008.

$2008 + 283$

Write the subtraction problem as an addition problem by adding 2008 and the opposite of -283. The opposite of -283 is 283.

$2008 + 283 = 2291$ Since the addends are both positive, add.

$2008 - (-283) = 2008 + 283$

$= 2291$

There are 2291 years separating this textbook from Euclid's *Elements*.

TRY-IT EXERCISE 5

Ovid, one of the classical poets of Latin literature, was born in 43 BC. William Shakespeare, one of the greatest English poets and playwrights, was born in 1564 AD. What is the difference between the years of their births?

Check your answer with the solution in Appendix A. ■

SECTION 9.3 REVIEW EXERCISES

Concept Check

1. The subtraction problem $a - b$ is the same as the addition problem $a +$ _____.

2. To solve the subtraction problem $3 - 7$, it is helpful to write it as _____.

Objective 9.3A   **Subtract signed numbers**

GUIDE PROBLEMS

3. Subtract $8 - 15$.

   a. Write the subtraction problem as an addition problem.

     $8 - 15 = 8 +$ _____

   b. Determine the absolute value of each addend in the addition problem of part a.

     $|8| =$ __ , $|$____$| =$ __

   c. Since the addends in part a have different signs, subtract the smaller absolute value from the larger.

     __ − __ = __

   d. Attach the sign of the addend having the larger absolute value to the difference of part c.

     $8 - 15 = 8 +$ _____ $=$ ____

4. Subtract $-1.2 - 1.7$.

   a. Write the subtraction problem as an addition problem.

     $-1.2 - 1.7 = -1.2 +$ _____

   b. Determine the absolute value of each addend in the addition problem of part a.

     $|-1.2| =$ __ , $|$____$| =$ __

   c. Since the addends in part a have the same sign, add the absolute values of the addends.

     $\begin{array}{r} 1.2 \\ + \underline{} \\ \hline \end{array}$

   d. Attach the common sign of the addends to the sum of part c.

     $-1.2 - 1.7 = -1.2 +$ _____ $=$ ____

Subtract. Simplify, if possible.

5. $13 - 6$

6. $18 - 7$

7. $27 - 11$

8. $35 - 23$

9. $5 - 11$

10. $6 - 14$

11. $15 - 32$

12. $28 - 55$

13. $13 - (-14)$

14. $18 - (-12)$

15. $48 - (-33)$

16. $45 - (-21)$

17. $413 - 106$

18. $215 - 163$

19. $-27 - (-10)$

20. $-10 - (-11)$

21. $-2145 - 1478$

22. $-182 - 807$

23. $1039 - 908$

24. $-656 - 450$

25. $-147 - (-409)$

26. $478 - 1249$

27. $540 - 1329$

28. $-874 - (-2197)$

29. $-\dfrac{1}{5} - \dfrac{3}{5}$

30. $\dfrac{2}{9} - \dfrac{5}{9}$

31. $\dfrac{1}{6} - \dfrac{3}{8}$

32. $-\dfrac{1}{12} - \dfrac{5}{8}$

33. $-\dfrac{2}{3} - \left(-\dfrac{1}{6}\right)$

34. $-\dfrac{1}{5} - \left(-\dfrac{1}{8}\right)$

35. $\dfrac{5}{12} - \left(-\dfrac{7}{18}\right)$

36. $\dfrac{3}{15} - \left(-\dfrac{7}{20}\right)$

37. $2\dfrac{1}{5} - 6\dfrac{3}{7}$

38. $3\dfrac{1}{3} - 8\dfrac{5}{7}$

39. $14\dfrac{2}{3} - \left(-11\dfrac{5}{9}\right)$

40. $6\dfrac{2}{21} - \left(-4\dfrac{3}{14}\right)$

41. $5\dfrac{1}{8} - 7\dfrac{7}{28}$

42. $-8\dfrac{2}{9} - 6\dfrac{3}{15}$

43. $1\dfrac{8}{9} - 4\dfrac{11}{12}$

44. $9\dfrac{1}{2} - 17\dfrac{7}{23}$

45. $9.78 - 4.25$

46. $7.02 - 5.03$

47. $4.32 - 6.87$

48. $5.21 - 7.31$

49. $-7.64 - 1.32$

50. $-1.15 - 9.12$

51. $-4.18 - (-8.96)$

52. $-7.98 - (-10.86)$

53. $12.25 - 45.30$

54. $24.32 - 57.3$

55. $-35.14 - (-51.2)$

56. $-47.21 - (-61.6)$

57. $-120.3 - 35.8$

58. $187.2 - 95.1$

59. $143.8 - (-87.3)$

60. $-78.2 - 86.3$

| Objective 9.3B | **Apply your knowledge** |

61. Archimedes is generally regarded as the greatest ancient mathematician, while Carl Friedrich Gauss is upheld as the greatest modern mathematician. Archimedes died in 212 BC and Gauss was born in 1777 AD. How many years separate the greatest ancient mathematician and the greatest modern mathematician?

62. According to legend, Marco Polo introduced pasta to Italy on his return from China in 1295 AD. The Chinese have been eating noodles since 2000 BC. If the legend is true, how long were the Chinese eating pasta before the Italians?

63. The temperature at which radon boils is $-143.6\,°F$. The temperature at which water boils is $212\,°F$. What is the difference between these two temperatures?

64. The temperature at which water freezes is $32\,°F$. The temperature at which regular unleaded gasoline freezes is $-97\,°F$. What is the difference between these two temperatures?

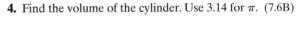

CUMULATIVE SKILLS REVIEW

1. Ariana and Claudia are thinking of starting their own business. They estimate they will need $225,000 to cover their first year expenses and together have saved $70,000. What percent of the total amount needed can Ariana and Claudia provide? Round to the nearest percent. (5.2C, 5.3C)

2. Elizabeth had a beginning balance of $12,388.14 in her checking account. She wrote checks in the amounts of $1420.12, $522.18, and $125.50. What is the new balance on Elizabeth's account? (3.2D)

3. Identify and name the figure. (7.1A)

4. Find the volume of the cylinder. Use 3.14 for π. (7.6B)

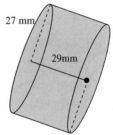

27 mm

29mm

5. Convert 24 square yards to square feet. (6.1B)

6. Add $42 + (-16) + (-18)$. (9.2B)

7. Compare the signed numbers 7 and -12. (9.1D)

8. Convert 45% to a fraction and simplify. (5.1A)

9. What is 150 increased by 35%? (5.5C)

10. Write 42 is to 3 as 14 is to 1 as a proportion. (4.3A)

9.4 MULTIPLYING AND DIVIDING SIGNED NUMBERS

LEARNING OBJECTIVES

A. Multiply signed numbers

B. Divide signed numbers

C. Apply your knowledge

Objective 9.4A   **Multiply signed numbers**

In mathematics, we can often recognize patterns that help us determine what happens next. For example, consider the following columns of products.

$5 \cdot 1 = 5$	$5 \cdot 2 = 10$	$5 \cdot 3 = 15$	$5 \cdot 4 = 20$	$5 \cdot 5 = 25$
$4 \cdot 1 = 4$	$4 \cdot 2 = 8$	$4 \cdot 3 = 12$	$4 \cdot 4 = 16$	$4 \cdot 5 = 20$
$3 \cdot 1 = 3$	$3 \cdot 2 = 6$	$3 \cdot 3 = 9$	$3 \cdot 4 = 12$	$3 \cdot 5 = 15$
$2 \cdot 1 = 2$	$2 \cdot 2 = 4$	$2 \cdot 3 = 6$	$2 \cdot 4 = 8$	$2 \cdot 5 = 10$
$1 \cdot 1 = 1$	$1 \cdot 2 = 2$	$1 \cdot 3 = 3$	$1 \cdot 4 = 4$	$1 \cdot 5 = 5$
$0 \cdot 1 = 0$	$0 \cdot 2 = 0$	$0 \cdot 3 = 0$	$0 \cdot 4 = 0$	$0 \cdot 5 = 0$
$-1 \cdot 1 = ?$	$-1 \cdot 2 = ?$	$-1 \cdot 3 = ?$	$-1 \cdot 4 = ?$	$-1 \cdot 5 = ?$

Looking down the first column, notice that as the numbers in blue decrease by 1, the numbers in red decrease by 1. This leads us to the conclusion that the "?" should be replaced by a number 1 less than 0. Thus, we replace the "?" by -1.

$$-1 \cdot 1 = -1$$

Now, looking down the second column, notice that as the numbers in blue decrease by 1, the numbers in red decrease by 2. This leads us to the conclusion that the "?" should be replaced by a number 2 less than 0. Thus, we replace the "?" by -2.

$$-1 \cdot 2 = -2$$

This same pattern continues. The "?" in the third column should be replaced by -3, in the fourth column by -4, and the fifth column by -5.

These results suggest that the product of two numbers with different signs is always negative. Based on our observations, we present the following for multiplying numbers with different signs.

Steps for Multiplying Numbers with Different Signs

Step 1. Determine the absolute value of each factor.

Step 2. Multiply the absolute values of the factors.

Step 3. Attach a negative sign to the result. The product is negative.

Let's now look at some examples of multiplying numbers with different signs. Refer to Section 2.4, Multiplying Fractions and Mixed Numbers, and Section 3.3, Multiplying Decimals, for a review of multiplying fractions, mixed numbers, and decimals.

EXAMPLE 1   Multiply numbers with different signs

Multiply. Simplify, if possible.

a. $2(-4)$ **b.** $-9 \cdot 7$ **c.** $\dfrac{2}{3}\left(-\dfrac{5}{8}\right)$ **d.** $2\dfrac{2}{5}\left(-4\dfrac{1}{6}\right)$ **e.** $(1.2)(-0.6)$

SOLUTION STRATEGY

a. $2(-4)$

$\lvert 2 \rvert = 2, \lvert -4 \rvert = 4$	Determine the absolute value of each factor.
$2 \cdot 4 = 8$	Multiply the absolute values.
$2(-4) = -8$	Since the factors have different signs, the product is negative.

b. $-9 \cdot 7$

$\lvert -9 \rvert = 9, \lvert 7 \rvert = 7$	Determine the absolute value of each factor.
$9 \cdot 7 = 63$	Multiply the absolute values.
$-9 \cdot 7 = -63$	Since the factors have different signs, the product is negative.

c. $\dfrac{2}{3}\left(-\dfrac{5}{8}\right)$

$\left\lvert \dfrac{2}{3} \right\rvert = \dfrac{2}{3}, \left\lvert -\dfrac{5}{8} \right\rvert = \dfrac{5}{8}$	Determine the absolute value of each factor.
$\dfrac{\overset{1}{2}}{3} \cdot \dfrac{5}{\underset{4}{8}} = \dfrac{5}{12}$	Multiply the absolute values.
$\dfrac{2}{3}\left(-\dfrac{5}{8}\right) = -\dfrac{5}{12}$	Since the factors have different signs, the product is negative.

d. $2\dfrac{2}{5}\left(-4\dfrac{1}{6}\right)$

$\left\lvert 2\dfrac{2}{5} \right\rvert = 2\dfrac{2}{5}, \left\lvert -4\dfrac{1}{6} \right\rvert = 4\dfrac{1}{6}$	Determine the absolute value of each factor.
$2\dfrac{2}{5} \cdot 4\dfrac{1}{6} = \dfrac{\overset{2}{12}}{\underset{1}{5}} \cdot \dfrac{\overset{5}{25}}{\underset{1}{6}} = \dfrac{10}{1} = 10$	Multiply the absolute values.
$2\dfrac{2}{5}\left(-4\dfrac{1}{6}\right) = -10$	Since the factors have different signs, the product is negative.

e. $(1.2)(-0.6)$

$\lvert 1.2 \rvert = 1.2, \lvert -0.6 \rvert = 0.6$	Determine the absolute value of each factor.
$(1.2)(0.6) = 0.72$	Multiply the absolute values.
$(1.2)(-0.6) = -0.72$	Since the factors have different signs, the product is negative.

TRY-IT EXERCISE 1

Multiply. Simplify, if possible.

a. $9(-5)$ **b.** $-4 \cdot 10$ **c.** $\dfrac{8}{21}\left(-\dfrac{3}{16}\right)$ **d.** $-3\dfrac{1}{4} \cdot 2\dfrac{2}{5}$ **e.** $(1.5)(-0.4)$

Check your answers with the solutions in Appendix A. ∎

Just as we looked at a pattern to understand how to multiply two numbers with different signs, we can analyze a pattern to see how to multiply two numbers with the same sign. Consider the following columns of products.

$$
\begin{array}{lllll}
5(-1) = -5 & 5(-2) = -10 & 5(-3) = -15 & 5(-4) = -20 & 5(-5) = -25 \\
4(-1) = -4 & 4(-2) = -8 & 4(-3) = -12 & 4(-4) = -16 & 4(-5) = -20 \\
3(-1) = -3 & 3(-2) = -6 & 3(-3) = -9 & 3(-4) = -12 & 3(-5) = -15 \\
2(-1) = -2 & 2(-2) = -4 & 2(-3) = -6 & 2(-4) = -8 & 2(-5) = -10 \\
1(-1) = -1 & 1(-2) = -2 & 1(-3) = -3 & 1(-4) = -4 & 1(-5) = -5 \\
0(-1) = 0 & 0(-2) = 0 & 0(-3) = 0 & 0(-4) = 0 & 0(-5) = 0 \\
-1(-1) = ? & -1(-2) = ? & -1(-3) = ? & -1(-4) = ? & -1(-5) = ?
\end{array}
$$

Looking down the first column, notice that as the numbers in blue decrease by 1, the numbers in red increase by 1. This leads us to the conclusion that the "?" should be replaced by a number 1 more than 0. Thus, we replace the "?" by 1.

$$-1 \cdot -1 = 1$$

Now looking down the second column, notice that as the numbers in blue decrease by 1, the numbers in red increase by 2. This leads us to the conclusion that the "?" should be replaced by a number 2 more than 0. Thus, we replace the "?" by 2.

$$-1 \cdot -2 = 2$$

This same pattern continues. The "?" in the third column should be replaced by 3, in the fourth column by 4, and the fifth column by 5.

These results suggest that the product of two numbers with the same sign is always positive. Based on our observations, we present the following for multiplying numbers with the same sign.

 *Learning Tip*

You may find the following helpful.

positive · positive = positive
negative · negative = positive
positive · negative = negative
negative · positive = negative

Steps for Multiplying Numbers with the Same Sign

Step 1. Determine the absolute value of each factor.

Step 2. Multiply the absolute values of the two numbers. The product is positive.

Since we are already very familiar with multiplying positive numbers, we'll look at some examples in which we multiply negative numbers.

EXAMPLE 2   Multiply numbers with the same sign

Multiply. Simplify, if possible.

a. $-3(-9)$ **b.** $(-9)(-11)$ **c.** $-\dfrac{2}{7}\left(-\dfrac{14}{15}\right)$ **d.** $-3\dfrac{1}{8}\left(-1\dfrac{1}{7}\right)$ **e.** $-0.6(-0.13)$

SOLUTION STRATEGY

a. $-3(-9)$

$|-3| = 3, |-9| = 9$ Determine the absolute value of each factor.

$3 \cdot 9 = 27$ Multiply the absolute values.

$-3(-9) = 27$ Since the factors have the same signs, the product is positive.

b. $(-9)(-11)$

$|-9| = 9, |-11| = 11$ Determine the absolute value of each factor.

$9 \cdot 11 = 99$ Multiply the absolute values.

$(-9)(-11) = 99$ Since the factors have the same signs, the product is positive.

c. $-\dfrac{2}{7}\left(-\dfrac{14}{15}\right)$

$\left|-\dfrac{2}{7}\right| = \dfrac{2}{7}, \left|-\dfrac{14}{15}\right| = \dfrac{14}{15}$ Determine the absolute value of each factor.

$\dfrac{2}{\overset{}{\underset{1}{7}}} \cdot \dfrac{\overset{2}{14}}{15} = \dfrac{4}{15}$ Multiply the absolute values.

$-\dfrac{2}{7}\left(-\dfrac{14}{15}\right) = \dfrac{4}{15}$ Since the factors have the same signs, the product is positive.

d. $-3\dfrac{1}{8}\left(-1\dfrac{1}{7}\right)$

$\left|-3\dfrac{1}{8}\right| = 3\dfrac{1}{8}, \left|-1\dfrac{1}{7}\right| = 1\dfrac{1}{7}$ Determine the absolute value of each factor.

$3\dfrac{1}{8} \cdot 1\dfrac{1}{7} = \dfrac{25}{8} \cdot \dfrac{\overset{1}{8}}{7} = \dfrac{25}{7} = 3\dfrac{4}{7}$ Multiply the absolute values.

$-3\dfrac{1}{8}\left(-1\dfrac{1}{7}\right) = 3\dfrac{4}{7}$ Since the factors have the same signs, the product is positive.

e. $-0.6(-0.13)$

$|-0.6| = 0.6, |-0.13| = 0.13$ Determine the absolute value of each factor.

$0.6 \cdot 0.13 = 0.078$ Multiply the absolute values.

$-0.6(-0.13) = 0.078$ Since the factors have the same signs, the product is positive.

TRY-IT EXERCISE 2

Multiply. Simplify, if possible.

a. $-8(-7)$ **b.** $-15(-5)$ **c.** $-\dfrac{4}{15}\left(-\dfrac{7}{8}\right)$ **d.** $-4\dfrac{1}{2}\left(-3\dfrac{1}{9}\right)$ **e.** $-12(-11)$

Check your answers with the solutions in Appendix A. ■

EXAMPLE 3   **Multiply signed numbers**

Multiply.

a. $2 \cdot 8(-9)$ **b.** $-5(-6)(4)$ **c.** $-\dfrac{2}{3}\left(-\dfrac{15}{34}\right)\left(\dfrac{1}{4}\right)$ **d.** $-0.3(-4)(-0.007)$

SOLUTION STRATEGY

a. $2 \cdot 8(-9)$

    $16(-9)$ Multiply $2 \cdot 8$. (positive · positive = positive)

    -144 Multiply $16(-9)$. (positive · negative = negative)

b. $-5(-6)(4)$

    $30(4)$ Multiply $-5(-6)$. (negative · negative = positive)

    120 Multiply $30(4)$. (positive · positive = positive)

c. $-\dfrac{2}{3}\left(-\dfrac{15}{34}\right)\left(\dfrac{1}{4}\right)$

    $-\dfrac{\overset{1}{\cancel{2}}}{\underset{1}{\cancel{3}}}\left(-\dfrac{\overset{5}{\cancel{15}}}{\underset{17}{\cancel{34}}}\right)\left(\dfrac{1}{4}\right)$ Divide out common factors.

    $\dfrac{5}{17}\left(\dfrac{1}{4}\right)$ Multiply $-\dfrac{1}{1}\left(-\dfrac{5}{17}\right)$. (negative · negative = positive)

    $\dfrac{5}{68}$ Multiply $\dfrac{5}{17}\left(\dfrac{1}{4}\right)$. (positive · positive = positive)

d. $-0.3(-4)(-0.007)$

    $1.2(-0.007)$ Multiply $-0.3(-4)$. (negative · negative = positive)

    -0.0084 Multiply $1.2(-0.007)$. (positive · negative = negative)

TRY-IT EXERCISE 3

Multiply. Simplify, if possible.

a. $3 \cdot 2(-6)$ **b.** $-7(4)(-5)$ **c.** $-\dfrac{1}{5}\left(\dfrac{2}{3}\right)\left(-\dfrac{9}{14}\right)$ **d.** $-0.2(-3.4)(0.8)$

Check your answers with the solutions in Appendix A. ■

Objective 9.4B	Divide signed numbers

To understand division of signed numbers, consider the following.

$$15 \div (-3)$$

If $15 \div (-3) = q$, then $q(-3) = 15$. But, since $-5(-3) = 15$, we know that q must be -5. Therefore, the answer to our division problem must be -5.

$$15 \div (-3) = -5$$

This makes sense because division is the inverse of multiplication. Consequently, the rules for dividing signed numbers are very similar to those for multiplying signed numbers. When we divide two numbers with different signs, the quotient is negative. When we divide two numbers with the same sign, the quotient is positive.

Steps for Dividing Numbers with Different Signs

Step 1. Determine the absolute values of the dividend and the divisor.

Step 2. Divide the absolute values from step 1.

Step 3. Attach a negative sign to the result. The quotient is negative.

Steps for Dividing Signed Numbers with the Same Sign

Step 1. Determine the absolute values of the dividend and the divisor.

Step 2. Divide the absolute values from step 1. The quotient is positive.

We'll now look at some examples of dividing signed numbers. Refer to Section 2.5, Dividing Fractions and Mixed Numbers, and Section 3.4, Dividing Decimals, for a review of dividing fractions, mixed numbers, and decimals.

EXAMPLE 4   Divide signed numbers with different signs

Divide. Simplify, if possible.

a. $25 \div (-5)$ **b.** $-39 \div 13$ **c.** $\dfrac{5}{6} \div \left(-\dfrac{1}{12}\right)$ **d.** $2\dfrac{2}{3} \div \left(-1\dfrac{7}{9}\right)$ **e.** $81 \div (-0.9)$

SOLUTION STRATEGY

a. $25 \div (-5)$

$|25| = 25, |-5| = 5$ Determine the absolute values of the dividend and divisor.

$25 \div 5 = 5$ Divide the absolute values.

$25 \div (-5) = -5$ Attach a negative sign to the result. The quotient is negative.

b. $-39 \div 13$

$|-39| = 39, |13| = 13$ — Determine the absolute values of the dividend and divisor.

$39 \div 13 = 3$ — Divide the absolute values.

$-39 \div 13 = -3$ — Attach a negative sign to the result. The quotient is negative.

c. $\dfrac{5}{6} \div \left(-\dfrac{1}{12}\right)$

$\left|\dfrac{5}{6}\right| = \dfrac{5}{6}, \left|-\dfrac{1}{12}\right| = \dfrac{1}{12}$ — Determine the absolute values of the dividend and divisor.

$\dfrac{5}{6} \div \dfrac{1}{12} = \dfrac{5}{\overset{}{\underset{1}{6}}} \cdot \dfrac{\overset{2}{\cancel{12}}}{1} = \dfrac{10}{1} = 10$ — Divide the absolute values.

$\dfrac{5}{6} \div \left(-\dfrac{1}{12}\right) = -10$ — Attach a negative sign to the result. The quotient is negative.

d. $2\dfrac{2}{3} \div \left(-1\dfrac{7}{9}\right)$

$\left|2\dfrac{2}{3}\right| = 2\dfrac{2}{3}, \left|-1\dfrac{7}{9}\right| = 1\dfrac{7}{9}$ — Determine the absolute values of the dividend and divisor.

$2\dfrac{2}{3} \div 1\dfrac{7}{9} = \dfrac{8}{3} \div \dfrac{16}{9}$

$= \dfrac{\overset{1}{\cancel{8}}}{\underset{1}{\cancel{3}}} \cdot \dfrac{\overset{3}{\cancel{9}}}{\underset{2}{\cancel{16}}} = \dfrac{3}{2} = 1\dfrac{1}{2}$ — Divide the absolute values.

$2\dfrac{2}{3} \div \left(-1\dfrac{7}{9}\right) = -1\dfrac{1}{2}$ — Attach a negative sign to the result. The quotient is negative.

e. $81 \div (-0.9)$

$|81| = 81, |-0.9| = 0.9$ — Determine the absolute values of the dividend and divisor.

$0.9\overline{)81.0}$ — Divide the absolute values.

$9\overline{)810}^{\,90}$

$81 \div (-0.9) = -90$ — Attach a negative sign to the result. The quotient is negative.

TRY-IT EXERCISE 4

Divide.

a. $28 \div (-4)$ **b.** $-49 \div 7$ **c.** $\dfrac{3}{22} \div \left(-\dfrac{15}{11}\right)$ **d.** $-5\dfrac{2}{3} \div 3\dfrac{1}{9}$ **e.** $6.3 \div (-0.3)$

Check your answers with the solutions in Appendix A. ∎

EXAMPLE 5   Divide numbers with the same sign

Divide.

a. $-18 \div (-3)$ 　　　　**b.** $-44 \div (-4)$ 　　　　**c.** $-\dfrac{8}{27} \div \left(-\dfrac{16}{45}\right)$

d. $-8\dfrac{3}{4} \div \left(-2\dfrac{1}{12}\right)$ 　　　**e.** $-3.2 \div (-0.16)$

SOLUTION STRATEGY

a. $-18 \div (-3)$

$|-18| = 18, |-3| = 3$ 　　　　　Determine the absolute values of the dividend and divisor.

$18 \div 3 = 6$ 　　　　　　　　Divide the absolute values.

$-18 \div (-3) = 6$ 　　　　　　Since the dividend and divisor are negative, the quotient is positive.

b. $-44 \div (-4)$

$|-44| = 44, |-4| = 4$ 　　　　　Determine the absolute values of the dividend and divisor.

$44 \div 4 = 11$ 　　　　　　　　Divide the absolute values.

$-44 \div (-4) = 11$ 　　　　　　Since the dividend and divisor are negative, the quotient is positive.

c. $-\dfrac{8}{27} \div \left(-\dfrac{16}{45}\right)$

$\left|-\dfrac{8}{27}\right| = \dfrac{8}{27}, \left|-\dfrac{16}{45}\right| = \dfrac{16}{45}$ 　　Determine the absolute values of the dividend and divisor.

$\dfrac{8}{27} \div \dfrac{16}{45} = \dfrac{\overset{1}{\cancel{8}}}{\underset{3}{\cancel{27}}} \cdot \dfrac{\overset{5}{\cancel{45}}}{\underset{2}{\cancel{16}}} = \dfrac{5}{6}$ 　　Divide the absolute values.

$-\dfrac{8}{27} \div \left(-\dfrac{16}{45}\right) = \dfrac{5}{6}$ 　　Since the dividend and divisor are negative, the quotient is positive.

d. $-8\dfrac{3}{4} \div \left(-2\dfrac{1}{12}\right)$

$\left|-8\dfrac{3}{4}\right| = 8\dfrac{3}{4}, \left|-2\dfrac{1}{12}\right| = 2\dfrac{1}{12}$ 　　Determine the absolute value of the dividend and divisor.

$8\dfrac{3}{4} \div \left(2\dfrac{1}{12}\right) = \dfrac{35}{4} \cdot \dfrac{12}{25}$ 　　Divide the absolute values.

$\qquad = \dfrac{\overset{7}{\cancel{35}}}{\underset{1}{\cancel{4}}} \cdot \dfrac{\overset{3}{\cancel{12}}}{\underset{5}{\cancel{25}}}$

$\qquad = \dfrac{21}{5} = 4\dfrac{1}{5}$

$-8\dfrac{3}{4} \div \left(-2\dfrac{1}{12}\right) = 4\dfrac{1}{5}$ 　　Since the dividend and divisor are negative, the quotient is positive.

e. $-3.2 \div (-0.16)$

$|-3.2| = 3.2, |-0.16| = 0.16$ Determine the absolute value of the dividend and divisor.

$0.16\overline{)3.20}$ Divide the absolute values.

$\dfrac{20}{16\overline{)320}}$

$-3.2 \div (-0.16) = 20$ Since the dividend and divisor are negative, the quotient is positive.

TRY-IT EXERCISE 5

Divide.

a. $-48 \div (-12)$ **b.** $-54 \div (-6)$ **c.** $-\dfrac{4}{21} \div \left(-\dfrac{8}{3}\right)$

d. $-1\dfrac{1}{5} \div \left(-2\dfrac{3}{10}\right)$ **e.** $-7.2 \div (-0.08)$

Check your answers with the solutions in Appendix A. ■

Objective 9.4C   Apply your knowledge

EXAMPLE 6   Apply your knowledge

In a particular quarter, United Airlines reported earnings of $-\$495$ million. If this trend were to continue for the next two quarters, how much more money would the airline lose?

SOLUTION STRATEGY

$-\$495 \cdot 2$ Multiply $-\$495$ by 2.

$|-\$495| = \$495, |2| = 2$ Determine the absolute values of the dividend and divisor.

$\$495 \cdot 2 = \$990$ Multiply the absolute values.

$-\$990$ Since the factors have different signs, attach a negative sign to the result.

The airline would lose an additional $990 million.   The negative result indicates that the airline would lose more money.

TRY-IT EXERCISE 6

A college's enrollment recently decreased by 2400 students. If this trend continues for the next three semesters, how many more students will the college lose?

Check your answers with the solutions in Appendix A. ■

SECTION 9.4 REVIEW EXERCISES

Concept Check

1. The product or quotient of two numbers with different signs is always _____ .

2. The product or quotient of two numbers with the same sign is always _____ .

Objective 9.4A   **Multiply signed numbers**

GUIDE PROBLEMS

3. Multiply $-7 \cdot 12$.

    a. Determine the absolute value of each factor.

    $|-7| =$ __, $|12| =$ ___

    b. Multiply the absolute values.

    $7 \cdot$ ___ $=$ ___

    c. Since the factors have different signs, the product is negative. Attach a negative sign to the result of part b.

    $-7 \cdot 12 =$ ____

4. Multiply $-8 \cdot (-1.1)$.

    a. Determine the absolute value of each factor.

    $|-8| =$ __, $|-1.1| =$ ___

    b. Multiply the absolute values.

    $8 \cdot$ ___ $=$ ___

    c. Since the factors have the same sign, the product is positive.

    $-8 \cdot (-1.1) =$ ___

5. Multiply $-\dfrac{12}{25} \cdot \dfrac{5}{32}$. Simplify, if possible.

    a. Determine the absolute value of each factor.

    $\left|-\dfrac{12}{25}\right| =$ ___, $\left|\dfrac{5}{32}\right| =$ ___

    b. Multiply the absolute values.

    $\dfrac{12}{25} \cdot$ ___ $=$ ___

    c. Since the factors have different signs, the product is negative. Attach a negative sign to the result of part b.

    $-\dfrac{12}{25} \cdot \dfrac{5}{32} =$ ___

6. Multiply $-6\dfrac{2}{3} \cdot \left(-1\dfrac{1}{5}\right)$. Simplify, if possible.

    a. Determine the absolute value of each factor.

    $\left|-6\dfrac{2}{3}\right| =$ ___, $\left|-1\dfrac{1}{5}\right| =$ ___

    b. Multiply the absolute values.

    $6\dfrac{2}{3} \cdot$ ___ $= \dfrac{20}{3} \cdot$ ___ $=$ ___

    c. Since the factors have the same sign, the product is positive.

    $-6\dfrac{2}{3} \cdot \left(-1\dfrac{1}{5}\right) =$ ___

Multiply. Simplify, if possible.

7. $6 \cdot 4$

8. $4 \cdot 12$

9. $-3 \cdot 9$

10. $-6 \cdot 10$

11. $5 \cdot (-20)$

12. $6 \cdot (-13)$

13. $-11 \cdot (-12)$

14. $-15 \cdot (-12)$

15. $128 \cdot (-4)$

16. $201 \cdot (-5)$

17. $-103 \cdot (-7)$

18. $-141 \cdot (-8)$

19. $11 \cdot (-312)$

20. $15 \cdot (-407)$

21. $-13 \cdot (-514)$

22. $-28 \cdot (-182)$

23. $\frac{3}{6} \cdot \left(-\frac{4}{11}\right)$

24. $-\frac{4}{9} \cdot \frac{6}{13}$

25. $-\frac{5}{4} \cdot \left(-\frac{2}{7}\right)$

26. $-\frac{3}{8} \cdot \left(-\frac{4}{5}\right)$

27. $-\frac{4}{9} \cdot \frac{5}{12}$

28. $\frac{7}{12} \cdot \left(-\frac{3}{5}\right)$

29. $-\frac{2}{5} \cdot \left(-\frac{5}{8}\right)$

30. $\frac{4}{3} \cdot \frac{3}{8}$

31. $\frac{5}{12} \cdot \frac{9}{10}$

32. $-\frac{4}{9} \cdot \left(-\frac{3}{16}\right)$

33. $-\frac{5}{21} \cdot \frac{14}{25}$

34. $\frac{5}{24} \left(-\frac{18}{25}\right)$

35. $-7\frac{1}{2} \cdot 3\frac{1}{5}$

36. $3\frac{1}{3} \cdot \left(-5\frac{1}{4}\right)$

37. $-3\frac{4}{5} \cdot \left(-3\frac{3}{4}\right)$

38. $-3\frac{3}{11} \cdot \left(-2\frac{1}{5}\right)$

39. $\frac{1}{7} \cdot 2$

40. $-\frac{2}{11} \cdot (-5)$

41. $-4 \cdot \frac{5}{8}$

42. $2\frac{3}{13} \cdot (-3)$

43. $6.1 \cdot 34$

44. $7.9 \cdot 0.61$

45. $10.2 \cdot (-1.8)$

46. $410 \cdot (-0.25)$

47. $-0.13 \cdot 0.018$

48. $-0.15 \cdot 0.23$

49. $2.7 \cdot (-0.51)$

50. $3.1 \cdot (-0.72)$

51. $-49 \cdot 12$

52. $-51 \cdot 14$

53. $72 \cdot (-218)$

54. $46 \cdot (-349)$

55. $11 \cdot 10 \cdot (-2)$

56. $12 \cdot (-3) \cdot (10)$

57. $24 \cdot (-3) \cdot (-2)$

58. $18 \cdot (-6) \cdot (-9)$

59. $2 \cdot (-45) \cdot 18$

60. $-5 \cdot 14 \cdot 20$

61. $-\frac{6}{7} \cdot \frac{1}{3} \cdot \frac{3}{14}$

62. $\frac{21}{5}\left(-\frac{5}{4}\right)\left(-\frac{4}{21}\right)$

63. $-3\frac{1}{2}\left(-3\frac{3}{4}\right)\left(-\frac{1}{5}\right)$

64. $\left(-4\frac{1}{3}\right)(-2)\left(-3\frac{1}{2}\right)$

65. $-2.3(-3.1)(0.2)$

66. $5.1(-0.3)(2.2)$

| **Objective 9.4B** | **Divide signed numbers** |

GUIDE PROBLEMS

67. Divide $-56 \div 8$.

   a. Determine the absolute values of the dividend and divisor.

      $|-56| = \underline{\hspace{1em}}, |8| = \underline{\hspace{1em}}$

   b. Divide the absolute values.

      $56 \div \underline{\hspace{1em}} = \underline{\hspace{1em}}$

   c. Since the dividend and divisor have different signs, the quotient is negative. Attach a negative sign to the result of part b.

      $-56 \div 8 = \underline{\hspace{2em}}$

68. Divide $-1.08 \div (-0.9)$.

   a. Determine the absolute values of the dividend and divisor.

      $|-1.08| = \underline{\hspace{1em}}, |-0.9| = \underline{\hspace{1em}}$

   b. Divide the absolute values.

      $0.9\overline{)\underline{\hspace{2em}}}$ $9\overline{)\overline{\underline{\hspace{2em}}}}$

   c. Since the dividend and divisor have the same sign, the quotient is positive.

      $-1.08 \div (-0.9) = \underline{\hspace{1em}}$

69. Divide $-\dfrac{3}{8} \div \left(-\dfrac{9}{4}\right)$. Simplify, if possible.

   a. Determine the absolute values of the dividend and divisor.

      $\left|-\dfrac{3}{8}\right| = \underline{\hspace{1em}}, \left|-\dfrac{9}{4}\right| = \underline{\hspace{1em}}$

   b. Divide the absolute values.

      $\dfrac{3}{8} \div \underline{\hspace{1em}} = \dfrac{3}{8} \cdot \underline{\hspace{1em}} = \underline{\hspace{1em}}$

   c. Since the dividend and divisor have the same sign, the quotient is positive.

      $-\dfrac{3}{8} \div \left(-\dfrac{9}{4}\right) = \underline{\hspace{1em}}$

70. Divide $-1\dfrac{3}{7} \div 2\dfrac{4}{5}$. Simplify, if possible.

   a. Determine the absolute values of the dividend and divisor.

      $\left|-1\dfrac{3}{7}\right| = \underline{\hspace{1em}}, \left|2\dfrac{4}{5}\right| = \underline{\hspace{1em}}$

   b. Divide the absolute values.

      $1\dfrac{3}{7} \div \underline{\hspace{1em}} = \dfrac{10}{7} \div \underline{\hspace{1em}} = \dfrac{10}{7} \cdot \underline{\hspace{1em}} = \underline{\hspace{1em}}$

   c. Since the dividend and divisor have different signs, the quotient is negative. Attach a negative sign to the result of part b.

      $-1\dfrac{3}{7} \div 2\dfrac{4}{5} = \underline{\hspace{2em}}$

Divide. Simplify, if possible.

71. $12 \div 4$

72. $-15 \div 5$

73. $21 \div 3$

74. $-32 \div 4$

75. $49 \div (-7)$

76. $56 \div (-8)$

77. $-81 \div (-9)$

78. $-63 \div (-9)$

79. $132 \div (-4)$

80. $213 \div (-3)$

81. $-135 \div 9$

82. $-126 \div 7$

83. $266 \div (-14)$

84. $-630 \div (-18)$

85. $273 \div (-21)$

86. $-495 \div (-45)$

87. $\dfrac{2}{3} \div \left(-\dfrac{2}{7}\right)$

88. $-\dfrac{1}{3} \div \left(-\dfrac{2}{3}\right)$

89. $-\dfrac{7}{14} \div \dfrac{1}{7}$

90. $-\dfrac{4}{7} \div \left(-\dfrac{8}{11}\right)$

91. $\dfrac{3}{4} \div \left(-\dfrac{1}{8}\right)$

92. $-\dfrac{8}{9} \div \left(-\dfrac{4}{5}\right)$

93. $-\dfrac{1}{10} \div \dfrac{6}{11}$

94. $\dfrac{1}{4} \div \left(-\dfrac{5}{9}\right)$

95. $-\dfrac{2}{3} \div 2\dfrac{1}{3}$

96. $2 \div \left(-3\dfrac{1}{6}\right)$

97. $-5\dfrac{3}{4} \div \left(-1\dfrac{1}{2}\right)$

98. $-5\dfrac{3}{8} \div \left(-2\dfrac{3}{4}\right)$

99. $2\dfrac{2}{3} \div \left(-3\dfrac{1}{2}\right)$

100. $-36\dfrac{2}{3} \div \left(3\dfrac{2}{3}\right)$

101. $-51 \div 1\dfrac{1}{2}$

102. $49 \div \left(-1\dfrac{3}{4}\right)$

103. $\dfrac{-2.2}{-50}$

104. $\dfrac{-6.586}{7.4}$

105. $\dfrac{-4.69}{-67}$

106. $\dfrac{15.18}{-0.69}$

107. $36.668 \div (-4.12)$

108. $89.27 \div (-11.3)$

109. $-1.786 \div 89.3$

110. $-6.885 \div 76.5$

111. $-67.95 \div (-1.5)$

112. $-195.25 \div (-2.5)$

113. $643.786 \div (-45.02)$

114. $1067.781 \div (-51.09)$

Objective 9.4C   **Apply your knowledge**

115. In 2005, General Motors posted a net loss of $10.6 billion. If this trend were to continue for the next 3 years, how much more money would General Motors lose?

116. The stock market changed −18 points in 3 days. Find the average daily change.

117. Suppose that you purchased 75 bonds at a price of $12 per bond. The following month, you sold each bond for $15. How much money did you make on the investment?

118. The temperature outside is dropping at a constant rate. If the temperature is 80°F at 5:00 PM and drops to 59°F by 8:00 PM, by how many degrees did the temperature change each hour?

CUMULATIVE SKILLS REVIEW

1. Express 288 students for 24 pecan pies as a unit rate. (4.2B)

2. Dana purchased a new iPod for $375. The sales tax rate is 7%. What is the amount of the sales tax? (5.4B)

3. Convert 12.5 years to months. (6.3C)

4. What is the mean of the set of numbers 12, 23, 57, 8, and 42? (8.2B)

5. Find the volume of the rectangular solid. (7.6A)

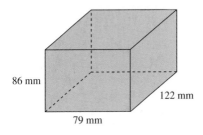

86 mm   122 mm   79 mm

6. Find the perimeter of the triangle. (7.3A)

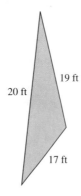

19 ft   20 ft   17 ft

7. Add $-25 + (-33)$. (9.2A)

8. Add $-8.3 + 7.4$. (9.2B)

9. Subtract $-55 - 7$. (9.3A)

10. Subtract $23 - 49$. (9.3A)

9.5 SIGNED NUMBERS AND ORDER OF OPERATIONS

LEARNING OBJECTIVES

A. Simplify an expression containing signed numbers

B. Apply your knowledge

Objective 9.5A   **Simplify an expression containing signed numbers**

This section serves as a review of order of operations. Once again, here are the rules for order of operations.

> **Order of Operations**
>
> **Step 1.** Perform all operations within grouping symbols: parentheses ( ), brackets [ ], curly braces { }, and fraction bars. When grouping symbols occur within grouping symbols, begin with the innermost grouping symbols.
>
> **Step 2.** Evaluate all exponential expressions.
>
> **Step 3.** Perform all multiplications and divisions as they appear in reading from left to right.
>
> **Step 5.** Perform all additions and subtractions as they appear in reading from left to right.

The following examples demonstrate how to apply the rules for order of operations to simplify expressions with signed numbers.

EXAMPLE 1 **Simplify an expression**

Simplify each expression.

a. $2 - (-5) \cdot 6$ **b.** $16 \div 4 - (-3) \cdot 2$

c. $-\dfrac{1}{7} \div \dfrac{2}{35} - \dfrac{1}{3} \cdot \dfrac{1}{4}$ **d.** $3.72 \div (-0.4) + 3(-0.05)$

SOLUTION STRATEGY

a. $2 - (-5) \cdot 6$

    $2 - (-30)$ Multiply $-5 \cdot 6$.

    $2 + 30$ Write subtraction as addition of the opposite.

    32 Add.

b. $16 \div 4 - (-3) \cdot 2$

    $4 - (-6)$ Divide $16 \div 4$. Multiply $-3 \cdot 2$.

    $4 + 6$ Write subtraction as addition of the opposite.

    10 Add.

c. $-\dfrac{1}{7} \div \dfrac{2}{35} - \dfrac{1}{3} \cdot \dfrac{1}{4}$

    $-\dfrac{1}{7} \cdot \dfrac{35}{2} - \dfrac{1}{3} \cdot \dfrac{1}{4}$ Multiply $-\dfrac{1}{7}$ by $\dfrac{35}{2}$, the reciprocal of $\dfrac{2}{35}$.

    $-\dfrac{5}{2} - \dfrac{1}{12}$ Multiply $-\dfrac{1}{7} \cdot \dfrac{35}{2}$ and $\dfrac{1}{3} \cdot \dfrac{1}{4}$.

    $-\dfrac{30}{12} - \dfrac{1}{12}$ Write equivalent fractions with the LCD, 12.

    $-\dfrac{30}{12} + \left(-\dfrac{1}{12}\right)$ Write subtraction as addition of the opposite.

    $-\dfrac{31}{12}$ Add.

d. $3.72 \div (-0.4) + 3(-0.05)$

    $-9.3 + (-0.15)$ Divide $3.72 \div (-0.4)$. Multiply $3(-0.05)$.

    -9.45 Add.

TRY-IT EXERCISE 1

Simplify each expression.

a. $7 - (-2) \cdot 4$ **b.** $20 \div 5 + 5 \cdot 3$

c. $\dfrac{2}{3} \div \left(-\dfrac{1}{9}\right) - \dfrac{1}{5} \cdot 2$ **d.** $-2.6(5.1 - 3.2) \div (-0.8)$

Check your answers with the solutions in Appendix A. ∎

We must exercise care when working with exponents and signed numbers. For example, consider $(-5)^2$. Here, we are squaring -5, that is, we are multiplying -5 by itself.

$$(-5)^2 = (-5)(-5) = 25$$

Note that we get a positive result.

Now let's consider -5^2. Note that -5 is not in parentheses, and so this problem is different from the previous one. In this example, we are squaring 5 and then taking the negative of the result, that is, we multiply 5 by itself and then take its negative.

$$-5^2 = -(5 \cdot 5) = -25$$

EXAMPLE 2   **Simplify an expression with exponents**

Simplify each expression.

a. $2^2 + (-3)^2 + (-4)$ **b.** $\left(-\dfrac{1}{2}\right)^4 + \left(\dfrac{1}{2}\right)^3 \div \left(-\dfrac{1}{7}\right)$ **c.** $(-0.3)^2 + 0.2(-9)$

SOLUTION STRATEGY

a. $2^2 + (-3)^2 + (-4)$

$\quad 4 + 9 + (-4)$ Evaluate 2^2. Evaluate $(-3)^2$.

$\quad 9$ Add.

b. $\left(-\dfrac{1}{2}\right)^4 + \left(\dfrac{1}{2}\right)^3 \div \left(-\dfrac{1}{7}\right)$

$\quad \dfrac{1}{16} + \dfrac{1}{8} \div \left(-\dfrac{1}{7}\right)$ Evaluate $\left(-\dfrac{1}{2}\right)^4$. Evaluate $\left(\dfrac{1}{2}\right)^3$.

$\quad \dfrac{1}{16} + \dfrac{1}{8}\left(-\dfrac{7}{1}\right)$ Multiply $\dfrac{1}{8}$ by $-\dfrac{7}{1}$, the reciprocal of $-\dfrac{1}{7}$.

$\quad \dfrac{1}{16} + \left(-\dfrac{7}{8}\right)$

$\quad \dfrac{1}{16} + \left(-\dfrac{14}{16}\right)$ Write equivalent fractions with the LCD, 16.

$\quad -\dfrac{13}{16}$ Add.

c. $(-0.3)^2 + 0.2(-9)$

$\quad 0.09 + 0.2(-9)$ Evaluate $(-0.3)^2$.

$\quad 0.09 + (-1.8)$ Multiply $0.2(-9)$.

$\quad -1.71$ Add.

TRY-IT EXERCISE 2

Simplify each expression.

a. $4^3 + 12 \cdot (-4) + 6$ **b.** $\left(-\dfrac{1}{5}\right)^2 + \left(\dfrac{2}{5}\right)^2 \div \left(\dfrac{2}{3}\right)^2$ **c.** $(-0.5)^3 \div 0.04 + 1.46$

Check your answers with the solutions in Appendix A. ∎

EXAMPLE 3   Simplify an expression with parentheses

Simplify each expression.

a. $(8 + 2 \cdot 3) - (-4)^2$ **b.** $\left[\dfrac{1}{2} + \left(\dfrac{5}{2}\right)^2\right] \div \dfrac{9}{2}$ **c.** $(1.4 - 0.2^3)^2 + 5(-0.6)$

SOLUTION STRATEGY

a. $(8 + 2 \cdot 3) - (-4)^2$

$(8 + 6) - (-4)^2$ Multiply $2 \cdot 3$ inside the parentheses.

$14 - (-4)^2$ Add $8 + 6$ inside the parentheses.

$14 - 16$ Simplify $(-4)^2$.

-2 Subtract.

b. $\left[\dfrac{1}{2} + \left(\dfrac{5}{2}\right)^2\right] \div \dfrac{9}{2}$

$\left[\dfrac{1}{2} + \dfrac{25}{4}\right] \div \dfrac{9}{2}$ Evaluate $\left(\dfrac{5}{2}\right)^2$ inside the brackets.

$\left[\dfrac{2}{4} + \dfrac{25}{4}\right] \div \dfrac{9}{2}$ Write equivalent fractions inside the brackets with the LCD, 4.

$\dfrac{27}{4} \div \dfrac{9}{2}$ Add $\dfrac{2}{4} + \dfrac{25}{4}$.

$\dfrac{27}{4} \cdot \dfrac{2}{9}$ Multiply $\dfrac{27}{4}$ by $\dfrac{2}{9}$, the reciprocal of $\dfrac{9}{2}$.

$\dfrac{\overset{3}{27}}{\underset{2}{4}} \cdot \dfrac{1}{9}$ Divide out common factors.

$\dfrac{3}{2}$ or $1\dfrac{1}{2}$ Multiply.

c. $(1.4 - 0.2^3) + 5(-0.6)$

$(1.4 - 0.008) + 5(-0.6)$ Evaluate 0.2^3 inside the parentheses.

$1.392 + 5(-0.6)$ Subtract $1.4 - 0.008$ inside the parentheses.

$1.392 + (-3.0)$ Multiply $5(-0.6)$.

-1.608 Add.

TRY-IT EXERCISE 3

Simplify each expression.

a. $8 + [6 + 2 \cdot (-3)] - 2^3$ **b.** $\left[-\dfrac{1}{4} \div \left(\dfrac{2}{3}\right)^2\right] \div \left(\dfrac{1}{2}\right)^4$ **c.** $(3.4 - 5.6)^2 + 3(-0.1)^2$

Check your answers with the solutions in Appendix A. ■

EXAMPLE 4   **Simplify an expression with a fraction bar**

Simplify $2^2 + \dfrac{15 - 2^3}{(-2)^2 + 3} + 1$.

SOLUTION STRATEGY

$2^2 + \dfrac{15 - 2^3}{(-2)^2 + 3} + 1$ Recall that a fraction bar acts as a grouping symbol.

$2^2 + \dfrac{15 - 8}{4 + 3} + 1$ Evaluate 2^3. Evaluate $(-2)^2$.

$2^2 + \dfrac{7}{7} + 1$ Subtract $15 - 8$ in the numerator. Add $4 + 3$ in the denominator.

$4 + \dfrac{7}{7} + 1$ Evaluate 2^2.

$4 + 1 + 1$ Divide $\dfrac{7}{7}$.

6 Add.

TRY-IT EXERCISE 4

Simplify $\dfrac{14 - 3^2}{5^2} + \left(\dfrac{1}{2}\right)^2$.

Check your answer with the solution in Appendix A. ■

Objective 9.5B   **Apply your knowledge**

EXAMPLE 5   **Write and evaluate an expression in an application problem**

In golf, scores are expressed in terms of *par*, the number of skillful strokes established for any hole. A *birdie* is one stroke under par, an *eagle* is two strokes under par, and a *bogie* is one stroke over par.

Chad played 9 holes of golf. He had three birdies, two eagles, and par, and three bogies.

a. Write an expression that represents how far over or under par Chad was for his golf game.

b. Evaluate the expression in part a.

SOLUTION STRATEGY

a. $3(-1) + 2(-2) + 1(0) + 3(1)$ Represent a birdie (one stroke under par) by -1, an eagle (two strokes under par) by -2, a par by 0, and a bogie (one stroke over par) by 1.

b. $3(-1) + 2(-2) + 1(0) + 3(1)$

$-3 + (-4) + 0 + 3$ Multiply.

-4 Add.

TRY-IT EXERCISE 5

Karen played 18 holes of golf. She had four birdies, three eagles, six pars, and five bogies.

a. Write an expression that represents how far over or under par Karen was for her golf game.

b. Evaluate the expression in part a.

Check your answers with the solutions in Appendix A. ■

SECTION 9.5 REVIEW EXERCISES

Concept Check

1. When applying the rules for order of operations, we perform all operations within _____ _____ first.

2. Next, we evaluate expressions with _____.

3. Then, we perform all _____ and _____ as they occur from left to right.

4. Finally, we perform all _____ and _____ as they occur from left to right.

Objective 9.5A   Simplify expressions containing signed numbers

GUIDE PROBLEMS

5. Simplify $7 + 2^4 \cdot 5$ using order of operations.

$7 + 2^4 \cdot 5 = 7 + \underline{\quad} \cdot 5$

$= 7 + \underline{\quad}$

$= \underline{\quad}$

6. Simplify $5^3 - (4 + 3 \cdot 2)^2 \div 4$ using order of operations.

$5^3 - (4 + 3 \cdot 2)^2 \div 4 = 5^3 - (4 + \underline{\quad})^2 \div 4$

$= 5^3 - (\underline{\quad})^2 \div 4$

$= \underline{\quad} - \underline{\quad} \div 4$

$= \underline{\quad} - \underline{\quad}$

$= \underline{\quad}$

Simplify each expression using order of operations.

7. $6 + 5 + (-4)$

8. $12 + (-8) + 4$

9. $8 - 2 \cdot (-3) - 4$

10. $9 - 4 \times (-2) + 5$

11. $8 \div 4 + (-3)(-5)$

12. $42 \div 7 - 2(-4)$

13. $-18 \div 2 + (-5) \cdot 4 + (-3)$

14. $-15 \div 5 + (-9) \cdot 3 + (-12)$

15. $-5 \cdot 2^2 \cdot 3^2$

16. $2^2 \cdot (-2) \cdot 4^2$

17. $(-8)^2 + 5 - 12$

18. $(-7)^2 + 21 - 8$

19. $6 + (-2)^4 \cdot 7$

20. $8 + (-6)^2 - 30$

21. $(7^2 - 9) \div (-5)$

22. $(2^5 - 12) \div (-4)$

23. $-6 - (-3)^2 - (-4)$

24. $-12 - (4)^2 + (-3)^2$

25. $(36 + 4) \div (20 \div 4)$

26. $(41 + 7) \div (16 \div 2)$

27. $-3 + [2 \cdot 3 + (-4)]^2 \div 4$

28. $[9^2 - 5 \cdot 12 + 9] \div (-3)$

29. $12^2 - (4 \cdot 5^2 - 20) \div 2^3$

30. $10^2 - (4^2 + 8 \cdot 9) \div 2^2$

31. $(8 - 4)^2 \div [3^2 + (-5)]$

32. $(8 + 4)^2 \div [(-3)^2 - 7]$

33. $2 + (7 - 5)^2 \cdot (5^2 - 13)$

34. $12 + (4 - 5)^2 \cdot (12 - 3^2)$

35. $-\dfrac{3}{8} - \dfrac{1}{4}\left(-\dfrac{1}{3}\right)$

36. $-\dfrac{2}{5} \div \dfrac{6}{25} + \dfrac{2}{3}\left(\dfrac{1}{10}\right)$

37. $-\dfrac{5}{27} - \left(-\dfrac{2}{3}\right)^2$

38. $\left(-\dfrac{1}{3}\right)^2 + \left(-\dfrac{1}{2}\right) \div \dfrac{3}{16}$

39. $2^2 + \left[-\dfrac{2}{3} \div \left(\dfrac{1}{2}\right)^2\right] \cdot \dfrac{3}{4}$

40. $(-2)^3 - \left[\dfrac{1}{3} + \dfrac{5}{6}\left(\dfrac{2}{15}\right)\right] \div \dfrac{1}{9}$

41. $4.21(-0.3) + 4(-0.06)$

42. $0.31(6.4 - 2.5) \div (-0.4)$

43. $(-0.5)^2 + 0.3(-8)$

44. $0.8 + (0.6)^2(-4)$

45. $-(1.5 + 0.1^2)^2 - 4(-0.2)^2$

46. $(-8.6 + 7.5)^3 - 3(0.4)^3$

47. $196 \div 2[10 + (4 - 2)^2] - (-5)^2$

48. $180 \div 3[(5 - 3)^3 - (-4)] - 4^3$

49. $6 + \dfrac{16 - 2^3}{(-2)^2 + 4} - 2$

50. $12 + \dfrac{32 - 4^2}{4^2 - 2^3} - 5$

51. $4^3 + \left(\dfrac{5^2 - 15}{3^2 - 4}\right)^2 - 14$

52. $7^2 + \left(\dfrac{6^2 - 2^4}{4^2 - 6}\right)^2 - 21$

Objective 9.5B   Apply your knowledge

53. Dom played 9 holes of golf. He had three birdies, three eagles, two pars, and one bogie.

 a. Write an expression that represents how far over or under par Dom was for his golf game.

 b. Evaluate the expression in part a.

54. Nancy played 18 holes of golf. She had two eagles, six pars, six bogies, and twice as many birdies as eagles.

 a. Write an expression that represents how far over or under par Nancy was for her golf game.

 b. Evaluate the expression in part a.

55. Physicists have determined that, after t seconds, the location of an object launched upward from a particular point with a speed of 80-feet-per-second is given by the expression $-16(t)^2 + 80(t)$. How far above or below that point will the object be after 4 seconds?

56. In aviation, air temperature decreases 3°F for every 1000 foot increase in altitude. If the average air temperature is 59°F at sea level, what is the average air temperature at 10,000 feet? What is the average air temperature at 20,000 feet?

CUMULATIVE SKILLS REVIEW

1. Divide $(-36) \div 6$. (9.4B)

2. Convert 22.5 miles to feet. (6.1A)

3. Use $<$ or $>$ to write a true statement for the decimals 78.322 and 78.32. (3.1B)

4. Simplify $(6 + 3 \cdot 8) - 2^2$. (9.5A)

5. Write a reduced rate for 24 bottles for every 4 cases of water. (4.1A)

6. Home prices have skyrocketed in the past few years. According to some reports, home prices have increased by 20% in the past two years. Write the percent increase of home prices in decimal form. (5.1C)

7. Add $24 + (-9)$. (9.3A)

8. Round 1417.7877 to the nearest tenth. (3.1C)

9. Find the volume of the rectangular solid. (7.6A)

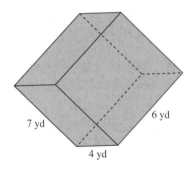

7 yd   6 yd   4 yd

10. Classify the triangle as equilateral, isosceles, or scalene; and as acute, right, or obtuse. (7.1D)

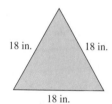

18 in.   18 in.   18 in.

10-MINUTE CHAPTER REVIEW

9.1 Introduction to Signed Numbers

Objective	Important Concepts	Illustrative Examples
A. Find the opposite of a number (page 636)	**positive number** A number that is greater than 0. **negative number** A number that is less than 0. **origin** The number 0 on a number line. **signed number** A number that is either positive or negative. **opposites** Two numbers that lie the same distance from the origin on opposite sides of the origin.	Find the opposite of each number. **a.** 7 The opposite of 7 is -7. **b.** 18 The opposite of 18 is -18. **c.** -32 The opposite of -32 is 32. **d.** 11 The opposite of 11 is -11. **e.** -4 The opposite of -4 is 4.
B. Graph a signed number on a number line (page 637)	**integers** The whole numbers together with the opposites of the positive whole numbers, that is, the numbers $\ldots -3, -2, -1, 0, 1, 2, 3, \ldots$. **rational number** A number that can be written in the form $\dfrac{a}{b}$, where a and b are integers and $b \neq 0$.	Graph each signed number. $$-5, 2, -3.5, \frac{3}{4}, 5\frac{1}{2}$$
C. Find the absolute value of a number (page 639)	**absolute value of a number** The distance between the number and 0 on the number line. **Properties of the Absolute Value of a Number** The absolute value of a positive number is the number itself. The absolute value of a negative number is the opposite of the number. The absolute value of 0 is 0.	Evaluate. **a.** $\lvert 95 \rvert = 95$ **b.** $\lvert -8 \rvert = 8$ **c.** $\lvert 5.6 \rvert = 5.6$ **d.** $\left\lvert -\dfrac{9}{11} \right\rvert = \dfrac{9}{11}$
D. Compare signed numbers (page 641)	On a number line, a number to the left is *less than* a number to the right, and a number to the right is *greater than* a number to the left. The less than symbol ($<$) represents "less than," and the greater than symbol ($>$) represents "greater than."	Compare the signed numbers. **a.** -4 and 4 $-4 < 4$ and $4 > -4$

b. 2 and −3

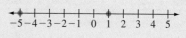

$2 > -3$ and $-3 < 2$

c. −5 and 1

$-5 < 1$ and $1 > -5$

E. Apply your knowledge (page 642)	Median home prices in Miami for the first quarters of 2004 and 2005 increased 28.4%. Express the percent increase as a signed number.	

$+28.4\%$ or 28.4%

Jaime started a weight-loss program. He currently weighs 192 pounds. He expects to lose 22 pounds after six months. Express this weight loss as a signed number.

-22 pounds

In 2004, the average price for a movie ticket in the United States was $6.21. The average price for a movie ticket in 1984 was $2.85 lower, or $3.36. Express each quantity as a signed number.

$6.21, $−$2.85, 3.36

9.2 Adding Signed Numbers

Topic	Important Concepts	Illustrative Examples
A. Add numbers with the same sign (page 647)	**Steps for Adding Numbers with the Same Sign** **Step 1.** Determine the absolute values of each addend. **Step 2.** Add the absolute values of the addends. **Step 3.** Attach the common sign of the addends to the sum of step 2.	Add. Simplify, if possible. **a.** $-\dfrac{1}{2} + \left(-\dfrac{2}{3}\right)$ $\left\|-\dfrac{1}{2}\right\| = \dfrac{1}{2},\ \left\|-\dfrac{2}{3}\right\| = \dfrac{2}{3}$ $\dfrac{1}{2} + \dfrac{2}{3} = \dfrac{3}{6} + \dfrac{4}{6} = \dfrac{7}{6} = 1\dfrac{1}{6}$ $-\dfrac{1}{2} + \left(-\dfrac{2}{3}\right) = -1\dfrac{1}{6}$ **b.** $-1.03 + (-9.1)$ $\|-1.03\| = 1.03,\ \|-9.1\| = 9.1$ $1.03 + 9.1 = 10.13$ $-1.03 + (-9.1) = -10.13$
B. Add numbers with different signs (page 650)	**Steps for Adding Signed Numbers with Different Signs** **Step 1.** Determine the absolute values of each addend. **Step 2.** Subtract the smaller absolute value from the larger.	Add. Simplify, if possible. **a.** $3.7 + (-1.2)$ $\|3.7\| = 3.7,\ \|-1.2\| = 1.2$ $3.7 - 1.2 = 2.5$ $3.7 + (-1.2) = 2.5$

Step 3. Attach the sign of the addend having the larger absolute value to the difference of step 2. If the absolute values are equal, then the sum is 0.

b. $-\dfrac{4}{5} + \dfrac{1}{3}$

$$\left|-\dfrac{4}{5}\right| = \dfrac{4}{5}, \; \left|\dfrac{1}{3}\right| = \dfrac{1}{3}$$

LCD = 15

$$\dfrac{4}{5} = \dfrac{12}{15}, \; \dfrac{1}{3} = \dfrac{5}{15}$$

$$\dfrac{12}{15} - \dfrac{5}{15} = \dfrac{7}{15}$$

$$-\dfrac{4}{5} + \dfrac{1}{3} = -\dfrac{7}{15}$$

C. Apply your knowledge (page 653)

Charlie has been with Technology Developers Corporation for one year and just received a raise of $3000. He has also received a bonus of $1000 of which $300 will go toward taxes.

a. If Charlie's salary was $61,000 per year, what is his new salary?

$61,000 + $3000 = $64,000

b. What portion of the bonus does Charlie get to keep after paying taxes?

$1000 + (−$300) = $700

c. What is Charlie's total income expected to be this year with the new raise and bonus?

$64,000 + $700 = $64,700

9.3 Subtracting Signed Numbers

Topic	Important Concepts	Illustrative Examples
A. Subtract signed numbers (page 658)	**Steps for Subtracting Signed Numbers** **Step 1.** Write the subtraction problem as an addition problem by adding the first number to the opposite of the second number. **Step 2.** Add using the steps in Section 9.2, Adding Signed Numbers.	Subtract. Simplify, if possible. **a.** $5 - 16$ $5 + (-16)$ $\|5\| = 5, \|-16\| = 16$ $16 - 5 = 11$ $5 - 16 = -11$ **b.** $-3.01 - 5.4$ $-3.01 + (-5.4)$ $\|-3.01\| = 3.01, \|-5.4\| = 5.4$ $5.4 + 3.01 = 8.41$ $-3.01 - 5.4 = -8.41$ **c.** $\dfrac{2}{5} - \left(-\dfrac{3}{10}\right)$ $\dfrac{2}{5} + \dfrac{3}{10} = \dfrac{4}{10} + \dfrac{3}{10} = \dfrac{7}{10}$ $\dfrac{2}{5} - \left(-\dfrac{3}{10}\right) = \dfrac{2}{5} + \dfrac{3}{10} = \dfrac{7}{10}$
B. Apply your knowledge (page 664)	On three consecutive hands of blackjack, a gambler wins $20, loses $50, and wins $30. What are the gambler's net winnings? $20 − $50 + $30 = $20 + (−$50) + $30 = $0	

9.4 Multiplying and Dividing Signed Numbers

Topic	Important Concepts	Illustrative Examples
A. Multiply signed numbers (page 668)	**Steps for Multiplying Numbers with Different Signs** **Step 1.** Determine the absolute value of each factor. **Step 2.** Multiply the absolute values of the factors. **Step 3.** Attach a negative sign to the result. The product is negative. **Steps for Multiplying Numbers with the Same Sign** **Step 1.** Determine the absolute value of each factor. **Step 2.** Multiply the absolute values of the two numbers. The product is positive.	Multiply. Simplify, if possible. **a.** $4 \cdot (-8)$ $\qquad \lvert 4 \rvert = 4, \lvert -8 \rvert = 8$ $\qquad 4 \cdot 8 = 32$ $\qquad 4 \cdot (-8) = -32$ **b.** $-\dfrac{2}{15} \cdot \dfrac{5}{8}$ $\qquad \left\lvert -\dfrac{2}{15} \right\rvert = \dfrac{2}{15}, \left\lvert \dfrac{5}{8} \right\rvert = \dfrac{5}{8}$ $\qquad \dfrac{\overset{1}{2}}{\underset{3}{15}} \cdot \dfrac{\overset{1}{5}}{\underset{4}{8}} = \dfrac{1}{12}$ $\qquad -\dfrac{2}{15} \cdot \dfrac{5}{8} = -\dfrac{1}{12}$ **c.** $\left(-2\dfrac{1}{4}\right)\left(-3\dfrac{1}{9}\right)$ $\qquad \left\lvert -2\dfrac{1}{4} \right\rvert = 2\dfrac{1}{4}, \left\lvert -3\dfrac{1}{9} \right\rvert = 3\dfrac{1}{9}$ $\qquad 2\dfrac{1}{4} \cdot 3\dfrac{1}{9} = \dfrac{9}{\underset{1}{4}} \cdot \dfrac{\overset{7}{28}}{\underset{1}{9}} = \dfrac{7}{1} = 7$ $\qquad \left(-2\dfrac{1}{4}\right)\left(-3\dfrac{1}{9}\right) = 7$ **d.** $(-2.1)(-0.3)$ $\qquad \lvert -2.1 \rvert = 2.1, \lvert -0.3 \rvert = 0.3$ $\qquad 2.1 \cdot 0.3 = 0.63$ $\qquad (-2.1)(-0.3) = 0.63$
B. Divide signed numbers (page 673)	**Steps for Dividing Numbers with Different Signs** **Step 1.** Determine the absolute values of the dividend and divisor. **Step 2.** Divide the absolute values from step 1. **Step 3.** Attach a negative sign to the result. The quotient is negative. **Steps for Dividing Signed Numbers with the Same Sign** **Step 1.** Determine the absolute values of the dividend and divisor. **Step 2.** Divide the absolute values from step 1. The quotient is positive.	Divide. Simplify, if possible. **a.** $36 \div (-6)$ $\qquad \lvert 36 \rvert = 36, \lvert -6 \rvert = 6$ $\qquad 36 \div 6 = 6$ $\qquad 36 \div (-6) = -6$ **b.** $-90 \div (-10)$ $\qquad \lvert -90 \rvert = 90, \lvert -10 \rvert = 10$ $\qquad 90 \div 10 = 9$ $\qquad -90 \div (-10) = 9$

C. Apply your knowledge (page 676)	Ten people invest $100,000 each into a piece of land. If after one year the land sells for $750,000, how much does each investor make or lose?

$100,000 \cdot 10 = \$1,000,000$

$750,000 - \$1,000,000 = -\$250,000$

$$\frac{-\$250,000}{10} = -\$25,000$$

Each investor's net profit was $-\$25,000$, that is, each investor lost $25,000.

9.5 Signed Numbers and Order of Operations

Topic	Important Concepts	Illustrative Examples
A. Simplify an expression containing signed numbers (page 681)	Order of Operations **Step 1.** Perform all operations within grouping symbols: parentheses ( ), brackets [ ], curly braces { }, and fraction bars. When grouping symbols occur within grouping symbols, begin with the innermost grouping symbols. **Step 2.** Evaluate all exponential expressions. **Step 3.** Perform all multiplications and divisions as they appear in reading from left to right. **Step 4.** Perform all additions and subtractions as they appear in reading from left to right.	Simplify each expression. **a.** $37 + 55 \div 5 + 2 \cdot 4 + (-3)$ $37 + 11 + 8 + (-3)$ 53 **b.** $(-9)^2 + (-7)(5) + 6$ $81 + (-7)(5) + 6$ $81 + (-35) + 6$ 52 **c.** $(-4)^4 \div 8 + 3 \cdot 5 + (-9)$ $256 \div 8 + 3 \cdot 5 + (-9)$ $32 + 15 + (-9)$ 38
B. Apply your knowledge (page 685)	Henry and Aida own Greek Tours, Inc. They offer a 4-day hiking tour package that explores the island of Crete. The schedule for the hike includes traveling 3 miles on day one, twice as many miles on day two, 5 miles on day three, and 3 miles less than the previous day on day four. How many total miles will each vacationer travel on this tour? $3 + (3 \cdot 2) + 5 + (5 - 3)$ $3 + 6 + 5 + (5 - 3)$ $3 + 6 + 5 + 2$ 16

Numerical Facts of Life

Estimating Wind Chill

Wind Chill Chart

Temperature (°F)

Calm	40	35	30	25	20	15	10	5	0	−5	−10	−15	−20	−25	−30	−35	−40	−45
5	36	31	25	19	13	7	1	−5	−11	−16	−22	−28	−34	−40	−46	−52	−57	−63
10	36	27	21	15	9	3	−4	−10	−16	−22	−28	−35	−41	−47	−53	−59	−66	−72
15	32	25	19	13	6	0	−7	−13	−19	−26	−32	−39	−45	−51	−58	−64	−71	−77
20	30	24	17	11	4	−2	−9	−15	−22	−29	−35	−42	−18	−55	−61	−68	−74	−81
25	29	23	16	9	3	−4	−11	−17	−24	−31	−37	−44	−51	−58	−64	−71	−78	−84
30	28	22	15	8	1	−5	−12	−19	−26	−33	−39	−46	−53	−60	−67	−73	−80	−87
35	28	21	14	7	0	−7	−14	−21	−27	−34	−41	−48	−55	−62	−59	−76	−82	−89
40	27	20	13	6	−1	−8	−15	−22	−29	−36	−43	−50	−57	−64	−71	−78	−84	−91
45	26	19	12	5	−2	−9	−16	−23	−30	−37	−44	−51	−58	−65	−72	−79	−86	−93
50	26	19	12	4	−3	−10	−17	−24	−31	−38	−45	−52	−60	−67	−74	−81	−88	−95
55	25	18	11	4	−3	−11	−18	−25	−32	−39	−46	−54	−61	−68	−75	−82	−89	−97
60	25	17	10	3	−4	−11	−19	−26	−33	−40	−48	−55	−62	−69	−76	−84	−91	−98

Wind (mph)

Frostbite Times
- 30 minutes
- 10 minutes
- 5 minutes

According to the National Oceanic and Atmospheric Administration (NOAA), wind chill describes a person's heat loss resulting from a combination of low temperatures and wind. Wind chill describes what the temperature *feels like* when the actual temperature and wind speed are combined. For example, if the actual temperature was 5°F and the wind speed was 25 mph, then the wind chill would be −17°F. To determine this, find 5°F along the top of the table and 25 mph along the left side. Then, go down the column below 5°F and across the row next to 25 mph. We note that the row and column intersect at −17°F.

Suppose that the actual temperature is −5°F and the wind speed is 30 mph.

1. Determine the wind chill.

2. Write a subtraction problem that represents the difference between the actual temperature and the wind chill in question 1. Calculate this difference.

3. If the actual temperature decreased by 10 degrees and the wind speed increased by 5 mph, what would be the new wind chill?

4. Write a subtraction problem that represents the difference between the new wind chill and the original wind chill. Calculate this difference.

CHAPTER REVIEW EXERCISES

Find the opposite of each number. (9.1A)

1. 15

2. 2.34

3. -47

4. -8.094

Graph each signed number. (9.1B)

5. $0.25, 2.5, -2, -5$

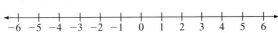

6. $\frac{1}{2}, 3, -3, -\frac{1}{2}$

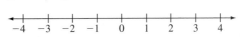

Evaluate. (9.1C)

7. $|12|$

8. $|-52|$

9. $|-2.314|$

10. $|7436|$

Compare each pair of signed numbers. (9.1D)

11. 2 and 7

12. -3 and -8

13. -2.05 and -2

14. 7 and 7.4

Express the quantity in each scenario as a signed number. (9.1E)

15. Oxygen freezes at two hundred ten degrees below zero on the Fahrenheit scale.

16. The sun's innermost region is estimated to have a temperature of one million degrees Kelvin.

17. You overdrew your checking account by $45.00.

18. A rocket is fired three thousand five hundred feet into the air.

Add. Simplify, if possible. (9.2A, B)

19. $21 + 89$

20. $-117 + (-37)$

21. $\frac{4}{5} + \left(-\frac{1}{6}\right)$

22. $-\frac{8}{9} + \frac{5}{12}$

23. $-2\frac{1}{2} + 1\frac{3}{7}$

24. $4\frac{5}{6} + \left(-1\frac{1}{8}\right)$

25. $-0.45 + 2.01$

26. $-12.1 + (-4.8)$

Subtract. (9.3A)

27. $54 - 82$

28. $2.3 - (-5.41)$

29. $\frac{1}{4} - \frac{5}{8}$

30. $5\frac{2}{9} - 7\frac{1}{3}$

Multiply. (9.4A)

31. $-3 \cdot 5$

32. $-0.6 \cdot (-1.5)$

33. $\frac{2}{3}\left(-\frac{7}{8}\right)$

34. $\left(-1\frac{2}{5}\right)\left(-2\frac{6}{7}\right)$

Divide. (9.4B)

35. $81 \div (-9)$

36. $-1.21 \div (-0.11)$

37. $-\dfrac{2}{9} \div \dfrac{1}{3}$

38. $-2\dfrac{7}{8} \div 3\dfrac{3}{4}$

Simplify each expression. (9.5A)

39. $[9^2 - (3 - 8)^2] \div 8$

40. $-2 + [-2^2 - (21 + 7)]^2 + 10$

41. $(-4)^2 + \dfrac{3^2 - 1}{2^2} - 3$

42. $5 - \left(\dfrac{8^2 - 1}{2^4 + 5}\right)^2$

Solve each application problem.

43. At the beginning of the month, Mr. Cortez had $250 in his savings account. In the middle of the month, he deposited $105. Then, at the end of the month, he deposited $215 and withdrew $55.

    a. Write an addition problem corresponding to this scenario.

    b. Determine how much Mr. Cortez has in his savings account at the end of the month.

44. Alexander the Great died in 323 BC. Most of the information about Alexander the Great comes from the writings of the historian Plutarch who was born in 46 AD.

    a. Write a subtraction problem that corresponds to the number of years that separate Alexander the Great and Plutarch.

    b. How many years separate Alexander the Great from his primary historian?

45. A construction crane positioned at ground level is 188 feet tall. The difference between the top of the crane and the base of a construction site is 226 feet. How far below ground level is the base of the construction site?

46. You purchased 500 shares of Comstock Mining Company stock. Suppose that the price decreases by $2.40 per share and you decide to sell your stock.

    a. Write a product that represents the change in the stock's value.

    b. What was the outcome of your investment?

47. Because of a recent promotion, your salary increased $175 per month. If your federal income tax increased $62 and your social security deduction increased $27, what is your net raise?

ASSESSMENT TEST

Find the opposite of each number.

1. 457

2. -5713

Graph each signed number.

3. $-3, 4, -8, 0$

4. $-1\frac{1}{3}, -\frac{1}{4}, 2\frac{2}{5}, \frac{10}{3}$

Evaluate.

5. $|350|$

6. $|-453|$

Compare each pair of signed numbers.

7. 7 and 4

8. -19.5 and -19.0

Express the quantity in each scenario as a signed number.

9. Mercury freezes at thirty-nine degrees below zero on the Celsius scale.

10. Didier overdrew his checking account by \$3.24.

Add.

11. $-25 + (-78)$

12. $-91 + 118$

13. $-14.7 + 2.64$

14. $13.05 + (-7.2)$

15. $-\frac{1}{12} + \left(-\frac{5}{16}\right)$

16. $2\frac{4}{5} + \left(-5\frac{1}{2}\right)$

Subtract.

17. $75 - 48$

18. $-0.47 - 8.9$

19. $\frac{5}{6} - \frac{4}{9}$

20. $-3\frac{7}{8} - 1\frac{1}{6}$

Multiply.

21. $1.2 \cdot (-0.5)$

22. $\left(-\frac{8}{15}\right)\left(-\frac{1}{6}\right)$

Divide.

23. $-72 \div (-0.9)$

24. $1\frac{4}{5} \div \left(-4\frac{1}{2}\right)$

Simplify each expression.

25. $4^3 + (3^3 - 30)^2 + (-65)$

26. $100 - \dfrac{(-12)^2 + 6}{(-4)^2 - 1} + (-50)$

Solve each application problem.

27. The Dead Sea is approximately 1300 feet below sea level and Mount Everest is approximately 29,000 feet above sea level. Find the difference in altitude.

28. Steven's checking account was overdrawn by $37.21. He deposited $150.00 and then later that day withdrew $60.00. What's his new balance?

29. Over the last 12 years, enrollment at a particular two-year college decreased by 3420 students. What was the average change in enrollment each year?

30. The Barbeque Barn offers a large order of ribs for $10.00 and a medium order for $8.00. Side dishes cost $2.50 each. There is a $4.00 charge for all deliveries. Suppose that you purchase two large and two medium orders along with two side dishes for each order. If you tip the delivery person $6.00 and use a coupon for $3.00 off, what is the total cost of the order?

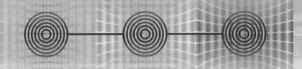

Introduction to Algebra

Civil Engineer

Much of the infrastructure in the industrialized world is due to the design efforts of civil engineers. Civil engineers design and supervise the construction of roads, airports, buildings, bridges, tunnels, dams, and sewage systems.[1] They must consider many factors in the design process, from construction costs and government regulations to environmental hazards such as earthquakes and hurricanes.

Civil engineers must have a strong mathematics background. Solving equations involving variables is an important skill that engineers and engineering students alike must possess. The ability to solve equations is the backbone of the more advanced courses that all engineers must take, including trigonometry and calculus.

We begin this chapter with a look at algebraic expressions. Then, we will learn to solve equations containing variables. Once we have developed this skill, we will present a strategy for analyzing a wide range of application problems that require us to solve equations.

[1] from *U.S. Bureau of Labor Statistics Occupational Outlook Handbook.*

10.1 ALGEBRAIC EXPRESSIONS

LEARNING OBJECTIVES

A. Evaluate an algebraic expression

B. Combine like terms

C. Multiply expressions

D. Apply your knowledge

variable
A letter or some other symbol that represents a number whose value is unknown.

algebraic expression or **expression**
A mathematical statement that consists of numbers, variables, operation symbols, and possibly grouping symbols.

evaluate an expression
To replace each variable of an algebraic expression with a particular value and find the value of the expression.

Objective 10.1A **Evaluate an algebraic expression**

In algebra, we often work with problems that involve variables. A **variable** is a letter or some other symbol that represents a number whose value is unknown. The letter t may represent time in a problem, or the letter d may represent distance.

An **algebraic expression**, or **expression**, is a mathematical statement that consists of numbers, variables, operation symbols, and possibly grouping symbols. Here are some examples of algebraic expressions.

$$x + 5 \qquad 3x \qquad yz + 3(y - 4)$$

If a number and a variable expression or two variable expressions are written next to each other, then we understand that the two are being multiplied. For example, $3x$ means $3 \cdot x$, yz means $y \cdot z$, and $3(y - 4)$ means $3 \cdot (y - 4)$.

When we replace each variable in an algebraic expression with a particular value and find the value of the expression, we **evaluate the expression**.

Steps for Evaluating Algebraic Expressions

Step 1. Substitute a value for the indicated variable into the algebraic expression.

Step 2. Find the value of the expression by performing the indicated operations.

EXAMPLE 1 Evaluate an algebraic expression

Evaluate each algebraic expression when $x = 2$.

a. $2x$ **b.** $3x + 7$ **c.** $5(x - 1)$

SOLUTION STRATEGY

a. $2x$

$2 \cdot 2$	Substitute 2 for x.
4	Multiply.

b. $3x + 7$

$3 \cdot 2 + 7$	Substitute 2 for x.
$6 + 7$	Multiply.
13	Add.

c. $5(x - 1)$

$5(2 - 1)$	Substitute 2 for x.
$5(1)$	Simplify within parentheses.
5	Multiply.

TRY-IT EXERCISE 1

Evaluate each algebraic expression when $t = 3$.

a. $-2t$ **b.** $6t - 5$ **c.** $7(2t - 3)$

Check your answers with the solutions in Appendix A. ■

EXAMPLE 2   Evaluate an algebraic expression

Evaluate each algebraic expression when $x = 12$ and $y = 3$.

a. $x + y$ **b.** $x - y$ **c.** xy **d.** $\dfrac{x}{y}$

SOLUTION STRATEGY

a. $x + y$

     $12 + 3$ Substitute 12 for x and 3 for y.

     15 Add.

b. $x - y$

     $12 - 3$ Substitute 12 for x and 3 for y.

     9 Subtract.

c. xy

     $12 \cdot 3$ Substitute 12 for x and 3 for y.

     36 Multiply.

d. $\dfrac{x}{y}$

     $\dfrac{12}{3}$ Substitute 12 for x and 3 for y.

     4 Divide.

TRY-IT EXERCISE 2

Evaluate each algebraic expression when $p = 16$ and $q = 8$.

a. $p + q$ **b.** $p - q$ **c.** pq **d.** $\dfrac{p}{q}$

Check your answers with the solutions in Appendix A. ■

Objective 10.1B   Combine like terms

Each addend in an algebraic expression is called a **term**. A term that contains a variable is called a **variable term**, while a term that is only a number is called a **constant term**.

Consider the following algebraic expression.

$$x + 2y + 3$$

term
An addend in an algebraic expression.

variable term
A term that contains a variable.

constant term
A term that is a number.

This expression contains three terms: x, $2y$, and 3. The variable terms are x and $2y$, and the constant term is 3.

A number factor in a variable term is called a **numerical coefficient**, or **coefficient**. The coefficient in the variable term $2y$ is 2, and the coefficient in the variable term x is 1. Indeed, if a variable term does not have an explicit number factor, then the coefficient is understood to be 1. Note that $1x = x$.

As another example, consider the following algebraic expression.

$$5x + 7y - 4z$$

To identify the terms, we must first write the expression as a sum. This requires that we write subtraction as addition of the opposite.

$$5x + 7y + (-4z)$$

We now see that the terms are $5x$, $7y$, and $-4z$. The coefficient in the variable term $5x$ is 5, the coefficient in the variable term $7y$ is 7, and the coefficient in the variable term $-4z$ is -4.

numerical coefficient or coefficient
A number factor in a variable term.

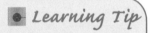 *Learning Tip*

In an algebraic expression involving subtraction, the minus sign always goes "along for the ride" with the term.

EXAMPLE 3   Identify terms

Identify the variable and constant terms in each expression. Also, identify the coefficient in each variable term.

a. $3x + 4 + 7y$ **b.** $9a + b - 7c - 3$ **c.** $x^3 - 8y^2 + 6z - 11$

SOLUTION STRATEGY

a. $3x + 4 + 7y$

Variable terms: $3x$ and $7y$
Constant term: 4
Coefficient in $3x$: 3
Coefficient in $7y$: 7

b. $9a + b - 7c - 3$

$9a + b + (-7c) + (-3)$ Write subtraction as addition of the opposite.

Variable terms: $9a$, b, and $-7c$
Constant term: -3
Coefficient in $9a$: 9
Coefficient in b: 1
Coefficient in $-7c$: -7

c. $x^3 - 8y^2 + 6z - 11$

$x^3 + (-8y^2) + 6z + (-11)$ Write subtraction as addition of the opposite.

Variable terms: x^3, $-8y^2$, and $6z$
Constant term: -11
Coefficient in x^3: 1
Coefficient in $-8y^2$: -8
Coefficient in $6z$: 6

TRY-IT EXERCISE 3

Identify the variable and constant terms in each expression. Also, identify the coefficient in each variable term.

a. $3 + 5k + 9k + 2$ **b.** $-13x - 6y + 8z$ **c.** $p^4 - 2p^3 + 9p^2 - 13p + 6$

Check your answers with the solutions in Appendix A. ■

like terms
Terms with the same variable factors.

Like terms are terms with the same variable factors. For instance, consider the following algebraic expression.

$$2x + 3x$$

In this expression, $2x$ and $3x$ are like terms. Even though the terms have different coefficients, both terms have the same variable factor, x.

As another example, consider the following:

$$4x^2 + 3x + 5x^2 - 7x$$

In this expression, $4x^2$ and $5x^2$ are like terms since they have the same variable factors. In particular, each term has two factors of x. Also, $3x$ and $-7x$ are like terms. Note that each term has only one factor of x.

Learning Tip

Like terms have the same variables and same exponents. Thus, $4x^2$ and $3x$ are not like terms since they do not have the same exponent.

Whenever an algebraic expression contains like terms, we can simplify the expression using properties of numbers with which we are already familiar. One such property is the distributive property. In Section 1.4, we learned that we can use the distributive property to manipulate the algebraic expression $a(b + c)$.

$$a(b + c) = ab + ac$$

In a similar way, the distributive property allows us to manipulate the algebraic expression $(a + b)c$.

$$(a + b)c = ac + bc$$

Interchanging the algebraic expressions on the left and right sides of the previous equation give us the following.

$$ac + bc = (a + b)c$$

Therefore, we can restate the distributive property as follows.

Distributive Property

For any numbers a, b, and c, we have the following.

$$ac + bc = (a + b)c \quad \text{and} \quad ac - bc = (a - b)c$$

To see how the distributive property is useful in simplifying an algebraic expression containing like terms, let's again consider $2x + 3x$.

$$2x + 3x = (2 + 3)x \quad \text{Apply the distributive property.}$$
$$= 5x \quad \text{Add } 2 + 3.$$

The commutative and associative properties are also useful in simplifying algebraic expressions that contain like terms. We introduced these properties in Sections 1.2 and 1.4. The commutative property tells us that the order in which we add or multiply two numbers does not affect the result. The associative property tells us that the way we group numbers in an addition or multiplication problem does not affect the result.

Commutative Property

Changing the order of the addends does not change the sum. Likewise, changing the order of factors does not change the product. That is, for any numbers a and b, we have the following.

$$a + b = b + a \quad \text{and} \quad a \cdot b = b \cdot a$$

Associative Property

Changing the grouping of addends does not change the sum. Likewise, changing the grouping of factors does not change the product. That is, for any numbers a, b, and c, we have the following.

$$a + (b + c) = (a + b) + c \quad \text{and} \quad a(bc) = (ab)c$$

To see how these properties apply to simplifying an algebraic expression containing like terms, consider $4x + 9y + 8x - 2y$.

$$4x + 9y + 8x - 2y$$
$$= 4x + 9y + 8x + (-2y) \quad \text{Write subtraction as addition of the opposite.}$$
$$= 4x + 8x + 9y + (-2y) \quad \text{Apply the commutative property.}$$
$$= (4x + 8x) + (9y + (-2y)) \quad \text{Apply the associative property by grouping like terms.}$$
$$= (4 + 8)x + (9 + (-2))y \quad \text{Apply the distributive property.}$$
$$= 12x + 7y \quad \text{Add } 4 + 8. \text{ Add } 9 + (-2).$$

collecting like terms
Changing the order of terms using the commutative property and grouping like terms using the associative property.

combining like terms
Adding like terms in an algebraic expression.

Note that $12x$ and $7y$ have different variable factors. As such, they are not like terms and hence cannot be added together.

Changing the order of terms using the commutative property and grouping like terms using the associative property is called **collecting like terms**. Adding all like terms in an algebraic expression is called **combining like terms**. Once we combine all like terms in an algebraic expression, we say that the expression is simplified.

EXAMPLE 4   Combine like terms

Combine like terms to simplify each expression.

a. $5x + 7y + x + 4y$ **b.** $12a - 5b - 7a + b$ **c.** $3y^2 + 4 - y^2 - 6$

SOLUTION STRATEGY

a. $5x + 7y + x + 4y$

$(5x + x) + (7y + 4y)$ Collect like terms

$6x + 11y$ Combine like terms. Note that the coefficient in $5x$ is 5, while the coefficient in x is 1. Thus, $5x + x$ is the same as $5x + 1x = (5 + 1)x = 6x$.

b. $12a - 5b - 7a + b$

$12a + (-5b) + (-7a) + b$ Write subtraction as addition of the opposite.

$[12a + (-7a)] + [(-5b) + b]$ Collect like terms.

$5a + (-4b)$ Combine like terms. Again, note that the coefficient of $-5b$ is -5, while the coefficient of b is 1. Thus, $-5b + b$ is the same as $-5b + 1b = (-5 + 1)b = -4b$.

$5a - 4b$ Write as a difference.

c. $3y^2 + 4 - y^2 - 6$

$3y^2 + 4 + (-y^2) + (-6)$ Write subtraction as addition of the opposite.

$[3y^2 + (-y^2)] + [4 + (-6)]$ Collect like terms.

$2y^2 + (-2)$ Combine like terms.

$2y^2 - 2$ Write as a difference.

> **Learning Tip**
>
> Recall that $x + (-y) = x - y$. Accordingly, in Example 4b, we can write $5a + (-4b)$ more concisely as $5a - 4b$.

TRY-IT EXERCISE 4

Combine like terms to simplify each expression.

a. $12x + 3y + 5x + y$ **b.** $6p + 3q - 8q - 12p$ **c.** $8d^3 - 5 - d^3 + 3$

Check your answers with the solutions in Appendix A. ∎

Objective 10.1C   Multiply expressions

We can also use the properties of numbers to multiply expressions. For example, in the expression $2(4y)$, we are multiplying 2 and $4y$. Using the associative property of multiplication, we can regroup the number factors to determine the product.

$2(4y) = (2 \cdot 4)y$ Apply the associative property of multiplication.

$= 8y$ Multiply $2 \cdot 4$.

EXAMPLE 5   Multiply expressions

Multiply. Simplify, if possible.

a. $2(6x)$ **b.** $0.3(-4y)$ **c.** $-\dfrac{3}{8}\left(-\dfrac{4}{9}z\right)$

SOLUTION STRATEGY

a. $2(6x)$

$\quad (2 \cdot 6)x$ \qquad Apply the associative property of multiplication.

$\quad 12x$ \qquad Multiply $2 \cdot 6$.

b. $0.3(-4y)$

$\quad [0.3(-4)]y$ \qquad Apply the associative property of multiplication.

$\quad -1.2y$ \qquad Multiply $0.3(-4)$.

c. $-\dfrac{3}{8}\left(-\dfrac{4}{9}z\right)$

$\quad \left(-\dfrac{3}{8} \cdot -\dfrac{4}{9}\right)z$ \qquad Apply the associative property of multiplication.

$\quad \dfrac{1}{6}z$ \qquad Multiply $-\dfrac{3}{8} \cdot -\dfrac{4}{9}$.

TRY-IT EXERCISE 5

Multiply.

a. $3(9a)$ **b.** $-1.5(-0.2b)$ **c.** $-\dfrac{4}{9}\left(\dfrac{3}{5}x^2\right)$

Check your answers with the solutions in Appendix A. ■

We can also use the distributive property to multiply expressions. As an example, consider $2(x + 9)$.

$$2(x + 9) = 2 \cdot x + 2 \cdot 9 \qquad \text{Apply the distributive property.}$$
$$= 2x + 18 \qquad \text{Multiply } 2 \cdot x. \text{ Multiply } 2 \cdot 9.$$

EXAMPLE 6   Apply the distributive property

Simplify each expression by applying the distributive property.

a. $3(2x + 7)$ **b.** $-(5y - 3)$ **c.** $-\dfrac{1}{2}(x + 8)$ **d.** $(3y - 7)0.2$ **e.** $(z + 7)(-3)$

SOLUTION STRATEGY

a. $3(2x + 7) = 3(2x) + 3(7)$ \qquad Apply the distributive property over addition.

$\qquad\qquad = 6x + 21$ \qquad Multiply $3(2x)$. Multiply $3(7)$.

b. $-(5y - 3) = -1(5y - 3)$

$\qquad\qquad = -1(5y) - (-1)(3)$ \qquad Apply the distributive property over subtraction.

$\qquad\qquad = -5y - (-3)$ \qquad Multiply $-1(5y)$. Multiply $-1(3)$.

$\qquad\qquad = -5y + 3$ \qquad Write subtraction as addition of the opposite.

c. $-\dfrac{1}{2}(x + 8) = -\dfrac{1}{2}x + \left(-\dfrac{1}{2}\right)8$ Apply the distributive property over addition.

$\qquad\qquad = -\dfrac{1}{2}x + (-4)$ Multiply $\left(-\dfrac{1}{2}\right)8$.

$\qquad\qquad = -\dfrac{1}{2}x - 4$ Write as a difference.

d. $(3y - 7)0.2 = 3y(0.2) - 7(0.2)$ Apply the distributive property over subtraction.

$\qquad\qquad\;\; = 0.6y - 1.4$ Multiply $3y(0.2)$. Multiply $7(0.2)$.

e. $(z + 7)(-3) = z(-3) + 7(-3)$ Apply the distributive property over addition.

$\qquad\qquad\;\; = -3z - 21$ Multiply $z(-3)$. Multiply $7(-3)$.

TRY-IT EXERCISE 6

Simplify each expression by applying the distributive property.

a. $8(3x + 7)$ **b.** $0.5(2y - 3)$ **c.** $-\dfrac{1}{3}(z + 12)$ **d.** $(2y - 6)4$ **e.** $(z + 8)(-4)$

Check your answers with the solutions in Appendix A. ■

Objective 10.1D   **Apply your knowledge**

In Section 1.7, we introduced a number of key words and phrases that are used to indicate the basic operations. In the following example, we use these key words and phrases to translate a statement into an algebraic expression. In Section 10.5, we will translate sentences into equations.

EXAMPLE 7   **Write an algebraic expression**

Write an algebraic expression to represent the sum of twice a number and 15.

SOLUTION STRATEGY

Let x represent the number.

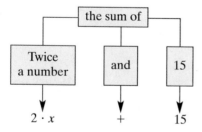

The key word *twice* indicates multiplication by 2.
The phrase *the sum of* indicates addition.

$2x + 15$

TRY-IT EXERCISE 7

Write an algebraic expression to represent the difference of 81 and nine times a number.

Check your answers with the solutions in Appendix A. ■

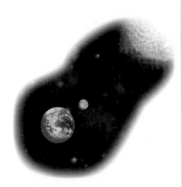

EXAMPLE 8 Write and evaluate an algebraic expression

The distance from the earth to the sun is approximately 390 times the distance from the earth to the moon. Let d represent the distance from the earth to the moon.

a. Write an algebraic expression that represents the distance from the earth to the sun in terms of d.

b. If the distance from the earth to the moon is approximately 239,000 miles, evaluate the expression you came up with in part a.

SOLUTION STRATEGY

a. Let d represent the distance from the earth to the moon.

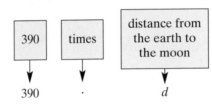

The key word *times* indicates multiplication.

390 · d

390d

b. $390 \cdot 239,000 = 93,210,000$ Substitute 239,000 for d.

The earth is approximately 93,210,000 miles from the sun.

TRY-IT EXERCISE 8

Mount Everest is 14,625 feet higher than Mount Rainier. Let x represent the height of Mount Rainier.

a. Write an algebraic expression that represents the height of Mount Everest in terms of x.

b. If Mount Rainier is 14,410 feet tall, evaluate the expression you came up with in part a.

Check your answers with the solutions in Appendix A. ∎

SECTION 10.1 REVIEW EXERCISES

Concept Check

1. A letter or some other symbol that represents a number whose value is unknown is called a _____.

2. A mathematical statement that consists of numbers, variables, operation symbols, and possibly grouping symbols is called an _____ expression.

3. When we _____ an expression, we replace each variable of an algebraic expression by a particular value and find the value of the expression.

4. A _____ is an addend in an algebraic expression.

5. A term that contains a variable is known as a _____ term, whereas a term that is a number is called a _____ term.

6. A _____ is a number factor in a variable term.

7. Terms with the same variable factors are called _____ terms.

8. The process of adding like terms in an algebraic expression is called _____ like terms.

| **Objective 10.A** | **Evaluate an algebraic expression** |

GUIDE PROBLEMS

9. Evaluate each algebraic expression when $x = 7$.

  a. $3x$

    $3(\_\_) = \_\_$

  b. $2 - x$

    $2 - \_\_ = \_\_$

  c. $4(x + 1)$

    $4(\_\_ + 1) = 4(\_\_) = \_\_$

10. Evaluate each algebraic expression when $a = 1$ and $b = -3$.

  a. $a - b$

    $\_\_ - (\_\_) = \_\_ + \_\_ = \_\_$

  b. $5a + b$

    $5(\_\_) + (\_\_) = \_\_ - \_\_ = \_\_$

  c. ab

    $\_\_(\_\_) = \_\_$

Evaluate each algebraic expression when $x = 7$.

11. $31 - x + 5$ **12.** $9 \div (x - 4)$ **13.** $5x + 4x$ **14.** $(x + 5) \div 3$ **15.** $2 + 3x + x^2$

Evaluate each algebraic expression when $y = 5$.

16. $-3y$ **17.** $2y + 7$ **18.** $3(y + 5)$ **19.** $-9y - 7$ **20.** $4y^2 + 3y$

Evaluate each algebraic expression when $x = -3$ and $y = 2$.

21. $3x - 2y$ **22.** $13y - 5x$ **23.** $\dfrac{8x^2}{3y}$ **24.** $\dfrac{2x + 1}{3y + 4}$ **25.** $(x + 1)(y + 3)$

Evaluate each algebraic expression when $x = 10$ and $y = 15$.

26. $2x + 3y$ **27.** $3x - 4y$ **28.** $(-3x)(4y)$ **29.** $6y \div x$ **30.** $\dfrac{8x + 6}{3y - 2}$

| **Objective 10.1B** | **Combine like terms** |

GUIDE PROBLEMS

31. Consider $3x^4 - 2x^3 - 9x^2 + x - 1$.

 a. The variable terms are _____, _____, _____, and _____.

 b. The constant term is ___.

 c. The coefficient in the first term is _____.
 The coefficient in the second term is _____.
 The coefficient in the third term is _____.
 The coefficient in the fourth term is _____ .

32. Combine like terms to simplify
$3x^2 + 7x + 8y - 5x^2 - 5x + 9y$.

 a. Collect like terms.

  $(3x^2 + (\_\_\_)) + (\_\_\_ + (-5x)) + (8y + \_\_\_)$

 b. Combine like terms.

  $\_\_ x^2 + \_\_ x + \_\_ y$

Identify the variable and constant terms in each expression. Also, identify the coefficient of each variable term.

33. $4a^3 + 3a^2 - 9a - 5$

34. $-7x^5 + 8x^4 - 3x^3 + 6x^2 - 10$

35. $-y^4 - y^2 - 3y - 9$

36. $-3m^3 + 2m^2 - 3m - 7$

Combine like terms to simplify each expression.

37. $5t + 7s + 2t + s$

38. $5a + 3b - a + 6b$

39. $2x + \dfrac{1}{4}y + \dfrac{3}{4}x + y$

40. $5m + 7n + \dfrac{1}{2}m - \dfrac{2}{3}n$

41. $x^2 - xy - xy + y^2$

42. $a^3 - a^2b + 4a^2b + b^3$

43. $2u^2v - 3uv^2 + 6u^2v - 2uv^2$

44. $2p^2q - 8pq^2 - 4p^2q + 10pq^2$

45. $3rst - 5r^2s + 4rst + 7rs - 3rs - 4r^2s$

46. $3x^2yz^3 - 2xy^2 + x^2yz^3 + x^2y^2 + 2xy^2$

47. $5x^2 + 10xy + 5y^2 - 3x^2 - 6xy - 3y^2$

48. $3p^2 + 4pq + q^2 - 2p^2 - pq + 7q^2$

49. $\dfrac{1}{5}m^4 + \dfrac{1}{5} - 2m^2 + \dfrac{1}{10} - \dfrac{2}{15}m^4 + 4m^2$

50. $\dfrac{1}{3}d^2 + \dfrac{1}{4} - d + \dfrac{1}{2} + \dfrac{2}{3}d^2 + 3d$

| **Objective 10.1C** | **Multiply expressions** |

GUIDE PROBLEMS

51. Multiply. Simplify, if possible.

   a. $3(5x) = (3 \cdot \underline{\hspace{1cm}})x$

   $\qquad = \underline{\hspace{1cm}} x$

   b. $-0.4(5y) = (-0.4 \cdot \underline{\hspace{1cm}})y$

   $\qquad = \underline{\hspace{1cm}} y$

   c. $\dfrac{2}{9}\left(-\dfrac{3}{5}z\right) = \left(\dfrac{2}{9} \cdot \underline{\hspace{1cm}}\right)z$

   $\qquad = \underline{\hspace{1cm}} z$

52. Simplify each expression by applying the distributive property.

   a. $5(4x + 3) = 5(\underline{\hspace{1cm}}) + 5(\underline{\hspace{1cm}})$

   $\qquad = \underline{\hspace{1cm}} + \underline{\hspace{1cm}}$

   b. $0.7(2a - 9) = 0.7(\underline{\hspace{1cm}}) - 0.7(\underline{\hspace{1cm}})$

   $\qquad = \underline{\hspace{1cm}} - \underline{\hspace{1cm}}$

   c. $-\dfrac{1}{2}(2r + 4) = -\dfrac{1}{2}(\underline{\hspace{1cm}}) + \left(-\dfrac{1}{2}\right)(\underline{\hspace{1cm}})$

   $\qquad = \underline{\hspace{1cm}} - \underline{\hspace{1cm}}$

Multiply. Simplify, if possible.

53. $7(3x)$

54. $8(3m)$

55. $(-7b)5$

56. $(-8y)4$

57. $-(8n)$

58. $-(15x)$

59. $0.3(8d)$

60. $0.9(0.1a)$

61. $(0.5n)0.4$

62. $(-1.1b)5$

63. $-\dfrac{4}{7}\left(-\dfrac{5}{8}x\right)$

64. $\dfrac{9}{20}\left(-\dfrac{5}{12}y\right)$

Simplify each expression by applying the distributive property.

65. $5(x + 2)$

66. $7(r + 5)$

67. $4(a - 1)$

68. $3(y - 4)$

69. $-2(n - 2)$

70. $-5(a + 7)$

71. $9(3x - 8)$

72. $7(5d - 3)$

73. $(3n + 7)3$

74. $(4s + 3)5$

75. $(6x + 7y)8$

76. $(13 - 3x)6$

77. $-\dfrac{1}{2}(4t - 6)$

78. $-\dfrac{1}{4}(12d - 72)$

79. $\dfrac{5}{7}\left(\dfrac{3}{4}x - 6\right)$

80. $\dfrac{3}{8}\left(\dfrac{1}{5}z - 7\right)$

81. $0.1(0.4y + 3)$

82. $0.3(0.5v + 8)$

83. $0.3(2.4d - 9)$

84. $0.1(3.5b - 7)$

85. $3(y^2 - 2y + 6)$

86. $4(a^2 - 3a - 5)$

87. $-2(k^2 + 2k - 3)$

88. $-3(x^2 + 3x + 5)$

Objective 10.1D   **Apply your knowledge**

89. Write an algebraic expression to represent the total of seventeen times a number and three.

90. Write an algebraic expression to represent five less than 3 times x.

91. The Taipei 101 Building in Taipei, Taiwan, is 421 feet taller than the Empire State Building in New York City. Let x represent the height of Taipei 101.

    a. Write an algebraic expression that represents the height of the Empire State Building in terms of x.

    b. If Taipei 101 is 1671 feet tall, determine the height of the Empire State Building using the expression in part a.

92. The Sears Tower in Chicago is 324 feet taller than that city's John Hancock Building. Let x represent the height of the John Hancock Building.

    a. Write an algebraic expression that represents the height of the Sears Tower in terms of x.

    b. If the John Hancock Building is 1127 feet tall, determine the height of the Sears Tower using the expression in part a.

CUMULATIVE SKILLS REVIEW

1. Convert 2 days to minutes. (6.5A)

2. Convert $14\frac{3}{8}\%$ to a decimal. (5.1A)

3. Use the Pythagorean theorem to find the measure of the unknown side of the right triangle. Round to the nearest tenth. (7.5C)

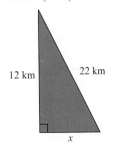

4. Find the circumference of the circle below. Use 3.14 for π. (7.3B)

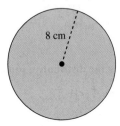

5. Write "17 is to 100" as a ratio in three ways. (4.1A)

6. Convert 190 degrees Fahrenheit to degrees Celsius. Round to the nearest whole degree. (6.5B)

7. Multiply $99.12444 \cdot 100$. (3.3B)

8. Solve $\dfrac{4.25}{18} = \dfrac{x}{108}$. (4.3C)

9. Graph $-3.5, -1, 1, 4,$ and 0 on the number line. (9.1B)

$$\overset{\longleftarrow \hspace{2em} \longrightarrow}{\underset{-5 \quad -4 \quad -3 \quad -2 \quad -1 \quad 0 \quad 1 \quad 2 \quad 3 \quad 4 \quad 5}{\big|\ \big|\ \big|\ \big|\ \big|\ \big|\ \big|\ \big|\ \big|\ \big|\ \big|}}$$

10. Calculate the median for the following set of numbers: 25, 32, 10, 67, 70. (8.2B)

10.2 SOLVING AN EQUATION USING THE ADDITION PROPERTY OF EQUALITY

Objective 10.2A	Verify a solution to an equation

Recall that an **equation** is a mathematical statement consisting of two expressions on either side of an equals (=) sign. The following are examples of equations.

$$4 + 5 = 9 \quad \text{and} \quad x + 6 = 10$$

A value of the variable that makes the equation a true statement is called a **solution** of the equation. For example, 4 is a solution of the equation $x + 6 = 10$ since substituting 4 for x makes the equation into a true statement. Note that 2 is not a solution of this equation since substituting 2 for x yields a false statement.

A. Verify a solution to an equation

B. Solve an equation using the addition property of equality

C. Apply your knowledge

equation
A mathematical statement consisting of two expressions on either side of an equals (=) sign.

solution
A value of the variable that makes the equation a true statement.

EXAMPLE 1 **Determine whether a given value is a solution to a given equation**

Determine whether 8 is a solution of $x + 3 = 11$.

SOLUTION STRATEGY

$8 + 3 \overset{?}{=} 11$ Substitute 8 for x.

$11 = 11$ ✓   Simplify. $11 = 11$ is a true statement.

8 is a solution.

TRY-IT EXERCISE 1

Determine whether 4 is a solution of $x + 13 = 17$.

Check your answer with the solution in Appendix A. ■

EXAMPLE 2 **Determine whether a given value is a solution to a given equation**

Determine whether 2 is a solution of $x + 6 = 9$.

SOLUTION STRATEGY

$2 + 6 \overset{?}{=} 9$ Substitute 2 for x.

$8 = 9$ ✗   Simplify. $8 = 9$ is a false statement.

2 is *not* a solution.

TRY-IT EXERCISE 2

Determine whether 4 is a solution of $x + 5 = 10$.

Check your answer with the solution in Appendix A. ■

Learning Tip

When determining whether a number is a solution to an equation, we often use "$\overset{?}{=}$" instead of "=". If we get a true statement, we use the "=" symbol. If we get a false statement, we use the "≠" symbol.

Objective 10.2B **Solve an equation using the addition property of equality**

For the equation $x + 6 = 9$ given in Example 2, we discovered that 2 is not a solution. Our experience tells us that $x = 3$ is a solution. After all, $3 + 6 = 9$. But if we did not know this, how would we determine this?

To find the solution to this equation and others like it, we use the following important rule.

What we do to one side of an equation, we must do to the other side.

Our goal is to apply this rule in order to isolate the variable on one side of the equation. The **addition property of equality** (or **addition property**, for short) helps us do just that. The addition property of equality states that adding the same value to each side of an equation preserves equality. In other words, if we add the same number to each side of an equation, then we will still have equality. Formally, we have the following.

addition property of equality
or **addition property**
Property stating that adding the same value to each side of an equation preserves equality.

The Addition Property of Equality

If a, b, and c are real numbers and if $a = b$, then $a + c = b + c$.

---

solving an equation
The process of finding a solution to an equation involving a variable.

The process of finding a solution to an equation involving a variable is referred to as **solving an equation**. As an example, consider the following equation.

$$x - 4 = 9$$

Our goal is to isolate x by adding the same value to each side of the equation. What can we add to each side of the equation so as to get x alone? We can add 4.

$x - 4 = 9$ Original equation.

$$\begin{array}{r} x - 4 = 9 \\ \underline{+\,4 \quad +\,4} \\ x + 0 = 13 \end{array}$$ Apply the addition property by adding 4 to each side.

$x = 13$ Simplify.

The solution is $x = 13$.

As another example, let's return to the problem of example 2.

$$x + 6 = 9$$

Once again, our goal is to isolate x by adding a value to each side of the equation. What number can we add to each side of the equation so as to get x alone? We can add the opposite of 6, which is -6. But, adding -6 is the same as subtracting 6. Thus, to solve $x + 6 = 9$, we can either add -6 to each side or subtract 6 from each side; the result will be the same.

$x + 6 = 9$ Original equation.

$$\begin{array}{r} x + 6 = 9 \\ \underline{-\,6 \quad -6} \\ x + 0 = 3 \end{array}$$ Apply the addition property by adding the opposite of 6 to both sides. Adding -6 is the same as subtracting 6.

$x = 3$ Simplify.

Learning Tip

Subtracting a number from an expression is the same as adding the opposite of that number to the expression.

The solution is $x = 3$.

In the examples above, we had to isolate x. To do so, we had to add the same value to each side of the equation. In general, to remove a term from one side of an equation, add the opposite of that term to each side of the equation.

A task that goes hand in hand with solving an equation is **checking the answer**. Checking the answer is the process of verifying that we get a true statement when we substitute the answer into the original equation. As an example, we can check that $x = 13$ is a solution for the equation $x - 4 = 9$.

$$x - 4 = 9 \qquad \text{Original equation.}$$
$$13 - 4 \stackrel{?}{=} 9 \qquad \text{Substitute 13 for } x.$$
$$9 = 9 \qquad \text{Simplify.}$$

checking the answer
The process of verifying that we get a true statement when we substitute the answer into the original equation.

Because substitution yields a true statement, $x = 13$ is a solution.

The following steps will guide us in solving equations using the addition property of equality.

Steps for Solving an Equation Using the Addition Property of Equality

To solve an equation of the form $x + b = c$, where b and c are numbers and x is a variable, follow these steps.

Step 1. Apply the addition property of equality by adding the opposite of b to each side of the equation.

Step 2. Simplify and solve for x.

Step 3. Check the solution by substituting into the original equation.

EXAMPLE 3   Solve an equation using the addition property of equality

Solve $x + 7 = 15$.

SOLUTION STRATEGY

$$x + 7 = 15$$
$$\underline{-7 \quad -7} \qquad \text{Add } -7 \text{ to each side, or, equivalently, subtract 7 from each side.}$$
$$x + 0 = 8$$
$$x = 8 \qquad \text{Simplify.}$$
$$8 + 7 \stackrel{?}{=} 15 \qquad \text{Check the solution.}$$
$$15 = 15 \checkmark$$

TRY-IT EXERCISE 3

Solve $x + 13 = 24$.

Check your answer with the solution in Appendix A. ■

EXAMPLE 4 **Solve an equation using the addition property of equality**

Solve $x - 1.7 = 3.2$.

SOLUTION STRATEGY

$$x - 1.7 = 3.2$$
$$\underline{+1.7 \quad +1.7} \qquad \text{Add 1.7 to each side.}$$
$$x + 0 = 4.9$$
$$x = 4.9 \qquad \text{Simplify.}$$
$$4.9 - 1.7 \overset{?}{=} 3.2 \qquad \text{Check the solution.}$$
$$3.2 = 3.2 \checkmark$$

TRY-IT EXERCISE 4

Solve $x - 1.2 = 11.4$.

Check your answer with the solution in Appendix A. ∎

EXAMPLE 5 **Solve an equation using the addition property of equality**

Solve $x + \dfrac{1}{3} = \dfrac{2}{9}$.

SOLUTION STRATEGY

$$x + \frac{1}{3} - \frac{1}{3} = \frac{2}{9} - \frac{1}{3} \qquad \text{Add } -\frac{1}{3} \text{ to each side, or, equivalently, subtract } \frac{1}{3} \text{ from each side.}$$

$$x + 0 = \frac{2}{9} - \frac{3}{9} \qquad \text{LCD} = 9.$$

$$x = -\frac{1}{9} \qquad \text{Simplify.}$$

$$-\frac{1}{9} + \frac{1}{3} \overset{?}{=} \frac{2}{9} \qquad \text{Check the solution.}$$

$$-\frac{1}{9} + \frac{3}{9} \overset{?}{=} \frac{2}{9}$$

$$\frac{2}{9} = \frac{2}{9} \checkmark$$

TRY-IT EXERCISE 5

Solve $x + \dfrac{1}{2} = \dfrac{3}{8}$.

Check your answer with the solution in Appendix A. ∎

Objective 10.2C	**Apply your knowledge**

Many real-world applications can be represented by algebraic equations whose solutions require us to use the addition property. In the following example, we'll analyze a company's income and expenses by using the formula $R - C = P$. In this formula, R represents a company's revenue (how much money the company made from the sale of goods or services), C represents a company's cost (how much the company had to spend on labor, supplies, and other expenses), and P represents a company's profit (how much is left for the company's owners after all expenses are paid).

EXAMPLE 6   Apply your knowledge

For the quarter ending March 31, 2007, Microsoft Corporation incurred costs of $7,809,000,000. Their net profit during this time period was $6,589,000,000. What was Microsoft's revenue for this quarter? (Source: Microsoft Corporation)

SOLUTION STRATEGY

$$R - C = P$$

$$R - 7{,}809{,}000{,}000 = 6{,}589{,}000{,}000 \qquad \text{Substitute } 7{,}809{,}000{,}000 \text{ for } C \text{ and } 6{,}589{,}000{,}000 \text{ for } P.$$

$$R - 7{,}809{,}000{,}000 = 6{,}589{,}000{,}000$$
$$\underline{+\ 7{,}809{,}000{,}000 \qquad +7{,}809{,}000{,}000} \qquad \text{Add } 7{,}809{,}000{,}000 \text{ to each side.}$$
$$R + 0 \qquad\qquad = 14{,}398{,}000{,}000$$

$$R = 14{,}398{,}000{,}000 \qquad \text{Simplify.}$$

$$\text{Check the solution.}$$
$$14{,}398{,}000{,}000 - 7{,}809{,}000{,}000 \overset{?}{=} 6{,}589{,}000{,}000$$
$$6{,}589{,}000{,}000 = 6{,}589{,}000{,}000 \quad \checkmark$$

Microsoft's revenue for the quarter was $14,398,000,000.

TRY-IT EXERCISE 6

Bed, Bath, and Beyond had a net profit of $2,835,000,000 during fiscal year 2006. Their total operating costs for the year were $3,782,000,000. What was Bed, Bath, and Beyond's revenue for 2006? (Source: Bed, Bath, and Beyond)

Check your answer with the solution in Appendix A. ■

SECTION 10.2 REVIEW EXERCISES

Concept Check

1. An _____ is a mathematical statement consisting of two expressions on either side of an equals (=) sign.

2. A value of the variable that makes the equation a true statement is called a _____ of an equation.

3. The _____ property of equality states that adding the same value to each side of an equation preserves equality.

4. Adding a negative number to each side of an equation is the same as _____ the opposite of the negative number.

5. The process of finding a solution to an equation involving a variable is known as _____ an equation.

6. The process of verifying that we get a true statement when we substitute the answer into the original equation is called _____ the solution.

Objective 10.2A   Verify a solution to an equation

GUIDE PROBLEMS

7. Determine whether 3 is a solution of the equation $3x + 9 = 18$.

$$3x + 9 = 18$$
$$3(\underline{\quad}) + 9 \stackrel{?}{=} 18$$
$$\underline{\quad} + 9 \stackrel{?}{=} 18$$
$$\underline{\quad} \stackrel{?}{=} 18$$

8. Determine whether 7 is a solution of the equation $-2x + 5 = -10$.

$$-2x + 5 = -10$$
$$-2(\underline{\quad}) + 5 \stackrel{?}{=} -10$$
$$(\underline{\quad}) + 5 \stackrel{?}{=} -10$$
$$\underline{\quad} \stackrel{?}{=} -10$$

Determine whether the given value is a solution to the given equation.

9. $s = 12; s + 10 = 22$

10. $y = 8; y + 7 = 15$

11. $b = 32; b - 8 = 22$

12. $v = 15; v + 6 = 19$

13. $s = 18; 6 + s = 12$

14. $a = 21; a + 13 = 33$

15. $x = 49; x - 17 = 32$

16. $p = 24; p - 5 = 19$

17. $k = 105; k + 27 = 132$

18. $h = 306; h + 19 = 325$

19. $x = 213; x - 35 = 168$

20. $m = 219; m - 19 = 210$

21. $t = \dfrac{5}{3}; t - \dfrac{2}{3} = 1$

22. $b = -\dfrac{9}{8}; b + \dfrac{5}{8} = -\dfrac{1}{2}$

23. $c = 34; 21 - c = -13$

24. $y = 54; 35 - y = -19$

25. $q = -20; 7 - q = 27$

26. $p = -40; 18 - q = 58$

27. $x = -30; 8 - x = 22$

28. $r = -12; 30 - r = 18$

29. $r = 2.5; r - 1.3 = 3.8$

30. $y = 6.90; y - 2.07 = 4.73$

31. $n = 1.6; n + 2.3 = 3.9$

32. $s = 6.25; s + 7.50 = 13.75$

33. $m = -6; m - 6 = 0$

34. $x = -8; x + 8 = 0$

35. $t = 10; t - 5 = 5$

36. $y = 12; 6 - y = 6$

Objective 10.2B   Solve an equation using the addition property of equality

GUIDE PROBLEMS

37. Solve $x + 8 = 21$.

$$x + 8 = 21$$
$$\frac{-\ \ \ -}{x + 0} = \frac{--}{--}$$
$$x = \underline{\ \ }$$

Check:

$$\underline{\ \ \ } + 8 \stackrel{?}{=} 21$$
$$21 = 21 \ \checkmark$$

38. Solve $11 + x = -5$

$$11 + x = -5$$
$$\frac{-\ \ \ }{0 + x} = \frac{-\ \ }{\underline{\ \ }}$$
$$x = \underline{\ \ }$$

Check:

$$11 + \underline{\ \ } \stackrel{?}{=} -5$$
$$-5 = -5 \ \checkmark$$

Solve each equation.

39. $x + 6 = 14$

40. $b + 5 = 44$

41. $n + 18 = 30$

42. $d + 13 = 35$

43. $t + 9 = 7$

44. $m + 13 = 8$

45. $9 = s + 5$

46. $12 = p + 5$

47. $3 = k + 8$

48. $7 = y + 11$

49. $a + 6 = 0$

50. $q + 15 = 0$

51. $k - 5 = 15$

52. $m - 11 = 27$

53. $v - 16 = 32$

54. $x - 19 = 50$

55. $40 = x - 27$

56. $37 = p - 35$

57. $21 = x - 34$

58. $76 = t - 13$

59. $d - 28 = 28$

60. $c - 32 = 32$

61. $m - 13 = 0$

62. $b - 29 = 0$

63. $t - 9 = -9$

64. $s - 12 = -12$

65. $k + 17 = 27$

66. $b + 4 = 19$

67. $0.8 = x - 2.7$

68. $2.1 = y - 1.3$

69. $0 = d - 1.47$

70. $0 = m - 1.6$

71. $b - 2.45 = 13.35$

72. $t - 1.25 = 30$

73. $p + \dfrac{3}{4} = \dfrac{7}{12}$

74. $k + \dfrac{1}{2} = -\dfrac{2}{3}$

75. $\dfrac{7}{8} = \dfrac{1}{4} + z$

76. $\dfrac{3}{4} = v - \dfrac{1}{2}$

77. $a + 1\dfrac{1}{2} = 6$

78. $n + 2\dfrac{2}{3} = 7$

Objective 10.2C   **Apply your knowledge**

For problems 79–81, use the formula $R - C = P$, where R represents a company's revenue, C represents a company's cost, and P represents a company's profit.

79. For the quarter ending March 31, 2007, Verizon incurred costs of $18,788,000,000. Their net profit during this time period was $3,796,000,000. What was Verizon's revenue for the quarter? (Source: Verizon Corporation)

80. For fiscal year 2006, McDonald's incurred costs of $18,042,000,000. Their net profit for the year was $3,544,000,000. What was McDonald's revenue for 2006? (Source: McDonald's)

81. At the end of the second quarter of fiscal year 2007, Apple, Inc. incurred costs of $4,490,000,000. Their net profit was $770,000,000. What was Apple's revenue for this quarter? (Source: Apple, Inc.)

CUMULATIVE SKILLS REVIEW

1. Rudy had a beginning balance of $21,125.34 in his checking account. Determine Rudy's balance after checks for $302.45, $18.99, and $57.76 were written. (3.2D)

2. Add $-75 + (-122)$. (9.2A)

3. Convert 32 weeks to days. (6.4A)

4. Write 3.108, 3.0865, 3.405, and 3.4284 in descending order. (3.1D)

5. Write "14 is what percent of 98" as a percent proportion. (5.3A)

6. Evaluate $28 - 8a$ when $a = 3$. (10.1A)

7. Apply the distributive property to simplify $-8(q + 15)$. (10.1C)

8. Write the ratio "16 cats to 6 dogs" as a simplified fraction. (4.1A)

9. What is the length of the diameter of this circle? (7.2B)

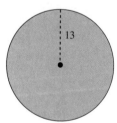

10. Find the mode, if any, of the set of numbers: 25, 62, 27, 56, 25, 67, 25. (8.2C)

10.3 SOLVING AN EQUATION USING THE MULTIPLICATION PROPERTY OF EQUALITY

| Objective 10.3A | Solve an equation using the multiplication property of equality |

In the previous section, we stated a rule that will serve as a guide in solving equations.

What we do to one side of an equation, we must do to the other side.

The **multiplication property of equality** (or **multiplication property**, for short) states that multiplying each side of an equation by the same value preserves equality. Formally, we have the following.

The Multiplication Property of Equality

If a, b, and c are real numbers and if $a = b$, then $a \cdot c = b \cdot c$.

To demonstrate the multiplication property, consider the following equation.

$$2 \cdot 9 = 3 \cdot 6$$

Because both sides simplify to 18, this is a true statement. By the multiplication property, we still have a true statement when we multiply each side of the equation by the same quantity. For example, when we multiply each side by 2, we obtain the following.

$$2 \cdot 9 \cdot 2 = 3 \cdot 6 \cdot 2$$

Note that each side of the equation simplifies to 36.

Now let's consider the following equation.

$$\frac{1}{4}x = 5$$

Our goal is to solve the equation, that is, we must get x by itself on one side of the equation. To do so, we can apply the multiplication property. In particular, we can multiply each side of the equation by 4.

$\frac{1}{4}x = 5$	Original equation.
$4 \cdot \frac{1}{4}x = 4 \cdot 5$	Apply the multiplication property by multiplying each side by 4.
$x = 20$	Simplify.

The solution is $x = 20$. We check the answer as follows.

$\frac{1}{4}(20) \stackrel{?}{=} 5$	Substitute 20 for x.
$5 = 5$	Simplify.

As another example, consider the following equation.

$$3x = 24$$

Once again, our goal is to isolate x by applying the multiplication property of equality. By what number can we multiply each side of the equation to get x alone?

We can multiply by the reciprocal of 3, which is $\frac{1}{3}$.

<table>
<tr><td>$3x = 24$</td><td>Original equation.</td></tr>
<tr><td>$\frac{1}{3} \cdot 3x = \frac{1}{3} \cdot 24$</td><td>Apply the multiplication property by multiplying both sides by $\frac{1}{3}$.</td></tr>
<tr><td>$x = 8$</td><td>Simplify.</td></tr>
</table>

Note that multiplying by $\frac{1}{3}$ is equivalent to dividing by 3. To solve the equation $3x = 24$, we can either multiply each side by $\frac{1}{3}$ or divide each side by 3; the result is the same.

Some times it is useful to think in terms of multiplying by the reciprocal of the coefficient and other times it is more advantageous to think in terms of division. In particular, when the coefficient is a fraction, it is better to multiply each side by the reciprocal of the coefficient. When the coefficient is an integer or a decimal, it is better to divide each side by the coefficient.

The following steps will guide us in solving equations using the multiplication property of equality.

> **◉ Learning Tip**
>
> In general, dividing an expression by a nonzero number is the same as multiplying the expression by the reciprocal of that number.

Steps for Solving an Equation Using the Multiplication Property of Equality

To solve an equation of the form $bx = c$, where b and c are numbers, $b \neq 0$, and x is a variable, perform the following steps.

Step 1. Apply the multiplication property of equality by multiplying each side of the equation by the reciprocal of b. Equivalently, divide each side by b.

Step 2. Simplify and solve for x.

Step 3. Check the solution by substituting into the original equation.

EXAMPLE 1   **Solve an equation using the multiplication property of equality**

Solve $2x = 18$.

SOLUTION STRATEGY

$$\frac{2x}{2} = \frac{18}{2} \qquad \text{Multiply each side by } \frac{1}{2}, \text{ or, equivalently, divide each side by 2.}$$

$$x = 9 \qquad \text{Simplify and solve for } x.$$

$$2 \cdot 9 \overset{?}{=} 18 \qquad \text{Check the solution.}$$

$$18 = 18 \ \checkmark$$

TRY-IT EXERCISE 1

Solve $6x = 48$.

Check your answer with the solution in Appendix A. ■

EXAMPLE 2   Solve an equation using the multiplication property of equality

Solve $-x = -21$.

SOLUTION STRATEGY

$$-1x = -21 \qquad \text{Note that the coefficient of } x \text{ is } -1.$$

$$\frac{-1x}{-1} = \frac{-21}{-1} \qquad \text{Multiply both sides by } -1, \text{ or, equivalently, divide both sides by } -1.$$

$$x = 21 \qquad \text{Simplify and solve for } x.$$

$$-1 \cdot 21 \overset{?}{=} -21 \qquad \text{Check the solution.}$$

$$-21 = -21 \ \checkmark$$

TRY-IT EXERCISE 2

Solve $-x = 15$.

Check your answer with the solution in Appendix A. ■

EXAMPLE 3   Solve an equation using the multiplication property of equality

Solve $\dfrac{2}{3}x = \dfrac{5}{3}$.

SOLUTION STRATEGY

$$\frac{3}{2} \cdot \frac{2}{3}x = \frac{3}{2} \cdot \frac{5}{3} \qquad \text{Multiply each side by } \frac{3}{2}, \text{ the reciprocal of } \frac{2}{3}.$$

$$x = \frac{5}{2} \qquad \text{Simplify and solve for } x.$$

$$\frac{2}{3} \cdot \frac{5}{2} \overset{?}{=} \frac{5}{3} \qquad \text{Check the solution.}$$

$$\frac{5}{3} = \frac{5}{3} \qquad \checkmark$$

TRY-IT EXERCISE 3

Solve $\dfrac{3}{8}x = \dfrac{3}{4}$.

Check your answer with the solution in Appendix A. ■

EXAMPLE 4 **Solve an equation using the multiplication property of equality**

Solve $31.2x = 780$.

SOLUTION STRATEGY

$$\frac{31.2x}{31.2} = \frac{780}{31.2} \qquad \text{Divide each side by 31.2.}$$

$$x = 25 \qquad \text{Simplify and solve for } x.$$

$$31.2 \cdot 25 \overset{?}{=} 780 \qquad \text{Check the solution.}$$

$$780 = 780 \checkmark$$

TRY-IT EXERCISE 4

Solve $58.75x = 940$.

Check your answer with the solution in Appendix A. ■

Objective 10.3B **Apply your knowledge**

In the following problems, we'll use the distance formula, $d = rt$. Here, d represents distance, r represents the rate, and t represents time.

EXAMPLE 5 **Apply your knowledge**

Vicki and Tom decide to take a trip from Milwaukee to Madison. The two cities are 78 miles apart. If Vicki drives at a speed of 60 mph, how long will it take them to make the trip?

SOLUTION STRATEGY

$$rt = d$$

$$60t = 78 \qquad \text{Substitute 60 for } r \text{ and 78 for } d.$$

$$\frac{60t}{60} = \frac{78}{60} \qquad \text{Divide each side by 60.}$$

$$t = \frac{\overset{13}{\cancel{78}}}{\underset{10}{\cancel{60}}} \qquad \text{Simplify and solve for } t.$$

$$t = \frac{13}{10} = 1\frac{3}{10}$$

$$60 \cdot \frac{13}{10} \overset{?}{=} 78 \qquad \text{Check the solution.}$$

$$6 \cdot 13 \overset{?}{=} 78 \qquad \text{Note that } 1\frac{3}{10} \text{ hours is 1 hour and } \frac{3}{10} \text{ of an hour. } \frac{3}{10} \text{ of an hour}$$

$$78 = 78 \; \checkmark$$

$$\text{is 18 minutes. } \frac{3}{\underset{1}{10}} \text{ hour} \cdot \frac{\overset{6}{\cancel{60} \text{ minutes}}}{1 \text{ hour}} = 18 \text{ minutes}$$

It will take Vicki and Tom
1 hour and 18 minutes
to make the trip.

TRY-IT EXERCISE 5

Dominique and her friends in Florida are planning to travel from Miami to Tampa for a
weekend getaway. The two cities are 275 miles apart. If Dominique drives at a speed of
50 mph, how long will it take them to make the trip?

Check your answer with the solution in Appendix A. ■

 SECTION 10.3 REVIEW EXERCISES

Concept Check

1. The _____ property of equality states that multiplying each side of an equation by the same value preserves
equality.

2. To solve equations of the form $bx = c$, where b and c are
numbers, $b \neq 0$, and x is a variable, either multiply each
side of the equation by the _____ of b or, equivalently, divide each side by _____ .

| Objective 10.3A | **Solve an equation using the multiplication property of equality** |

GUIDE PROBLEMS

3. Solve $9x = 45$.

$$\frac{9x}{\underline{}} = \frac{45}{\underline{}}$$

$$x = \underline{}$$

Check:

$$9 \cdot \underline{} \overset{?}{=} 45$$
$$45 = 45 \; \checkmark$$

4. Solve $2.5x = 100$.

$$\frac{2.5x}{\underline{}} = \frac{100}{\underline{}}$$

$$x = \underline{}$$

Check:

$$2.5 \cdot \underline{} \overset{?}{=} 100$$
$$100 = 100 \; \checkmark$$

5. Solve $\dfrac{2}{7}x = \dfrac{1}{3}$.

$$\dfrac{\underline{\quad}}{\underline{\quad}} \cdot \dfrac{2}{7}x = \dfrac{1}{3} \cdot \dfrac{\underline{\quad}}{\underline{\quad}}$$

$$x = \underline{\quad}$$

Check:

$$\dfrac{2}{7} \cdot \dfrac{\underline{\quad}}{\underline{\quad}} \overset{?}{=} \dfrac{1}{3}$$

$$\dfrac{1}{3} = \dfrac{1}{3} \checkmark$$

6. Solve $-x = 15$.

$$\dfrac{-x}{\underline{\quad}} = \dfrac{15}{\underline{\quad}}$$

$$x = \underline{\quad}$$

Check:

$$-(\underline{\quad}) \overset{?}{=} 15$$

$$15 = 15 \checkmark$$

Solve each equation.

7. $3x = 12$

8. $2x = 18$

9. $9t = -45$

10. $6s = -48$

11. $-r = -3$

12. $-k = -13$

13. $-p = 5$

14. $-n = 1$

15. $72 = 6a$

16. $36 = 4b$

17. $50 = -2m$

18. $64 = -8q$

19. $\dfrac{1}{2}x = 3$

20. $\dfrac{1}{3}r = 6$

21. $-\dfrac{b}{2} = 7$

22. $-\dfrac{h}{3} = 7$

23. $\dfrac{1}{2}x = 23$

24. $\dfrac{1}{5}y = 16$

25. $\dfrac{1}{2}r = \dfrac{3}{10}$

26. $\dfrac{2}{3}k = \dfrac{2}{9}$

27. $-5m = \dfrac{1}{4}$

28. $-7a = \dfrac{1}{6}$

29. $-\dfrac{5}{8}z = -12$

30. $-\dfrac{6}{11}p = -21$

31. $-\dfrac{3}{8}x = 9$

32. $-\dfrac{3}{5}r = 12$

33. $\dfrac{1}{9} = \dfrac{2}{7}b$

34. $\dfrac{3}{11} = \dfrac{1}{2}l$

35. $-2.5v = 10$

36. $-3.5w = 21$

37. $-3.3c = 24.75$

38. $3.4d = 7.004$

39. $6.3x = 88.2$

40. $0.8p = 6.4$

41. $1.6r = 5.44$

42. $0.9y = 0.63$

Objective 10.3B   **Apply your knowledge**

In problems 43–45, use the distance formula, $d = rt$, where d represents distance, r represents the rate, and t represents time.

43. Ian and his brother are driving from Detroit to Cincinnati. The two cities are approximately 270 miles apart. If Ian drives at 60 mph, how long will it take them to make the trip?

44. Deana's nonstop flight from Houston to Los Angeles took 3.5 hours. If the total distance traveled was 1463 miles, what was the plane's average speed?

45. A trip from Chicago to London aboard a Boeing 777 aircraft takes 7 hours and 30 minutes. If the distance between the two cities is 4000 miles, what is the average speed of the plane?

CUMULATIVE SKILLS REVIEW

1. Convert 89.9% to a decimal. (5.1A)

2. Convert 65% to a fraction and simplify. (5.1A)

3. Identify and name this figure. (7.1A)

P   D

4. Crop circles are thought to date back to the 17th century. What is the circumference of a crop circle with a radius of 60 feet? Use 3.14 for π. Round to the nearest tenth of a foot. (7.3C)

5. Convert 11.75 km to meters. (6.3A)

6. Apply the distributive property to $7(6p - 5q + 2)$. (10.1C)

7. Evaluate $-20 - 7w + 82$ when $w = 4$. (10.1A)

8. Identify the terms of $40x + 18y + 25z - 99$. (10.1B)

9. Is $t = 9$ a solution of $17 - t = 8$? (10.2A)

10. Solve $a + 16 = 29$. (10.2B)

10.4 SOLVING AN EQUATION USING THE ADDITION AND MULTIPLICATION PROPERTIES

LEARNING OBJECTIVES

A. Solve an equation using the addition and multiplication properties of equality

B. Solve an equation that has parentheses

C. Apply your knowledge

Objective 10.4A   **Solve an equation using the addition and multiplication properties of equality**

To solve an equation such as $3x + 2 = 11$, we cannot *just* add or subtract the same number to or from each side, nor can we *just* multiply or divide each side of the equation by the same number. Rather, we must use a combination of the properties introduced in the previous two sections. The following steps are applied in solving equations like the one above.

Steps for Solving an Equation Using the Addition and Multiplication Properties

To solve an equation of the form $ax + b = c$, where a, b, and c are numbers, $a \neq 0$, and x is a variable, follow these steps.

Step 1. Apply the addition property. That is, add or subtract the same terms to or from each side of the equation so that the variable term is isolated on one side of the equation.

Step 2. Apply the multiplication property. That is, multiply or divide each side of the equation by the same quantity to solve for the variable.

Step 3. Check the solution by substituting into the original equation.

EXAMPLE 1   **Solve an equation that has the variable term on the left side**

Solve $3x + 2 = 11$.

SOLUTION STRATEGY

$$3x + 2 = 11$$
$$\underline{-2 \quad -2}$$ Subtract 2 from each side.
$$3x + 0 = 9$$

$$3x = 9$$ Simplify.

$$\frac{3x}{3} = \frac{9}{3}$$ Divide each side by 3.

$$x = 3$$ Simplify and solve for x.

$$3(3) + 2 \stackrel{?}{=} 11$$ Check the solution.

$$9 + 2 \stackrel{?}{=} 11$$

$$11 = 11 \checkmark$$

TRY-IT EXERCISE 1

Solve $7x + 15 = 71$.

Check your answer with the solution in Appendix A. ∎

It does not matter which side of the equation the variable is on as long as it is isolated. In Example 2, the variable term is on the right side.

EXAMPLE 2   Solve an equation that has the variable term on the right side

Solve $45 = 8t + 13$.

SOLUTION STRATEGY

$$45 = 8t + 13$$
$$\underline{-13 \qquad -13}$$
$$32 = 8t + 0 \qquad \text{Subtract 13 from each side.}$$

$$32 = 8t \qquad \text{Simplify.}$$

$$\frac{32}{8} = \frac{8t}{8} \qquad \text{Divide each side by 8.}$$

$$4 = t \qquad \text{Simplify and solve for } t.$$

$$45 \stackrel{?}{=} 8(4) + 13 \qquad \text{Check the solution.}$$

$$45 \stackrel{?}{=} 32 + 13$$

$$45 = 45 \checkmark$$

TRY-IT EXERCISE 2

Solve $14 = 4y - 22$.

Check your answer with the solution in Appendix A. ■

When a variable term appears on each side of an equation, we must get the variable terms on the same side of the equation so that we can solve the equation. We do so by applying the addition property, as demonstrated in the following example.

EXAMPLE 3   Solve an equation that has variable terms on both sides

Solve $6m = 2m + 28$.

SOLUTION STRATEGY

$$6m = 2m + 28$$
$$\underline{-2m \quad -2m}$$
$$4m = 0m + 28 \qquad \text{Subtract } 2m \text{ from both sides.}$$

$$4m = 28 \qquad \text{Simplify.}$$

$$\frac{4m}{4} = \frac{28}{4} \qquad \text{Divide both sides by 4.}$$

$$m = 7 \qquad \text{Simplify and solve for } m.$$

$$6(7) \stackrel{?}{=} 2(7) + 28 \qquad \text{Check the solution.}$$

$$42 \stackrel{?}{=} 14 + 28$$

$$42 = 42 \checkmark$$

TRY-IT EXERCISE 3

Solve $5k = 2k + 27$.

Check your answer with the solution in Appendix A. ■

When both a variable term and a constant term appear on each side of an equation, we must get the variable terms on one side and the constant terms on the other so that we can solve the equation. We do so by applying the addition property twice, once for the variable term and once for the constant term. The next example illustrates this.

EXAMPLE 4   **Solve an equation that has variable and constant terms on both sides**

Solve $5d + 13 = 3d + 29$.

SOLUTION STRATEGY

$$
\begin{array}{rcl}
5d + 13 &=& 3d + 29 \\
\underline{-3d} && \underline{-3d} \\
2d + 13 &=& 0d + 29
\end{array}
$$
Subtract $3d$ from each side to get the variable terms on one side of the equation.

$2d + 13 = 29$ Simplify.

$$
\begin{array}{rcl}
2d + 13 &=& 29 \\
\underline{-13} && \underline{-13} \\
2d + 0 &=& 16
\end{array}
$$
Subtract 13 from each side to get the constant terms on the other side of the equation.

$2d = 16$ Simplify.

$\dfrac{2d}{2} = \dfrac{16}{2}$ Divide each side by 2.

$d = 8$ Simplify and solve for d.

$5(8) + 13 \stackrel{?}{=} 3(8) + 29$ Check the solution.

$40 + 13 \stackrel{?}{=} 24 + 29$

$53 = 53$ ✓

TRY-IT EXERCISE 4

Solve $7b + 14 = 4b + 35$.

Check your answer with the solution in Appendix A. ■

Objective 10.4B   **Solve an equation that has parentheses**

When an equation contains parentheses, first simplify within the parentheses, if possible. Then, apply the distributive property to remove the parentheses. Finally, collect and combine like terms and continue to solve the equation in the usual way. The following general equation-solving strategy summarizes this process.

Steps for Solving an Equation

Step 1. Simplify within parentheses, if possible.

Step 2. Apply the distributive property. Collect and combine like terms, if necessary.

Step 3. Apply the addition property. Isolate variable terms on one side and constant terms on the other.

Step 4. Apply the multiplication property to solve for the variable.

Step 5. Check the solution by substituting into the original equation.

EXAMPLE 5   Solve an equation that has parentheses

Solve $2(2x + 1) + 3x = 3(x + 3) + 1$.

SOLUTION STRATEGY

$$2(2x + 1) + 3x = 3(x + 3) + 1$$

$$4x + 2 + 3x = 3x + 9 + 1 \qquad \text{Apply the distributive property.}$$

$$7x + 2 = 3x + 10 \qquad \text{Collect and combine like terms.}$$

$$\begin{array}{r} 7x + 2 = 3x + 10 \\ -3x \qquad -3x \\ \hline 4x + 2 = 0x + 10 \end{array} \qquad \text{Subtract } 3x \text{ from each side.}$$

$$4x + 2 = 10 \qquad \text{Simplify.}$$

$$\begin{array}{r} 4x + 2 = 10 \\ -2 \quad -2 \\ \hline 4x + 0 = 8 \end{array} \qquad \text{Subtract 2 from each side.}$$

$$4x = 8 \qquad \text{Simplify.}$$

$$\frac{4x}{4} = \frac{8}{4} \qquad \text{Divide each side by 4.}$$

$$x = 2 \qquad \text{Simplify and solve for } x.$$

$$2(2 \cdot 2 + 1) + 3 \cdot 2 \stackrel{?}{=} 3(2 + 3) + 1 \qquad \text{Check the solution.}$$

$$2(4 + 1) + 6 \stackrel{?}{=} 3(2 + 3) + 1$$

$$2(5) + 6 \stackrel{?}{=} 3(5) + 1$$

$$10 + 6 \stackrel{?}{=} 15 + 1$$

$$16 = 16 \checkmark$$

TRY-IT EXERCISE 5

Solve $3(-3x + 5 + 7x) - 2x = 5(-4 + x + 2)$.

Check your answer with the solution in Appendix A. ■

EXAMPLE 6 **Solve an equation that has parentheses**

Solve $2(x + 4) + x = -(x + 5) + 13$.

SOLUTION STRATEGY

$$2(x + 4) + x = -(x + 5) + 13$$

$$2x + 8 + x = -x + (-5) + 13 \qquad \text{Apply the distributive property.}$$

$$3x + 8 = -x + 8 \qquad \text{Collect and combine like terms.}$$

$$\begin{array}{r} 3x + 8 = -x + 8 \\ \underline{+\ x \qquad\quad +x} \\ 4x + 8 = \ 0x + 8 \end{array} \qquad \text{Add } x \text{ to each side.}$$

$$4x + 8 = 8 \qquad \text{Simplify.}$$

$$\begin{array}{r} 4x + 8 = \ 8 \\ \underline{-8 \quad -8} \\ 4x + 0 = \ 0 \end{array} \qquad \text{Subtract 8 from each side.}$$

$$4x = 0 \qquad \text{Simplify.}$$

$$\frac{4x}{4} = \frac{0}{4} \qquad \text{Divide each side by 4.}$$

$$x = 0 \qquad \text{Simplify and solve for } x.$$

$$2(0 + 4) + 0 \stackrel{?}{=} -(0 + 5) + 13 \qquad \text{Check the solution.}$$

$$2(4) + 0 \stackrel{?}{=} -(5) + 13$$

$$8 + 0 \stackrel{?}{=} -5 + 13$$

$$8 = 8 \ \checkmark$$

> ● *Learning Tip*
>
> Zero can be a valid
> solution to an equation.
> If 0 makes the equation
> a true statement, then it is
> a solution.

TRY-IT EXERCISE 6

Solve $5(x + 4) - 3x = 4x + 2(x + 10)$.

Check your answer with the solution in Appendix A. ■

Objective 10.4C **Apply your knowledge**

In the following problems, we'll use the formula for the perimeter of a rectangle,
$P = 2l + 2w$.

EXAMPLE 7 **Apply your knowledge**

A rectangular plot garden has a perimeter of 34 feet. If the length is 11 feet, find the width.

SOLUTION STRATEGY

$$P = 2l + 2w$$

$$34 = 2(11) + 2w \qquad \text{Substitute 34 for } P \text{ and 11 for } l.$$

$$34 = 22 + 2w \qquad \text{Multiply 2(11).}$$

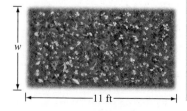

w

├──────11 ft──────┤

$$34 = 22 + 2w$$
$$\underline{-22 \quad -22}$$ Subtract 22 from each side.
$$12 = \quad 0 + 2w$$

$$12 = 2w$$

$$\frac{12}{2} = \frac{2w}{2}$$ Divide each side by 2.

$$6 = w$$ Simplify and solve for w.

$$34 \overset{?}{=} 2(11) + 2(6)$$ Check the solution.

$$34 \overset{?}{=} 22 + 12$$

$$34 = 34 \checkmark$$

The width of the garden is 6 feet.

TRY-IT EXERCISE 7

A rectangular living room has a perimeter of 70 feet. If the width is 14 feet, find the length.

Check your answer with the solution in Appendix A. ■

SECTION 10.4 REVIEW EXERCISES

Concept Check

1. To solve the equation $2x + 1 = 7$, first _____ 1 from each side of the equation. Then, _____ each side of the equation by 2.

2. To solve the equation $\dfrac{2}{3}x - 3 = 4$, first _____ 3 to each side of the equation. Then, _____ both sides of the equation by $\dfrac{3}{2}$.

Objective 10.4A   Solve an equation using the addition and multiplication properties of equality

GUIDE PROBLEMS

3. Solve $3x + 14 = 35$.

   a. Apply the addition property to isolate the variable term on one side of the equation.

$$3x + 14 = 35$$
$$\underline{- \quad \quad -}$$
$$3x + \quad 0 = \_\_\_$$
$$3x = \_\_\_$$

   b. Apply the multiplication property to solve for the variable.

$$\frac{3x}{\_\_} = \frac{21}{\_\_}$$
$$x = \_\_$$

4. Solve $5 - x = 11$.

   a. Apply the addition property to isolate the variable term on one side of the equation.

$$5 - x = 11$$
$$\underline{- \quad \quad -}$$
$$0 - x = \_\_\_$$
$$-x = \_\_\_$$

   b. Apply the multiplication property of equality to solve for the variable.

$$\frac{-x}{\_\_} = \frac{6}{\_\_}$$
$$x = \_\_$$

c. Check the solution.

$$3(\underline{}) + 14 \overset{?}{=} 35$$
$$\underline{} + 14 \overset{?}{=} 35$$
$$\underline{} = 35$$

5. Solve $4x = 2x + 36$.

  a. Apply the addition property to isolate the variable term on one side of the equation.

$$4x = 2x + 36$$
$$\underline{} = \underline{}$$
$$\underline{} = \ 0 \ + 36$$
$$\underline{} = 36$$

  b. Apply the multiplication property to solve for the variable.

$$\frac{2x}{\underline{}} = \frac{36}{\underline{}}$$
$$x = \underline{}$$

  c. Check the solution.

$$4(\underline{}) \overset{?}{=} 2(\underline{}) + 36$$
$$\underline{} \overset{?}{=} \underline{} + 36$$
$$72 = 72 \ \checkmark$$

c. Check the solution.

$$5 - (\underline{}) \overset{?}{=} 1$$
$$\underline{} = 11$$

6. Solve $5x + 11 = 3x + 33$.

  a. Apply the addition property to get the variable term on one side of the equation.

$$5x + 11 = \ 3x + 33$$
$$\underline{} = \ \underline{}$$
$$\underline{} + 11 = \ 0x + 33$$
$$\underline{} + 11 = 33$$

  b. Apply the addition property to isolate the variable term on one side of the equation.

$$\underline{} + 11 = \ 33$$
$$\underline{} = \ \underline{}$$
$$\underline{} + \ 0 = \ \underline{}$$
$$2x = \underline{}$$

  c. Apply the multiplication property to solve for the variable.

$$\frac{2x}{\underline{}} = \frac{22}{\underline{}}$$
$$x = \underline{}$$

  d. Check the solution.

$$5(\underline{}) + 11 \overset{?}{=} 3(\underline{}) + 33$$
$$\underline{} + 11 \overset{?}{=} \underline{} + 33$$
$$66 = 66 \ \checkmark$$

Solve each equation.

7. $2x + 6 = 12$

8. $4y + 3 = 19$

9. $3n + 6 = 24$

10. $5t + 8 = 43$

11. $5x + 7 = 7$

12. $4d - 3 = -3$

13. $3r - 6 = 21$

14. $7b - 8 = 48$

15. $3q + 4 = -14$

16. $5d + 3 = -22$

17. $-3p + 6 = 15$

18. $-8t + 3 = 27$

19. $-7m - 12 = 51$

20. $-6v - 7 = 53$

21. $\dfrac{x}{3} + 5 = 11$

22. $\dfrac{x}{8} + 1 = 8$

23. $\dfrac{y}{2} + 15 = -42$

24. $\dfrac{d}{7} - 3 = 2$

25. $\dfrac{z}{2} - 7 = -6$

26. $\dfrac{a}{4} - 4 = -6$

27. $-6 + \dfrac{x}{3} = 5$

28. $2 - \dfrac{2}{9}y = 8$

29. $4x + 9 = 3$

30. $3d + 2 = 3$

31. $\dfrac{1}{4} - \dfrac{x}{16} = \dfrac{1}{8}$

32. $\dfrac{x}{2} - \dfrac{1}{3} = \dfrac{1}{6}$

33. $\dfrac{1}{3}x + \dfrac{2}{3} = \dfrac{3}{4}$

34. $\dfrac{5}{6}x + \dfrac{2}{3} = \dfrac{5}{6}$

35. $6 - 5x = 24$

36. $7 + 2t = 18$

37. $3.3m - 2.1 = 7.8$

38. $2k - 3.1 = 6.9$

39. $3x = 2x + 6$

40. $5y = 4y + 9$

41. $12t = 3t + 72$

42. $10r = 2r + 16$

43. $9a - 3 = 3a$

44. $23 - 11b = 35b$

45. $5w = -7w + 8$

46. $2v = -6v + 5$

47. $2d - 2 = 6d + 6$

48. $5c - 6 = 3c - 12$

49. $6 + 2u = 3u - 12$

50. $5z + 3 = 6z - 6$

51. $6m - 1 = m - 26$

52. $5n + 2 = 3n - 6$

53. $2p - 17 = 3p - 3$

54. $41 - s = -1 - 7s$

55. $8.2q + 4.1 = 3.4q - 5.5$

56. $3.4t - 3.9 = 2.1t + 1.3$

57. $0.8x - 3.7 = 0.9x + 0.8$

58. $0.2y - 4.3 = 0.4y + 3.1$

59. $3c + 4 = c + 5$

60. $6b + 5 = 3b + 6$

61. $5q - 1 = 2q + 6$

62. $8v - 3 = 3v + 9$

63. $-\dfrac{1}{2}a - 2 = a + 4$

64. $2h + 3 = \dfrac{1}{2}h + 9$

65. $\dfrac{1}{3}m - \dfrac{1}{2} = -\dfrac{2}{3}m + \dfrac{1}{4}$

66. $\dfrac{2}{5}k + \dfrac{1}{3} = \dfrac{2}{3}k - \dfrac{3}{5}$

Objective 10.4B	Solve an equation that has parentheses

GUIDE PROBLEMS

67. Solve the equation $3(x + 2) = 2(x + 6)$.

  a. Apply the distributive property.
  $$3(x + 2) = 2(x + 6)$$
  $$3x + 6 = \underline{} + \underline{}$$

  b. Use the addition property to get the variable term on one side of the equation.
  $$3x + 6 = \underline{} + \underline{}$$
  $$\underline{-2x} \qquad \underline{} - \underline{}$$
  $$\underline{} + 6 = 0x + \underline{}$$
  $$\underline{} + 6 = \underline{}$$

  c. Use the addition property to isolate the variable term on one side of the equation.
  $$\underline{} + 6 = \underline{}$$
  $$\underline{} - \underline{} \quad \underline{} - \underline{}$$
  $$\underline{} + 0 = \underline{}$$
  $$x = \underline{}$$

  d. Check the solution.
  $$3(\underline{} + 2) \stackrel{?}{=} 2(\underline{} + 6)$$
  $$3(\underline{}) \stackrel{?}{=} 2(\underline{})$$
  $$24 = 24 \checkmark$$

68. Solve the equation $2(x + 9) = 3(3x - 1)$.

  a. Apply the distributive property.
  $$2(x + 9) = 3(3x - 1)$$
  $$2x + 18 = \underline{} - \underline{}$$

  b. Apply the addition property to get the variable term on one side of the equation.
  $$2x + 18 = \underline{} - \underline{}$$
  $$\underline{} \qquad \underline{-2x}$$
  $$0x + 18 = \underline{} - \underline{}$$
  $$18 = \underline{} - \underline{}$$

  c. Apply the addition property to isolate the variable term on one side of the equation.
  $$18 = \underline{} - \underline{}$$
  $$+\underline{} \qquad +\underline{}$$
  $$\underline{} = \underline{} + 0$$
  $$21 = \underline{}$$

  d. Use the multiplication property to solve for the variable.
  $$\frac{21}{\underline{}} = \frac{\underline{}}{\underline{}}$$
  $$\underline{} \qquad \underline{}$$
  $$\underline{} = x$$

  e. Check the solution.
  $$2(\underline{} + 9) \stackrel{?}{=} 3(3 \cdot \underline{} - 1)$$
  $$2(\underline{}) \stackrel{?}{=} 3(\underline{} - 1)$$
  $$24 \stackrel{?}{=} 3(\underline{})$$
  $$24 = 24 \checkmark$$

Solve each equation.

69. $3(2x - 5) = 21$

70. $5(3x - 4) = 40$

71. $6(5r + 2) = 36$

72. $7(3p + 4) = 40$

73. $2(3s - 5) = 8s$

74. $6(3t - 7) = 11t$

75. $12x - 3(x - 5) = -12$

76. $5p - (3p + 4) = 16$

77. $5(x + 8) = 7(x - 4)$

78. $5(y + 4) = 6(y - 2)$

79. $4(2a - 1) = 2(3a - 2)$

80. $5(4 - 3q) = -5(q - 4)$

81. $\dfrac{1}{3}(4b + 9) = \dfrac{2}{3}b - 7$

82. $\dfrac{5}{7}(v - 2) = \dfrac{2}{7}v - 4$

83. $\dfrac{1}{3}(x - 2) = \dfrac{4}{3} - x$

84. $\dfrac{1}{5}(y + 4) = \dfrac{3}{5}y + 3$

| Objective 10.4C | Apply your knowledge |

In problems 85–87, use the formula for the perimeter of a rectangle, $P = 2l + 2w$.

85. The perimeter of a rectangle is 32 inches. If the width is 7 inches, find the length.

86. A standard note card has a perimeter of 16 inches. If the length is 5 inches, find the width.

87. A rectangular serving tray with a perimeter of 52 inches can fit 16 tightly packed square hors d'oeuvres along each of its longest sides. If each hors d'oeuvre has an area of 1 square inch, how many can fit side by side along each of the tray's shortest sides?

CUMULATIVE SKILLS REVIEW

1. Write "3 course credits is to $750 as 12 course credits is to $3000" as a proportion. (4.3A)

2. Solve $3x = 30$. (10.3A)

3. Solve $110.4z = 552$. (10.3A)

4. What number is 30% of $1500? (5.2B, 5.3B)

5. Combine like terms and evaluate $8v - 17y - 3y + 21v$ when $y = 2$, $v = 3$. (10.1A, B)

6. Apply the distributive property to $(8r + 7f - 10)6$ and evaluate when $r = 5$ and $f = -2$. (10.1B, C)

7. According to the CIA World Factbook, the life expectancy for females is about 80.67 years and about 74.89 years for males. How many more years are females expected to live? About how many more days are females expected to live? Round to the nearest whole day. (6.5A)

8. The game of billiards can be played in many ways. A regulation size billiard ball has a diameter of 2.25 inches. What is the circumference? Use 3.14 for π. Round to the nearest hundredth if necessary. (7.3C)

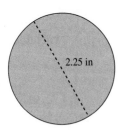

2.25 in

9. Use the addition property of equality to solve $23 + s = 55$. (10.3B)

10. Calculate the GPA using this information. (8.2A)

COURSE	CREDITS	GRADE
Architecture	3	B
English	3	A
AP Math	4	B

10.5 SOLVING APPLICATION PROBLEMS

In this chapter, we learned to solve equations using the addition and multiplication properties of equality. At the end of each section, we solved some applied problems by substituting values into a formula and solving for the unknown quantity. In this section, we will solve applied problems by translating sentences into equations. We'll then develop a problem-solving strategy for solving applied problems.

Objective 10.5A   **Translate a sentence to an equation**

In Section 1.7, we introduced a number of key words and phrases that are used to indicate the basic operations and equality. Below is our list of these common key words and phrases.

KEY WORDS AND PHRASES FOR SOLVING APPLICATION PROBLEMS

ADDITION +	SUBTRACTION −	MULTIPLICATION ×	DIVISION ÷	EQUALS SIGN =
add	subtract	multiply	divide	equals
plus	minus	times	divided by	is
sum	difference	product	quotient	are
increased by	decreased by	product of	quotient of	yields
total of	take away	multiplied by	divided into	leaves
more than	reduced by	of	goes into	gives
greater than	deducted from	at	ratio of	makes
and	less than	twice	average of	results in
added to	fewer than	double	per	provides
gain of	subtracted from	triple	equally divided	produces

We will use these key words and phrases to translate sentences involving unknown quantities into equations. In doing this, we will represent the unknown by a variable.

EXAMPLE 1   **Translate sentences into equations**

Translate each sentence into an equation.

a. A number increased by 2 is 14.

b. A number reduced by 8 equals 11.

c. The product of 4 and a number is 48.

d. The quotient of a number and 8 yields 7.

e. Five times the sum of a number and 3 is 35.

SOLUTION STRATEGY

a.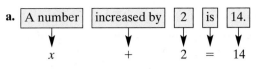

$x + 2 = 14$

The phrase *increased by* indicates addition.

The key word *is* indicates equality.

b.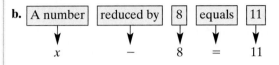

$x - 8 = 11$

The phrase *reduced by* indicates subtraction.

The key word *equals* indicates equality.

c.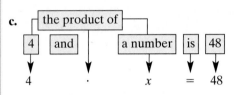

$4x = 48$

The phrase *the product of* indicates multiplication.

The key word *is* indicates equality.

d.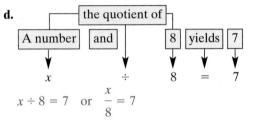

$x \div 8 = 7$ or $\dfrac{x}{8} = 7$

The phrase *the quotient of* indicates division.

The key word *yields* indicates equality.

e.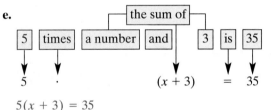

$5(x + 3) = 35$

The key word *times* indicates multiplication. The phrase *the sum of* indicates addition.

The key word *is* indicates equality.

TRY-IT EXERCISE 1

Translate each sentence into an equation.

a. A number added to 10 gives 29.

b. Fifteen decreased by a number yields 12.

c. A number multiplied by 8 gives -32.

d. Ten divided by a number is $\dfrac{1}{2}$.

e. Twenty-five divided by the difference of 7 and a number is 5.

Check your answer with the solution in Appendix A. ■

Objective 10.5B   **Apply your knowledge**

One of the primary objectives of studying arithmetic and algebra is to develop the skill needed to solve applied problems. In Section 1.7, we outlined a problem-solving strategy. Below is a slightly revised version of this strategy.

Steps for Solving Application Problems

Step 1. *Read and understand the problem.* You may have to read the problem several times. To visualize the problem, draw a picture if possible.

Step 2. *Assign a variable to the unknown quantity.* If there is more than one unknown, express the others in terms of the chosen variable.

Step 3. *Translate the problem into an equation.*

Step 4. *Solve the equation.*

Step 5. *Check the solution.*

Step 6. *Clearly state the result using units, if necessary.*

EXAMPLE 2   Find an unknown number

Twice a number decreased by 5 is equal to the number increased by 9. Determine the number.

SOLUTION STRATEGY   *Read and understand the problem.*

Let $x =$ the number.   *Assign a variable to the unknown quantity.*

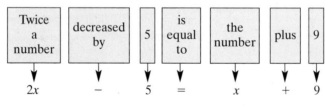

Translate the problem into an equation.

$2x - 5 = x + 9$

$$
\begin{array}{l}
2x - 5 = x + 9 \\
\underline{-x \qquad -x} \\
\ \ x - 5 = 0x + 9
\end{array}
$$

Subtract x from each side.

$x - 5 = 9$

Simplify.

$$
\begin{array}{l}
x - 5 = \ \ 9 \\
\underline{+5 \quad +5} \\
x + 0 = 14
\end{array}
$$

Add 5 to each side.

$x = 14$

Simplify and solve for x.

$2(14) - 5 \stackrel{?}{=} 14 + 9$

Check the solution.

$28 - 5 \stackrel{?}{=} 23$

$23 = 23$

The number is 14.   *State the result.*

TRY-IT EXERCISE 2

Three times a number added to 5 is 26. Determine the number.

Check your answer with the solution in Appendix A. ■

EXAMPLE 3   Find an unknown quantity

ABC Truck Rentals rents a small truck for $29.95 per day plus $0.90 per mile. Wanda needs to move several pieces of furniture across the state in a single day. If her budget is $250, how many miles can she drive?

SOLUTION STRATEGY

Read and understand the problem.

Let x = the number of miles Wanda can drive

Assign a variable to the unknown quantity.

daily rate	plus	cost per mile	times	number of miles	equals	total budget
$\downarrow$	$\downarrow$	$\downarrow$	$\downarrow$	$\downarrow$	$\downarrow$	$\downarrow$
29.95	+	0.90	·	x	=	250

Translate the problem into an equation.

$29.95 + 0.90x = 250.00$

Solve the equation.

$$29.95 + 0.90x = 250.00$$
$$\underline{-29.95 \qquad\qquad -29.95}$$
$$0 + 0.90x = 220.05$$

Subtract 29.95 from each side.

$$0.90x = 220.05$$

Simplify.

$$\frac{0.90x}{0.90} = \frac{220.05}{0.90}$$

Divide each side by 0.90.

$$x = 244.5$$

Simplify and solve for x.

$29.95 + 0.90 \cdot 244.5 \stackrel{?}{=} 250$

Check the solution.

$29.95 + 220.05 \stackrel{?}{=} 250$

$250 = 250$ ✓

Wanda can drive 244.5 miles.

State the result.

TRY-IT EXERCISE 3

Lights Plus sells a 72-inch brushed-steel track lighting fixture for $180. Each fixture has 6 outlets for bulbs. If each bulb costs $5, determine how many such fixtures with bulbs you can purchase for $630.

Check your answer with the solution in Appendix A. ■

In the next example, we are given a triangle in which the lengths of all three sides are unknown. We do this problem by choosing a variable to represent the lengths of one of the sides. We then express the lengths of the remaining sides in terms of the chosen variable.

EXAMPLE 4 Find the perimeter of a triangle

The triangle shown in the illustration is such that side b is four times as long as side a, and side c is 10 inches shorter than side b. The perimeter of the triangle is 71 inches. Determine the lengths of sides a, b, and c.

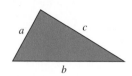

SOLUTION STRATEGY

Read and understand the problem.

In this problem, only the perimeter is known; it is 71 inches. The lengths of the three sides are not known, but we are given information about them. In particular, we know that side b is four times as long as side a, and c is 10 inches less than side b.

Let $a =$ length of side a *Assign a variable to the unknown quantity.*
Let $4a =$ length of side b
Let $4a - 10 =$ length of side c

$a + 4a + 4a - 10 = 71$ *Translate the problem into an equation.*

The perimeter of a triangle with sides of length a, b, and c is given by the formula $P = a + b + c$.

$a + 4a + 4a - 10 = 71$ *Solve the equation.*

$9a - 10 = 71$ Combine like terms.

$$\begin{array}{rr} 9a - 10 = & 71 \\ + 10 & +10 \\ \hline 9a + 0 = & 81 \end{array}$$ Add 10 to each side.

$9a = 81$ Simplify.

$\dfrac{9a}{9} = \dfrac{81}{9}$ Divide each side by 9.

$a = 9$ Simplify and solve for a.

$9 + 4(9) + 4(9) - 10 \overset{?}{=} 71$ *Check the solution.*
$9 + 36 + 36 - 10 \overset{?}{=} 71$
$71 = 71 \checkmark$

length of side a: 9 inches   *State the result.*
length of side b: 36 inches
length of side c: 26 inches

TRY-IT EXERCISE 4

The length of a rectangle is 3 less than four times its width. The perimeter of the rectangle is 24 meters. Determine the length and width of the rectangle.

Check your answer with the solution in Appendix A. ∎

SECTION 10.5 REVIEW EXERCISES

Concept Check

1. To solve an application problem, first _____ and understand the problem.

2. Next, assign a _____ to the unknown quantity. Express other unknowns in terms of the chosen variable.

3. Next, translate the problem into an _____ .

4. Once you have an equation, _____ it.

5. Always _____ the solution.

6. Once you have checked the solution, clearly _____ the result using units, if necessary.

Objective 10.5A   **Translate a sentence to an equation**

GUIDE PROBLEMS

7. A number decreased by 15 is 23.

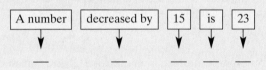

8. The product of 7 and a number is 12.

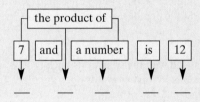

Translate each sentence into an equation.

9. A number increased by 7 is 15.

10. The difference of 8 and a number is -3.

11. Three times a number is 15.

12. The quotient of 48 and a number is 6.

13. The product of -8 and a number is $\dfrac{1}{2}$.

14. Five times a number is $-\dfrac{2}{3}$.

15. Twice a number added to 8 is 38.

16. Ten subtracted from twice a number is 12.

17. Eighteen decreased by two-thirds of a number is 10.

18. Half of a number plus 19 is 15.

19. The product of 3 and the sum of a number and 10 is 36.

20. The quotient of 54 and the difference of a number and 6 is 9.

Write an equation to represent each situation. Then, solve the equation.

21. A number increased by 8 is 15. Find the number.

22. The difference between a number and 18 is 41. Find the number.

23. Three times a number is $\frac{1}{4}$. Find the number.

24. The quotient of 63 and a number is 7. Find the number.

25. Five subtracted from twice a number is 3. Find the number.

26. Seven subtracted from 5 times a number is 33. Find the number.

27. The sum of a number and 4 is equal to twice the number. Find the number.

28. The sum of 12 and twice a number is equal to four times the number. Find the number.

29. Six less than a number is three times the sum of 4 and the number. Find the number.

30. Six times the difference of a number and 3 is 2 less than twice the number. Find the number.

31. An airplane's speed with the wind at its back is 505 mph. If the wind speed is 55 mph, how fast does the plane fly without the wind?

32. An exercise machine is on sale for $120 less than the regular price. The sale price is $599. Find the regular price.

33. The length of a house is 21.5 feet more than its width. If the length of the house is 78 feet, what is the width?

34. A trail begins at an altitude of 487 meters and ends at an altitude of 973 meters. If a hiker climbs from the beginning to the end of the trail, what is the net change in altitude?

35. Taipei 101, a building in Taipei, Taiwan, is 979 feet shorter than the Burj Dubai, a building in Dubai, UAE. If Taipei 101 is 1671 feet tall, find the height of the Burj Dubai.

36. One hundred thirty-five seniors made the honor roll. This represents one-fourth of the senior class. How many students are in the senior class?

37. After conducting research on ocean kelp, a scientist found that it grows at a steady rate of 0.45 meters per day. If the kelp grew 12.6 meters, determine the number of days that the experiment lasted.

38. An auditorium can seat 45 people in each row. How many full rows will be needed if 675 people are expected to attend a lecture?

39. If a large 8-slice margherita pizza from Skeeter's Pizza costs $14.00, how much does each slice cost?

40. One case of DVDs containing 48 units sold for $408.00. Find the cost of each DVD.

41. A parking garage charges $3.00 for the first hour or part thereof. Each additional hour or part thereof costs $1.50. If Eric has exactly $15.00 to spend on parking, how many hours can he park in this lot?

42. At Phones West, long distance phone calls cost $0.55 for the first minute and $0.25 for each additional minute, plus an additional $1.50 service charge. If the total charge of a call is $10.30, how long did the call last?

43. Carmen is selling tickets to a school function. The tickets are $7.50 for adults and $4.00 for students. She sells three times as many adult tickets as student tickets. If the ticket sales totaled $795.00, how many of each type of ticket did Carmen sell?

44. Marty's salary started at $26,000 per year with annual raises of $3000. Janice's salary started at $29,000 per year with annual raises of $2000. Marty and Janice were hired at the same time. After how many years will both employees earn the same salary?

45. The triangle shown in the illustration is such that side a is four times as long as side b, and side c is 5 inches shorter than side a. The perimeter of the triangle is 40 inches. Determine the lengths of sides a, b, and c.

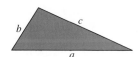

46. A rectangle is such that its length is twice the difference of its width and 4 inches. The perimeter of the rectangle is 38 inches. Determine the length and width.

47. A 250-foot piece of rope is cut into three pieces. The first piece is twice as long as the third piece and the second piece is 4 feet longer than three times the third piece. What is the length of each piece?

48. A 10-foot board is cut into three pieces. The second piece is twice as long as the first, and the third piece is a foot longer than the first. How long is each piece?

CUMULATIVE SKILLS REVIEW

1. Simplify $16 \cdot 3 - (5 + 1)^2$. (1.6C)

2. Multiply $2\dfrac{1}{2} \cdot 9\dfrac{2}{3}$. Simplify, if possible. (2.4B)

3. Divide $\dfrac{23.12}{4}$. (3.4A)

4. A 12-ounce can of soda costs \$1.00. What is the unit price? Round to the nearest cent. (4.2C)

5. What is 15% of 600? (5.2B, 5.3B)

6. Convert 5 yards to feet. (6.1A)

7. Calculate the mean of the following set of numbers: 7, 4, 6, 4, 2, 9, 5, 3 (8.2A)

8. Subtract $-\dfrac{1}{5} - \left(-\dfrac{2}{3}\right)$. (9.3A)

9. Apply the distribution property to simplify $(7l - 6)8$. (10.1C)

10. Solve $15h + 5 = 72.5$. (10.4A)

10-MINUTE CHAPTER REVIEW

10.1 Algebraic Expressions

Objective	Important Concepts	Illustrative Examples
A. Evaluate an algebraic expression (page 700)	**variable** A letter or some other symbol that represents a number whose value is unknown. **algebraic expression or expression** A mathematical statement that consists of numbers, variables, operation symbols, and possibly grouping symbols. **evaluate an expression** To replace each variable of an algebraic expression with a particular value and find the value of the expression. **Steps for Evaluating Algebraic Expressions** **Step 1.** Substitute a value for the indicated variable into the algebraic expression. **Step 2.** Find the value of the expression by performing the indicated operations.	Evaluate each algebraic expression when $n = 5$. **a.** $18 - 3n$ $18 - 3(5)$ $18 - 15$ 3 **b.** $21n + 45$ $21(5) + 45$ $105 + 45$ 150 **c.** $7n - 10$ $7(5) - 10$ $35 - 10$ 25
B. Combine like terms (page 701)	**term** An addend in an algebraic expression. **variable term** A term that contains a variable. **constant term** A term that is a number. **numerical coefficient or coefficient** A number factor in a variable term. **Distributive Property** For any numbers a, b, and c, we have the following. $$ac + bc = (a + b)c$$ and $$ac - bc = (a - b)c$$ **Commutative Property** Changing the order of the addends does not change the sum. Likewise, changing the order of factors does not change the product. That is, for any numbers a and b, we have the following. $$a + b = b + a \text{ and } ab = ba$$	Identify the variable and constant terms in each expression. Also, identify the coefficient of each variable term. **a.** $18 + 3p - 12 + 6$ Variable term: $3p$ Constant terms: $18, -12, 6$ Coefficient of $3p$: 3 **b.** $55 - 7x - 9 + 33y$ Variable terms: $-7x, 33y$ Constant terms: $55, -9$ Coefficient of $-7x$: -7 Coefficient of $33y$: 33 **c.** $200 + 8r + 5s - 7$ Variable terms: $8r, 5s$ Constant terms: $200, -7$ Coefficient of $8r$: 8 Coefficient of $5s$: 5 Combine like terms to simplify each expression. **a.** $33x + 2 - 8x + 7$ $(33x - 8x) + (2 + 7)$ $25x + 9$

Associative Property

Changing the grouping of addends does not change the sum. Likewise, changing the grouping of factors does not change the product. That is, for any numbers a, b, and c, we have the following.

$$a + (b + c) = (a + b) + c \quad \text{and}$$
$$a(bc) = (ab)c$$

collecting like terms
Changing the order of terms using the commutative property and grouping like terms using the associative property.

combining like terms
Adding like terms in an algebraic expression.

b. $20a - 4 + 5a + 13$

$(20a + 5a) + (-4 + 13)$

$25a + 9$

c. $x^2 + 3x - 5x^2 + 7x$

$(x^2 - 5x^2) + (3x + 7x)$

$-4x^2 + 10x$

C. Multiply expressions (page 705)

Use the associative property of multiplication to regroup number factors to determine a product such as $4(5x)$.

$$4(5x) = (4 \cdot 5)x = 20x$$

Use the distributive property to multiply expressions such as $3(x + 4)$.

$$3(x + 4) = 3 \cdot x + 3 \cdot 4 = 3x + 12$$

Multiply. Simplify, if possible.

a. $9(8x)$

$(9 \cdot 8)x$

$72x$

b. $-3(12y)$

$(-3 \cdot 12)y$

$-36y$

Simplify each expression by applying the distributive property.

a. $4(3x + 12)$

$12x + 48$

b. $(11 - 2y)5$

$55 - 10y$

c. $(-9)(8 + 2v - 5)$

$-72 - 18v + 45$

D. Apply your knowledge (page 707)

The AC Master Company stock did extremely well this past year. The stock price gained $10.76 between January 5, 2007, and January 5, 2008. Let b represent the stock price on January 5, 2007.

a. Write an algebraic expression that represents the stock price on January 5, 2008, in terms of b.

$b + \$10.76$

b. If the AC Master Company stock price was $23.27 on January 5, 2007, evaluate the expression in part a.

$34.03

10.2 Solving an Equation Using the Addition Property of Equality

Objective	Important Concepts	Illustrative Examples
A. Verify a solution to an equation (page 713)	**equation** A mathematical statement consisting of two expressions on either side of an equals (=) sign. **solution** A value of the variable that makes the equation a true statement.	Determine whether the given value is the solution to the given equation. **a.** $h = 2$; $5h + 3 = 13$ $5(2) + 3 \stackrel{?}{=} 13$ $10 + 3 \stackrel{?}{=} 13$ $13 = 13$ ✓ 2 is a solution.

b. $w = 4; -5 + 8w = 19$

$$-5 + 8(4) \stackrel{?}{=} 19$$
$$-5 + 32 \stackrel{?}{=} 19$$
$$27 = 19 ✗$$

4 is not a solution.

B. Solve an equation using the addition property of equality (page 714)

addition property of equality or **addition property**
Property stating that adding the same value to each side of an equation preserves equality.

The Addition Property of Equality
If a, b, and c are real numbers and if $a = b$, then $a + c = b + c$.

solving an equation
The process of finding a solution to an equation involving a variable.

checking the answer
The process of verifying that we get a true statement when we substitute the answer into the original equation.

Steps for Solving an Equation Using the Addition Property of Equality

To solve an equation of the form $x + b = c$, where b and c are numbers and x is a variable, follow these steps.

Step 1. Apply the addition property of equality by adding the opposite of b to each side of the equation.

Step 2. Simplify and solve for x.

Step 3. Check the solution by substituting into the original equation.

Solve each equation.

a. $6 + k = 19$

$$\begin{array}{r} 6 + k = 19 \\ -6 \quad\; -6 \\ \hline 0 + k = 13 \end{array}$$
$$k = 13$$
$$6 + 13 \stackrel{?}{=} 19$$
$$19 = 19 ✓$$

b. $u - 6 = 22$

$$\begin{array}{r} u - 6 = 22 \\ +6 \quad +6 \\ \hline u + 0 = 28 \end{array}$$
$$u = 28$$
$$28 - 6 \stackrel{?}{=} 22$$
$$22 = 22 ✓$$

C. Apply your knowledge (page 717)

For the quarter ending March 31, 2007, Google incurred costs of $972,000,000. Their net profit during this time period was $2,688,000,000. What was Google's revenue for this quarter? Use the formula $R - C = P$. (Source: Google)

$$R - C = P$$
$$\begin{array}{r} R - 972,000,000 = 2,688,000,000 \\ + 972,000,000 \quad + 972,000,000 \\ \hline R + 0 \qquad\qquad = 3,660,000,000 \end{array}$$
$$R = 3,660,000,000$$
$$3,660,000,000 - 972,000,000 \stackrel{?}{=} 2,688,000,000$$
$$2,688,000,000 = 2,688,000,000 ✓$$

Google's revenue for the quarter was $3,660,000,000.

10.3 Solving an Equation Using the Multiplication Property of Equality

Objective	Important Concepts	Illustrative Examples
A. Solve an equation using the multiplication property of equality (page 721)	**multiplication property of equality** or **multiplication property** Property stating that multiplying each side of an equation by the same value preserves equality. **The Multiplication Property of Equality** If a, b, and c are real numbers and if $a = b$, then $a \cdot c = b \cdot c$. **Steps for Solving an Equation Using the Multiplication Property of Equality** To solve an equation of the form $bx = c$, when b and c are numbers, $b \neq 0$, and x is a variable, perform the following steps. **Step 1.** Apply the multiplication property of equality by multiplying each side of the equation by the reciprocal of b. Equivalently, divide both sides by b. **Step 2.** Simplify and solve for x. **Step 3.** Check the solution by substituting into the original equation.	Solve each equation. **a.** $4z = 40$ $$\frac{4z}{4} = \frac{40}{4}$$ $$z = 10$$ $4 \cdot 10 \overset{?}{=} 40$ $40 = 40 \checkmark$ **b.** $\frac{1}{5}y = \frac{4}{7}$ $$\frac{5}{1} \cdot \frac{1}{5}y = \frac{4}{7} \cdot \frac{5}{1}$$ $$y = \frac{20}{7}$$ $\frac{1}{5} \cdot \frac{20}{7} \overset{?}{=} \frac{4}{7}$ $\frac{4}{7} = \frac{4}{7} \checkmark$
B. Apply your knowledge (page 724)	Nolan drove from Cleveland to Chicago. The two cities are 320 miles apart. If Nolan's average speed was 60 mph, how long did it take him to make the trip? $$rt = d$$ $$60t = 320$$ $$\frac{60t}{60} = \frac{320}{60}$$ $$t = \frac{\overset{16}{\cancel{320}}}{\underset{3}{\cancel{60}}}$$ $$t = \frac{16}{3} = 5\frac{1}{3}$$ $60 \cdot \frac{16}{3} \overset{?}{=} 320$ $20 \cdot 16 \overset{?}{=} 320$ $320 = 320 \checkmark$ $$5\frac{1}{3}\text{ hours} = 5\text{ hours} + \frac{1}{3}\text{ hours}$$ $$\frac{1}{3}\cancel{\text{hour}} \cdot \frac{\overset{20}{\cancel{60}}\text{ minutes}}{1\cancel{\text{hour}}} = 20\text{ minutes}$$ Nolan made the trip in 5 hours and 20 minutes.	

10.4 Solving an Equation Using the Addition and Multiplication Properties

Topic	Important Concepts	Illustrative Examples
A. Solve an equation using the addition and multiplication properties of equality (Page 728)	**Steps for Solving an Equation Using the Addition and Multiplication Properties** To solve an equation of the form $ax + b = c$, where a, b, and c are numbers, $a \neq 0$, and x is a variable, follow these steps. **Step 1.** Apply the addition property. That is, add or subtract the same terms to or from each side of the equation so that the variable term is isolated on one side of the equation. **Step 2.** Apply the multiplication property. That is, multiply or divide each side of the equation by the same quantity to solve for the variable. **Step 3.** Check the solution by substituting into the original equation.	Solve each equation using both the addition and multiplication properties of equality. **a.** $5r + 18 = 28$ $$5r + 18 = 28$$ $$\underline{\quad -18 \quad -18}$$ $$5r + 0 = 10$$ $$\frac{5r}{5} = \frac{10}{5}$$ $$r = 2$$ $$5(2) + 18 \stackrel{?}{=} 28$$ $$10 + 18 \stackrel{?}{=} 28$$ $$28 = 28 \checkmark$$ **b.** $88 = 2k - 16$ $$88 = 2k - 16$$ $$\underline{+16 \qquad +16}$$ $$104 = 2k + 0$$ $$\frac{104}{2} = \frac{2k}{2}$$ $$52 = k$$ $$88 \stackrel{?}{=} 2(52) - 16$$ $$88 \stackrel{?}{=} 104 - 16$$ $$88 = 88 \checkmark$$
B. Solve an equation that has parentheses (Page 730)	**Steps for Solving an Equation** **Step 1.** Simplify within parentheses, if possible. **Step 2.** Apply the distributive property. Collect and combine like terms, if necessary. **Step 3.** Apply the addition property. Isolate variable terms on one side and constant terms on the other. **Step 4.** Apply the multiplication property to solve for the variable. **Step 5.** Check the solution by substituting into the original equation.	Solve $5(3h + 1) - 7h = 3(h - 10) + 5$. $$15h + 5 - 7h = 3h - 30 + 5$$ $$8h + 5 = 3h - 25$$ $$8h + 5 = 3h - 25$$ $$\underline{-3h \qquad -3h}$$ $$5h + 5 = 0h - 25$$ $$5h + 5 = -25$$ $$\underline{\quad -5 \qquad -5}$$ $$5h + 0 = -30$$ $$5h = -30$$ $$\frac{5h}{5} = \frac{-30}{5}$$ $$h = -6$$ $$5[3(-6) + 1] - 7(-6) \stackrel{?}{=} 3(-6 - 10) + 5$$ $$5(-18 + 1) - (-42) \stackrel{?}{=} 3(-6 - 10) + 5$$ $$5(-17) + 42 \stackrel{?}{=} 3(-16) + 5$$ $$-85 + 42 \stackrel{?}{=} -48 + 5$$ $$-43 = -43 \checkmark$$

C. Apply your knowledge (page 732)	A rectangular garden plot has a perimeter of 58 feet. If the length is 16 feet, find the width.

$$P = 2l + 2w$$
$$58 = 2(16) + 2w$$
$$58 = 32 + 2w$$

$$\begin{array}{r} 58 = 32 + 2w \\ -32 \quad -32 \\ \hline 26 = \ 0 \ + 2w \end{array}$$

$$26 = 2w$$
$$\frac{26}{2} = \frac{2w}{2}$$
$$13 = w$$

$$58 \overset{?}{=} 2(16) + 2(13)$$
$$58 \overset{?}{=} 32 + 26$$
$$58 = 58 \ \checkmark$$

The width of the garden is 13 feet.

10.5 Solving Application Problems

Objective	Important Concepts	Illustrative Examples
A. Translate a sentence to an equation (page 738)	Use key words and phrases to translate sentences involving unknown quantities into equations.	Translate the following sentence into an equation. Twice a number decreased by 8 is 10. $2x - 8 = 10$
B. Apply your knowledge (page 740)	**Steps for Solving Application Problems** **Step 1.** *Read and understand the problem.* You may have to read the problem several times. To visualize the problem, draw a picture if possible. **Step 2.** *Assign a variable to the unknown quantity.* If there is more than one unknown, express the others in terms of the chosen variable. **Step 3.** *Translate the problem into an equation.* **Step 4.** *Solve the equation.* **Step 5.** *Check the solution.* **Step 6.** *Clearly state the result using units, if necessary.*	Many car lease programs offer a limit on the total miles per year that a consumer can use before a penalty is imposed. If Henry is spending \$275 per month on his lease, what is the maximum number of additional miles that he can use at a \$0.10 per mile penalty if his budget is \$3500 for the year? Let *m* represent the number of miles over the lease allowance. $12 \text{ months} \cdot \dfrac{\$275}{\text{month}} = \$3300$ $3300 + 0.10m = 3500$ $\begin{array}{r} 3300 + 0.10m = \ \ 3500 \\ -3300 \qquad\qquad -3300 \\ \hline 0.10m \qquad\ \ 200 \end{array}$ $\dfrac{0.10m}{0.10} = \dfrac{200}{0.10}$ $m = 2000$ $3300 + 0.10(2000) \overset{?}{=} 3500$ $3300 + 200 \overset{?}{=} 3500$ $3500 = 3500 \ \checkmark$ Henry can drive 2000 miles over the lease allowance.

Numerical Facts of Life

Population Changes

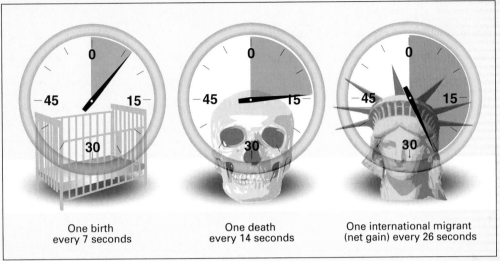

One birth
every 7 seconds

One death
every 14 seconds

One international migrant
(net gain) every 26 seconds

Source: U.S. Census Bureau's U.S. POPClock Projection

According to the U.S. Census Bureau, there is one birth every 7 seconds, one death every 14 seconds, and one international migrant every 26 seconds. From this information, we can construct three ratios.

$$\frac{1 \text{ birth}}{7 \text{ seconds}} \qquad \frac{1 \text{ death}}{14 \text{ seconds}} \qquad \frac{1 \text{ migrant}}{26 \text{ seconds}}$$

1. Let P represents the initial population and T represents the population after t seconds. Using the above ratios, write an equation representing the total population T after t seconds.

2. Approximately how long does it take to effect a net gain of one person?

3. On October 17, 2006, the U.S. population hit 300,000,000. Approximately how many days did it take to add an additional 1,000,000 people?

CHAPTER REVIEW EXERCISES

Evaluate each algebraic expression when $x = 2$ and $y = 3$. (10.1A)

1. $2x - 3y$

2. $x^2 - y$

3. $xy + 6y - 3x - 18$

4. $8x + 12y - 5xy$

Combine like terms to simplify each expression. (10.1B)

5. $9a - 4b + 2a + 8b$

6. $4x + 7y - 5y + 12x$

7. $4z + 5v + 6z - 8v$

8. $2rt + 4r - 7rt + 5t - 6r$

9. $a^2 + 5a - 4a - 8a^2$

10. $m^3 + m^2n - 4m^3 + 8mn^2$

11. $gh + g^2 - gh + h^2$

12. $7x^3y + 3x^2y - 36x^3y + 5x^2y$

Multiply. Simplify, if possible. (10.1C)

13. $2(3x)$

14. $-5(5y)$

15. $2.1(3a)$

16. $\dfrac{1}{2}(8d)$

Simplify each expression by applying the distributive property. (10.1C)

17. $3(x - 15)$

18. $8(2k^2 + 1)$

19. $-(b - 7)$

20. $-(4z + 8 - y)$

21. $-3(8p + 7)$

22. $-4(5t^2 - 2)$

23. $-2(-3m^2 + 2mn - 9n^2)$

24. $-5(7y^2 - 3yz + 2z^2)$

Determine whether the given value is a solution to the given equation. (10.2A)

25. $x = 2; 7x + 15 = 29$

26. $y = 2; 4 - (2y + 6) = -8$

27. $b = 6; 5b - 9 = 7b + 3$

28. $k = -20; k + 20 = 0$

29. $p = 3; p^2 - 3 = 5$

30. $m = 4; m^2 + 9 = 25$

31. $a = 8; 63 - a^2 = 1$

32. $t = 10; 109 - t^2 = 9$

Solve each equation. (10.2B)

33. $v + 15 = 34$

34. $x + 21 = 8$

35. $m - 2.3 = 5.4$

36. $b - 5.7 = 8.4$

37. $12 + p = 4$

38. $20 + r = 7$

39. $a + \dfrac{1}{3} = \dfrac{1}{2}$

40. $n + \dfrac{2}{5} = \dfrac{1}{2}$

Solve each equation. (10.3A)

41. $4k = 48$

42. $7q = 56$

43. $2z = 25$

44. $3h = 47$

45. $-\dfrac{2}{5}t = 12$

46. $-\dfrac{3}{7}t = 24$

47. $0.3p = 3.9$

48. $0.5x = 4.5$

Solve each equation using the addition and multiplication properties of equality. (10.4A)

49. $12t + 3 = 39$

50. $8b - 9 = 31$

51. $9x = 5x + 40$

52. $7s = 3s + 52$

53. $2(m + 6) = 4(2m + 3)$

54. $6(z - 5) = 3(4z + 8)$

55. $5(2n - 11) - 7n = 5$

56. $7(3c + 10) + 2c = 1$

Solve each application problem.

57. Write an algebraic expression to represent twelve subtracted from twice the difference between ten and a number.

58. An airplane flying at an altitude of 32,000 feet suddenly has to change altitude to 29,500 feet. What is the net change in altitude?

59. A new radio sells for $58.99. If this is $17.68 above the wholesale price, find the wholesale price.

60. Martha was paid $348.75 for 45 hours of work. Find her rate of pay.

61. There are 32 students in a beginning algebra class. The number of males is seven less than two times the number of females. Find the number of each.

ASSESSMENT TEST

Evaluate each algebraic expression when $a = 3$ **and** $b = 8$.

1. $a^2 + 7(b - 4)$

2. $4b - a^2 + (a - b)^2$

Combine like terms to simplify each expression.

3. $6m^4n^3 + 8m^4n - m^4n^3 + 12m^4n + 3m^4n^3$

4. $a^2 + 2ab - b^2 + 5ab - 8a^2 + 3b^2$

Simplify each expression by applying the distributive property.

5. $-3(9d - 8)$

6. $5(8m - 7)$

Determine whether the given value is a solution to the given equation.

7. $x = 12, 2x + 3(2x - 4) = 9x$

8. $y = -7, 6y + 14(y + 5) = 10y$

Solve each equation.

9. $x + 45 = 38$

10. $p + 12.5 = 9.5$

Solve each equation.

11. $9q = 108$

12. $\dfrac{1}{5}w = \dfrac{2}{3}$

Solve each equation using the addition and multiplication properties of equality.

13. $7(x - 8) = 3(2x - 5)$

14. $7(2t + 3) = 3(t - 4)$

15. $8y + 3 = 12y$

16. $24(p + 1) = 3p$

Solve each application problem.

17. Write an algebraic expression to represent three times a number decreased by 24.

18. Write an algebraic expression to represent the product of three and the sum of the square of a number and 15.

19. The temperature this morning was 34 degrees. By noon, the temperature had risen 7 degrees. Find the new temperature.

20. A jet flew a distance of 3300 miles in 6 hours. What was the average speed of the jet in terms of miles per hour?

21. You are planning to advertise your car for sale on the Internet. *Car Showroom* charges $1.80 for a photo plus $0.09 per word. *Car Bazaar* charges $1.00 for the photo plus $0.11 per word. For what number of words will the charges be the same?

A

absolute value of a number The distance between the number and 0 on the number line.

abstract number A number without an associated unit of measure.

acute angle An angle whose measure is greater than 0° and less than 90°.

acute triangle A triangle that has three acute angles.

addends Numbers that are added together.

addition The mathematical process of combining two or more numbers to find the total.

addition property of equality or **addition property** The property stating that adding the same value to each side of an equation preserves equality.

algebraic expression or **expression** A mathematical expression that consists of numbers, variables, operation symbols, and/or grouping symbols.

amount In a percent problem, the number that represents part of a whole.

angle The construct formed by uniting the endpoints of two rays.

area The measure associated with the interior of a closed, flat geometric figure (that is, a closed plane figure).

average A numerical value that represents an entire set of numbers.

B

bar graph A graphical representation of quantities using horizontal or vertical bars.

base (1) In exponential notation, the factor that is multiplied repeatedly. (2) In a percent problem, the number that represents the whole or 100%.

C

capacity A measure of a liquid's content or volume.

center The fixed point that defines a circle.

checking the answer The process of verifying that we get a true statement when we substitute the answer into the original equation.

circle A plane figure that consists of all points that lie the same distance from some fixed point.

circle graph or **pie chart** A circle divided into sections or segments that represent the component parts of a whole.

circumference The distance around a circle.

collecting like terms Changing the order of terms using the commutative property and grouping like terms using the associative property.

combining like terms Adding like terms in an algebraic expression.

commission A form of compensation based on a percent of sales.

common denominator A common multiple of all the denominators for a set of fractions.

common multiple A multiple that is shared by a set of two or more natural numbers.

comparative bar graph A bar graph with side-by-side bars to illustrate two or more related variables.

complementary angles Two angles, the sum of whose degree measures is 90°.

complex fraction A quotient of the form $\dfrac{A}{B}$ where A or B or both are fractions and where B is not zero.

composite number A natural number greater than 1 that has more than two factors (divisors).

compound denominate numbers Two or more denominate numbers that are combined.

cone A solid with a circular base in which all points of the base are joined by line segments to a single point in a different plane.

constant term A term that is a number.

credit An addition to a checkbook balance.

cube A rectangular solid in which all six faces are squares.

cylinder A solid with two identical plane figure bases joined by line segments that are perpendicular to these bases.

D

debit A subtraction from a checkbook balance.

decimal fraction A fraction whose denominator is a power of 10.

decimal number or **decimal** A number written in decimal notation.

degree A unit used to measure an angle.

denominate number A number together with a unit of measure.

denominator The bottom number in a fraction.

diameter The length of a line segment that passes through the center of a circle and whose endpoints lie on the circle.

difference The result of subtracting numbers.

digits The numbers 0, 1, 2, 3, 4, 5, 6, 7, 8, and 9.

dividend The number being divided.

division The mathematical process of repeated subtraction of a value.

divisor The number by which the dividend is divided.

E

endpoint A point at the end of a line segment.

equation A mathematical statement consisting of two expressions on either side of an equals (=) sign.

equilateral triangle A triangle with sides of equal length and angles of equal measure.

equivalent fractions Fractions that represent the same quantity.

evaluate an expression To replace each variable of an algebraic expression by a particular value and find the value of the expression.

expanded notation or **expanded form** A representation of a number as a sum of its units place, tens place, hundreds place, and so on, beginning with the highest place value.

exponent or **power** In exponential notation, the number that indicates how many times the base is used as a factor.

exponential notation A shorthand way of expressing repeated multiplication.

F

factor (1) *noun* In a multiplication problem, one of the numbers that are multiplied together. (2) *verb* To express a quantity as a product of factors.

factor tree An illustration used to determine the prime factorization of a composite number.

factors Numbers that are multiplied together.

fraction A number written in the form $\frac{a}{b}$ where a and b are whole numbers and b is not zero.

fraction bar The line between the numerator and the denominator.

fraction simplified to lowest terms A fraction in which the numerator and denominator have no common factor other than 1.

G

geometry The branch of mathematics that deals with the measurements, properties, and relationships of shapes and sizes.

gram The amount of mass of water contained in a cube whose sides measure 1 centimeter each.

greatest common factor or **GCF** The largest factor common to two or more numbers.

H

Hindu-Arabic or **decimal number system** A system that uses the digits to represent numbers.

hypotenuse In a right triangle, the side opposite the right angle.

I

improper fraction A fraction in which the numerator is greater than or equal to the denominator.

integers The whole numbers together with the opposites of the positive whole numbers, that is, the numbers ... $-3, -2, -1, 0, 1, 2, 3, \ldots$.

intersecting lines Lines that lie in the same plane and cross at some point in the plane.

invoice A business document detailing the sales of goods or services.

isosceles triangle A triangle with at least two sides of equal length in which the angles opposite these sides have equal measure.

L

least common denominator or **LCD** The least common multiple (LCM) of all the denominators for a set of fractions.

least common multiple or **LCM** The smallest multiple shared by a set of two or more numbers.

legs The two sides that meet to form the right angle of a right triangle.

like fractions Fractions with the same denominator.

like terms Terms with the same variable factors.

line A straight row of points that extends forever in both directions.

line graph A picture of selected data changing over a period of time.

line segment A finite portion of a line with a point at each end.

liter The capacity or volume of a cube whose sides measure 10 centimeters.

M

mass The measure of the amount of material in an object.

mean The sum of the values of a set of numbers divided by the number of values in that set.

measure A number together with a unit assigned to something to represent its size or magnitude.

median The middle value of a set of numbers when the numbers are listed in numerical order.

meter The basic unit of length used in the metric system.

minuend The number from which another number is subtracted.

mixed number A number that combines whole number with a fraction.

mode The value or values in a set that occur most often.

multiple of a number The product of the number and any natural number.

multiplication property of equality or **multiplication property** The property stating that multiplying each side of an equation by the same value preserves equality.

multiplication The mathematical process of repeated addition of a value a specified number of times.

N

natural or **counting numbers** Any of the numbers 1, 2, 3, 4, 5, 6, 7, 8, 9, 10, 11, 12, 13, 14, 15 ....

negative number A number that is less than 0.

numerator The top number in a fraction.

numerical coefficient or **coefficient** The number factor in a variable term.

O

obtuse angle An angle whose measure is greater than 90° and less than 180°.

obtuse triangle A triangle that has an obtuse angle.

opposites Two numbers that lie the same distance from the origin on opposite sides of the origin.

order of operations A set of rules that establishes the procedure for simplifying a mathematical expression.

origin The number 0 on a number line.

P

parallel lines Lines that lie in the same plane but never cross.

parallelogram A quadrilateral whose opposite sides are parallel and equal in length.

percent (1) A part per 100. (2) In a percent problem, the number that defines what part the amount is of the whole.

percent equation An equation of the form Amount = Percent · Base.

percent proportion A proportion of the form $\dfrac{\text{Amount}}{\text{Base}} = \dfrac{\text{Part}}{100}$.

percent sign The % symbol.

perfect square A whole number or fraction that is the square of another whole number or fraction.

perimeter of a polygon The distance around a polygon. Alternatively, the sum of the lengths of its sides.

plane A flat surface that has infinite width, infinite length, and no depth.

plane figure A figure that lies entirely in a plane.

point An exact location or position in space.

polygon A closed, flat geometric figure (that is, a closed plane figure) in which all sides are line segments.

positive number A number that is greater than 0.

prime factorization A factorization of a whole number in which each factor is prime.

prime number or **prime** A natural number greater than 1 that has only two factors (divisors), namely, 1 and itself.

principal square root of a number, n A number whose square is n.

product The result of multiplying numbers.

proper fraction or **common fraction** A fraction in which the numerator is less than the denominator.

proportion A mathematical statement showing that two ratios are equal.

protractor A device used to measure an angle.

pyramid A solid with three or more triangular-shaped faces that share a common vertex.

Q

quadrilateral A four-sided polygon.

quality points The value of each course in the GPA. It is the product of the number of credits and the value of the grade earned.

quotient The result of dividing numbers.

R

radical sign The symbol $\sqrt{}$

radicand The number underneath the radical sign.

radius The length of a line segment from the center of a circle to any point of the circle.

range The difference between the largest and the smallest values in a set; used as a measure of spread or dispersion.

rate A ratio that compares two quantities that have different kinds of units.

ratio A comparison of two quantities by division.

rational number A number that can be written in the form $\dfrac{a}{b}$, where a and b are integers and $b \neq 0$.

ray A portion of a line that has one endpoint and extends forever in one direction.

reciprocal of the fraction $\dfrac{a}{b}$ The fraction $\dfrac{b}{a}$ where $a \neq 0$ and $b \neq 0$.

rectangle A polygon with four right angles in which opposite sides are parallel and of equal length. Alternatively, a parallelogram that has four right angles.

rectangular solid A solid that consists of six sides known as *faces*, all of which are rectangles.

remainder The number that remains after division is complete.

repeating decimal A decimal that continues indefinitely with one or more repeating digits.

rhombus A parallelogram in which all sides are of equal length.

right angle An angle whose measure is 90°.

right triangle A triangle that has a right angle.

rounded number An approximation of an exact number.

S

sales tax A state tax based on the retail price or rental cost of certain items.

scalene triangle A triangle with all three sides of different lengths and angles of different measures.

set A collection of numbers or objects.

sides of an angle The rays that form an angle.

signed number A number that is either positive or negative.

similar geometric figures Geometric figures with the same shape in which the ratios of the lengths of their corresponding sides are equal.

solid An object with length, width, and depth that resides in space.

solution A value of the variable that makes the equation a true statement.

solving an equation The process of finding a solution to an equation involving a variable.

space The expanse that has infinite length, infinite width, and infinite depth.

sphere A solid that consists of all points in space that lie the same distance from some fixed point.

square A rectangle with all sides of equal length.

square of a number A number times itself.

Standard International Metric System or **metric system** A decimal-based system of weights and measures that uses a series of prefixes representing powers of 10.

standard notation or standard form A representation for a number in which each period is separated by a comma.

statistic A number that is computed from, and describes, numerical data about a particular situation.

statistics The science of collecting, interpreting, and presenting numerical data.

straight angle An angle whose measure is 180°.

subtraction The mathematical process of taking away or deducting an amount from a given number.

subtrahend The number that is subtracted from a given number.

sum The result of adding numbers.

supplementary angles Two angles, the sum of whose degree measures is 180°.

T

table A collection of data arranged in rows and columns for ease of reference.

temperature A measure of the warmth or coldness of an object, substance, or environment.

term An addend in an algebraic expression.

terminating decimal A decimal whose expansion ends.

terms of the ratio The quantities being compared.

trapezoid A quadrilateral that has exactly one pair of parallel sides.

triangle A three-sided polygon.

U

U.S. Customary System or **English System** A system of weights and measures that uses units such as inches, feet, and yards to measure length; pounds and tons to measure weight; and pints, quarts, and gallons to measure capacity.

unit price A rate expressed as price per single item of something.

unit rate A rate in which the number in the denominator is 1.

unit ratio A ratio that is equivalent to 1.

V

variable A letter or some other symbol that represents a number whose value is unknown.

variable term A term that contains a variable.

vertex The common endpoint of the two rays that form an angle.

volume The measure of the amount of interior space of a solid.

W

weight A measure of an object's heaviness.

weighted mean An average used when some numbers in a set count more heavily than others.

whole numbers Any of the numbers $0, 1, 2, 3, 4, 5, 6, 7, 8, 9, 10, 11, 12, 13, 14, 15$.

X

x-axis The *horizontal* axis of a graph.

Y

y-axis The *vertical* axis of a graph.

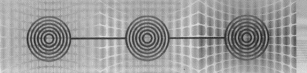

Try-It Exercise Solutions

Chapter 1

SECTION 1.1

TRY-IT EXERCISE 1

a. 8,395,470   millions

b. 57,675   ones

c. 214,355   thousands

d. 19   tens

e. 134,221   ten thousands

TRY-IT EXERCISE 2

	NUMBER	STANDARD NOTATION	WORD FORM
a.	1146	1146	one thousand, one hundred forty-six
b.	9038124	9,038,124	nine million, thirty-eight thousand, one hundred twenty-four
c.	773618	773,618	seven hundred seventy-three thousand, six hundred eighteen
d.	27009	27,009	twenty-seven thousand, nine
e.	583408992	583,408,992	five hundred eighty-three million, four hundred eight thousand, nine hundred ninety-two

TRY-IT EXERCISE 3

a. 8000 + 200 + 90 or 8 thousands + 2 hundreds + 9 tens

b. 70,000 + 5000 + 40 + 1 or 7 ten thousands + 5 thousands + 4 tens + 1 one

c. 700,000 + 9000 + 300 + 80 + 5 or 7 hundred thousands + 9 thousands + 3 hundreds + 8 tens + 5 ones

TRY-IT EXERCISE 4

	NUMBER	PLACE SPECIFIED	ROUNDED NUMBER
a.	67,499	67,499	67,000
b.	453	453	500
c.	6,383,440,004	6,383,440,004	6,380,000,000
d.	381,598	381,598	400,000
e.	1,119,632	1,119,632	1,000,000

TRY-IT EXERCISE 5

a. teacher

b. $68,120

c. eighteen thousand, nine hundred forty-five dollars

d. $76,000

SECTION 1.2

TRY-IT EXERCISE 1

a. 34 + 0 = 34

b. 81 + 15 = 96

    15 + 81 = 96

c. (5 + 2) + 8 = 7 + 8 = 15

    5 + (2 + 8) = 5 + 10 = 15

TRY-IT EXERCISE 2

a.   325
      + 504

       829

b.   16
        11
      + 151

       178

TRY-IT EXERCISE 3

a.   ₁
        78
      + 49

       127

b.   ₁₁₁
        492
      + 1538

       2030

c.   ₁₁
        4510
        8393
      + 190

       13,093

TRY-IT EXERCISE 4

$$
\begin{array}{r}
44 \\
78 \\
26 \\
+\,110 \\
\hline
258 \text{ miles}
\end{array}
$$

TRY-IT EXERCISE 5

a.
$$
\begin{array}{r}
6 \\
10 \\
+\,5 \\
\hline
21 \text{ inches}
\end{array}
$$

b.
$$
\begin{array}{r}
8 \\
8 \\
5 \\
5 \\
5 \\
+\,5 \\
\hline
36 \text{ centimeters}
\end{array}
$$

c.
$$
\begin{array}{r}
13 \\
13 \\
9 \\
+\,9 \\
\hline
44 \text{ yards}
\end{array}
$$

SECTION 1.3

TRY-IT EXERCISE 1

a.
$$
\begin{array}{r}
355 \\
-\,242 \\
\hline
113
\end{array}
$$

b.
$$
\begin{array}{r}
767 \\
-\,303 \\
\hline
464
\end{array}
$$

c.
$$
\begin{array}{r}
4578 \\
-\,2144 \\
\hline
2434
\end{array}
$$

TRY-IT EXERCISE 2

a.
$$
\begin{array}{r}
{}^{7\,14} \\
8\,\cancel{4} \\
-\,5\,7 \\
\hline
2\,7
\end{array}
$$

b.
$$
\begin{array}{r}
{}^{9} \\
{}^{6\,\cancel{10}\,14} \\
\cancel{7}\,\cancel{0}\,\cancel{4} \\
-\,5\,6\,6 \\
\hline
1\,3\,8
\end{array}
$$

c.
$$
\begin{array}{r}
{}^{9\;9} \\
{}^{2\;\cancel{10}\,\cancel{10}\,10} \\
\cancel{3}\,\cancel{0}\,\cancel{0}\,\cancel{0} \\
-\,1\,4\,5\,5 \\
\hline
1\,5\,4\,5
\end{array}
$$

TRY-IT EXERCISE 3

$29,334 - $26,559 = $2775

TRY-IT EXERCISE 4

a. Major general, Lieutenant general, General

b. $9051

c. $7233 - $6329 = $904

d. $11,875 - $9051 = $2824

e. $10,009 - $6329 = $3680

SECTION 1.4

TRY-IT EXERCISE 1

a. $0 \cdot 84 = 0$

b. $219 \cdot 0 = 0$

c. $16 \cdot 1 = 16$

d. $1 \cdot 500 = 500$

TRY-IT EXERCISE 2

a. $5 \cdot 8 = 40$

$8 \cdot 5 = 40$

b. $1(4 \cdot 2) = 1 \cdot 8 = 8$

$(1 \cdot 4)2 = 4 \cdot 2 = 8$

TRY-IT EXERCISE 3

a. $5(9 - 6) = 5(3) = 15$

$5 \cdot 9 - 5 \cdot 6 = 45 - 30 = 15$

b. $(3 + 4)2 = (7)2 = 14$

$3 \cdot 2 + 4 \cdot 2 = 6 + 8 = 14$

TRY-IT EXERCISE 4

$$
\begin{array}{r}
72 \\
\times\,3 \\
\hline
216
\end{array}
$$

TRY-IT EXERCISE 5

$$
\begin{array}{r}
{}^{21} \\
832 \\
\times\,7 \\
\hline
5824
\end{array}
$$

TRY-IT EXERCISE 6

a.
$$
\begin{array}{r}
{}^{1} \\
{}^{2} \\
93 \\
\times\,58 \\
\hline
744 \\
+\,4650 \\
\hline
5394
\end{array}
$$

b.
$$
\begin{array}{r}
{}^{1\;1} \\
{}^{1\;1} \\
256 \\
\times\,321 \\
\hline
256 \\
5120 \\
+\,76800 \\
\hline
82,176
\end{array}
$$

TRY-IT EXERCISE 7

$$
\begin{array}{r}
\overset{1}{721} \\
\times\ 207 \\
\hline
5047 \\
0000 \\
+144200 \\
\hline
149{,}247
\end{array}
$$

TRY-IT EXERCISE 8

$$
\begin{array}{r}
\overset{11}{4397} \\
\times\ \$12 \\
\hline
8794 \\
+43970 \\
\hline
\$52{,}764
\end{array}
$$

TRY-IT EXERCISE 9

a. 97 feet $\cdot$ 38 feet $=$ 3686 square feet

b. 3686($7 + $2)

$\qquad = 3686($9)$

$\qquad = \$33{,}174$

SECTION 1.5

TRY-IT EXERCISE 1

a. $29 \div 1 = 29$

b. $\dfrac{285}{285} = 1$

c. $0 \div 4 = 0$

d. $\dfrac{388}{0}$ undefined

TRY-IT EXERCISE 2

a.
$$
\begin{array}{r}
212 \\
4{\overline{)848}}
\end{array}
$$

b.
$$
\begin{array}{r}
52 \\
3{\overline{)156}} \\
-\ 15 \\
\hline
06 \\
-\ 6 \\
\hline
0
\end{array}
$$

TRY-IT EXERCISE 3

a.
$$
\begin{array}{r}
154 \\
4{\overline{)616}} \\
-\ 4 \\
\hline
21 \\
-\ 20 \\
\hline
16 \\
-\ 16 \\
\hline
0
\end{array}
$$

b.
$$
\begin{array}{r}
139 \\
31{\overline{)4309}} \\
-\ 31 \\
\hline
120 \\
-\ 93 \\
\hline
279 \\
-\ 279 \\
\hline
0
\end{array}
$$

TRY-IT EXERCISE 4

a.
$$
\begin{array}{r}
9\ R\ 25 \\
61{\overline{)574}} \\
-\ 549 \\
\hline
25
\end{array}
$$

b.
$$
\begin{array}{r}
85\ R\ 9 \\
73{\overline{)6214}} \\
-\ 584 \\
\hline
374 \\
-\ 365 \\
\hline
9
\end{array}
$$

TRY-IT EXERCISE 5

Donna must make 12 equal payments because there are 12 months in one year. So the price of the stereo, $2520, must be divided by 12 to calculate the monthly payment: $2520 \div 12 = \$210$.

TRY-IT EXERCISE 6

To find the average distance, we must add the distances driven each day, then take the total and divide by the number of days, 4: $(184 + 126 + 235 + 215) \div 4 = 760 \div 4 = 190$ miles.

SECTION 1.6

TRY-IT EXERCISE 1

a. $9^4 = $ "nine to the fourth power"

b. $4^6 = $ "four to the sixth power"

c. $6^1 = $ "six to the first power" or "six"

d. $12^3 \cdot 16^2 = $ "twelve cubed times sixteen squared"

TRY-IT EXERCISE 2

a. 11

b. 26

c. 1

d. 1

e. 1899

f. 1

TRY-IT EXERCISE 3

a. $4 \cdot 4 \cdot 4 = 64$

b. $5 \cdot 5 \cdot 5 \cdot 5 = 625$

c. $10 \cdot 10 \cdot 10 \cdot 10 \cdot 10 \cdot 10 \cdot 10 = 10{,}000{,}000$

TRY-IT EXERCISE 4

a. $33 + 6 \div 2 - 7$

$\quad 33 \; + \; 3 - 7$

$\qquad 36 - 7$

$\qquad\quad 29$

b. $6 \div 3 \cdot 7 - 6 + 3$

$\quad 2 \cdot 7 - 6 + 3$

$\quad\; 14 - 6 + 3$

$\qquad\; 8 + 3$

$\qquad\; 11$

c. $20 \cdot 3 + 4 - \left[\begin{array}{c} 112 \div 7 \\ \hline 21 - 17 \end{array}\right.$

$\qquad\qquad\qquad \dfrac{16}{4}$

$20 \cdot 3 + 4 - \dfrac{16}{4}$

$\quad 60 + 4 - 4$

$\qquad 64 - 4$

$\qquad\quad 60$

TRY-IT EXERCISE 5

a. $(35 - 14) \div 7 + 4 \cdot 3$

$\quad\; 21 \div 7 + 4 \cdot 3$

$\qquad 3 \;+\; 12$

$\qquad\quad 15$

b. $26 - [4 + (9 - 5)] \div 8$

$\quad 26 - [4 + 4] \div 8$

$\quad\; 26 - 8 \div 8$

$\qquad 26 - 1$

$\qquad\quad 25$

TRY-IT EXERCISE 6

a. $20 + 3(14 - 2^3) - (40 - 21)$

$\quad 20 + 3(14 - 8) - (40 - 21)$

$\qquad 20 + 3(6) \;-\; 19$

$\qquad\; 20 + 18 - 19$

$\qquad\quad 38 - 19$

$\qquad\qquad 19$

b. $40(3 - 8^0) \div [8 + (4 \cdot 3)]$

$\quad 40(3 - 1) \;\div\; [8 + 12]$

$\qquad 40(2) \;\div\; 20$

$\qquad\; 80 \div 20$

$\qquad\qquad 4$

TRY-IT EXERCISE 7

a. $48 \cdot 48 = 2304$ square inches

b. $\dfrac{2304}{144} = 16 \quad 16 \cdot 5 = \$80$

SECTION 1.7

TRY-IT EXERCISE 1

$\$162 + 34 + 51 + 5 = \$252$

TRY-IT EXERCISE 2

$1474 - 188 = 1286$ tons

TRY-IT EXERCISE 3

$540 \cdot \$89 = \$48,060$

TRY-IT EXERCISE 4

$\$300,000 \div 8 = \$37,500$

TRY-IT EXERCISE 5

Profit per guard per hour = $\$16 - \$11 = \$5$.
Total guard hours worked = $25 \cdot 30 = 750$.
Profit = $\$5 \cdot 750 = \$3750$

Chapter 2

SECTION 2.1

TRY-IT EXERCISE 1

a. $1, 2, 3, 4, 6, 8, 12, 24$

b. $1, 2, 3, 4, 5, 6, 8, 10, 12, 15, 20, 24, 30, 40, 60, 120$

TRY-IT EXERCISE 2

a. prime

b. neither

c. composite

d. composite

e. composite

f. prime

TRY-IT EXERCISE 3

a.

$2 \cdot 3 \cdot 7$

b.

$$2 \cdot 2 \cdot 2 \cdot 11 = 2^3 \cdot 11$$

c.

$$2 \cdot 11 \cdot 13$$

TRY-IT EXERCISE 4

$2, 4, 6, 8, 10, 12, 14, 16, 18, 20, 22, 24, 26, 28, \boxed{30}$

$5, 10, 15, 20, 25, \boxed{30}$

$6, 12, 18, 24, \boxed{30}$

$\text{LCM} = 30$

TRY-IT EXERCISE 5

$18 = 2 \cdot 3 \cdot 3$

$15 = 3 \cdot 5$

$12 = 2 \cdot 2 \cdot 3$

$\text{LCM} = 2 \cdot 2 \cdot 3 \cdot 3 \cdot 5 = 180$

TRY-IT EXERCISE 6

3	18	15	12
3	6	5	4
2	2	5	4
2	1	5	2
5	1	5	1
	1	1	1

$\text{LCM} = 3 \cdot 3 \cdot 2 \cdot 2 \cdot 5 = 180$

TRY-IT EXERCISE 7

A Formula I race car completes a lap every $3, 6, 9, \boxed{12}$ minutes

A Formula I Jr. race car completes a lap every $4, 8, \boxed{12}$ minutes

The cars complete a lap at the same time every 12 minutes.

SECTION 2.2

TRY-IT EXERCISE 1

a. mixed number

b. proper fraction

c. improper fraction

TRY-IT EXERCISE 2

a. $\dfrac{3}{4}$

b. $\dfrac{7}{10}$

c. $1\dfrac{3}{5}$

TRY-IT EXERCISE 3

a. $2\dfrac{1}{3}$

b. $6\dfrac{3}{4}$

c. 13

TRY-IT EXERCISE 4

a. $\dfrac{11}{4}$

b. $\dfrac{46}{5}$

c. $\dfrac{181}{8}$

d. $\dfrac{39}{7}$

TRY-IT EXERCISE 5

a. $\dfrac{19}{55}$

b. $\dfrac{23}{55}$

c. $\dfrac{13}{55}$

TRY-IT EXERCISE 6

a. $\dfrac{201}{365}$

b. 1

c. $\dfrac{448}{365}$ or $1\dfrac{83}{365}$

SECTION 2.3

TRY-IT EXERCISE 1

a. $\dfrac{2 \cdot 3 \cdot \overset{1}{\cancel{5}}}{\underset{1}{\cancel{5}} \cdot 11} = \dfrac{2 \cdot 3 \cdot 1}{1 \cdot 11} = \dfrac{6}{11}$

b. $\dfrac{\overset{1}{\cancel{2}} \cdot \overset{1}{\cancel{2}} \cdot 2 \cdot 3 \cdot 3}{\underset{1}{\cancel{2}} \cdot \underset{1}{\cancel{2}} \cdot 37} = \dfrac{1 \cdot 1 \cdot 2 \cdot 3 \cdot 3}{1 \cdot 1 \cdot 37} = \dfrac{18}{37}$

TRY-IT EXERCISE 2

a. $\dfrac{\overset{3}{\cancel{18}}}{\underset{7}{\cancel{42}}} = \dfrac{3}{7}$

b. $\dfrac{\overset{9}{\cancel{45}}}{\underset{16}{\cancel{80}}} = \dfrac{9}{16}$

TRY-IT EXERCISE 3

a. $\dfrac{3}{4} = \dfrac{3 \cdot 3}{4 \cdot 3} = \dfrac{9}{12}$

b. $\dfrac{5}{8} = \dfrac{5 \cdot 7}{8 \cdot 7} = \dfrac{35}{56}$

TRY-IT EXERCISE 4

a. LCD = 35

$\dfrac{2}{5} = \dfrac{2 \cdot 7}{5 \cdot 7} = \dfrac{14}{35}, \quad \dfrac{3}{7} = \dfrac{3 \cdot 5}{7 \cdot 5} = \dfrac{15}{35}$

$\dfrac{14}{35} < \dfrac{15}{35}, \quad \dfrac{2}{5} < \dfrac{3}{7}$

b. LCD = 40

$\dfrac{3}{8} = \dfrac{3 \cdot 5}{8 \cdot 5} = \dfrac{15}{40}, \quad \dfrac{2}{5} = \dfrac{2 \cdot 8}{5 \cdot 8} = \dfrac{16}{40}, \quad \dfrac{1}{4} = \dfrac{1 \cdot 10}{4 \cdot 10} = \dfrac{10}{40}$

$\dfrac{10}{40} < \dfrac{15}{40} < \dfrac{16}{40}, \quad \dfrac{1}{4} < \dfrac{3}{8} < \dfrac{2}{5}$

TRY-IT EXERCISE 5

a. $\dfrac{160}{582} = \dfrac{80}{291}$

b. $\dfrac{422}{582} = \dfrac{211}{291}$

SECTION 2.4

TRY-IT EXERCISE 1

a. $\dfrac{12}{35}$

b. $\dfrac{15}{32}$

c. $\dfrac{12}{75} = \dfrac{4}{25}$

TRY-IT EXERCISE 2

a. $\dfrac{6}{90} = \dfrac{1}{15}$

b. $\dfrac{6}{160} = \dfrac{3}{8}$

TRY-IT EXERCISE 3

a. $\dfrac{\overset{21}{\cancel{42}}}{\underset{1}{\cancel{5}}} \cdot \dfrac{\overset{5}{\cancel{25}}}{\underset{2}{\cancel{4}}} = \dfrac{105}{4} = 52\dfrac{1}{2}$

b. $\dfrac{49}{\underset{1}{\cancel{9}}} \cdot \dfrac{\overset{1}{\cancel{9}}}{4} = \dfrac{49}{4} = 12\dfrac{1}{4}$

TRY-IT EXERCISE 4

a. $1\dfrac{5}{8} \cdot \dfrac{1}{2} = \dfrac{13}{8} \cdot \dfrac{1}{2} = \dfrac{13}{16}$ miles

b. $1\dfrac{5}{8} \cdot 3 = \dfrac{13}{8} \cdot \dfrac{3}{1} = \dfrac{39}{8} = 4\dfrac{7}{8}$ miles

SECTION 2.5

TRY-IT EXERCISE 1

a. $\dfrac{1}{\underset{4}{8}} \cdot \dfrac{\overset{3}{\cancel{6}}}{5} = \dfrac{3}{20}$

b. $\dfrac{1}{\underset{1}{\cancel{3}}} \cdot \dfrac{\overset{3}{\cancel{9}}}{5} = \dfrac{3}{5}$

c. $\dfrac{\overset{1}{\cancel{3}}}{\underset{1}{\cancel{7}}} \cdot \dfrac{\overset{1}{\cancel{7}}}{\underset{1}{\cancel{3}}} = \dfrac{1}{1} = 1$

d. $\dfrac{5}{\underset{2}{\cancel{16}}} \cdot \dfrac{\overset{1}{\cancel{8}}}{1} = \dfrac{5}{2} = 2\dfrac{1}{2}$

TRY-IT EXERCISE 2

a. $\dfrac{\overset{5}{\cancel{10}}}{1} \cdot \dfrac{7}{\underset{3}{\cancel{6}}} = \dfrac{35}{3} = 11\dfrac{2}{3}$

b. $\dfrac{35}{\underset{4}{\cancel{16}}} \cdot \dfrac{\overset{1}{\cancel{4}}}{17} = \dfrac{35}{68}$

c. $\dfrac{9}{1} \cdot \dfrac{5}{28} = \dfrac{45}{28} = 1\dfrac{17}{28}$

d. $\dfrac{\overset{9}{\cancel{27}}}{8} \cdot \dfrac{1}{\underset{2}{\cancel{6}}} = \dfrac{9}{16}$

TRY-IT EXERCISE 3

$280 \div 3\dfrac{1}{2} = \dfrac{280}{1} \div \dfrac{7}{2} = \dfrac{\overset{40}{\cancel{280}}}{1} \cdot \dfrac{2}{\underset{1}{\cancel{7}}} = 80$ bags

SECTION 2.6

TRY-IT EXERCISE 1

a. $\dfrac{3 + 9}{25} = \dfrac{12}{25}$

b. $\dfrac{4 + 1 + 3}{9} = \dfrac{8}{9}$

c. $\dfrac{5 + 11 + 7 + 13}{16} = \dfrac{36}{16} = 2\dfrac{1}{4}$

TRY-IT EXERCISE 2

a. $\dfrac{3 \cdot 3}{8 \cdot 3} + \dfrac{5 \cdot 4}{6 \cdot 4} = \dfrac{9}{24} + \dfrac{20}{24} = \dfrac{29}{24} = 1\dfrac{5}{24}$

b. $\dfrac{1 \cdot 5}{6 \cdot 5} + \dfrac{3 \cdot 6}{5 \cdot 6} + \dfrac{2 \cdot 10}{3 \cdot 10} = \dfrac{5 + 18 + 20}{30} = \dfrac{43}{30} = 1\dfrac{13}{30}$

c. $\dfrac{3 \cdot 15}{4 \cdot 15} + \dfrac{1 \cdot 10}{6 \cdot 10} + \dfrac{7 \cdot 4}{15 \cdot 4} = \dfrac{45 + 10 + 28}{60} = \dfrac{83}{60} = 1\dfrac{23}{60}$

TRY-IT EXERCISE 3

a.
$$\begin{array}{r} 4\dfrac{1}{9} \\ + 8\dfrac{4}{9} \\ \hline 12\dfrac{5}{9} \end{array}$$

b.
$$\begin{array}{r} 5\dfrac{1}{12} \\ + 9\dfrac{5}{12} \\ \hline 14\dfrac{6}{12} = 14\dfrac{1}{2} \end{array}$$

TRY-IT EXERCISE 4

a.
$$\begin{array}{r} 4\dfrac{1}{4} \rightarrow \quad 4\dfrac{3}{12} \\ + 6\dfrac{5}{12} \rightarrow \quad + 6\dfrac{5}{12} \\ \hline 10\dfrac{8}{12} = 10\dfrac{2}{3} \end{array}$$

b.
$$\begin{array}{r} 12\dfrac{1}{3} \rightarrow \quad 12\dfrac{5}{15} \\ + 18\dfrac{2}{5} \rightarrow \quad + 18\dfrac{6}{15} \\ \hline 30\dfrac{11}{15} \end{array}$$

TRY-IT EXERCISE 5

a.
$$\begin{array}{r} 2\dfrac{3}{4} \rightarrow \quad 2\dfrac{9}{12} \\ + 6\dfrac{5}{12} \rightarrow \quad + 6\dfrac{5}{12} \\ \hline 8\dfrac{14}{12} = 8 + \dfrac{14}{12} = 8 + \dfrac{7}{6} = 8 + 1\dfrac{1}{6} = 9\dfrac{1}{6} \end{array}$$

b.
$$\begin{array}{r} 10\dfrac{3}{5} \rightarrow \quad 10\dfrac{24}{40} \\ + 13\dfrac{7}{8} \rightarrow \quad + 13\dfrac{35}{40} \\ \hline 23\dfrac{59}{40} = 23 + \dfrac{59}{40} = 23 + 1\dfrac{19}{40} = 24\dfrac{19}{40} \end{array}$$

TRY-IT EXERCISE 6

$$\begin{array}{r} 6\dfrac{3}{8} \rightarrow \quad 6\dfrac{3}{8} \\ 7\dfrac{1}{2} \rightarrow \quad 7\dfrac{4}{8} \\ + 5\dfrac{3}{4} \rightarrow \quad + 5\dfrac{6}{8} \\ \hline 18\dfrac{13}{8} = 18 + \dfrac{13}{8} = 18 + 1\dfrac{5}{8} = 19\dfrac{5}{8} \text{ pounds} \end{array}$$

SECTION 2.7

TRY-IT EXERCISE 1

a. $\dfrac{11 - 6}{25} = \dfrac{5}{25} = \dfrac{1}{5}$

b. $\dfrac{13 - 5}{14} = \dfrac{8}{14} = \dfrac{4}{7}$

TRY-IT EXERCISE 2

a. $\dfrac{5 \cdot 3}{12 \cdot 3} - \dfrac{2 \cdot 4}{9 \cdot 4} = \dfrac{15 - 8}{36} = \dfrac{7}{36}$

b. $\dfrac{7 \cdot 3}{16 \cdot 3} + \dfrac{1 \cdot 8}{6 \cdot 8} = \dfrac{21 - 8}{48} = \dfrac{13}{48}$

c. $\dfrac{6 \cdot 3}{7 \cdot 3} - \dfrac{3}{21} = \dfrac{18 - 3}{21} = \dfrac{15}{21} = \dfrac{5}{7}$

TRY-IT EXERCISE 3

a.
$$\begin{array}{r} 12\dfrac{7}{8} \\ - 5\dfrac{3}{8} \\ \hline 7\dfrac{4}{8} = 7\dfrac{1}{2} \end{array}$$

b.
$$\begin{array}{r} 8\dfrac{5}{12} \rightarrow \quad 8\dfrac{5}{12} \\ - 3\dfrac{1}{4} \rightarrow \quad - 3\dfrac{3}{12} \\ \hline 5\dfrac{2}{12} = 5\dfrac{1}{6} \end{array}$$

TRY-IT EXERCISE 4

a.
$$\begin{array}{r} 11\dfrac{2}{7} \rightarrow \quad 11\dfrac{10}{35} \rightarrow \quad 10\dfrac{45}{35} \\ - 8\dfrac{3}{5} \rightarrow \quad - 8\dfrac{21}{35} \rightarrow \quad - 8\dfrac{21}{35} \\ \hline 2\dfrac{24}{35} \end{array}$$

b.
$$\begin{array}{r} 42\dfrac{2}{9} \rightarrow \quad 42\dfrac{10}{45} \rightarrow \quad 41\dfrac{55}{45} \\ - 7\dfrac{8}{15} \rightarrow \quad - 7\dfrac{24}{45} \rightarrow \quad - 7\dfrac{24}{45} \\ \hline 34\dfrac{31}{45} \end{array}$$

c. $21 \quad \rightarrow \quad 20\dfrac{11}{11}$

$\dfrac{-13\dfrac{8}{11} \rightarrow}{} \quad \dfrac{-13\dfrac{8}{11}}{7\dfrac{3}{11}}$

TRY-IT EXERCISE 5

$8 \quad \rightarrow \quad 7\dfrac{5}{5}$

$\dfrac{-3\dfrac{2}{5} \rightarrow}{} \quad \dfrac{-3\dfrac{2}{5}}{4\dfrac{3}{5} \text{ miles}}$

Chapter 3

SECTION 3.1

TRY-IT EXERCISE 1

a. hundredths

b. tenths

c. thousandths

d. hundred-thousandths

e. ten-millionths

TRY-IT EXERCISE 2

a. fifty-two hundredths

b. eighty-three thousand four hundred sixty-five hundred thousandths

c. nineteen and twenty-five hundredths

d. ninety and two hundred seventy-three ten thousandths

TRY-IT EXERCISE 3

a. 0.331

b. 1.05

c. 15.0011

TRY-IT EXERCISE 4

a. $\dfrac{31}{100}$

b. $\dfrac{19}{10,000}$

c. $57\dfrac{8}{10} = 57\dfrac{4}{5}$

d. $132\dfrac{75}{1000} = 132\dfrac{3}{40}$

TRY-IT EXERCISE 5

a. $0.9384 < 0.93870$

b. $143.00502 > 143.005$

TRY-IT EXERCISE 6

a. 0.18

b. 0.0555

c. 6.7

d. 337.87163

TRY-IT EXERCISE 7

a. $\$2085.63$

b. three thousand two hundred forty-four and $\dfrac{19}{100}$

SECTION 3.2

TRY-IT EXERCISE 1

a. $\begin{array}{r} 3.229 \\ +0.660 \\ \hline 3.889 \end{array}$

b. $\begin{array}{r} 1.65410 \\ +0.00282 \\ \hline 1.65692 \end{array}$

TRY-IT EXERCISE 2

a. $\begin{array}{r} 5.06900 \\ 4.00000 \\ +0.00918 \\ \hline 9.07818 \end{array}$

b. $\begin{array}{r} 1.30000 \\ 0.88470 \\ 0.34221 \\ +0.19000 \\ \hline 2.71691 \end{array}$

TRY-IT EXERCISE 3

a. $\begin{array}{r} 4.3178 \\ -2.1001 \\ \hline 2.2177 \end{array}$

b. $\begin{array}{r} 0.08720 \\ -0.04635 \\ \hline 0.04085 \end{array}$

c. $\begin{array}{r} 12.0000 \\ -3.4485 \\ \hline 8.5515 \end{array}$

TRY-IT EXERCISE 4

a. $\begin{array}{r} 75.98 \\ +2.62 \\ \hline 78.60 \end{array} \begin{array}{r} \rightarrow \\ \rightarrow \end{array} \begin{array}{r} 76 \\ +3 \\ \hline 79 \end{array}$

TRY-IT EXERCISE 5

a. $\begin{array}{rcl} 8.430 & \to & 8 \\ -1.391 & \to & -1 \\ \hline 7.039 & & 7 \end{array}$

TRY-IT EXERCISE 6

Number or Code	Date	Transaction Description	Payment, Fee, Withdrawal (–)		✓	Deposit, Credit (+)		$ Balance	
	May 1							1264	59
183	May 4	Shell Oil	$327	68				936	91
184	May 9	Gardner's Market	36	50				900	41
	May 26					116	81	1017	22

SECTION 3.3

TRY-IT EXERCISE 1

a.
$\begin{array}{r} 76.4 \\ \times 15.1 \\ \hline 764 \\ 3820 \\ 764 \\ \hline 1153.64 \end{array}$

b.
$\begin{array}{r} 1.0012 \\ \times 0.27 \\ \hline 70084 \\ 20024 \\ \hline 0.270324 \end{array}$

c.
$\begin{array}{r} 143 \\ \times 11.28 \\ \hline 1144 \\ 286 \\ 143 \\ 143 \\ \hline 1613.04 \end{array}$

TRY-IT EXERCISE 2

a. $42.769 \cdot 100 = 4276.9$

b. $0.0035 \cdot 1000 = 3.5$

c. $78.42 \cdot 0.01 = 0.7842$

d. $0.047 \cdot 0.0001 = 0.0000047$

TRY-IT EXERCISE 3

a. 41,300,000

b. 8,690,000,000

c. 1,500,000,000,000

TRY-IT EXERCISE 4

a. $\begin{array}{rcl} 54.30 & \to & 50.0 \\ \times 0.48 & \to & \times 0.5 \\ \hline 4344 & & 25.0 \\ 2172 & & \\ \hline 26.064 & & \end{array}$

TRY-IT EXERCISE 5

SPARKWELL ELECTRONICS

Quantity	Description	Cost per Item	Total
430	MP3 Players	$115.20	$ 49,536.00
300	DVD Burners	160.00	48,000.00
500	Pkg. of blank DVDs	7.25	3625.00
	Merchandise total		$101,161.00
	Shipping and handling		590.00
	Insurance		345.50
	Invoice total		$102,096.50

SECTION 3.4

TRY-IT EXERCISE 1

a.
$$\begin{array}{r} 16.83 \\ 2\overline{)33.66} \\ \underline{32} \\ 16 \\ \underline{16} \\ 06 \\ \underline{6} \\ 0 \end{array}$$

b.
$$\begin{array}{r} 7.58 \\ 10\overline{)75.80} \\ \underline{70} \\ 58 \\ \underline{50} \\ 80 \\ \underline{80} \\ 0 \end{array}$$

c.
$$\begin{array}{r} 0.0229 \\ 4\overline{)0.0916} \\ \underline{8} \\ 11 \\ \underline{8} \\ 36 \\ \underline{36} \\ 0 \end{array}$$

TRY-IT EXERCISE 2

a. 48,300

b. 1.528661

c. 28

d. 0.1357

TRY-IT EXERCISE 3

a. $0.094\overline{)0.0916} = 94\overline{)1880}$ with $\begin{array}{r} 20 \\ \underline{188} \\ 00 \end{array}$

b. $3.735\overline{)62.67330} = 3735\overline{)62673.30}$

$$
\begin{array}{r}
16.78 \\
\underline{3735} \\
25323 \\
\underline{22410} \\
29133 \\
\underline{26145} \\
29880 \\
\underline{29880} \\
0
\end{array}
$$

c. $13.39\overline{)4.2} = 1339\overline{)420.000}$ $\quad 0.313 \approx 0.31$

$$
\begin{array}{r}
\underline{4017} \\
1830 \\
\underline{1339} \\
4910 \\
\underline{4017}
\end{array}
$$

TRY-IT EXERCISE 4

$19.7\overline{)61.07} = 197\overline{)610.7}\ \ 3.1 \qquad 20\overline{)60}\ \ 3$

$$
\begin{array}{r}
\underline{591} \\
197 \\
\underline{197} \\
0
\end{array}
\qquad
\begin{array}{r}
\underline{60} \\
0
\end{array}
$$

TRY-IT EXERCISE 5

$$\frac{36.6 + 25.8 + 175 + 58.5}{4} = \frac{295}{4} = 73.975 \approx 74 \text{ pounds}$$

SECTION 3.5

TRY-IT EXERCISE 1

a. $\dfrac{3}{40} = 0.075$

b. $\dfrac{15}{16} = 0.9375$

c. $\dfrac{5}{6} = 0.8\overline{3}$

d. $\dfrac{1}{6} = 0.1\overline{6}$

e. $\dfrac{4}{15} = 0.2\overline{6}$

TRY-IT EXERCISE 2

a. $0.875 - 0.6 = 0.275$

b. $\dfrac{375}{1000} \cdot \dfrac{5}{21} = \dfrac{\overset{5}{\cancel{15}}}{\underset{8}{\cancel{40}}} \cdot \dfrac{\overset{1}{\cancel{5}}}{\underset{7}{\cancel{21}}} = \dfrac{5}{56}$

c. $\dfrac{2}{3} \div 1\dfrac{3}{4} = \dfrac{2}{3} \div \dfrac{7}{4} = \dfrac{2}{3} \cdot \dfrac{4}{7} = \dfrac{8}{21}$

TRY-IT EXERCISE 3

a. $4(10 - 2.5^2) \div \dfrac{1}{10}$

$4(10 - 2.5^2) \div 0.1$

$4(10 - 6.25) \div 0.1$

$4(3.75) \div 0.1$

$15 \div 0.1$

150

b. $5^3 + \left(4^2 - 2\dfrac{1}{2}\right)$

$5^3 + (4^2 - 2.5)$

$5^3 + (16 - 2.5)$

$5^3 + 13.5$

$125 + 13.5$

138.5

c. $\dfrac{3^2 - 4\dfrac{1}{10}}{10 - 2^3}$

$\dfrac{3^2 - 4.1}{10 - 2^3}$

$\dfrac{9 - 4.1}{10 - 8}$

$\dfrac{4.9}{2} = 2.45$

TRY-IT EXERCISE 4

a. Living room:

$24\dfrac{1}{2} \cdot (\$34.50 + \$3.60 + \$2.40) = 24.5 \cdot \$40.50 = \$992.25$

Bedroom:

$18\dfrac{1}{4} \cdot (\$17.00 + \$3.60 + \$2.40) = 18.25 \cdot \$23.00 = \$419.75$

b. $\begin{array}{r} \$992.25 \\ +419.75 \\ \hline \$1412.00 \end{array}$

TRY-IT EXERCISE 5

$$28\dfrac{1}{5} \rightarrow 28\dfrac{2}{10} \rightarrow 27\dfrac{12}{10}$$
$$-6\dfrac{4}{10} \rightarrow -6\dfrac{4}{10} \rightarrow -6\dfrac{4}{10}$$
$$21\dfrac{8}{10} = 21\dfrac{4}{5} \text{ feet}$$

Chapter 4

SECTION 4.1

TRY-IT EXERCISE 1

a. $\frac{4}{9}$ 4:9   4 to 9

b. $\frac{14}{5}$ 14:5   14 to 5

TRY-IT EXERCISE 2

a. $\frac{25}{40} = \frac{5}{8}$

b. $\frac{33}{72} = \frac{11}{24}$

c. $\frac{38}{4} = \frac{19}{2}$

TRY-IT EXERCISE 3

$\frac{18.5}{5.5} \cdot \frac{10}{10} = \frac{185}{55} = \frac{37}{11}$

TRY-IT EXERCISE 4

$\frac{3\frac{1}{8}}{2\frac{1}{2}} = \frac{\frac{25}{8}}{\frac{5}{2}} = \frac{25}{8} \cdot \frac{2}{5} = \frac{5}{4}$

TRY-IT EXERCISE 5

a. $\frac{20 \cdot 60}{300} = \frac{1200}{300} = \frac{4}{1}$

b. $\frac{15}{2.5 \cdot 12} = \frac{15}{30} = \frac{1}{2}$

c. $\frac{5}{4 \cdot 2} = \frac{5}{8}$

TRY-IT EXERCISE 6

a. $\frac{26}{2 \cdot 16} = \frac{26}{32} = \frac{13}{16}$

b. $\frac{2 \cdot 4}{3} = \frac{8}{3}$

c. $\frac{1.5 \cdot 24}{9} = \frac{36}{9} = \frac{4}{1}$

TRY-IT EXERCISE 7

a. $\frac{18}{15} = \frac{6}{5}$ 6 to 5   6:5

b. $\frac{25}{90} = \frac{5}{18}$ 5 to 18   5:18

c. $\frac{15}{32}$ 15 to 32   15:32

d. $\frac{90}{18} = \frac{5}{1}$ 5 to 1   5:1

e. $\frac{18 + 25}{15} = \frac{43}{15}$ 43 to 15   43:15

SECTION 4.2

TRY-IT EXERCISE 1

a. $\frac{6 \text{ computers}}{15 \text{ students}} = \frac{2 \text{ computers}}{5 \text{ students}}$

2 computers for every 5 students

b. $\frac{22 \text{ inches of snow}}{8 \text{ hours}} = \frac{11 \text{ inches of snow}}{4 \text{ hours}}$

11 inches of snow for every 4 hours

c. $\frac{\$35,000}{14 \text{ weeks}} = \frac{\$2500}{1 \text{ week}}$

$2500 for every week

TRY-IT EXERCISE 2

a. $\frac{\$5400}{6 \text{ months}} = \$900$ per month

b. $\frac{349 \text{ gallons}}{2.8 \text{ hours}} = 124.6$ gallons per hour

TRY-IT EXERCISE 3

a. $\frac{98 \text{ pitches}}{7 \text{ innings}} = 14$ pitches per inning

b. $\frac{10,000 \text{ pounds}}{7 \text{ trucks}} = 1428.6$ pounds per truck

TRY-IT EXERCISE 4

a. $\frac{\$1350}{5 \text{ days}} = \$270$ per day

b. $\frac{\$3300}{2.48 \text{ carats}} = \$1330.65$ per carat

TRY-IT EXERCISE 5

a.

SIZE	PRICE	UNIT PRICE
16 ounces	$3.29	$\frac{\$3.29}{16} = \$0.21$
24 ounces	$4.50	$\frac{\$4.50}{24} = \$0.19$
31 ounces	$5.39	$\frac{\$5.39}{31} = \$0.17$

b. Based on unit price, the 31-ounce size is the best buy.

SECTION 4.3

TRY-IT EXERCISE 1

a. $\frac{5}{12} = \frac{15}{36}$

b. $\frac{14 \text{ grams}}{6 \text{ ounces}} = \frac{7 \text{ grams}}{3 \text{ ounces}}$

TRY-IT EXERCISE 2

a. 3 is to 40 as 6 is to 80

b. 22 pounds is to 6 weeks as 11 pounds is to 3 weeks

TRY-IT EXERCISE 3

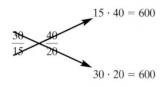

$15 \cdot 40 = 600$

$30 \cdot 20 = 600$

Cross products are equal.
The ratios are proportional.

$$\frac{30}{15} = \frac{40}{20}$$

TRY-IT EXERCISE 4

$4 \cdot 140 = 560$

$52 \cdot 10 = 520$

Cross products are not equal.
The ratios are not proportional.

TRY-IT EXERCISE 5

$$\frac{w}{12} = \frac{1}{3}$$

$12 \cdot 1 = w \cdot 3$

$12 = 3w$

$$\frac{12}{3} = \frac{3w}{3}$$

$4 = w$

Verify:

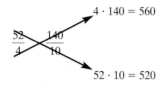

$12 \cdot 1 = 12$

Cross products are equal.

$4 \cdot 3 = 12$

TRY-IT EXERCISE 6

$$\frac{12}{x} = \frac{15}{2.5}$$

$x \cdot 15 = 12 \cdot 2.5$

$15x = 30$

$$\frac{15x}{15} = \frac{30}{15}$$

$x = 2$

Verify:

$2 \cdot 15 = 30$

Cross products are equal.

$12 \cdot 2.5 = 30$

TRY-IT EXERCISE 7

$$\frac{180 \text{ miles}}{12 \text{ gallons}} = \frac{330 \text{ miles}}{x \text{ gallons}}$$

$12 \cdot 330 = 180x$

$3960 = 180x$

$22 = x$

The trip would require 22 gallons of gasoline.

TRY-IT EXERCISE 8

$$\frac{24 \text{ square yards}}{6 \text{ chairs}} = \frac{x \text{ square yards}}{11 \text{ chairs}}$$

$6 \cdot x = 24 \cdot 11$

$6x = 264$

$x = 44$

It takes 44 square yards of material to make 11 chairs.

TRY-IT EXERCISE 9

$$\frac{5.25}{x} = \frac{7}{20}$$

$x \cdot 7 = 5.25 \cdot 20$

$7x = 105$

$x = 15$

The height of the new photo is 15 inches.

TRY-IT EXERCISE 10

$$\frac{5}{x} = \frac{4}{13}$$

$x \cdot 4 = 5 \cdot 13$

$4x = 65$

$x = 16.25$

The tree is 16.25 feet tall.

Chapter 5

SECTION 5.1

TRY-IT EXERCISE 1

a. $\dfrac{19}{100}$

b. $\dfrac{38}{100} = \dfrac{19}{50}$

c. $\dfrac{266}{100} = 2\dfrac{66}{100} = 2\dfrac{33}{50}$

d. $\dfrac{18.4}{100} = \dfrac{184}{1000} = \dfrac{23}{125}$

e. $\dfrac{9}{16}\% = \dfrac{0.5625}{100} = \dfrac{5625}{1,000,000} = \dfrac{9}{1600}$

TRY-IT EXERCISE 2

a. $89 \cdot 0.01 = 0.89$

b. $7 \cdot 0.01 = 0.07$

c. $420 \cdot 0.01 = 4.20$

d. $32.6 \cdot 0.01 = 0.326$

e. $0.008 \cdot 0.01 = 0.00008$

f. $3\dfrac{7}{8} \cdot 0.01 = 3.875 \cdot 0.01 = 0.03875$

TRY-IT EXERCISE 3

a. $0.91 \cdot 100\% = 91\%$

b. $7.2 \cdot 100\% = 720\%$

c. $0.009 \cdot 100\% = 0.9\%$

d. $3.0 = 3.0 \cdot 100\% = 300\%$

e. $1.84 \cdot 100\% = 184\%$

TRY-IT EXERCISE 4

a. $\dfrac{3}{8} = 0.375$

    $0.375 \cdot 100\% = 37.5\%$

b. $\dfrac{49}{100} = 0.49$

    $0.49 \cdot 100\% = 49\%$

c. $2\dfrac{1}{4} = 2 + \dfrac{1}{4} = 2 + 0.25 = 2.25$

    $2.25 \cdot 100\% = 225\%$

d. $\dfrac{22}{5} = 4.4$

    $4.4 \cdot 100\% = 440\%$

e. $\dfrac{1}{3} = 0.33\overline{3}$

    $0.33\overline{3} \cdot 100\% = 33.\overline{3}\% = 33\dfrac{1}{3}\%$

TRY-IT EXERCISE 5

a. $0.263 \cdot 100\% = 26.3\%$

b. $0.014 \cdot 100\% = 1.4\%$

TRY-IT EXERCISE 6

a. $68.3\% = 68.3 \cdot 0.01 = 0.683$

b. $13.4\% = 13.4 \cdot 0.01 = 0.134$

c. $5.3\% = 5.3 \cdot 0.01 = 0.053$

TRY-IT EXERCISE 7

a. $0.552 \cdot 100\% = 55.2\%$

b. $0.581 \cdot 100\% = 58.1\%$

c. $0.575 \cdot 100\% = 57.5\%$

TRY-IT EXERCISE 8

a. $\dfrac{2}{3} = 0.66\overline{6}$

    $0.66\overline{6} \cdot 100\% = 66.\overline{6}\% \approx 66.7\%$

b. $\dfrac{2900}{1500} = 1.93\overline{3}$

    $1.93\overline{3} \cdot 100\% = 193.\overline{3}\% \approx 193\%$

TRY-IT EXERCISE 9

a. $26\% = 0.26$

    $0.26 = \dfrac{26}{100} = \dfrac{13}{50}$

b. $24\% = 0.24$

    $0.24 = \dfrac{24}{100} = \dfrac{6}{25}$

SECTION 5.2

TRY-IT EXERCISE 1

a. $x = 34\% \cdot 80$

b. $x = 130\% \cdot 68$

TRY-IT EXERCISE 2

a. $57 = x \cdot 239$

b. $x \cdot 96 = 33$

TRY-IT EXERCISE 3

a. $x = 135\% \cdot 90$

b. $0.55\% \cdot x = 104$

TRY-IT EXERCISE 4

$a = 36\% \cdot 150$

$a = 0.36 \cdot 150$

$a = 54$

TRY-IT EXERCISE 5

$115\% \cdot 38 = a$

$1.15 \cdot 38 = a$

$a = 43.7$

TRY-IT EXERCISE 6

$45\% \cdot b = 216$

$b = \dfrac{216}{0.45} = 480$

TRY-IT EXERCISE 7

$55 = 22\% \cdot b$

$b = \dfrac{55}{0.22} = 250$

TRY-IT EXERCISE 8

$300 = p \cdot 500$

$p = \dfrac{300}{500} = 0.6 = 60\%$

TRY-IT EXERCISE 9

$p \cdot 56 = 123.2$

$p = \dfrac{123.2}{56} = 2.2 = 220\%$

TRY-IT EXERCISE 10

a. $a = 40\% \cdot 180$

$a = 0.4 \cdot 180 = 72$

b. $a = 14\% \cdot 1850$

$a = 0.14 \cdot 1850 = 259$

TRY-IT EXERCISE 11

a. $38\% \cdot b = 15,400$

$b = \dfrac{15,400}{0.38} \approx 40,526.3 \approx 40,526 \text{ ft}^2$

b. $61.3\% \cdot b = 245$

$b = \dfrac{245}{0.613} \approx 399.67 \approx 400 \text{ degrees}$

TRY-IT EXERCISE 12

a. $p \cdot 382 = 158$

$p = \dfrac{158}{382} \approx 0.4136 \approx 41.4\%$

b. $p \cdot 112 = 42$

$p = \dfrac{42}{112} = 0.375 = 37.5\%$

TRY-IT EXERCISE 13

a. $p \cdot 67,500 = 72,300$

$p = \dfrac{72,300}{67,500} \approx 1.071 \approx 107\%$

b. $p \cdot 75,000 = 67,500$

$p = \dfrac{67,500}{75,000} = 0.9 = 90\%$

c. $p \cdot 67,500 = 75,000$

$p = \dfrac{75,000}{67,500} \approx 1.1111 \approx 111.1\%$

d. $a = 60\% \cdot \dfrac{67,500 + 75,000}{2}$

$a = 0.6 \cdot 71,250 = \$42,750$

SECTION 5.3

TRY-IT EXERCISE 1

a. $\dfrac{64}{262} = \dfrac{p}{100}$

b. $\dfrac{a}{120} = \dfrac{89}{100}$

TRY-IT EXERCISE 2

a. $\dfrac{85}{b} = \dfrac{28}{100}$

b. $\dfrac{a}{90} = \dfrac{7}{100}$

TRY-IT EXERCISE 3

a. $\dfrac{620}{b} = \dfrac{8.37}{100}$

b. $\dfrac{10.5}{13.9} = \dfrac{p}{100}$

TRY-IT EXERCISE 4

a. $\dfrac{a}{220} = \dfrac{35}{100}$

$220 \cdot 35 = a \cdot 100$

$7700 = 100 \cdot a$

$a = \dfrac{7700}{100} = 77$

b. $\dfrac{a}{1800} = \dfrac{67}{100}$

$1800 \cdot 67 = a \cdot 100$

$120,600 = 100 \cdot a$

$a = \dfrac{120,600}{100} = 1206$

TRY-IT EXERCISE 5

a. $\dfrac{45}{b} = \dfrac{30}{100}$

$b \cdot 30 = 45 \cdot 100$

$30 \cdot b = 4500$

$b = \dfrac{4500}{30} = 150$

b. $\dfrac{196}{b} = \dfrac{140}{100}$

$b \cdot 140 = 196 \cdot 100$

$140 \cdot b = 19,600$

$b = \dfrac{19,600}{140} = 140$

TRY-IT EXERCISE 6

a. $\dfrac{21}{300} = \dfrac{p}{100}$

$300 \cdot p = 21 \cdot 100$

$300 \cdot p = 2100$

$p = \dfrac{2100}{300} = 7\%$

b. $\dfrac{66}{165} = \dfrac{p}{100}$

$165 \cdot p = 66 \cdot 100$

$165 \cdot p = 6600$

$p = \dfrac{6600}{165} = 40\%$

TRY-IT EXERCISE 7

a. $\dfrac{a}{68} = \dfrac{25}{100}$

$68 \cdot 25 = a \cdot 100$

$1700 = 100 \cdot a$

$a = \dfrac{1700}{100} = 17 \text{ hits}$

b. $\dfrac{a}{2400} = \dfrac{6}{100}$

$2400 \cdot 6 = a \cdot 100$

$14{,}400 = 100 \cdot a$

$a = \dfrac{14{,}400}{100} = 144 \text{ broken pieces}$

TRY-IT EXERCISE 8

a. $\dfrac{40}{b} = \dfrac{80}{100}$

$b \cdot 80 = 40 \cdot 100$

$80 \cdot b = 4000$

$b = \dfrac{4000}{80} = 50 \text{ questions}$

b. $\dfrac{3550}{b} = \dfrac{19.7}{100}$

$b \cdot 19.7 = 3550 \cdot 100$

$19.7 \cdot b = 355{,}000$

$b = \dfrac{355{,}000}{19.7} \approx 18{,}020.3 \approx 18{,}020 \text{ people}$

TRY-IT EXERCISE 9

a. $\dfrac{1}{2.5} = \dfrac{p}{100}$

$2.5 \cdot p = 1 \cdot 100$

$2.5 \cdot p = 100$

$p = \dfrac{100}{2.5} = 40\%$

b. $\dfrac{47}{160} = \dfrac{p}{100}$

$160 \cdot p = 47 \cdot 100$

$160 \cdot p = 4700$

$p = \dfrac{4700}{160} \approx 29.3 \approx 29\%$

TRY-IT EXERCISE 10

a. $\dfrac{a}{32} = \dfrac{25.5}{100}$

$32 \cdot 25.5 = a \cdot 100$

$816 = 100 \cdot a$

$a = \dfrac{816}{100} = 8.16$

$8.16 \cdot 1{,}000{,}000 = 8{,}160{,}000 \text{ people}$

b. $\dfrac{a}{32} = \dfrac{14}{100}$

$32 \cdot 14 = a \cdot 100$

$448 = 100 \cdot a$

$a = \dfrac{448}{100} = 4.48$

$4.48 \cdot 1{,}000{,}000 = 4{,}480{,}000 \text{ people}$

c. $\dfrac{a}{32} = \dfrac{36.4}{100}$

$32 \cdot 36.4 = a \cdot 100$

$1164.8 = 100 \cdot a$

$a = \dfrac{1164.8}{100} = 11.648$

$11.648 \cdot 1{,}000{,}000 = 11{,}648{,}000 \text{ people}$

SECTION 5.4

TRY-IT EXERCISE 1

a. amount of change $= 312 - 260 = 52$

$\dfrac{52}{260} = 0.2 = 20\% \text{ increase}$

b. amount of change $= 4250 - 1820 = 2430$

$$\frac{2430}{4250} \approx 0.5717 \approx 57.2\% \text{ decrease}$$

TRY-IT EXERCISE 2

a. Sales tax = Sales tax rate · Item cost

$$t \quad = \quad 7.5\% \quad \cdot \quad \$54.25$$

$t = 7.5\% \cdot \$54.25$

$t \approx \$4.068 \approx \$4.07$

The sales tax amount is \$4.07.

b. Item cost + Sales tax = Total purchase price

$\$54.25 + \$4.07 = \$58.32$

The total purchase price is \$58.32

TRY-IT EXERCISE 3

a. Tip = Tip rate · Bill amount

$$t \quad = \quad 22\% \quad \cdot \quad \$35.70$$

$t = 0.22 \cdot \$35.70$

$t \approx \$7.854 \approx \$7.85$

The tip amount is \$7.85.

b. Bill amount + Tip amount = Total

$\$35.70 + \$7.85 = \$43.55$

The total including tip is \$43.55

TRY-IT EXERCISE 4

Commission = Commission rate · sales amount

$$c \quad = \quad 6\% \quad \cdot \quad \$158,000$$

$c = 0.06 \cdot \$158,000$

$c = \$9480$

Coastal made \$9480 commission.

TRY-IT EXERCISE 5

Discount = Discount rate · Original cost

$$\$178.20 \quad = \quad r \quad \cdot \quad \$990.00$$

$\$178.20 = r \cdot \$990.00$

$$\frac{\$178.20}{\$990.00} = \frac{\$990.00r}{\$990.00}$$

$0.18 = r$

$18\% = r$

The discount rate is 18%.

TRY-IT EXERCISE 6

a. $100\% + 120\% = 220\%$

What is 220% of 260?

$$a \quad = \quad 2.2 \quad \cdot \quad 260$$

$a = 2.2 \cdot 260$

$a = 572$

260 increased by 120% is 572

b. $100\% - 15\% = 85\%$

What is 85% of 1400?

$$a \quad = 0.85 \quad \cdot \quad 1400$$

$a = 0.85 \cdot 1400$

$a = 1190$

1400 decreased by 15% is 1190

TRY-IT EXERCISE 7

a. $100\% - 30\% = 70\%$

714 is 70% of what number?

$$714 = \quad 0.7 \quad \cdot \quad b$$

$714 = 0.7 \cdot b$

$$\frac{714}{0.7} = \frac{0.7b}{0.7}$$

$1020 = b$

714 is 70% of 1020

b. $100\% + 40\% = 140\%$

1764 is 140% of what number?

$$1764 = \quad 1.4 \quad \cdot \quad b$$

$1764 = 1.4 \cdot b$

$$\frac{1764}{1.4} = \frac{1.4b}{1.4}$$

$1260 = b$

1764 is 140% of 1260

TRY-IT EXERCISE 8

a. $5.2 - 3.5 = 1.7$

$$\frac{1.7}{3.5} \approx 0.4857 \approx 48.6\% \text{ increase}$$

b. $58 - 42 = 16$

$$\frac{16}{58} \approx 0.275 \approx 28\% \text{ decrease}$$

TRY-IT EXERCISE 9

a. $100\% + 20\% = 120\%$

What is 120% of 180?

$$\begin{array}{ccc} \downarrow & \downarrow & \downarrow \quad \downarrow \quad \downarrow \\ a & = \ 1.2 & \cdot \ 180 \end{array}$$

$a = 1.2 \cdot 180$

$a = 216$

Jiffy Lube expects to service 216 cars this week.

b. $100\% - 10\% = 90\%$

What is 90% of 260?

$$\begin{array}{ccc} \downarrow & \downarrow & \downarrow \quad \downarrow \quad \downarrow \\ a & = \ 0.9 & \cdot \ 260 \end{array}$$

$a = 0.9 \cdot 260$

$a = 234$

234 handlers work each shift during the normal months.

TRY-IT EXERCISE 10

a. $100\% + 10\% = 110\%$

1353 is 110% of what number?

$$\begin{array}{ccccc} \downarrow & \downarrow & \downarrow & \downarrow & \downarrow \\ 1353 = & 1.1 & \cdot & & b \end{array}$$

$1353 = 1.1 \cdot b$

$\dfrac{1353}{1.1} = \dfrac{1.1b}{1.1}$

$1230 = b$

Dr. Mager had 1230 patients last year.

b. $100\% - 25\% = 75\%$

$28,500 is 75% of what number?

$$\begin{array}{ccccc} \downarrow & \downarrow & \downarrow & \downarrow & \downarrow \\ \$28,500 = & 0.75 & \cdot & & b \end{array}$$

$\$28,500 = 0.75 \cdot b$

$\dfrac{\$28,500}{0.75} = \dfrac{0.75b}{0.75}$

$\$38,000 = b$

$38,000 was the original price of the car.

TRY-IT EXERCISE 11

a. $25.5 - 20.3 = 5.2$

$\dfrac{5.2}{20.3} \approx 0.256 \approx 26\%$ increase

b. $27.0 - 26.1 = 0.9$

$\dfrac{0.9}{27.0} \approx 0.0333 \approx 3.3\%$ decrease

Chapter 6

SECTION 6.1

TRY-IT EXERCISE 1

$2 \ \text{miles} \cdot \dfrac{5280 \ \text{feet}}{1 \ \text{mile}} = 10{,}560 \ \text{feet}$

TRY-IT EXERCISE 2

$1 \ \text{mile} \cdot \dfrac{5280 \ \text{feet}}{1 \ \text{mile}} \cdot \dfrac{12 \ \text{inches}}{1 \ \text{foot}} = 63{,}360 \ \text{inches}$

TRY-IT EXERCISE 3

$1500 \ \text{pounds} \cdot \dfrac{1 \ \text{ton}}{2000 \ \text{pounds}} = \dfrac{3}{4} \ \text{ton}$

TRY-IT EXERCISE 4

$150 \ \text{gallons} \cdot \dfrac{4 \ \text{quarts}}{1 \ \text{gallon}} = 600 \ \text{quarts}$

TRY-IT EXERCISE 5

$2.5 \ \text{miles} \cdot \dfrac{5280 \ \text{feet}}{1 \ \text{mile}} \cdot 13{,}200 \ \text{feet}$

$\dfrac{13{,}200 \ \text{feet}}{15 \ \text{“distances” between sites}} = 880 \ \text{feet between sites}$

SECTION 6.2

TRY-IT EXERCISE 1

$$\begin{array}{r} 25 \ \text{ft} \ 10 \ \text{in.} \\ 12\overline{)310} \\ -\underline{24} \\ 70 \\ \underline{60} \\ 10 \end{array}$$

TRY-IT EXERCISE 2

a. 5 gal 6 qt = 5 gal + 1 gal + 2 qt

   = 6 gal + 2 qt

   = 6 gal 2 qt

b. 2 tons 4300 lbs = 2 tons + 2 tons + 300 lbs

   = 4 tons + 300 lbs

   = 4 tons 300 lbs

TRY-IT EXERCISE 3

a.
$$\begin{array}{r} 2 \ \text{qt} \ \ 1 \ \text{pt} \\ +\underline{3 \ \text{qt} \ \ 4 \ \text{pt}} \\ 5 \ \text{qt} \ \ 5 \ \text{pt} \end{array}$$

5 qt 5 pt = 5 qt + 2 qt + 1 pt

   = 7 qt + 1 pt

   = 7 qt 1 pt

b.
$$\begin{array}{r} 7 \text{ ft } 9 \text{ in.} \\ -\ 2 \text{ ft } 3 \text{ in.} \\ \hline 5 \text{ ft } 6 \text{ in.} \end{array}$$

c.
$$\begin{array}{r} 19 \text{ lbs } 2 \text{ oz} \\ -\ 5 \text{ lbs } 12 \text{ oz} \end{array}$$

$$\begin{array}{r} 18 \text{ lbs } 18 \text{ oz} \\ \cancel{19 \text{ lbs}} \ \cancel{2 \text{ oz}} \\ -\ 5 \text{ lbs } 12 \text{ oz} \\ \hline 13 \text{ lbs } 6 \text{ oz} \end{array}$$

TRY-IT EXERCISE 4

a.
$$\begin{array}{r} 5 \text{ qt } 3 \text{ pt} \\ \times \qquad\ 4 \\ \hline 20 \text{ qt } 12 \text{ pt} \end{array}$$

$$20 \text{ qt } 12 \text{ pt} = 20 \text{ qt} + 6 \text{ qt} = 26 \text{ qt}$$

b.
$$\begin{array}{r} 1 \text{ gal} \\ 3\overline{)5 \text{ gal } 1 \text{ qt}} \\ \underline{3 \text{ gal}} \\ 2 \text{ gal } 1 \text{ qt} \end{array}$$

$$\begin{array}{r} 1 \text{ gal } 3 \text{ qt} \\ 3\overline{)5 \text{ gal } 1 \text{ qt}} \\ \underline{3 \text{ gal}} \\ 9 \text{ qt} \\ \underline{9 \text{ qt}} \\ 0 \end{array}$$

TRY-IT EXERCISE 5

a.
$$\begin{array}{r} 6 \text{ gal } 3 \text{ qt} \\ +\ 12 \text{ gal } 2 \text{ qt} \\ \hline 18 \text{ gal } 5 \text{ qt} \end{array}$$

$$\begin{aligned} 18 \text{ gal } 5 \text{ qt} &= 18 \text{ gal} + 1 \text{ gal} + 1 \text{ qt} \\ &= 19 \text{ gal} + 1 \text{ qt} \\ &= 19 \text{ gal } 1 \text{ qt} \end{aligned}$$

b.
$$\begin{array}{r} 9 \text{ gal} \\ 2\overline{)19 \text{ gal } 1 \text{ qt}} \\ \underline{18 \text{ gal}} \\ 1 \text{ gal } 1 \text{ qt} \end{array}$$

$$\begin{array}{r} 9 \text{ gal } 2 \text{ qt} \\ 2\overline{)19 \text{ gal } 1 \text{ qt}} \\ \underline{18 \text{ gal}} \\ 5 \text{ qt} \\ \underline{4 \text{ qt}} \\ 1 \text{ qt} \end{array}$$

$$\begin{array}{r} 9 \text{ gal } 2 \text{ qt } 1 \text{ pt} \\ 2\overline{)19 \text{ gal } 1 \text{ qt}} \\ \underline{18 \text{ gal}} \\ 5 \text{ qt} \\ \underline{4 \text{ qt}} \\ 2 \text{ pt} \\ \underline{2 \text{ pt}} \\ 0 \end{array}$$

SECTION 6.3

TRY-IT EXERCISE 1

$$18.3 \,\cancel{\text{km}} \cdot \frac{1000 \text{ m}}{1 \,\cancel{\text{km}}} = 18{,}300 \text{ meters}$$

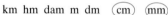

$$\text{(km)} \quad \text{hm} \quad \text{dam} \quad \text{(m)} \quad \text{dm} \quad \text{cm} \quad \text{mm}$$

$$18.3 \text{ km} = 18{,}300 \text{ m}$$

TRY-IT EXERCISE 2

$$26.4 \,\cancel{\text{mm}} \cdot \frac{1 \text{ cm}}{10 \,\cancel{\text{mm}}} = 2.64 \text{ cm}$$

$$\text{km} \quad \text{hm} \quad \text{dam} \quad \text{m} \quad \text{dm} \quad \text{(cm)} \quad \text{(mm)}$$

$$26.4 \text{ mm} = 2.64 \text{ cm}$$

TRY-IT EXERCISE 3

$$6.2 \,\cancel{\text{kg}} \cdot \frac{1000 \text{ g}}{1 \,\cancel{\text{kg}}} = 6200 \text{ g}$$

$$\text{(kg)} \quad \text{hg} \quad \text{dag} \quad \text{(g)} \quad \text{dg} \quad \text{cg} \quad \text{mg}$$

$$6.2 \text{ kg} = 6200 \text{ g}$$

TRY-IT EXERCISE 4

$$41 \,\cancel{\text{kL}} \cdot \frac{1000 \text{ L}}{1 \,\cancel{\text{kL}}} = 41{,}000 \text{ L}$$

$$\text{(kL)} \quad \text{hL} \quad \text{daL} \quad \text{(L)} \quad \text{dL} \quad \text{cL} \quad \text{mL}$$

$$41 \text{ kL} = 41{,}000 \text{ L}$$

TRY-IT EXERCISE 5

a.
$$\frac{190 \,\cancel{\text{pounds}}}{100 \,\cancel{\text{pounds}}} = 1.9$$

$$1.9 \cdot 1100 \text{ milligrams} = 2090 \text{ milligrams}$$

b.
$$2090 \,\cancel{\text{mg}} \cdot \frac{1 \text{ g}}{1000 \,\cancel{\text{mg}}} = 2.09 \text{ grams}$$

$$\text{kg} \quad \text{hg} \quad \text{dag} \quad \text{(g)} \quad \text{dg} \quad \text{cg} \quad \text{(mg)}$$

$$2090 \text{ mg} = 2.09 \text{ g}$$

SECTION 6.4

TRY-IT EXERCISE 1

$$1011 \,\cancel{\text{m}} \cdot \frac{3.3 \text{ ft}}{1 \,\cancel{\text{m}}} = 3336.3 \approx 3336 \text{ ft}$$

TRY-IT EXERCISE 2

$$10.5 \text{ oz} \cdot \frac{28.35 \text{ g}}{1 \text{ oz}} = 297.675 \approx 298 \text{ g}$$

TRY-IT EXERCISE 3

$$25 \text{ mg} \cdot \frac{1000 \text{ mcg}}{1 \text{ mg}} = 25{,}000 \text{ mcg}$$

SECTION 6.5

TRY-IT EXERCISE 1

a. $2 \text{ yr} \cdot \dfrac{4 \text{ qtrs}}{1 \text{ yr}} = 8 \text{ qtrs}$

b. $68{,}400 \text{ min} \cdot \dfrac{1 \text{ hr}}{60 \text{ min}} = 1140 \text{ hrs}$

TRY-IT EXERCISE 2

$$C = \frac{5}{9}(68 - 32)$$

$$= \frac{5}{9}(36) = 20^\circ C$$

TRY-IT EXERCISE 3

$$F = \frac{9}{5} \cdot 30 + 32$$

$$= 9 \cdot 6 + 32 = 54 + 32 = 86^\circ F$$

Chapter 7

SECTION 7.1

TRY-IT EXERCISE 1

a. line segment, $\overline{PA}$ or $\overline{AP}$

b. ray, $\overrightarrow{IS}$

c. line, $\overleftrightarrow{ZK}$ or $\overleftrightarrow{KZ}$

TRY-IT EXERCISE 2

a. $\angle U$, $\angle HUS$, $\angle SUH$ acute

b. $\angle Z$, $\angle YZB$, $\angle BZY$ right

c. $\angle Z$ straight

d. $\angle P$, $\angle GPA$, $\angle APG$ obtuse

TRY-IT EXERCISE 3

a. $90^\circ - 48^\circ = 42^\circ$

b. $90^\circ - 77^\circ = 13^\circ$

c. $90^\circ - 12^\circ = 78^\circ$

TRY-IT EXERCISE 4

a. $180^\circ - 95^\circ = 85^\circ$

b. $180^\circ - 140^\circ = 40^\circ$

c. $180^\circ - 103^\circ = 77^\circ$

TRY-IT EXERCISE 5

a. $180^\circ - 53^\circ = 127^\circ$

b. $90^\circ - 72^\circ = 18^\circ$

SECTION 7.2

TRY-IT EXERCISE 1

a. isosceles

b. scalene

c. equilateral

TRY-IT EXERCISE 2

a. right

b. acute

c. obtuse

TRY-IT EXERCISE 3

a. $90^\circ + 75^\circ = 165^\circ$
   $180^\circ - 165^\circ = 15^\circ$

b. $80^\circ + 75^\circ = 155^\circ$
   $180^\circ - 155^\circ = 25^\circ$

TRY-IT EXERCISE 4

a. square   **b.** trapezoid

c. rhombus   **d.** rectangle

TRY-IT EXERCISE 5

a. pentagon   **b.** hexagon

c. octagon   **d.** triangle

TRY-IT EXERCISE 6

a. Radius $= \dfrac{8 \text{ inches}}{2} = 4 \text{ inches}$

b. Diameter $= 2 \text{ yards} \cdot 2 = 4 \text{ yards}$

TRY-IT EXERCISE 7

a. pyramid   **b.** rectangular solid

c. cylinder   **d.** cone

SECTION 7.3

TRY-IT EXERCISE 1

$$88 + 110 + 75 + 122 + 135 = 530 \text{ mm}$$

TRY-IT EXERCISE 2

$P = (2 \cdot 90 \text{ in.}) + (2 \cdot 32 \text{ in.}) = 244 \text{ inches}$

TRY-IT EXERCISE 3

$p = 4 \cdot 7 \text{ in.} = 28 \text{ in.}$

TRY-IT EXERCISE 4

a. $C = (2)(3.14)(16 \text{ ft}) = 100.48 \text{ ft}$

b. $C = (3.14)(43 \text{ yd}) = 135.02 \text{ yards}$

TRY-IT EXERCISE 5

$p = 2.4 \text{ mi} + 1.8 \text{ mi} + 1.9 \text{ mi} + 0.5 \text{ mi} + 0.7 \text{ mi} + 1.6 \text{ mi}$
$\quad = 8.9 \text{ miles}$

$8.9 \text{ mi} \cdot \dfrac{\$2.50}{\text{mi}} = \$22.25 \text{ per person}$

TRY-IT EXERCISE 6

$C = (2)(3.14)(75 \text{ ft}) = 471 \text{ feet}$

SECTION 7.4

TRY-IT EXERCISE 1

$A = 4 \text{ m} \cdot 12 \text{ m} = 48 \text{ m}^2$

TRY-IT EXERCISE 2

$A = (8 \text{ yd})^2 = 64 \text{ yd}^2$

TRY-IT EXERCISE 3

$A = 7 \text{ ft} \cdot 2 \text{ ft} = 14 \text{ ft}^2$

TRY-IT EXERCISE 4

$A = \dfrac{1}{2}(5 \text{ m})(2 \text{ m}) = 5 \text{ m}^2$

TRY-IT EXERCISE 5

$A = \dfrac{1}{2}(2 \text{ yd} + 4 \text{ yd})(3) = 9 \text{ yd}^2$

TRY-IT EXERCISE 6

$A = (3.14)(4 \text{ in.})^2$

$A = (3.14)(16 \text{ in.}^2) = 50.24 \text{ in}^2$

TRY-IT EXERCISE 7

$A = (11 \text{ ft})(15 \text{ ft}) = 165 \text{ ft}^2$

$165 \text{ ft}^2 \cdot \dfrac{\$4.29}{\text{ft}^2} = \$707.85$

SECTION 7.5

TRY-IT EXERCISE 1

a. 1   **b.** 3   **c.** 13   **d.** 15

TRY-IT EXERCISE 2

a. 5.39   **b.** 7.42

TRY-IT EXERCISE 3

$c = \sqrt{5^2 + 12^2}$

$c = \sqrt{25 + 144}$

$c = \sqrt{169} = 13 \text{ inches}$

TRY-IT EXERCISE 4

$c = \sqrt{19^2 - 7^2}$

$c = \sqrt{361 - 49}$

$c = \sqrt{312} \approx 17.7 \text{ meters}$

TRY-IT EXERCISE 5

$c = \sqrt{30^2 + 20^2}$

$c = \sqrt{900 + 400}$

$c = \sqrt{1300} \approx 36 \text{ inches}$

SECTION 7.6

TRY-IT EXERCISE 1

$V = (5 \text{ m})(3 \text{ m})(1 \text{ m}) = 15 \text{ m}^3$

TRY-IT EXERCISE 2

$V = (5 \text{ m})^3 = 125 \text{ m}^3$

TRY-IT EXERCISE 3

$V = (3.14)(4 \text{ cm})^2(10 \text{ cm}) = 502.4 \text{ cm}^3$

TRY-IT EXERCISE 4

$V = \dfrac{1}{3}(3.14)(2 \text{ yd})^2(5.2 \text{ yd}) = 21.77 \text{ yd}^3$

TRY-IT EXERCISE 5

$V = \dfrac{1}{3}(2 \text{ m})^2(7 \text{ m})$

$V = \dfrac{1}{3}(4 \text{ m}^2)(7 \text{ m}) \approx 9.33 \text{ m}^3$

TRY-IT EXERCISE 6

$V = \dfrac{4}{3}(3.14)(2.1 \text{ ft})^3$

$V = \dfrac{4}{3}(3.14)(9.261 \text{ ft}^3) \approx 38.8 \text{ ft}^3$

TRY-IT EXERCISE 7

$V = (3.14)(6 \text{ ft})^2(46 - 6) + \dfrac{4}{3}(3.14)(6 \text{ ft})^3\left(\dfrac{1}{2}\right)$

$V = (3.14)(36 \text{ ft}^2)(40) + \dfrac{4}{3}(3.14)(216 \text{ ft}^3)\left(\dfrac{1}{2}\right) \approx 4973.8 \text{ ft}^3$

Chapter 8

SECTION 8.1

TRY-IT EXERCISE 1

a. $9000

b. February Appliance Sales

$240,000 Surfside

$190,000 Midway

c. April Clothing Sales

$\begin{array}{r} \$130{,}000 \text{ Midway} \\ -\$105{,}000 \text{ Surfside} \\ \hline \$25{,}000 \end{array}$

d.

MARCH PROFIT	SURFSIDE	MIDWAY
Appliances	$48,000	$35,000
Clothing	12,000	15,000
Garden Shop	9,000	6,000
Total Profit	$69,000	$56,000

TRY-IT EXERCISE 2

a. $1.20

b. June

c. May

d. $\begin{array}{r} \$1.25 \text{ January} \\ -\$0.85 \text{ March} \\ \hline \$0.40 \end{array}$

TRY-IT EXERCISE 3

a. $1.30

b. bananas

c. February, March, May, and June

d. $\begin{array}{r} \$1.25 \text{ bananas} \\ -\$0.90 \text{ strawberries} \\ \hline \$0.35 \end{array}$

TRY-IT EXERCISE 4

TRY-IT EXERCISE 5

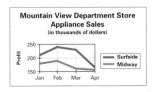

TRY-IT EXERCISE 6

a. The Rolling Stones

b. $80,000,000

c. Kenny Chesney

d. Neal Diamond and Jimmy Buffett

TRY-IT EXERCISE 7

a. Beta Corp.

b. 2006

c. 2003

d. 2005 and 2007

TRY-IT EXERCISE 8

TRY-IT EXERCISE 9

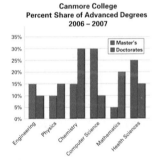

TRY-IT EXERCISE 10

a. 25.2%, Rock

b. 8.9%

c. $\begin{array}{r} 13.3\% \text{ Rap/Hip-Hop} \\ -5.8\% \text{ Religious} \\ \hline 7.5\% \end{array}$

d. Rock

TRY-IT EXERCISE 11

Car/station wagon $= \dfrac{342}{600} = 57\%$

$0.57 \cdot 360° = 205.2 \approx 205°$

Pickup truck $= \dfrac{108}{600} = 18\%$

$0.18 \cdot 360° = 64.8 \approx 65°$

Sport utility vehicle $= \dfrac{72}{600} = 12\%$

$0.12 \cdot 360° = 43.2 \approx 43°$

$$\text{Van} = \frac{54}{600} = 9\%$$

$$0.09 \cdot 360° = 32.4 \approx 32°$$

$$\text{Other} = \frac{24}{600} = 4\%$$

$$0.04 \cdot 360° = 14.4 \approx 14°$$

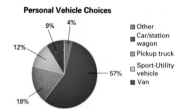

Personal Vehicle Choices

□ Other
□ Car/station wagon
□ Pickup truck
□ Sport-Utility vehicle
■ Van

SECTION 8.2

TRY-IT EXERCISE 1

a. $\dfrac{36 + 21 + 5 + 28 + 20}{5} = 22$

b. $\dfrac{88 + 74 + 99 + 77 + 82 + 86}{6} = 84.3$

TRY-IT EXERCISE 2

COURSE	CREDITS	GRADE VALUE	QUALITY POINTS
Real Estate	4	B = 3	12
Business Math	3	A = 4	12
Social Science	3	C = 2	6
Humanities	3	B = 3	9
Photography	2	B = 3	6
	15		45

$$\text{GPA} = \frac{45}{15} = 3.0$$

TRY-IT EXERCISE 3

a. Blender: $37 $54 $56 $69 $72 $88 $98

b. Dishwasher: $143 $190 $229 $235 $293 $327 $342
          $433 $494

TRY-IT EXERCISE 4

a. 54   96   121   130   135   157

$$\text{Median} = \frac{121 + 130}{2} = 125.5$$

b. $40 $48 $49 $56 $62 $74 $79 $88.

$$\text{Median} = \frac{\$56 + \$62}{2} = \$59$$

TRY-IT EXERCISE 5

a. 76   102   35   75   80   34   35

Mode

b. 126   119   80   139   143   139   141   126

Mode

Mode

c. 8   5   9   12   6   11

No Mode

TRY-IT EXERCISE 6

a. Range = 67 lbs − 19 lbs = 48 lbs

b. Range = 350° − 275° = 75°

TRY-IT EXERCISE 7

a. Mean = $240, Median = $280, Mode = $290,

Range = $280

b. The median is the better indicator of central tendency because there is one "extreme" value, $20, which makes the mean less than all but one of the other values in the set.

Chapter 9

SECTION 9.1

TRY-IT EXERCISE 1

a. +12

b. $-8\dfrac{3}{5}$

c. +2.25

TRY-IT EXERCISE 2

a.

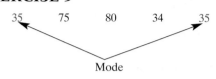

b.

c.

TRY-IT EXERCISE 3

a. 13.46

b. $\dfrac{3}{8}$

c. 18

TRY-IT EXERCISE 4

a. $6 < 11$ or $11 > 6$

b. $-4 < 7$ or $7 > -4$

c. $-3.18 < -2.57$ or $-2.57 > -3.18$

d. $\dfrac{1}{4} = \dfrac{1}{4} \cdot \dfrac{5}{5} = \dfrac{5}{20}$

$\dfrac{2}{5} = \dfrac{2}{5} \cdot \dfrac{4}{4} = \dfrac{8}{20}$

$\dfrac{1}{4} < \dfrac{2}{5}$ or $\dfrac{2}{5} > \dfrac{1}{4}$

TRY-IT EXERCISE 5

-4.03

SECTION 9.2

TRY-IT EXERCISE 1

a. $-30 + (-12)$

$|-30| = 30, |-12| = 12$

$30 + 12 = 42$

$-30 + (-12) = -42$

b. $-19 + (-33)$

$|-19| = 19, |-33| = 33$

$19 + 35 = 52$

$-19 + (-33) = -52$

c. $-59 + (-7)$

$|-59| = 59, |-7| = 7$

$59 + 7 = 66$

$-59 + (-7) = -66$

TRY-IT EXERCISE 2

a. $-\dfrac{3}{8} + \left(-\dfrac{1}{8}\right)$

$\left|-\dfrac{3}{8}\right| = \dfrac{3}{8}, \left|-\dfrac{1}{8}\right| = \dfrac{1}{8}$

$\dfrac{3}{8} + \dfrac{1}{8} = \dfrac{4}{8} = \dfrac{1}{2}$

$-\dfrac{3}{8} + \left(-\dfrac{1}{8}\right) = -\dfrac{1}{2}$

b. $-\dfrac{5}{7} + \left(-\dfrac{10}{21}\right)$

$\left|-\dfrac{5}{7}\right| = \dfrac{5}{7}, \left|-\dfrac{10}{21}\right| = \dfrac{10}{21}$

LCD = 21

$\dfrac{5}{7} = \dfrac{5}{7} \cdot \dfrac{3}{3} = \dfrac{15}{21}$

$\dfrac{10}{21} \rightarrow \dfrac{10}{21}$

$\dfrac{15}{21} + \dfrac{10}{21} = \dfrac{25}{21} = 1\dfrac{4}{21}$

$-\dfrac{5}{7} + \left(-\dfrac{10}{21}\right) = -1\dfrac{4}{21}$

c. $-3\dfrac{1}{4} + \left(-6\dfrac{2}{3}\right)$

$\left|-3\dfrac{1}{4}\right| = 3\dfrac{1}{4}, \left|-6\dfrac{2}{3}\right| = 6\dfrac{2}{3}$

LCD = 12

$3\dfrac{1}{4} \cdot \dfrac{3}{3} = 3\dfrac{3}{12}$

$6\dfrac{2}{3} \cdot \dfrac{4}{4} = 6\dfrac{8}{12}$

$3\dfrac{3}{12} + 6\dfrac{8}{12} = 9\dfrac{11}{12}$

$-3\dfrac{1}{4} + \left(-6\dfrac{2}{3}\right) = -9\dfrac{11}{12}$

d. $-12.2 + (-6.814)$

$|-12.2| = 12.2, |-6.814| = 6.814$

$\begin{array}{r} 12.200 \\ +6.814 \\ \hline 19.014 \end{array}$

$-12.2 + (-6.814) = -19.014$

TRY-IT EXERCISE 3

a. $7 + (-4)$

$|7| = 7, |-4| = 4$

$7 - 4 = 3$

$7 + (-4) = 3$

b. $4 + (-7)$

$|4| = 4, |-7| = 7$

$7 - 4 = 3$

$4 + (-7) = -3$

c. $-16 + 16$

$|-16| = 16, |16| = 16$

$16 - 16 = 0$

$-16 + 16 = 0$

TRY-IT EXERCISE 4

a. $-\dfrac{7}{9} + \dfrac{4}{9}$

$\left|-\dfrac{7}{9}\right| = \dfrac{7}{9}, \left|\dfrac{4}{9}\right| = \dfrac{4}{9}$

$\dfrac{7}{9} - \dfrac{4}{9} = \dfrac{3}{9} = \dfrac{1}{3}$

$-\dfrac{7}{9} + \dfrac{4}{9} = -\dfrac{1}{3}$

b. $-\dfrac{3}{8} + \dfrac{7}{16}$

$\left|-\dfrac{3}{8}\right| = \dfrac{3}{8}, \left|\dfrac{7}{16}\right| = \dfrac{7}{16}$

LCD = 16

$\dfrac{3}{8} = \dfrac{3}{8} \cdot \dfrac{2}{2} = \dfrac{6}{16}$

$\dfrac{7}{16} \rightarrow \dfrac{7}{16}$

$\dfrac{7}{16} - \dfrac{6}{16} = \dfrac{1}{16}$

$-\dfrac{3}{8} + \dfrac{7}{16} = \dfrac{1}{16}$

c. $4.381 + (-6.29)$

$|4.381| = 4.381, |-6.29| = 6.29$

$\begin{array}{r} 6.290 \\ -4.381 \\ \hline 1.909 \end{array}$

$4.381 + (-6.29) = -1.909$

TRY-IT EXERCISE 5

$-69 + 39$

$|-69| = 69, |39| = 39$

$69 - 39 = 30$

$-69 + 39 = -30$

Cleopatra died in 30 BC.

SECTION 9.3

TRY-IT EXERCISE 1

a. $7 - 12$

$7 + (-12)$

$|7| = 7, |-12| = 12$

$12 - 7 = 5$

$7 - 12 = -5$

b. $25 - 49$

$25 + (-49)$

$|25| = 25, |-49| = 49$

$49 - 25 = 24$

$25 - 49 = -24$

TRY-IT EXERCISE 2

a. $-24 - 19$

$-24 + (-19)$

$|-24| = 24, |-19| = 19$

$24 + 19 = 43$

$-24 - 19 = -24 + (-19) = -43$

b. $-39 - 52$

$-39 + (-52)$

$|-39| = 39, |-52| = 52$

$39 + 52 = 91$

$-39 - 52 = -39 + (-52) = -91$

TRY-IT EXERCISE 3

a. $14 - (-12)$

$14 + 12$

$14 + 12 = 26$

$14 - (-12) = 14 + 12 = 26$

b. $-48 - (-51)$

$-48 + 51$

$|-48| = 48, |51| = 51$

$51 - 48 = 3$

$-48 - (-51) = -48 + 51 = 3$

TRY-IT EXERCISE 4

a. $\dfrac{1}{8} - \dfrac{5}{12}$

$\dfrac{1}{8} + \left(-\dfrac{5}{12}\right)$

$\left|\dfrac{1}{8}\right| = \dfrac{1}{8}, \left|-\dfrac{5}{12}\right| = \dfrac{5}{12}$

LCD = 24

$$\frac{1}{8} = \frac{1}{8} \cdot \frac{3}{3} = \frac{3}{24}$$

$$\frac{5}{12} = \frac{5}{12} \cdot \frac{2}{2} = \frac{10}{24}$$

$$\frac{10}{24} - \frac{3}{24} = \frac{7}{24}$$

$$\frac{1}{8} - \frac{5}{12} = \frac{1}{8} + \left(-\frac{5}{12}\right) = -\frac{7}{24}$$

b. $-\frac{1}{4} - \frac{5}{9}$

$$-\frac{1}{4} + \left(-\frac{5}{9}\right)$$

$$\left|-\frac{1}{4}\right| = \frac{1}{4}, \left|-\frac{5}{9}\right| = \frac{5}{9}$$

LCD = 36

$$\frac{1}{4} = \frac{1}{4} \cdot \frac{9}{9} = \frac{9}{36}$$

$$\frac{5}{9} = \frac{5}{9} \cdot \frac{4}{4} = \frac{20}{36}$$

$$\frac{20}{36} + \frac{9}{36} = \frac{29}{36}$$

$$-\frac{1}{4} - \frac{5}{9} = -\frac{1}{4} + \left(-\frac{5}{9}\right) = -\frac{29}{36}$$

c. $1\frac{1}{5} - \left(-2\frac{2}{3}\right)$

$$1\frac{1}{5} + 2\frac{2}{3}$$

LCD = 15

$$1\frac{1}{5} \cdot \frac{3}{3} = 1\frac{3}{15}$$

$$2\frac{2}{3} \cdot \frac{5}{5} = 2\frac{10}{15}$$

$$1\frac{3}{15} + 2\frac{10}{15} = 3\frac{13}{15}$$

$$1\frac{1}{5} - \left(-2\frac{2}{3}\right) = 1\frac{1}{5} + 2\frac{2}{3} = 3\frac{13}{15}$$

d. $-2\frac{2}{5} - 4\frac{1}{4}$

$$-2\frac{2}{5} + \left(-4\frac{1}{4}\right)$$

$$\left|-2\frac{2}{5}\right| = 2\frac{2}{5}, \left|-4\frac{1}{4}\right| = 4\frac{1}{4}$$

LCD = 20

$$2\frac{2}{5} \cdot \frac{4}{4} = 2\frac{8}{20}$$

$$4\frac{1}{4} \cdot \frac{5}{5} = 4\frac{5}{20}$$

$$2\frac{8}{20} + 4\frac{5}{20} = 6\frac{13}{20}$$

$$-2\frac{2}{5} - 4\frac{1}{4} = -2\frac{2}{5} + \left(-4\frac{1}{4}\right) = -6\frac{13}{20}$$

e. $0.31 - (-0.28)$

$$0.31 + 0.28$$

$$0.31 + 0.28 = 0.59$$

$$0.31 - (-0.28) = 0.31 + 0.28 = 0.59$$

f. $-6.7 - 4.15$

$$-6.7 + (-4.15)$$

$$|-6.7| = 6.7, |-4.15| = 4.15$$

$$\begin{array}{r} 6.70 \\ +4.15 \\ \hline 10.85 \end{array}$$

$$-6.7 - 4.15 = -6.7 + (-4.15) = -10.85$$

TRY-IT EXERCISE 5

$$1564 - (-43)$$

$$1564 + 43$$

$$1564 + 43 = 1607$$

$$1564 - (-43) = 1564 + 43 = 1607$$

There were 1607 years separating the births of Ovid and Shakespeare.

SECTION 9.4

TRY-IT EXERCISE 1

a. $9(-5)$

$$|9| = 9, |-5| = 5$$

$$9 \cdot 5 = 45$$

$$9(-5) = -45$$

b. $-4 \cdot 10$

$$|-4| = 4, |10| = 10$$

$$-4 \cdot 10 = 40$$

$$-4 \cdot 10 = -40$$

c. $\dfrac{8}{21}\left(-\dfrac{3}{16}\right)$

$\left|\dfrac{8}{21}\right| = \dfrac{8}{21}, \left|-\dfrac{3}{16}\right| = \dfrac{3}{16}$

$\dfrac{\overset{1}{8}}{\underset{7}{21}} \cdot \dfrac{\overset{1}{3}}{\underset{2}{16}} = \dfrac{1}{14}$

$\dfrac{8}{21}\left(-\dfrac{3}{16}\right) = -\dfrac{1}{14}$

d. $-3\dfrac{1}{4} \cdot 2\dfrac{2}{5}$

$\left|3\dfrac{1}{4}\right| = 3\dfrac{1}{4}, \left|2\dfrac{2}{5}\right| = 2\dfrac{2}{5}$

$3\dfrac{1}{4} \cdot 2\dfrac{2}{5} = \dfrac{13}{\underset{1}{4}} \cdot \dfrac{\overset{3}{12}}{5} = \dfrac{39}{5} = 7\dfrac{4}{5}$

$-3\dfrac{1}{4} \cdot 2\dfrac{2}{5} = -7\dfrac{4}{5}$

e. $(1.5)(-0.4)$

$|1.5| = 1.5, |-0.4| = 0.4$

$(1.5)(0.4) = 0.6$

$(1.5)(-0.4) = -0.6$

TRY-IT EXERCISE 2

a. $-8(-7)$

$|-8| = 8, |-7| = 7$

$8 \cdot 7 = 56$

$-8(-7) = 56$

b. $-15(-5)$

$|-15| = 15, |-5| = 5$

$15 \cdot 5 = 75$

$-15(-5) = 75$

c. $-\dfrac{4}{15}\left(-\dfrac{7}{8}\right)$

$\left|-\dfrac{4}{15}\right| = \dfrac{4}{15}, \left|-\dfrac{7}{8}\right| = \dfrac{7}{8}$

$\dfrac{\overset{1}{4}}{15} \cdot \dfrac{7}{\underset{2}{8}} = \dfrac{7}{30}$

$-\dfrac{4}{15}\left(-\dfrac{7}{8}\right) = \dfrac{7}{30}$

d. $-4\dfrac{1}{2}\left(-3\dfrac{1}{9}\right)$

$\left|-4\dfrac{1}{2}\right| = 4\dfrac{1}{2}, \left|-3\dfrac{1}{19}\right| = 3\dfrac{1}{9}$

$4\dfrac{1}{2} \cdot 3\dfrac{1}{9} = \dfrac{\overset{1}{9}}{\underset{1}{2}} \cdot \dfrac{\overset{14}{28}}{\underset{1}{9}} = \dfrac{14}{1} = 14$

$-4\dfrac{1}{2}\left(-3\dfrac{1}{9}\right) = 14$

e. $-12(-11)$

$|-12| = 12, |-11| = 11$

$12 \cdot 11 = 132$

$-12(-11) = 132$

TRY-IT EXERCISE 3

a. $3 \cdot 2\,(-6)$

$6\,(-6)$

-36

b. $-7\,(4) - 5$

$(35)\,(4)$

140

c. $-\dfrac{1}{5}\left(\dfrac{2}{3}\right)\left(-\dfrac{9}{14}\right)$

$-\dfrac{1}{5}\left(\dfrac{\overset{1}{2}}{\underset{1}{3}}\right)\left(-\dfrac{\overset{3}{9}}{\underset{7}{14}}\right)$

$-\dfrac{1}{5} \cdot -\dfrac{3}{7} = \dfrac{3}{35}$

d. $-0.2(-3.4)(0.8)$

$0.68(0.8) = 0.544$

TRY-IT EXERCISE 4

a. $28 \div (-4)$

$|28| = 28, |-4| = 4$

$28 \div 4 = 7$

$28 \div (-4) = -7$

b. $-49 \div 7$

$|-49| = 49, |7| = 7$

$49 \div 7 = 7$

$-49 \div 7 = -7$

c. $\dfrac{3}{22} \div \left(-\dfrac{15}{11}\right)$

$\left|\dfrac{3}{22}\right| = \dfrac{3}{22}, \left|-\dfrac{15}{11}\right| = \dfrac{15}{11}$

$\dfrac{3}{22} \div \dfrac{15}{11} = \dfrac{\overset{1}{3}}{\underset{2}{22}} \cdot \dfrac{\overset{1}{11}}{\underset{5}{15}} = \dfrac{1}{10}$

$\dfrac{3}{22} \div \left(-\dfrac{15}{11}\right) = -\dfrac{1}{10}$

d. $-5\dfrac{2}{3} \div 3\dfrac{1}{9}$

$\left|-5\dfrac{2}{3}\right| = 5\dfrac{2}{3}, \left|3\dfrac{1}{9}\right| = 3\dfrac{1}{9}$

$5\dfrac{2}{3} \div 3\dfrac{1}{9} = \dfrac{17}{\underset{1}{3}} \cdot \dfrac{\overset{3}{9}}{28} = \dfrac{51}{28} = 1\dfrac{23}{28}$

$-5\dfrac{2}{3} \div 3\dfrac{1}{9} = -1\dfrac{23}{28}$

e. $6.3 \div (-0.3)$

$|6.3| = 6.3, |-0.3| = 0.3$

$0.3\overline{)6.3}$

$\begin{array}{r} 21 \\ 3\overline{)63} \end{array}$

$6.3 \div (-0.3) = -21$

TRY-IT EXERCISE 5

a. $-48 \div (-12)$

$|-48| = 48, |-12| = 12$

$48 \div 12 = 4$

$-48 \div (-12) = 4$

b. $-54 \div (-6)$

$|-54| = 54, |-6| = 6$

$54 \div 6 = 9$

$-54 \div (-6) = 9$

c. $-\dfrac{4}{21} \div \left(-\dfrac{8}{3}\right)$

$\left|-\dfrac{4}{21}\right| = \dfrac{4}{21}, \left|-\dfrac{8}{3}\right| = \dfrac{8}{3}$

$\dfrac{4}{21} \div \dfrac{8}{3} = \dfrac{\overset{1}{\cancel{4}}}{\underset{7}{\cancel{21}}} \cdot \dfrac{\overset{1}{\cancel{3}}}{\underset{2}{\cancel{8}}} = \dfrac{1}{14}$

$-\dfrac{4}{21} \div \left(-\dfrac{8}{3}\right) = \dfrac{1}{14}$

d. $-1\dfrac{1}{5} \div \left(-2\dfrac{3}{10}\right)$

$\left|-1\dfrac{1}{5}\right| = 1\dfrac{1}{5}, \left|-2\dfrac{3}{10}\right| = 2\dfrac{3}{10}$

$1\dfrac{1}{5} \div 2\dfrac{3}{10} = \dfrac{6}{5} \div \dfrac{23}{10} = \dfrac{6}{\underset{1}{\cancel{5}}} \cdot \dfrac{\overset{2}{\cancel{10}}}{23} = \dfrac{12}{23}$

$-1\dfrac{1}{5} \div \left(-2\dfrac{3}{10}\right) = \dfrac{12}{23}$

e. $-7.2 \div (-0.08)$

$|-7.2| = 7.2, |-0.08| = 0.08$

$0.08\overline{)7.2}$

$\begin{array}{r} 90 \\ 8\overline{)720} \end{array}$

$-7.2 \div (-0.08) = 90$

TRY-IT EXERCISE 6

$-2400 \cdot 3$

$|-2400| = 2400, |3| = 3$

$2400 \cdot 3 = 7200$

$-2400 \cdot 3 = -7200$

The college will lose 7200 more students.

SECTION 9.5

TRY-IT EXERCISE 1

a. $7 - (-2) \cdot 4$

$7 - (-8)$

$7 + 8 = 15$

b. $20 \div 5 + 5 \cdot 3$

$4 + 15 = 19$

c. $\dfrac{2}{3} \div \left(-\dfrac{1}{9}\right) - \dfrac{1}{5} \cdot 2$

$\dfrac{2}{3} \cdot \left(-\dfrac{9}{1}\right) - \dfrac{1}{5} \cdot \dfrac{2}{1}$

$-\dfrac{6}{1} - \dfrac{2}{5}$

$-6 + \left(-\dfrac{2}{5}\right) = -6\dfrac{2}{5}$

d. $-2.6(5.1 - 3.2) \div (-0.8)$

$-2.6(1.9) \div (-0.8)$

$-4.94 \div (-0.8) = 6.175$

TRY-IT EXERCISE 2

a. $4^3 + 12(-4) + 6$

$64 - 48 + 6 = 22$

b. $\left(-\dfrac{1}{5}\right)^2 + \left(\dfrac{2}{5}\right)^2 \div \left(\dfrac{2}{3}\right)^2$

$\dfrac{1}{25} + \dfrac{4}{25} \div \dfrac{4}{9}$

$\dfrac{5}{25} \div \dfrac{4}{9}$

$\dfrac{\overset{1}{\cancel{5}}}{\underset{5}{\cancel{25}}} \cdot \dfrac{9}{4} = \dfrac{9}{20}$

c. $(-0.5)^3 \div 0.04 + 1.46$

$-0.125 \div 0.04 + 1.46$

$-3.125 + 1.46 = -1.665$

TRY-IT EXERCISE 3

a. $8 + [6 + 2 \cdot (-3)] - 2^3$

$8 + [6 + (-6)] - 8$

$8 + 0 - 8 = 0$

b. $\left[-\dfrac{1}{4} \div \left(\dfrac{2}{3}\right)^2\right] \div \left(\dfrac{1}{2}\right)^4$

$\left[-\dfrac{1}{4} \div \dfrac{4}{9}\right] \div \dfrac{1}{16}$

$-\dfrac{1}{4} \cdot \dfrac{9}{4} \cdot \dfrac{\overset{4}{\cancel{16}}}{\underset{1}{1}} = \dfrac{36}{4} = -9$

c. $(3.4 - 5.6)^2 + 3(-0.1)^2$

$\quad (-2.2)^2 + 3(0.01)$

$\quad\quad 4.84 + 0.03 = 4.87$

TRY-IT EXERCISE 4

$\dfrac{14 - 3^2}{5^2} + \left(\dfrac{1}{2}\right)^2$

$\dfrac{14 - 9}{25} + \dfrac{1}{4}$

$\dfrac{5}{25} + \dfrac{1}{4} = \dfrac{1}{5} + \dfrac{1}{4}$

$\text{LCD} = 20$

$\dfrac{4}{20} + \dfrac{5}{20} = \dfrac{9}{20}$

TRY-IT EXERCISE 5

a. $4(-1) + 3(-2) + 6(0) + 5(1)$

b. $-4 + (-6) + 0 + 5 = -5$

Chapter 10

SECTION 10.1

TRY-IT EXERCISE 1

a. $-2t$

$\quad -2 \cdot 3 = -6$

b. $6t - 5$

$\quad 6 \cdot 3 - 5$

$\quad 18 - 5 = 13$

c. $7(2t - 3)$

$\quad 7(2 \cdot 3 - 3)$

$\quad 7(6 - 3)$

$\quad 7(3) = 21$

TRY-IT EXERCISE 2

a. $p + q$

$\quad 16 + 8 = 24$

b. $p - q$

$\quad 16 - 8 = 8$

c. pq

$\quad 16 \cdot 8 = 128$

d. $\dfrac{p}{q}$

$\quad \dfrac{16}{8} = 2$

TRY-IT EXERCISE 3

a. $3 + 5k + 9k + 2$

$\quad$ Variable terms: $5k$ and $9k$

$\quad$ Constant terms: 3 and 2

$\quad$ Coefficient of $5k$: 5

$\quad$ Coefficient of $9k$: 9

b. $-13x - 6y + 8z$

$\quad -13x + (-6y) + 8z$

$\quad$ Variable terms: $-13x, -6y$, and $8z$

$\quad$ Constant terms: none

$\quad$ Coefficient of $-13x$: -13

$\quad$ Coefficient of $-6y$: -6

$\quad$ Coefficient of $8z$: 8

c. $p^4 - 2p^3 + 9p^2 - 13p + 6$

$\quad p^4 + (-2p^3) + 9p^2 + (-13p) + 6$

$\quad$ Variable terms: $p^4, -2p^3, 9p^2$, and $-13p$

$\quad$ Constant term: 6

$\quad$ Coefficient of p^4: 1

$\quad$ Coefficient of $-2p^3$: -2

$\quad$ Coefficient of $9p^2$: 9

$\quad$ Coefficient of $-13p$: -13

TRY-IT EXERCISE 4

a. $12x + 3y + 5x + y$

$\quad (12x + 5x) + (3y + y)$

$\quad 17x + 4y$

b. $6p + 3q - 8q - 12p$

$\quad [6p - (-12p)] + [3q + (-8q)]$

$\quad -6p + (-5q)$

$\quad -6p - 5q$

c. $8d^3 - 5 - d^3 + 3$

$\quad [8d^3 + (-d^3)] + [(-5) + 3]$

$\quad 7d^3 + (-2)$

$\quad 7d^3 - 2$

TRY-IT EXERCISE 5

a. $3(9a)$

$\quad (3 \cdot 9)a$

$\quad 27a$

b. $-1.5(-0.2b)$

$\quad (-1.5 \cdot -0.2)b$

$\quad 0.3b$

c. $-\dfrac{4}{9}\left(\dfrac{3}{5}x^2\right)$

$\left[-\dfrac{4}{9}\left(\dfrac{3}{5}\right)\right]x^2$

$-\dfrac{4}{15}x^2$

TRY-IT EXERCISE 6

a. $8(3x + 7)$

$= 8(3x) + 8(7)$

$= 24x + 56$

b. $0.5(2y - 3)$

$= 0.5(2y) - 0.5(3)$

$= y - 1.5$

c. $-\dfrac{1}{3}(z + 12)$

$-\dfrac{1}{3}z + \left(-\dfrac{1}{3}\right)12$

$-\dfrac{1}{3}z + (-4)$

$-\dfrac{1}{3}z - 4$

d. $(2y - 6)4$

$= 2y(4) - 6(4)$

$= 8y - 24$

e. $(z + 8)(-4)$

$= z(-4) + 8(-4)$

$= -4z - 32$

TRY-IT EXERCISE 7

Let x represent the number.

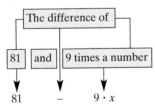

$81 \quad - \quad 9 \cdot x$

$81 - 9x$

TRY-IT EXERCISE 8

a.

| height of Mt. Rainer | higher than | 14,625 feet |

$x \qquad\qquad + \qquad\qquad 14,625 \text{ feet}$

$x + 14,625$

b. $14,410 + 14,625 = 29,035 \text{ feet}$

Mt. Everest is 29,035 feet high.

SECTION 10.2

TRY-IT EXERCISE 1

$x + 13 = 17$

$(4) + 13 \stackrel{?}{=} 17$

$17 = 17$

4 is a solution.

TRY-IT EXERCISE 2

$x + 5 = 10$

$(4) + 5 \stackrel{?}{=} 10$

$9 \neq 10$

4 is *not* a solution.

TRY-IT EXERCISE 3

$x + 13 = 24$

$x + 13 = 24$

$\dfrac{-13 \quad -13}{x + 0 = 11}$

$x = 11$

TRY-IT EXERCISE 4

$x - 1.2 = 11.4$

$\dfrac{+1.2 \quad\; +1.2}{x + 0 = 12.6}$

$x = 12.6$

TRY-IT EXERCISE 5

$x + \dfrac{1}{2} - \dfrac{1}{2} = \dfrac{3}{8} - \dfrac{1}{2}$

$x + 0 = \dfrac{3}{8} - \dfrac{4}{8}$

$x = -\dfrac{1}{8}$

TRY-IT EXERCISE 6

$R - C = P$

$R - 3,782,000,000 = \quad 2,835,000,000$

$\dfrac{+ \; 3,782,000,000 = +3,782,000,000}{R + 0 \qquad\quad = \quad 6,617,000,000}$

$R = \quad 6,617,000,000$

Bed, Bath, and Beyond's revenue for 2006 was $6,617,000,000.

SECTION 10.3

TRY-IT EXERCISE 1

$6x = 48$

$\dfrac{6x}{6} = \dfrac{48}{6}$

$x = 8$

TRY-IT EXERCISE 2

$-x = 15$

$-1x = 15$

$\dfrac{-1x}{-1} = \dfrac{15}{-1}$

$x = -15$

TRY-IT EXERCISE 3

$\dfrac{3}{8}x = \dfrac{3}{4}$

$\dfrac{8}{3} \cdot \dfrac{3}{8}x = \dfrac{8}{3} \cdot \dfrac{3}{4}$

$x = 2$

TRY-IT EXERCISE 4

$58.75x = 940$

$\dfrac{58.75x}{58.75} = \dfrac{940}{58.75}$

$x = 16$

TRY-IT EXERCISE 5

$rt = d$

$50t = 275$

$\dfrac{50t}{50} = \dfrac{275}{50}$

$t = \dfrac{275}{50} = \dfrac{55}{10} = 5\dfrac{1}{2}$

It will take Dominique and her friends 5 hours and 30 minutes to make the trip.

SECTION 10.4

TRY-IT EXERCISE 1

$$\begin{aligned} 7x + 15 &= 71 \\ -15 \quad &\quad -15 \\ \hline 7x + 0 &= 56 \end{aligned}$$

$\dfrac{7x}{7} = \dfrac{56}{7}$

$x = 8$

TRY-IT EXERCISE 2

$$\begin{aligned} 14 &= 4y - 22 \\ +22 &= \quad +22 \\ \hline 36 &= 4y + 0 \end{aligned}$$

$\dfrac{36}{4} = \dfrac{4y}{4}$

$9 = y$

TRY-IT EXERCISE 3

$$\begin{aligned} 5k &= 2k - 27 \\ -2k &= -2k + 27 \\ \hline 3k &= 0 + 27 \end{aligned}$$

$\dfrac{3k}{3} = \dfrac{27}{3}$

$k = 9$

TRY-IT EXERCISE 4

$$\begin{aligned} 7b + 14 &= 4b + 35 \\ -4b \quad &\quad -4b \\ \hline 3b + 14 &= 0b + 35 \end{aligned}$$

$3b + 14 = 35$

$$\begin{aligned} 3b + 14 &= 35 \\ -14 \quad &\quad -14 \\ \hline 3b + 0 &= 21 \end{aligned}$$

$3b = 21$

$\dfrac{3b}{3} = \dfrac{21}{3}$

$b = 7$

TRY-IT EXERCISE 5

$3(-3x + 5 + 7x) - 2x = 5(-4 + x + 2)$

$-9x + 15 + 21x - 2x = -20 + 5x + 10$

$10x + 15 = 5x - 10$

$$\begin{aligned} 10x + 15 &= 5x - 10 \\ -5x \quad &\quad -5x \\ \hline 5x + 15 &= 0x - 10 \end{aligned}$$

$5x + 15 = -10$

$$\begin{aligned} -15 \quad &\quad -15 \\ \hline 5x + 0 &= -25 \end{aligned}$$

$5x = -25$

$\dfrac{5x}{5} = \dfrac{-25}{5}$

$x = -5$

TRY-IT EXERCISE 6

$5(x + 4) - 3x = 4x + 2(x + 10)$

$5x + 20 - 3x = 4x + 2x + 20$

$2x + 20 = 6x + 20$

$$\begin{aligned} 2x + 20 &= 6x + 20 \\ -6x \quad &\quad -6x \\ \hline -4x + 20 &= 0x + 20 \end{aligned}$$

$$\begin{aligned} -4x + 20 &= 0x + 20 \\ -20 \quad &\quad -20 \\ \hline -4x + 0 &= 0 \end{aligned}$$

$\dfrac{-4x}{-4} = \dfrac{0}{-4}$

$x = 0$

TRY-IT EXERCISE 7

$P = 2l + 2w$

$70 = 2l + 2(14)$

$70 = 2l + 28$

$70 = 2l + 28$

$\underline{-28 = 2l - 28}$

$42 = 2l + 0$

$42 = 2l$

$\dfrac{42}{2} = \dfrac{2l}{2}$

$21 = l$

The length of the living room is 21 feet.

SECTION 10.5

TRY-IT EXERCISE 1

a.

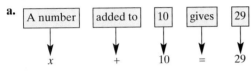

$x + 10 = 29$

b.

$15 - x = 12$

c.

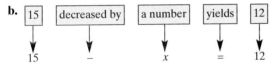

$8x = -32$

d.

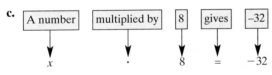

$\dfrac{10}{x} = \dfrac{1}{2}$

e.

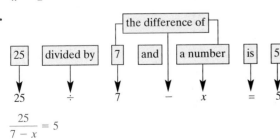

$\dfrac{25}{7 - x} = 5$

TRY-IT EXERCISE 2

Let x the number

$5 + 3x = 26$

$5 + 3x = 26$

$\underline{-5 \qquad\quad -5}$

$0 + 3x = 21$

$3x = 21$

$\dfrac{3x}{3} = \dfrac{21}{3}$

$x = 7$

TRY-IT EXERCISE 3

Let x the number of fixtures

$x = \dfrac{630}{180 + 6(5)}$

$x = \dfrac{630}{180 + 30}$

$x = \dfrac{630}{210}$

$x = 3$

3 fixtures with bulbs can be purchased for $630.

TRY-IT EXERCISE 4

Let width $= w$

Let length $= 4w - 3$

$P = 2l + 2w$

$24 = 2(4w - 3) + 2w$

$24 = 8w - 6 + 2w$

$24 = 10w - 6$

$24 = 10w - 6$

$\underline{+6 \qquad\qquad + 6}$

$30 = 10w + 0$

$30 = 10w$

$\dfrac{30}{10} = \dfrac{10w}{10}$

$3 = w = $ width

$4w - 3 = l$

$4(3) - 3 = l$

$12 - 3 = l$

$9 = l = $ length

The length of the rectangle is 9 meters.

The width of the rectangle is 3 meters.

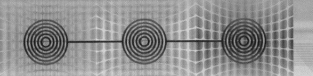

Answers to Selected Exercises

CHAPTER 1

Section 1.1 Review Exercises

1. digits **3.** natural, counting **5.** standard **7.** rounded **9.** zero **11. a.** 8 **b.** 2 **c.** 1 **13.** ones **15.** thousands **17.** hundreds **19.** ten thousands **21.** thousands **23.** hundred thousands **25.** millions **27.** ten millions **29.** seven hundred **31.** 32,809, nine **33.** 26; twenty-six **35.** 812; eight hundred twelve **37.** 9533 or 9,533; nine thousand, five hundred thirty-three **39.** 81,184; eighty-one thousand, one hundred eighty-four **41.** 58,245; fifty-eight thousand, two hundred forty-five **43.** 498,545; four hundred ninety-eight thousand, five hundred forty-five **45.** 70 **47.** 70 + 3; 7 tens + 3 ones **49.** 2000 + 700 + 40 + 6; 2 thousands + 7 hundreds + 4 tens + 6 ones **51.** 20,000 + 5000 + 300 + 70; 2 ten thousands + 5 thousands + 3 hundreds + 7 tens **53.** 800,000 + 90,000 + 6000 + 900 + 5; 8 hundred thousands + 9 ten thousands + 6 thousands + 9 hundreds + 5 ones **55. a.** 8 **b.** tens **c.** 5 **d.** Increase the specified digit, 8, by one, because the digit in the tens place is 5 or more. Next, change each digit to the right of the specified place value to zero. **e.** 900 **57.** 4550 **59.** 590,000 **61.** 430,000 **63.** 5,000,000 **65.** 90,000,000 **67.** 4,000,000 **69.** 752,128 **71.** $2,902,000,000,000 **73.** three thousand, four hundred ninety-seven dollars **75.** thirty million dollars **77.** nine hundred sixty-five; one hundred six; ninety-one thousand **79.** $1240 **81.** 47,000 pages **83.** fifty-one thousand, two hundred six dollars **85.** $18,700 **87.** $51,700

Section 1.2 Review Exercises

1. addition **3.** place values **5.** order **7.** carry **9.** 12, zero **11.** 34, commutative **13.** 128 **15.** 55 = 55 **17.** 13 + 8 = 3 + 18, 21 = 21 **19.** 9 **21.** 8 **23.** 92 **25.** 71 **27.** 88 **29.** 112 **31.** 409 **33.** 1285 **35.** 2257 **37.** 14,731 **39.** 1718 **41.** 1147 **43.** 4025 **45.** 11,305 **47.** 232 **49.** 12,175 **51.** 3717 **53.** 3097 **55.** 1104 **57.** 1250 **59.** 952 **61.** 26,900 feet **63.** $59,000 **65.** $1774 **67.** 1094, 1109, 1019, 976, 1123 **69.** 5321 **71.** 285 mg **73.** 97 cm **75.** 339 ft

Cumulative Skills Review

1. 261,809 **3.** 10,000 + 4000 + 700 + 30 + 9, 1 ten thousand + 4 thousands + 7 hundreds + 3 tens + 9 ones **5.** six thousand, one hundred fourteen **7.** hundreds **9. a.** 365.529 **b.** 366,000

Section 1.3 Review Exercises

1. subtraction **3.** subtrahend **5.** place values **7.** 0 **9.** 5 **11.** 7 **13.** 13 **15.** 52 **17.** 39 **19.** 22 **21.** 60 **23.** 26 **25.** 0

27. 56 **29.** 47 **31.** 51 **33.** 6 **35.** 504 **37.** 626 **39.** 708 **41.** 386 **43.** 3877 **45.** 61,097 **47.** 397 **49.** 104 **51.** 1050 **53.** 2006 **55.** 19 **57.** 34 **59.** 116 **61.** 639 **63.** 17 degrees **65.** 2040 gallons **67.** 880 shirts **69. a.** $190,000 **b.** $4,890,000 **c.** four million, eight hundred ninety thousand dollars **71. a.** $492 **b.** $280 **73.** $500 **75.** 5598 **77.** 13,240

Cumulative Skills Review

1. 2000 + 500 + 10, 2 thousands + 5 hundreds + 1 ten **3.** ten thousands **5.** 219,812 **7.** 1051 **9.** thirty-five thousand, four hundred twenty-nine

Section 1.4 Review Exercises

1. multiplication **3.** product **5.** 1 or one **7.** grouping **9.** 0, zero **11.** 21, commutative **13.** 7, 6, 14, 14, distributive, addition **15.** 0 **17.** 82 **19.** 32 = 32 **21.** 3(8) = (6)4, 24 = 24 **23.** 7(7) = 14 + 35, 49 = 49 **25.** 8 **27.** 2 **29.** 4 **31.** 4 **33.** 69 **35.** 208 **37.** 468 **39.** 354 **41.** 1716 **43.** 4700 **45.** 24,200 **47.** 5049 **49.** 444,000 **51.** 112,424 **53.** 1,199,880 **55.** 3,178,242 **57.** 22,875 **59.** 10,434 **61.** 420 **63.** $192 **65.** 4200 **67.** $780 **69.** $73,580,000 **71.** $3447 **73.** 604,800 people **75. a.** 4440 toys **b.** 319,680 toys **77. a.** 2808 square feet **b.** 2106 square feet **c.** 702 square feet **79.** $531,000 **81.** $31,000

Cumulative Skills Review

1. eighty-two thousand, one hundred eighty-four **3.** 2594 **5.** 532 **7.** $70 **9.** 1690 tickets

Section 1.5 Review Exercises

1. division **3.** divisor **5.** 8 ÷ 4, $4\overline{)8}$, $\frac{8}{4}$ **7.** one **9.** undefined **11.** 213 **13.** 0 **15.** 18 **17.** 1 **19.** 0 **21.** undefined **23.** undefined **25.** 0 **27.** 0 **29.** undefined **31.** 8 **33.** 8 **35.** 8 **37.** 6 **39.** 9 **41.** 45 **43.** 131 **45.** 114 **47.** 234 **49.** 5 R 4 **51.** 8 R 6 **53.** 10 R 56 **55.** 17 R 18 **57.** 47 R 17 **59.** 11 R 2 **61.** 52 R 12 **63.** 27 R 1 **65.** 28 R 98 **67.** 105 **69.** 426 R 5 **71.** 12 **73.** 40 minutes **75.** 14 pounds **77. a.** 80 pieces **b.** 16 boats **79.** $699 **81.** $800

Cumulative Skills Review

1. 103,200 **3.** 1135 **5.** 20,000 + 2000 + 100 + 80 + 5 **7.** 577 **9.** 42 hours

Section 1.6 Review Exercises

1. Exponential **3.** exponent or power **5.** exponent **7.** 15^3 **9.** one **11.** 3 **13.** 5 **15.** 8 · 8 · 8 **17.** 5, 3

19. 3^3, three to the third power, three cubed   **21.** 5^4, five to the fourth power   **23.** 9^1, nine to the first power, nine   **25.** 1^3, one to the third power one cubed   **27.** $4^3 \cdot 9^2$ **29.** $3^2 \cdot 4^3 \cdot 5$
31. $5^2 \cdot 8^3 \cdot 12$ **33.** $2 \cdot 5^2 \cdot 7 \cdot 9^3$ **35.** 0   **37.** 3, 27   **39.** 1   **41.** 14
43. 1   **45.** 25   **47.** 144   **49.** 343   **51.** 64   **53.** 1000   **55.** 86
57. 256   **59.** 1   **61.** 225   **63.** 54, 121   **65.** 25, 475, 473   **67.** 13
69. 26   **71.** 6   **73.** 162   **75.** 31   **77.** 2   **79.** 4   **81.** 79   **83.** 41
85. 32   **87.** 84   **89.** 26   **91.** 72   **93.** 2   **95.** 225 square inches
97. a. 400 square feet   **b.** $3600   **c.** $800

Cumulative Skills Review

1. 71,022   **3.** 26,366   **5.** 260,000   **7.** 0   **9.** $9870

Section 1.7 Review Exercises

1. addition   **3.** multiplication   **5.** equality or the equal sign
7. 575 horsepower   **9.** 128 photos   **11.** $4620   **13. a.** 66 pieces
b. $1980   **c.** $23,760   **15.** Townhouse = $140 per square foot; apartment = $175 per square foot. Townhouse is the better buy.
17. a. 34,650,000 miles   **b.** 25,350,000 miles   **19.** 105 calories
21. 3096 calories   **23.** $52,440   **25.** 25 minutes   **27.** $1650
29. 36 uses   **31.** $67,586   **33.** 3402   **35. a.** Yes, the load weighs 280,000 pounds.   **b.** Either 8 more cars or 1 more bus and 2 more cars could be accommodated.   **37.** $1008   **39.** $3670

Cumulative Skills Review

1. 163   **3.** 24   **5.** 2545   **7.** 173   **9.** 1000 + 500 + 40 + 9, 1 thousand + 5 hundreds + 4 tens + 9 ones

Numerical Facts of Life

Current Assets: 3640, 4720, 18,640;
Total Current Assets: 27,000;
Long-Term Assets:
    Investments: 67,880, 25,550, 15,960;
    Personal: 225,500, 32,300, 6400, 12,100, 7630;
Total Long-Term Assets: 393,320;
Total Assets: $420,320.
Current Liabilities: 1940, 8660, 0;
Total Current Liabilities: 10,600;
Long-Term Liabilities: 165,410, 13,200, 4580;
Total Long-Term Liabilities: 183,190;
Total Liabilities: $193,790;
Net Worth: $226,530.

Chapter Review Exercises

1. thousands   **2.** hundreds   **3.** millions   **4.** ones   **5.** tens
6. ten thousands   **7.** 336, three hundred thirty-six   **8.** 8,475 or 8475, eight thousand, four hundred seventy-five   **9.** 784,341, seven hundred eighty-four thousand, three hundred forty-one
10. 380,633, three hundred eighty thousand, six hundred thirty-three   **11.** 62,646, sixty-two thousand, six hundred forty-six
12. 1,326,554, one million, three hundred twenty-six thousand, five hundred fifty-four   **13.** 10,102, ten thousand, one hundred two
14. 6,653,634, six million, six hundred fifty-three thousand, six hundred thirty-four   **15.** 4,022,407,508, four billion, twenty-two million, four hundred seven thousand, five hundred eight
16. 20 + 3, 2 tens + 4 ones   **17.** 500 + 30 + 2, 5 hundreds + 3 tens + 2 ones   **18.** 100 + 9, 1 hundred + 9 ones   **19.** 20,000 + 6000 + 300 + 80 + 5, 2 ten thousands + 6 thousands + 3 hundreds + 8 tens + 5 ones   **20.** 2000 + 100 + 40 + 8, 2 thousands + 1 hundred + 4 tens + 8 ones   **21.** 1,000,000 + 900,000 + 20,000 +

8000 + 300 + 60 + 5, 1 million + 9 hundred thousands + 2 ten thousands + 8 thousands + 3 hundreds + 6 tens + 5 ones
22. 363,000   **23.** 18,140   **24.** 90,000   **25.** 601,900   **26.** 5,000,000
27. 3,100,000   **28.** 81,080   **29.** 196,000   **30.** 40,000,000   **31.** 89
32. 113   **33.** 379   **34.** 951   **35.** 595   **36.** 2295
37. 115,472   **38.** 2569   **39.** 1463   **40.** 3886   **41.** 258   **42.** 392
43. 64   **44.** 9   **45.** 27   **46.** 23   **47.** 683   **48.** 362   **49.** 423
50. 614   **51.** 6833   **52.** 1205   **53.** 4269   **54.** 6527   **55.** 64
56. 0   **57.** 1575   **58.** 4290   **59.** 3705   **60.** 12,654   **61.** 12,720
62. 6105   **63.** 810   **64.** 17,280   **65.** 48,900   **66.** 951,200
67. undefined   **68.** 0   **69.** 46   **70.** 1   **71.** 16   **72.** 21
73. 11 R 2   **74.** 21 R 26   **75.** 20 R 4   **76.** 34 R 4   **77.** 4 R 2
78. 31 R 2   **79.** 7^4 **80.** 13^3 **81.** 17^1 **82.** 5^6 **83.** $3^2 \cdot 5^3 \cdot 11^2$
84. $5^2 \cdot 7 \cdot 17^2 \cdot 19$ **85.** $2^4 \cdot 23^2 \cdot 29$ **86.** $11^3 \cdot 19^2$ **87.** 49   **88.** 16
89. 39   **90.** 243   **91.** 1000   **92.** 1   **93.** 361   **94.** 1
95. 1,000,000   **96.** 216   **97.** 0   **98.** 512   **99.** 349   **100.** 242
101. 25   **102.** 126   **103.** 0   **104.** 86   **105.** 2   **106.** 18   **107.** 60
108. 3000   **109.** 234   **110.** 20   **111. a.** 453,200 gallons   **b.** four hundred fifty-three thousand, two hundred   **112. a.** 1567 acres
b. 1238 acres   **113.** 4346 yards   **114.** $361,000   **115. a.** $216
b. $72   **116. a.** $6720   **b.** $42   **117.** 20   **118.** 17   **119.** 52
120. 104   **121.** 858   **122.** 10

Assessment Test

1. hundreds   **2.** ten thousands   **3.** 15,862, fifteen thousand, eight hundred sixty-two   **4.** 123,509, one hundred twenty-three thousand, five hundred nine   **5.** 400 + 70 + 5, 4 hundreds + 7 tens + 5 ones   **6.** 1000 + 300 + 90 + 7, 1 thousand + 3 hundreds + 9 tens + 7 ones   **7.** 35,000   **8.** 6,500,000   **9.** 488
10. 1485   **11.** 17   **12.** 741   **13.** 11,448   **14.** 181,656   **15.** 63
16. 14 R 1   **17.** 13^3 **18.** $3^2 \cdot 5^4 \cdot 7$ **19.** 36   **20.** 16   **21.** 20
22. 43   **23.** 23,939 miles   **24.** $180,000   **25. a.** 105 portions
b. 15 cartons   **26. a.** 520 feet   **b.** 16,500 square feet

CHAPTER 2

Section 2.1 Review Exercises

1. prime   **3.** factor   **5.** factor tree   **7.** common   **9.** 1, 2, 4, 5, 8, 10, 20, 40   **11.** 1, 5   **13.** 1, 2, 3, 6   **15.** 1, 7, 49   **17.** 1, 29   **19.** 1, 7, 11, 77   **21.** 1, 2, 4, 7, 14, 28   **23.** 1, 61   **25.** 1, 3, 5, 15, 25, 75
27. 1, 2, 3, 6, 9, 18, 27, 54   **29.** 1, 2, 4, 5, 10, 20, 25, 50, 100
31. composite   **33.** prime   **35.** neither   **37.** neither
39. composite   **41.** composite   **43.** prime   **45.** composite
47. prime   **49.** $2 \cdot 3 \cdot 5$ **51.** $2 \cdot 5$ **53.** $3 \cdot 17$ **55.** $2 \cdot 3 \cdot 7$
57. $7 \cdot 7$ or 7^2 **59.** $2 \cdot 2 \cdot 3$ or $2^2 \cdot 3$ **61.** $2 \cdot 2 \cdot 2 \cdot 2$ or 2^4
63. $3 \cdot 3 \cdot 3 \cdot 3$ or 3^4 **65.** $2 \cdot 2 \cdot 3 \cdot 3 \cdot 3$ or $2^2 \cdot 3^3$ **67.** $5 \cdot 5 \cdot 7$ or $5^2 \cdot 7$
69. $3 \cdot 3 \cdot 3 \cdot 5$ or $3^3 \cdot 5$ **71.** $2 \cdot 3 \cdot 5 \cdot 5$ or $2 \cdot 3 \cdot 5^2$ **73.** $2 \cdot 2 \cdot 2 \cdot 2 \cdot 5 \cdot 5$ or $2^4 \cdot 5^2$ **75. a.** 12, 16, 20, 24; 18, 24, 30, 36   **b.** 12
77. a. $8 = 2 \cdot 2 \cdot 2 = 2^3$; $18 = 2 \cdot 3 \cdot 3 = 2 \cdot 3^2$ **b.** three, two $2 \cdot 2 \cdot 2 \cdot 3 \cdot 3 = 72$.   **79.** 18   **81.** 20   **83.** 18   **85.** 72   **87.** 16
89. 60   **91.** 48   **93.** 84   **95.** 66   **97.** 72   **99.** Every 12th day
101. Every 60 minutes

Cumulative Skills Review

1. 2   **3.** 20,069   **5.** 79   **7.** $6^2 \cdot 7^3$ **9.** $34,233,000

Section 2.2 Review Exercises

1. fraction   **3.** denominator   **5.** proper   **7.** mixed number
9. a. proper fraction   **b.** improper fraction   **c.** mixed number

11. proper fraction   **13.** improper fraction   **15.** mixed number
17. improper fraction   **19.** improper fraction   **21.** mixed number
23. $9, 5, \frac{5}{9}$ **25.** $\frac{5}{8}$ **27.** $\frac{7}{18}$ **29.** $\frac{4}{7}$ **31.** $3\frac{3}{4}$ **33.** $\frac{11}{3}$ or $3\frac{2}{3}$

35. $\frac{6}{11}$ **37.** $6, 54, 0, 6$ **39.** $5, 3, 43$ **41.** 10 **43.** $6\frac{1}{2}$ **45.** $9\frac{7}{9}$

47. 13 **49.** $1\frac{7}{8}$ **51.** $13\frac{1}{3}$ **53.** $10\frac{1}{3}$ **55.** $10\frac{11}{12}$ **57.** $\frac{73}{7}$ **59.** $\frac{58}{5}$

61. $\frac{73}{10}$ **63.** $\frac{44}{5}$ **65.** $\frac{38}{3}$ **67.** $\frac{121}{10}$ **69.** $\frac{138}{13}$ **71.** $\frac{64}{7}$ **73. a.** $\frac{21}{37}$

b. $\frac{16}{37}$ **75.** $\frac{14}{55}$ **77. a.** $\frac{3}{7}$ **b.** $\frac{11}{7} = 1\frac{4}{7}$ **79. a.** $\frac{83}{200}$ **b.** $\frac{117}{200}$

81. a. $\frac{18,441}{30,000}$ **b.** $\frac{11,559}{36,000}$ **83.** $\frac{4}{9}$

Cumulative Skills Review

1. $1, 2, 4, 8, 16$ **3.** 63 **5.** $133,000$ **7.** composite   **9.** $125,662$; one
hundred twenty-five thousand, six hundred sixty-two

Section 2.3 Review Exercises

1. equivalent   **3.** greatest common factor, GCF   **5.** one
7. common denominator   **9.** LCD, equivalent, numerators

11. a. $2, 2, 5$ **b.** $2, 2, 2, 3$ **c.** $\frac{5}{6}$ **13. a.** 4 **b.** $\frac{3}{5}$ **15.** $\frac{3}{7}$

17. $\frac{1}{6}$ **19.** $\frac{2}{9}$ **21.** $\frac{1}{11}$ **23.** $\frac{4}{5}$ **25.** $\frac{7}{19}$ **27.** $\frac{1}{10}$ **29.** $\frac{4}{7}$ **31.** $\frac{3}{5}$

33. $\frac{7}{24}$ **35.** $\frac{3}{25}$ **37.** $\frac{13}{20}$ **39.** $\frac{7}{15}$ **41.** $\frac{43}{79}$ **43.** $\frac{11}{20}$ **45.** $\frac{20}{39}$

47. $\frac{31}{35}$ **49.** $\frac{65}{79}$ **51.** $10, 20$ **53.** $4, 4, 20$ **55.** $\frac{7}{56}$ **57.** $\frac{40}{64}$

59. $\frac{30}{48}$ **61.** $\frac{63}{99}$ **63.** $\frac{9}{27}$ **65.** $\frac{6}{78}$ **67.** $\frac{66}{78}$ **69.** $\frac{20}{52}$ **71.** $\frac{63}{98}$

73. $\frac{21}{28}$ **75.** $\frac{25}{40}$ **77.** $\frac{10}{65}$ **79.** $\frac{55}{70}$ **81.** $\frac{21}{48}$ **83.** $\frac{32}{34}$

85. $\frac{30}{84}$ **87. a.** 45 **b.** $9, 9, 27, 45, 5, 5, 25, 45$ **c.** $25, 45, < 27, 45,$

$< 3, 5$ **89.** $\frac{5}{8} < \frac{7}{10}$ **91.** $\frac{1}{14} < \frac{3}{8}$ **93.** $\frac{1}{6} < \frac{1}{4} < \frac{1}{2}$

95. $\frac{1}{2} < \frac{2}{3} < \frac{5}{6}$ **97.** $\frac{5}{24} < \frac{8}{32} < \frac{9}{16}$ **99.** $\frac{1}{18} < \frac{4}{9} < \frac{7}{12} < \frac{7}{8}$

101. $\frac{140}{380} = \frac{7}{19}$ **103.** $\frac{6000}{16,000} = \frac{3}{8}$ **105.** $\frac{26}{40} = \frac{13}{20}$ **107.** $\frac{8}{40} = \frac{1}{5}$

109. $\frac{4}{28} = \frac{1}{7}$ **111.** $\frac{122}{136} = \frac{61}{68}$ **113.** $\frac{3}{8}$ inches   **115.** $1\frac{7}{10}$ tons

Cumulative Skills Review

1. $4\frac{7}{12}$ **3.** 36 **5.** $144\ \text{ft}^2$ **7.** $\frac{68}{15}$ **9.** Every sixth day

Section 2.4 Review Exercises

1. numerators, denominators   **3.** common factor, divide   **5.** 21
7. $1, 7, 1, 7, 3, 7$ **9.** $\frac{1}{6}$ **11.** $\frac{4}{35}$ **13.** $\frac{8}{15}$ **15.** $\frac{15}{56}$ **17.** $\frac{24}{77}$ **19.** $\frac{21}{80}$

21. $\frac{1}{3}$ **23.** $\frac{2}{25}$ **25.** $\frac{2}{11}$ **27.** $\frac{10}{27}$ **29.** $\frac{3}{10}$ **31.** $\frac{5}{27}$ **33.** $\frac{1}{2}$

35. $\frac{1}{5}$ **37.** $\frac{3}{8}$ **39.** $\frac{2}{15}$ **41.** $\frac{7}{16}$ **43.** $\frac{2}{39}$ **45.** $\frac{3}{50}$ **47.** $\frac{7}{108}$

49. a. 6 **b.** $2, 1, 2, 1, 4, 1, 4$ **51.** 6 **53.** 24 **55.** 1 **57.** $41\frac{2}{3}$

59. $3\frac{1}{2}$ **61.** 9 **63.** $4\frac{1}{2}$ **65.** $1\frac{6}{7}$ **67.** $44\frac{1}{12}$ **69.** $3\frac{2}{3}$

71. $30\frac{1}{3}$ **73.** $\frac{2}{3}$ **75.** 6375 students   **77.** \$9840

79. 16 cups of flour   **81.** 1125 respondents   **83.** 5 inches

85. $38\frac{1}{4}$ square feet   **87.** 11,925 square feet   **89.** \$33 in dues

91. \$16   **93.** \$4000   **95.** 23 more chairs   **97. a.** $812\frac{1}{2}$ mg

b. $487\frac{1}{2}$ mg   **c.** $\frac{3}{8}$

Cumulative Skills Review

1. 156 **3.** $2\frac{1}{2}$ or $\frac{5}{2}$ **5.** $806,616$ **7.** $\frac{3}{7}$ **9.** $\frac{42}{5}$

Section 2.5 Review Exercises

1. dividend; divisor   **3.** multiply, reciprocal   **5. a.** $11, 9$ **b.** $11, 9$

c. $11, 9, 11, 9, 3; 11, 3, 11, 15$ **7.** $\frac{3}{4}$ **9.** $2\frac{1}{3}$ **11.** $3\frac{1}{2}$ **13.** 2 **15.** $\frac{4}{5}$

17. $\frac{9}{10}$ **19.** 6 **21.** $\frac{3}{5}$ **23.** 3 **25.** $\frac{11}{60}$ **27.** $1\frac{1}{9}$ **29.** 1 **31.** $1\frac{3}{7}$

33. $1\frac{1}{6}$ **35. a.** 9 **b.** $1, 9$ **c.** $1, 9$ **d.** $1, 9, 1, 9, 3; 3, 1, 12$ **37.** $3\frac{5}{6}$

39. $1\frac{21}{22}$ **41.** $3\frac{1}{2}$ **43.** $\frac{2}{7}$ **45.** 48 **47.** 10 **49.** $1\frac{4}{5}$ **51.** 43

53. $\frac{16}{21}$ **55.** 34 **57.** 28 **59.** 12 **61. a.** $21\frac{9}{10}$ miles per gallon

b. 50 gallons   **63.** $25\frac{3}{8}$ acres   **65.** 554 bins   **67.** 200 dinners

69. 44 signs   **71.** 600 loaves

Cumulative Skills Review

1. $19,584$ **3.** $\frac{1}{81}$ **5.** $2 \cdot 3 \cdot 3 \cdot 5$ or $2 \cdot 3^2 \cdot 5$ **7.** $\frac{6}{7}$ **9.** $18\frac{1}{3}$ cups

Section 2.6 Review Exercises

1. like   **3.** LCD, equivalent   **5.** mixed number   **7.** $4, 1, 5$

9. $\frac{5}{7}$ **11.** $\frac{11}{13}$ **13.** $\frac{6}{12} = \frac{1}{2}$ **15.** $\frac{9}{21} = \frac{3}{7}$ **17.** $\frac{10}{10} = 1$ **19.** $\frac{13}{9} = 1\frac{4}{9}$

21. $\frac{4}{3} = 1\frac{1}{3}$ **23.** $\frac{6}{5} = 1\frac{1}{5}$ **25. a.** 12 **b.** $4, 4, 4, 12; 3, 3, 9, 12$

c. $4, 9, 13, 1\frac{1}{12}$ **27.** $\frac{13}{16}$ **29.** $\frac{7}{24}$ **31.** $\frac{8}{9}$ **33.** $1\frac{3}{16}$ **35.** $2\frac{1}{18}$

37. $2\frac{1}{8}$ **39.** $1\frac{8}{45}$ **41.** $1\frac{29}{90}$ **43. a.** 12 **b.** $4, 4, 8, 12; 3, 3, 9, 12$

c. $8, 12, 9, 12, 17, 12, 17, 12, 5, 12, 5, 12$ **45.** $3\frac{47}{75}$ **47.** $1\frac{27}{40}$ **49.** $3\frac{1}{8}$

51. $1\frac{47}{80}$ **53.** $12\frac{49}{72}$ **55.** $15\frac{1}{4}$ **57.** $6\frac{22}{63}$ **59.** $7\frac{1}{40}$ **61.** $5\frac{23}{24}$

63. $2\frac{11}{30}$ **65.** $2\frac{19}{30}$ **67.** $8\frac{1}{24}$ **69.** $8\frac{2}{15}$ **71.** $6\frac{11}{20}$ **73.** $1\frac{15}{16}$ miles

75. $48\frac{19}{20}$ acres   **77.** $148\frac{3}{8}$ inches   **79.** $279\frac{53}{60}$ acres

81. a. $21\frac{4}{5}$ gallons   **b.** \$436

Cumulative Skills Review

1. 12,650   **3.** $25\frac{4}{15}$ pounds   **5.** $\frac{66}{84}$ **7.** $4\frac{9}{16} < 4\frac{7}{12}$ or $4\frac{7}{12} > 4\frac{9}{16}$
9. 21

Section 2.7 Review Exercises

1. numerator, denominator   **3.** fraction, whole numbers
5. $\frac{LCD}{LCD}$ **7.** 7, 3, 4   **9.** $\frac{3}{5}$ **11.** $\frac{5}{14}$ **13.** $\frac{2}{17}$ **15.** $\frac{1}{61}$ **17.** $\frac{1}{5}$
19. $\frac{5}{24}$ **21. a.** 12   **b.** 3, 3, 9, 12; 4, 4, 4, 12   **c.** 9, 4, 5   **23.** $\frac{5}{24}$
25. $\frac{1}{24}$ **27.** $\frac{2}{45}$ **29.** $\frac{1}{2}$ **31.** $\frac{27}{50}$ **33.** $\frac{17}{48}$ **35.** 2, 4, 1, 2   **37.** $1\frac{3}{5}$
39. $2\frac{1}{3}$ **41.** $1\frac{1}{2}$ **43.** $5\frac{8}{27}$ **45. a.** 4, 4, 5, 4   **b.** 5, 4, 2, 4, 10, 1, 2
47. $1\frac{3}{4}$ **49.** $3\frac{2}{3}$ **51.** $10\frac{3}{7}$ **53.** $4\frac{3}{4}$ **55. a.** 12   **b.** 4, 4, 8, 12, 3, 3,
3, 12   **c.** 8, 12, 3, 12, 5, 12   **57.** $1\frac{23}{30}$ **59.** $2\frac{7}{30}$ **61.** $8\frac{2}{3}$ **63.** $2\frac{1}{6}$
65. $3\frac{17}{24}$ **67.** $20\frac{9}{20}$ **69.** $7\frac{1}{30}$ **71.** $2\frac{1}{8}$ **73.** $8\frac{23}{90}$ **75.** $52\frac{1}{6}$

77. a. 6   **b.** 2, 2, 2, 6, 3, 3, 3, 6   **c.** 2, 6, 2, 6, 6, 6, 2, 6, 8, 6

d. 8, 6, 3, 6, 12, 5, 6   **79.** $3\frac{7}{15}$ **81.** $11\frac{13}{18}$ **83.** $30\frac{3}{4}$ **85.** $16\frac{3}{8}$
87. $2\frac{9}{16}$ **89.** $3\frac{2}{3}$ **91.** $5\frac{35}{48}$ **93.** $2\frac{1}{16}$ **95.** $\frac{11}{40}$ pound   **97.** $17\frac{5}{8}$ inches
99. $6\frac{3}{4}$ miles   **101.** $\frac{11}{16}$ pound   **103.** $16\frac{1}{24}$ pounds   **105.** $10\frac{1}{2}$ inches
107. $26\frac{79}{120}$ feet   **109.** $7\frac{5}{16}$ **111.** $132\frac{1}{8}$ pounds   **113. a.** Yes, the
weight is within the limit.   **b.** $\frac{5}{12}$ pounds under the limit

Cumulative Skills Review

1. $\frac{35}{60}$ **3.** 5226 gallons   **5.** 315   **7.** 221   **9.** 24

Numerical Facts of Life

1. 3   **3.** 2 cups   **5.** $\frac{69}{2}$ ounces, $34\frac{1}{2}$ ounces

Chapter Review Exercises

1. 1, 2, 5, 10   **2.** 1, 3, 5, 15   **3.** 1, 2, 4, 11, 22, 44
4. 1, 2, 3, 4, 6, 8, 12, 16, 24, 48   **5.** 1, 2, 23, 46   **6.** 1, 5, 17, 85
7. 1, 89   **8.** 1, 61   **9.** 1, 2, 3, 4, 6, 8, 12, 24   **10.** 1, 3, 7, 9, 21, 63
11. 1, 2, 3, 6, 11, 22, 33, 66   **12.** 1, 2, 4, 7, 8, 14, 16, 28, 56, 112
13. prime   **14.** composite   **15.** neither   **16.** composite
17. composite   **18.** neither   **19.** composite   **20.** prime
21. composite   **22.** prime   **23.** composite   **24.** prime
25. $3 \cdot 5 \cdot 5 = 3 \cdot 5^2$ **26.** $2 \cdot 2 \cdot 2 \cdot 5 = 2^3 \cdot 5$ **27.** $3 \cdot 19$
28. $2 \cdot 31$ **29.** $2 \cdot 2 \cdot 2 \cdot 11 = 2^3 \cdot 11$ **30.** $3 \cdot 5 \cdot 7$
31. $5 \cdot 5 \cdot 5 \cdot 5 = 5^4$ **32.** $2 \cdot 3 \cdot 3 \cdot 5 = 2 \cdot 3^2 \cdot 5$
33. $2 \cdot 2 \cdot 2 \cdot 5 \cdot 5 \cdot 5 = 2^3 \cdot 5^3$ **34.** $2 \cdot 2 \cdot 2 \cdot 3 \cdot 5 = 2^3 \cdot 3 \cdot 5$
35. $2 \cdot 5 \cdot 5 = 2 \cdot 5^2$ **36.** $2 \cdot 2 \cdot 2 \cdot 3 \cdot 3 \cdot 7 = 2^3 \cdot 3^2 \cdot 7$ **37.** 33
38. 26   **39.** 86   **40.** 40   **41.** 72   **42.** 504   **43.** 336   **44.** 144
45. 168   **46.** 252   **47.** 1008   **48.** 6006   **49.** improper
50. mixed   **51.** proper   **52.** mixed   **53.** proper   **54.** improper

55. $\frac{21}{24}$ **56.** $\frac{4}{9}$ **57.** $3\frac{3}{5}$ **58.** $1\frac{2}{3}$ **59. a.** $\frac{3}{8}$ **b.** $\frac{5}{8}$ **60. a.** $\frac{2}{7}$ **b.** $\frac{5}{7}$
61. $12\frac{1}{2}$ **62.** $4\frac{5}{8}$ **63.** 7   **64.** $17\frac{5}{6}$ **65.** 11   **66.** $11\frac{1}{7}$ **67.** $\frac{13}{5}$
68. $\frac{134}{9}$ **69.** $\frac{59}{8}$ **70.** $\frac{111}{5}$ **71.** $\frac{677}{15}$ **72.** $\frac{176}{17}$ **73.** $\frac{1}{8}$ **74.** $\frac{1}{5}$
75. $\frac{5}{8}$ **76.** $\frac{5}{8}$ **77.** $\frac{1}{3}$ **78.** $\frac{3}{10}$ **79.** $\frac{5}{18}$ **80.** $\frac{3}{5}$ **81.** $\frac{12}{56}$ **82.** $\frac{8}{80}$
83. $\frac{8}{44}$ **84.** $\frac{24}{64}$ **85.** $\frac{5}{6} < \frac{11}{12}$ **86.** $\frac{7}{9} < \frac{5}{6}$ **87.** $\frac{5}{8} < \frac{13}{16} < \frac{11}{12}$
88. $\frac{7}{9} < \frac{5}{6} < \frac{7}{8}$ **89.** $\frac{7}{27}$ **90.** $\frac{1}{16}$ **91.** $\frac{20}{33}$ **92.** $\frac{2}{15}$ **93.** $\frac{1}{5}$
94. $\frac{20}{171}$ **95.** $\frac{7}{640}$ **96.** $\frac{5}{8}$ **97.** $10\frac{19}{28}$ **98.** $33\frac{7}{12}$ **99.** $43\frac{7}{8}$
100. $37\frac{1}{8}$ **101.** $8\frac{26}{27}$ **102.** $18\frac{7}{45}$ **103.** $26\frac{23}{30}$ **104.** $109\frac{1}{3}$ **105.** 4
106. $\frac{5}{7}$ **107.** $\frac{2}{5}$ **108.** $2\frac{1}{6}$ **109.** $1\frac{1}{2}$ **110.** $\frac{8}{21}$ **111.** $\frac{4}{5}$ **112.** $1\frac{1}{2}$
113. $\frac{48}{85}$ **114.** 11   **115.** $9\frac{2}{9}$ **116.** $\frac{21}{25}$ **117.** $11\frac{1}{5}$ **118.** $3\frac{11}{48}$
119. $4\frac{13}{24}$ **120.** $2\frac{118}{299}$ **121.** $\frac{9}{20}$ **122.** 1   **123.** $\frac{1}{2}$ **124.** $1\frac{5}{24}$
125. $1\frac{2}{35}$ **126.** $1\frac{11}{63}$ **127.** $\frac{3}{4}$ **128.** $1\frac{3}{10}$ **129.** $55\frac{1}{6}$ **130.** $7\frac{1}{12}$
131. $43\frac{13}{20}$ **132.** $67\frac{13}{15}$ **133.** $20\frac{1}{4}$ **134.** $11\frac{1}{6}$ **135.** $54\frac{5}{6}$
136. $28\frac{17}{42}$ **137.** $\frac{1}{5}$ **138.** $\frac{22}{45}$ **139.** $\frac{1}{60}$ **140.** $\frac{7}{30}$ **141.** $\frac{1}{6}$
142. $\frac{11}{16}$ **143.** $\frac{1}{4}$ **144.** $\frac{5}{36}$ **145.** $37\frac{1}{2}$ **146.** $39\frac{1}{3}$ **147.** $21\frac{13}{16}$
148. $36\frac{2}{3}$ **149.** $9\frac{1}{4}$ **150.** $36\frac{1}{26}$ **151.** $6\frac{3}{4}$ **152.** $17\frac{1}{2}$
153. $\frac{3}{10}$ **154.** $\frac{4}{17}$ **155.** $6\frac{13}{28}$ pounds   **156.** $9\frac{3}{8}$ ounces
157. $13\frac{1}{7}$ yards   **158.** $10\frac{1}{3}$ feet   **159.** $62\frac{1}{2}$ jars   **160.** $1800
161. $716\frac{5}{8}$ square feet   **162.** $217\frac{1}{2}$ miles   **163.** $1\frac{15}{16}$ inches
164. $1\frac{29}{35}$ inches   **165.** $1885   **166.** $14\frac{1}{2}$ inches

Assessment Test

1. 1, 31   **2.** 1, 2, 4, 8, 16, 32, 64   **3.** composite   **4.** prime
5. $2 \cdot 2 \cdot 3 = 2^2 \cdot 3$ **6.** $3 \cdot 3 \cdot 3 \cdot 3 = 3^4$ **7.** 18   **8.** 56
9. improper   **10.** mixed   **11.** proper   **12.** $2\frac{1}{2}$ **13.** $\frac{11}{8}$ or $1\frac{3}{8}$
14. $3\frac{5}{6}$ **15.** $4\frac{19}{35}$ **16.** 3   **17.** $\frac{39}{5}$ **18.** $\frac{43}{16}$ **19.** $\frac{64}{3}$ **20.** $\frac{5}{6}$
21. $\frac{3}{7}$ **22.** $\frac{4}{9}$ **23.** $\frac{4}{15}$ **24.** $\frac{30}{48}$ **25.** $\frac{18}{81}$ **26.** $\frac{60}{24}$ **27.** $\frac{1}{2} < \frac{4}{7} < \frac{5}{8}$
28. $\frac{37}{70} < \frac{6}{10} < \frac{22}{35}$ **29.** $\frac{7}{15}$ **30.** $\frac{1}{6}$ **31.** $63\frac{3}{4}$ **32.** $\frac{11}{15}$ **33.** $1\frac{32}{33}$
34. 144   **35.** $1\frac{1}{18}$ **36.** $4\frac{7}{8}$ **37.** $5\frac{2}{5}$ **38.** $2\frac{1}{10}$ **39.** $6\frac{7}{12}$
40. $5\frac{19}{75}$ **41. a.** $\frac{2}{5}$ **b.** $\frac{8}{55}$ **c.** $\frac{47}{55}$ **42.** 120 signs   **43.** $194\frac{2}{5}$ miles
44. $18\frac{5}{12}$ inches   **45.** $36,000   **46.** $1\frac{17}{64}$ centimeters

CHAPTER 3

Section 3.1 Review Exercises

1. decimal fraction   **3.** decimal   **5.** ths   **7.** digits, place values
9. four, five   **11.** 3, 5, 1, 8   **13.** hundreds   **15.** tenths
17. ten-thousandths   **19.** millionths   **21. a.** sixteen   **b.** and
c. two   **d.** hundredths   **e.** seventy-four hundredths   **f.** sixteen
and seventy-four hundredths   **23.** nine tenths   **25.** fifty-four
ten-thousandths   **27.** one and thirty-four hundredths
29. twenty-five and three thousand six hundred fifty-two
ten-thousandths   **31.** sixty-two ten-thousandths   **33.** fifteen and
seven tenths   **35. a.** 67   **b.** .0015   **c.** 67.0015   **37.** 0.183
39. 0.0015   **41.** 598.8   **43.** 46.03   **45.** 14.35   **47.** 0.00029
49. a. 51   **b.** 100   **c.** 100   **51. a.** 37   **b.** 100   **c.** 37, 100
53. $\dfrac{7}{10}$ **55.** $\dfrac{1}{1000}$ **57.** $\dfrac{64}{100} = \dfrac{16}{25}$ **59.** $3\dfrac{75}{100} = 3\dfrac{3}{4}$
61. $26\dfrac{88}{1000} = 26\dfrac{11}{125}$ **63.** $14\dfrac{5003}{10,000}$ **65. a.** hundredths
b. 4.596   **c.** 4.596 > 4.587 or 4.587 < 4.596   **67.** 0.57 < 0.62
69. 4.017 < 4.170   **71.** 0.0023 = 0.00230   **73.** 243.33 > 242.33
75. 133.52 > 133.5   **77.** 0.730 > 0.7299   **79.** 0.5, 0.564, 0.5654
81. 4.6, 4.576, 4.57   **83.** 1.379, 1.3856, 1.3879, 1.3898   **85. a.** 8
b. 6   **c.** Increase the specified digit, 8, by one, because the digit in
the ten-thousandths place is 5 or more. Next, change each digit to
the right of the specified place value to zero.   **d.** 3.079
87. 14.573   **89.** 8.3   **91.** 240   **93.** 842.0   **95.** 0.003949
97. 10.350   **99.** thirty-four hundredths millimeters
101. 3.34 inches   **103.** 5.4318 seconds, 5.4132 seconds,
5.399 seconds   **105.** $350   **107.** 0.04 inches   **109. a.** seventeen
and $\dfrac{68}{100}$ dollars   **b.** $251.10

Cumulative Skills Review

1. 34,600   **3.** 853   **5.** 36   **7.** $2 \cdot 2 \cdot 5, 2^2 \cdot 5$ **9.** $\dfrac{53}{10}$

Section 3.2 Review Exercises

1. decimal points (decimal places)   **3.** whole

5. a.
$$\begin{array}{r} 4.60 \\ 2.09 \\ + 15.48 \end{array}$$
b.
$$\begin{array}{r} 1\ 1\ 1 \\ 4.60 \\ 2.09 \\ + 15.48 \\ \hline 22.17 \end{array}$$
7. 2.69   **9.** 69.18   **11.** 3.204
13. 5.769   **15.** 79.3695   **17.** 16.01   **19.** 34.725   **21.** 50.3428
23. 12.5122   **25.** 10.68   **27.** 36.158   **29.** 77.29   **31.** 13.2
33. 12.52   **35.** $6.91   **37. a.**
$$\begin{array}{r} 16.40 \\ - 2.91 \end{array}$$
b.
$$\begin{array}{r} 5\ 13 \\ 3\ 10 \\ 16.4\,\cancel{0} \\ - 2.9\ 1 \\ \hline 13.4\ 9 \end{array}$$
39. 0.4
41. 5.73   **43.** 53.64   **45.** 1.857   **47.** 5.2   **49.** 14.5   **51.** 65.37
53. 89.47   **55.** 7.097   **57.** 400.28   **59.** 683.511   **61.** 43.966
63. 5.97   **65.** 5.95   **67.** 14.7   **69.** 20, 220   **71.** 7   **73.** 28
75. 55.0   **77.** 14.62   **79.** 673.6 feet   **81.** 123.26 cm   **83.** $30.90
85. 79.1 °F   **87.** $3.03   **89. a.** 1.136 inches   **b.** 1.596 inches
91.

Number or Code	Date	Transaction Description	Payment, Fee, Withdrawal (−)		✓	Deposit, Credit (+)		$ Balance	
	11/1							2218	90
078	11/12	Castle Decor	451	25				1767	65
	11/19	Deposit				390	55	2158	20
079	11/27	Winton Realty	257	80				1900	40

Cumulative Skills Review

1. $\dfrac{3}{4}$ **3.** 1056   **5.** $\dfrac{163}{9}$ **7.** 21,450   **9.** $\dfrac{39}{72}$

Section 3.3 Review Exercises

1. factors   **3.** right   **5. a.** two   **b.** one   **c.** $2 + 1 = 3$
d. 5.26   **7.** 0.352   **9.** 36.1   **11.** 84.318   **13.** 1.8225   **15.** 29.68
$$\begin{array}{r} \times 1.4 \\ \hline 2104 \\ 526 \\ \hline 7.364 \end{array}$$
17. 0.3756   **19.** 0.099   **21.** 16.016   **23.** 20,734.5   **25.** $12,880.32
27. 204.5633   **29.** 15.06020582   **31.** $12.66   **33.** 5.356
35. two, two, right, 360.0   **37.** 2750   **39.** 19,550   **41.** 7500
43. 0.0054   **45.** 0.00072   **47.** 0.0003209   **49.** 298,990,000
51. $8,383,000,000,000   **53.** 4, 40   **55.** 1.5   **57.** 2.7   **59.** 82.5
61. 520   **63.** 2.94 miles   **65.** 11.25 inches   **67.** $146,542.15
69. $292.50   **71. a.** $20,000,000,000   **b.** $75,000,000
73. $269.10, $215.88   **75.** $352.28, $91.01   **77. a.** 3mg   **b.** 30mg
79. $428.04   **81.** $174.84
83.

CUISINEART			
Quantity	**Description**	**Cost per Item**	**Total**
200	Toasters	$69.50	$13,900.00
130	Blenders	75.80	9854.00
	Merchandise total		23,754.00
	Shipping and handling		1327.08
	Insurance		644.20
	Invoice total		$25,725.28

Cumulative Skills Review

1. 0   **3.** 13.959   **5.** six and eight hundred fifty-two thousandths
7. $\dfrac{53}{6}$ **9.** $3\dfrac{1}{10}$

Section 3.4 Review Exercises

1. dividend   **3.** quotient   **5.** last, dividend   **7.** left, zeros
9.
$$\begin{array}{r} 1.35 \\ 5\overline{)6.75} \\ -5 \\ \hline 17 \\ -15 \\ \hline 25 \\ -25 \\ \hline 0 \end{array}$$
11. 2.7   **13.** 5.6   **15.** 1.74   **17.** 0.4
19. 0.075   **21.** 6.27   **23.** 0.044   **25.** 0.07   **27.** two, two, left, 0.047
29. 0.2478   **31.** 67,000   **33.** 5,600,300   **35.** 0.00076
37. a. $35\overline{)19.6}$ **b.**
$$\begin{array}{r} 0.56 \\ 35\overline{)19.60} \\ -17\ 5 \\ \hline 2\ 10 \\ -2\ 10 \\ \hline 0 \end{array}$$
39. 80   **41.** 26.8   **43.** 3.1   **45.** 4.4
47. 0.89   **49.** 0.45   **51.** 19   **53.** 32   **55.** 2.7   **57.** 0.7   **59.** 0.08
61. 217.27   **63. a.** 40   **b.** $8\overset{5}{\overline{)40}}$ **65.** 5   **67.** 0.05   **69.** $0.22 per

bottle   **71.** 0.0134 inches per day   **73.** $12.50 per hour
75. a. 8.5 minutes per mile   **b.** 26.35 minutes   **77.** $3.26
79. $2.16 per can   **81.** 6.4 pounds per month
83. a. 110,000 square feet   **b.** $0.04

Cumulative Skills Review

1. 6.7925   **3.** $\frac{3}{5}$ **5.** 20.51   **7.** 118 house sites   **9.** 104 ounces

Section 3.5 Review Exercises

1. divide   **3.** $0.\overline{14}$
5.

$$\begin{array}{r} 0.3125 \\ 16\overline{)5.0000} \\ -\ 48 \\ \hline 20 \\ -\ 16 \\ \hline 40 \\ -\ 32 \\ \hline 80 \\ -\ 80 \\ \hline 0 \end{array}$$

$\frac{5}{16} = 0.3125$

7. 0.15   **9.** 0.5625   **11.** 0.38   **13.** $0.\overline{45}$ **15.** 1.6

17. 0.65   **19.** $1.8\overline{3}$ **21.** 0.1875   **23.** $4.3\overline{8}$ **25.** 5.125   **27.** 0.8
29. 10.4   **31.** 0.17   **33.** 1.15   **35. a.** 1   **b.** 1, 41.208, 47.478
37. 32.3   **39.** 19.12   **41.** 0.502   **43.** 2.8   **45.** 1   **47.** 22.1
49. 5.425   **51.** 17.1   **53.** 74.5064   **55.** $132.56
57. 1481.1 square inches   **59. a.** almonds, $14.14; pears, $12.79; grapes, $2.71   **b.** $29.64   **61.** $45\frac{4}{5}$ feet

Cumulative Skills Review

1. 0.586   **3.** $\frac{1}{10}$ **5.** 2.855   **7.** 3,080,000   **9.** $3\frac{7}{9}$

Numerical Facts of Life

1. 2006 Payroll Rounded to Millions	**3. 2006 Average Salary per Player 30-Player Roster**
$195,000,000	$6,500,000
$120,000,000	$4,000,000
$103,000,000	$3,433,333
$41,000,000	$1,366,667
$35,000,000	$1,166,667
$15,000,000	$500,000

Chapter Review Exercises

1. tenths   **2.** ten-thousandths   **3.** thousandths   **4.** hundredths
5. millionths   **6.** ten-millionths   **7.** twenty-eight and three hundred fifty-five thousandths   **8.** two hundred eleven hundred-thousandths   **9.** one hundred fifty-eight thousandths   **10.** one hundred forty-two and twelve hundredths   **11.** fifty-nine and six hundred twenty-five thousandths   **12.** thirty-nine hundredths
13. 0.0298   **14.** 22.324   **15.** 178.13   **16.** 0.0735   **17.** 912.25
18. 0.00016   **19.** $9\frac{57}{100}$ **20.** $\frac{63}{200}$ **21.** $5\frac{3}{500}$ **22.** $1\frac{19}{100}$
23. 23.512 < 23.519   **24.** 0.8124 < 0.8133
25. 3.45887 > 3.45877   **26.** 125.6127 > 124.78
27. 0.02324 = 0.02324   **28.** 55.398 > 55.389   **29.** 1.85
30. 2.149   **31.** 3.4   **32.** 4.1146   **33.** 1.58856   **34.** 7.451

35. 5.582   **36.** 7.309   **37.** 11.6234   **38.** 9.711   **39.** 15.7819
40. 13.501   **41.** 9.741   **42.** 6.292   **43.** 31.576   **44.** 30.153
45. 22.293   **46.** 12.175   **47.** 6.112   **48.** 2.008   **49.** 0.06848
50. 11.0673   **51.** 0.0268   **52.** 4.3361   **53.** 15.02   **54.** 0.952
55. 6.28125   **56.** 0.13902   **57.** 13.01904   **58.** 0.064989
59. 9.45   **60.** 113.3   **61.** 11.826   **62.** 27.405   **63.** 17.4984
64. 0.1057   **65.** 145,900,000   **66.** 1,250,000,000,000
67. 455,200,000,000   **68.** $16,780,000   **69.** 0.089   **70.** 1.409
71. 1.79   **72.** 1.595   **73.** 8.275   **74.** 36.352   **75.** 498.8   **76.** 12.6
77. 4.8   **78.** 40.3   **79.** 6.1   **80.** 34.4   **81.** 0.2   **82.** 0.04
83. $0.91666\ldots$, or $0.91\overline{6}$ **84.** $3.6363\ldots$, or $3.\overline{63}$ **85.** 0.86
86. 4.19   **87.** 127.9   **88.** 92.64   **89.** 543.375   **90.** 15.3   **91.** 14.6
92. 1548   **93.** 12.18 feet, 12.27 feet, 12.65 feet
94. 189.44 pounds, 155.65 pounds, 126.32 pounds, 114.18 pounds
95. 2654.5 feet   **96.** $52.70   **97.** $1836.44   **98.** 41.62 feet
99. $69.72   **100.** $42,923.40 per year
101. 161,270,000 kilometers   **102.** 778,100,000 kilometers
103. 797.5 miles   **104.** $19.95   **105. a.** $894.00   **b.** $6.33
c. $900.33   **d.** nine hundred dollars and thirty-three cents
106. a. $1131.00   **b.** $12.86   **c.** $1143.86   **d.** eleven hundred forty-three dollars and eighty-six cents

107.

Number or Code	Date	Transaction Description	Payment, Fee, Withdrawal (−)		✓	Deposit, Credit (+)		$ Balance	
	7/1				·			1694	20
228	7/12	Wal-Mart	183	40				1510	80
	7/16	Deposit				325	50	1836	30
	7/24	ATM withdrawal	200	00				1636	30

108.

Number or Code	Date	Transaction Description	Payment, Fee, Withdrawal (−)		✓	Deposit, Credit (+)		$ Balance	
	3/1							2336	40
	3/11	Deposit				1550	35	3886	75
357	3/19	Visa	253	70				3633	05
358	3/23	FedEx	45	10				3587	95

109. a. $170.25   **b.** $54.75   **110. a.** $76.92   **b.** 30 weeks
111. 45.4°F   **112.** 3.66   **113. a.** $17.58   **b.** $5.86
114. a. $138,862.50   **b.** $19,837.50   **115.** $15\frac{1}{10}$ pounds
116. $7\frac{13}{20}$ pounds   **117.** $47.50   **118.** 12.5 pounds

Assessment Test

1. hundredths   **2.** ten-thousandths   **3.** forty-two and nine hundred forty-nine thousandths   **4.** three hundred sixty-five ten-thousandths   **5.** 0.00021   **6.** 61.211   **7.** $8\frac{17}{20}$ **8.** $\frac{1}{8}$
9. 0.6643 > 0.66349   **10.** 12.118 < 12.181
11. 2.14530 = 2.145300   **12.** 1.6   **13.** 4.11   **14.** 9.296
15. 24.4779   **16.** 27.517   **17.** 0.0893   **18.** 9.3964   **19.** 0.12336
20. 218,600,000   **21.** 3,370,000,000   **22.** 0.0928   **23.** 25.6
24. 9.02   **25.** 5.843   **26. a.** $269.50   **b.** $184.68   **27. a.** $74.77
b. $5.23   **28.** 20.2 mpg   **29.** 48.4°F   **30.** $161.96   **31.** $116.00
32. $15.08

CHAPTER 4

Section 4.1 Review Exercises

1. ratio   **3.** to, colon (:), fraction   **5.** whole, part   **7.** Step 1:

Write the ratio in fraction notation; Step 2: Rewrite as a ratio of whole numbers. Multiply by 1 in the form $\frac{n}{n}$, where n is a power of 10 large enough to remove any decimals in both the numerator and the denominator; Step 3: Simplify, if possible.   **9. a.** 7 to 12   **b.** 7:12   **c.** $\frac{7}{12}$ **11.** 5 to 17, 5:17, $\frac{5}{17}$ **13.** 3 to $8\frac{1}{4}$, $3{:}8\frac{1}{4}$, $\frac{3}{8\frac{1}{4}}$

15. 2.7 to 9, 2.7:9, $\frac{2.7}{9}$ **17.** 5 to 2, 5:2, $\frac{5}{2}$ **19.** 8 to 15, 8:15, $\frac{8}{15}$

21. 44 to 1.2, 44:1.2, $\frac{44}{1.2}$ **23. a.** $\frac{18}{27}$ **b.** $\frac{2}{3}$ **25. a.** $\frac{2.6}{50}$ **b.** $\frac{10}{10}$

c. $\frac{2.6}{50} \cdot \frac{10}{10} = \frac{26}{500}$ **d.** $\frac{13}{250}$ **27.** $\frac{10}{3}$ **29.** $\frac{12}{1}$ **31.** $\frac{1}{4}$ **33.** $\frac{1}{2}$

35. $\frac{3}{11}$ **37.** $\frac{8}{15}$ **39.** $\frac{5}{4}$ **41.** $\frac{4}{1}$ **43.** $\frac{4}{5}$ **45.** $\frac{27}{4}$ **47. a.** quarts

b. 1 gallon = 4 quarts, 2 gallons = $2 \cdot 4$ quarts = 8 quarts   **c.** $\frac{6}{8}$

d. $\frac{3}{4}$ **49.** $\frac{1}{4}$ **51.** $\frac{2}{5}$ **53.** $\frac{24}{7}$ **55.** $\frac{16}{15}$ **57.** $\frac{18}{1}$ **59.** $\frac{4}{1}$

61. a. $\frac{9}{12} = \frac{3}{4}$, 3 to 4, 3:4   **b.** $\frac{152}{284} = \frac{38}{71}$, 38 to 71, 38:71

63. a. $\frac{3}{7}$ **b.** $\frac{7}{1}$ **c.** $\frac{1}{11}$ **65.** $\frac{1}{4}$ **67.** $\frac{9}{4}$ **69.** $\frac{10}{6} = \frac{5}{3}$ **71.** $\frac{12}{7}$

73. 741 to 1156, 741:1156, $\frac{741}{1156}$ **75.** $\frac{578}{1000} = \frac{289}{500}$

77. $\frac{31,100}{6700} = \frac{311}{67}$ **79.** $\frac{11,200}{37,800} = \frac{8}{27}$ **81.** $\frac{3.7}{7.0} = \frac{37}{70}$, 37 to 70,

37:70   **83.** $\frac{7.0}{42.2} = \frac{70}{422} = \frac{35}{211}$, 35 to 211, 35:211

Cumulative Skills Review

1. 4   **3.** 19.163   **5.** 16,179   **7.** $\frac{4}{5}, \frac{8}{15}, \frac{23}{47}$ **9.** 8975.46

Section 4.2 Review Exercises

1. rate   **3.** divide   **5.** divide   **7.** price, quantity (number of items or units)   **9. a.** $\frac{8 \text{ pages}}{12 \text{ minutes}}$ **b.** $\frac{2 \text{ pages}}{3 \text{ minutes}}$ **c.** 2 pages for every 3 minutes

11. $\frac{17 \text{ fence panels}}{270 \text{ feet}}$; 17 fence panels for every 270 feet

13. $\frac{3 \text{ vans}}{26 \text{ people}}$; 3 vans for every 26 people   **15.** $\frac{4 \text{ bags}}{3 \text{ passengers}}$; 4 bags for every 3 passengers   **17.** $\frac{625 \text{ revolutions}}{2 \text{ minutes}}$; 625 revolutions for every 2 minutes   **19.** $\frac{25 \text{ patients}}{3 \text{ doctors}}$; 25 patients for every 3 doctors   **21.** $\frac{91 \text{ gallons}}{17 \text{ cows}}$; 91 gallons of milk for every 17 cows   **23.** $\frac{281 \text{ students}}{14 \text{ teachers}}$; 281 students for every 14 teachers

25. $\frac{3142 \text{ square feet}}{7 \text{ gallons of paint}}$; 3142 square feet for every 7 gallons of paint

27. $\frac{11 \text{ hits}}{36 \text{ at bats}}$; 11 hits for every 36 at bats   **29. a.** $\frac{280 \text{ miles}}{20 \text{ gallons}}$

b. $\frac{14 \text{ miles}}{1 \text{ gallon}}$ **c.** 14 miles per gallon or 14 miles/gallon or 14 mpg

31. \$300 per month   **33.** 5.3 touchdowns per game   **35.** 1 parking space per apartment   **37.** 3.8 yards of material per shirt   **39.** 4 servings per pizza   **41.** 22 roses per vase   **43.** 3.2 kilowatts per hour   **45.** 93 branches per tree

47. 420 words per page   **49. a.** $\frac{\$22.50}{12 \text{ golf balls}}$ **b.** $\frac{\$1.875}{1 \text{ golf ball}}$

c. \$1.88 per golf ball   **51.** \$0.08 per minute of long distance   **53.** \$0.13 per ounce of detergent   **55.** \$0.28 per orange   **57.** \$1.55 per milkshake   **59.** \$1.16 per battery   **61.** \$1.45 per pound of turkey   **63.** \$8.95 per pie   **65.** \$0.23 per bottle of spring water   **67.** $\frac{7 \text{ patients}}{3 \text{ nurses}}$, 7 patients for every 3 nurses

69. $\frac{4 \text{ pounds}}{3 \text{ orders}}$, 4 pounds of cheese for every 3 orders

71. a. 6.7 miles per hour   **b.** 6.3 miles per hour   **c.** Todd   **73. a.** 1.7 inches per second   **b.** 1.6 inches per second   **c.** X400   **75.** $\frac{306,137}{105,723}$, 306,137 total pilots for every 105,723 general aviation

aircraft   **77.** $\frac{134,350}{1}$, 134,350 passengers for every public airport

79. 20 purses at \$45.80 per purse   **81.** 12-ounce tube at \$0.30 per ounce   **83.** \$1.65, \$1.73, \$1.50; 45 pounds at \$1.50 per pound   **85.** \$16.25, \$15.82, \$16.75; 5 gallons at \$15.82 per gallon   **87. a.** \$0.07 per ounce   **b.** \$0.06 per ounce   **c.** 45-ounce gel for \$2.25 at \$0.05 per ounce

Cumulative Skills Review

1. not defined   **3.** $9\frac{1}{4}$ **5.** 39.001   **7. a.** $\frac{12}{7}$ **b.** $\frac{9}{7}$ **9.** $16\frac{5}{8}$ pounds

Section 4.3 Review Exercises

1. equal   **3.** $\frac{a}{b} = \frac{c}{d}$ **5.** cross multiplication, equal   **7.** solve

9. cross products   **11. a.** $\frac{5}{10}$ **b.** $\frac{9}{18}$ **c.** $\frac{5}{10} = \frac{9}{18}$ **13.** $\frac{22}{44} = \frac{7}{14}$

15. $\frac{8 \text{ suits}}{3 \text{ weeks}} = \frac{32 \text{ suits}}{12 \text{ weeks}}$ **17.** $\frac{3.6}{5.8} = \frac{14.4}{23.2}$ **19.** $\frac{5 \text{ cans}}{\$8} = \frac{15 \text{ cans}}{\$24}$

21. $\frac{12}{7} = \frac{3.6}{2.1}$ **23.** $\frac{150 \text{ calories}}{7 \text{ ounces}} = \frac{300 \text{ calories}}{14 \text{ ounces}}$ **25.** 6 is to 3 as 30 is to 15.   **27.** 15 pages is to 2 minutes as 75 pages is to 10 minutes.   **29.** 3 strikeouts is to 2 hits as 27 strikeouts is to 18 hits.   **31.** 16 is to 5 as 80 is to 25.   **33.** 22.2 is to 65.3 as 44.4 is to 130.6.   **35.** 25 songs is to 2 CDs as 125 songs is to 10 CDs.   **37. a.** $11 \cdot 80 = 880$ **b.** $55 \cdot 16 = 880$ **c.** yes   **d.** yes   **e.** $\frac{55}{11} = \frac{80}{16}$ **39.** no   **41.** no   **43.** yes; $\frac{80}{5} = \frac{400}{25}$ **45.** yes; $\frac{5}{17} = \frac{35}{119}$ **47.** no   **49.** yes; $\frac{25}{39} = \frac{75}{117}$ **51.** yes; $\frac{54}{13} = \frac{108}{26}$

53. a. $20 \cdot 14 = 280$; $c \cdot 56 = 56c$ **b.** $280 = 56c$ **c.** $\frac{280}{56} = \frac{56c}{56}$

$$20 \cdot 14 = 280$$
Cross products are equal.
d. $c = 5$ **e.** $\frac{5}{20} = \frac{14}{56}$
$$5 \cdot 56 = 280$$

55. $w = 144$ **57.** $c = 24$ **59.** $m = 30$ **61.** $v = 100$ **63.** $j = 3$ **65.** $h = 3.6$ **67.** $b = 30$ **69.** $q = 56$ **71.** $y = 5$ **73.** yes   **75.** no   **77.** 24 passenger flights   **79.** 14 buses   **81.** 7 ounces of whipped cream   **83.** \$93.15 interest   **85. a.** 2400 children

b. 4200 bags of popcorn **c.** $18,900   **87.** 2085 births
89. 350,000 people   **91.** 13.2   **93.** 33 inches   **95.** 14 feet

Cumulative Skills Review

1. 3.25   **3. a.** $2\frac{1}{6}$ **b.** $\frac{5}{6}$ **c.** 1 **d.** $2\frac{1}{4}$ **5.** sixty-two and three
hundred ninety-nine ten thousandths   **7.** $33

9. 18 to 25, 18:25, $\frac{18}{25}$

Numerical Facts of Life

1. $\frac{1230}{170} = \frac{x}{185}$ $x = 1339$ calories per hour

3. $\frac{1339}{588} = 2.3$ calories burned running for each
calorie burned playing tennis

Chapter Review Exercises

1. 3 to 8   3:8 $\frac{3}{8}$ **2.** 62 to 7   62:7 $\frac{62}{7}$ **3.** 12 to 5.2   12:5.2 $\frac{12}{5.2}$

4. 9 to 14.3   9:14.3 $\frac{9}{14.3}$ **5.** 3 to $\frac{5}{9}$ 3:$\frac{5}{9}$ $\frac{3}{\frac{5}{9}}$

6. $2\frac{1}{2}$ to $\frac{1}{16}$ $2\frac{1}{2}$:$\frac{1}{16}$ $\frac{2\frac{1}{2}}{\frac{1}{16}}$ **7.** $\frac{5}{8}$ **8.** $\frac{29}{3}$ **9.** $\frac{4}{13}$ **10.** $\frac{8}{7}$ **11.** $\frac{2}{5}$

12. $\frac{11}{150}$ **13.** $\frac{16}{7}$ **14.** $\frac{9}{119}$ **15.** $\frac{55}{24}$ **16.** $\frac{12}{5}$ **17.** $\frac{36}{11}$ **18.** $\frac{125}{264}$

19. $\frac{17}{20}$ **20.** $\frac{12}{25}$ **21.** $\frac{5}{2}$ **22.** $\frac{11}{6}$ **23.** $\frac{25 \text{ sprinklers}}{2 \text{ acres}}$; 25 sprinklers

for every 2 acres   **24.** $\frac{49 \text{ avocados}}{5 \text{ trees}}$; 49 avocados for every 5 trees

25. $\frac{38 \text{ kittens}}{3 \text{ pet stores}}$; 38 kittens for every 3 pet stores   **26.** $\frac{\$49}{2 \text{ tires}}$;

$49 for every 2 tires   **27.** $\frac{5 \text{ ponies}}{2 \text{ trainers}}$; 5 ponies for every 2 trainers

28. $\frac{3 \text{ cheeseburgers}}{\$5}$; 3 cheeseburgers for every $5   **29.** 12 miles

per day   **30.** 794 pounds per truck   **31.** 2.6 yards per minute
32. 801.3 jellybeans per bag   **33.** 28 cars per lane   **34.** 1445 bees
per beehive   **35.** 15.7 tons of fuel per cruise   **36.** 3.1 pounds per
week   **37.** $18 per ticket   **38.** $12.50 per T-shirt   **39.** $7 per car
wash   **40.** $173.75 per day   **41.** $85 per flight lesson
42. $0.65 per sugar cookie   **43.** $1.58 per tennis ball

44. $4300 per sales event   **45.** $\frac{9}{11} = \frac{36}{44}$

46. $\frac{124 \text{ graduates}}{3 \text{ schools}} = \frac{248 \text{ graduates}}{6 \text{ schools}}$ **47.** $\frac{3}{5} = \frac{300}{500}$

48. $\frac{2 \text{ days}}{95 \text{ mail orders}} = \frac{6 \text{ days}}{285 \text{ mail orders}}$ **49.** $\frac{2.1}{6.5} = \frac{16.8}{52}$

50. $\frac{5 \text{ concerts}}{7 \text{ days}} = \frac{15 \text{ concerts}}{21 \text{ days}}$ **51.** 30 violins is to 5 orchestras as
90 violins is to 15 orchestras.   **52.** 9 is to 13 as 81 is to 117.
53. 3 tours is to 450 bicycles as 6 tours is to 900 bicycles.
54. 12 is to 33 as 36 is to 99.   **55.** 8 swings is to 3 playgrounds as
16 swings is to 6 playgrounds.   **56.** 3.7 is to 1.2 as 37 is to 12.
57. yes, $\frac{18}{17} = \frac{54}{51}$ **58.** no   **59.** no   **60.** yes, $\frac{35}{21} = \frac{70}{42}$

61. yes, $\frac{7.5}{11} = \frac{60}{88}$ **62.** yes, $\frac{2.3}{5.5} = \frac{9.2}{22}$ **63.** $g = 35$ **64.** $y = 7$

65. $m = 69$ **66.** $t = 22$ **67.** $a = 108$ **68.** $f = 16$ **69.** $u = 3$
70. $b = 5$ **71.** $q = 40$ **72.** $r = 3$ **73.** $h = 3$ **74.** $x = 8$

75. a. 14 to 27, 14:27, $\frac{14}{27}$ **b.** 27 to 41, 27:41, $\frac{27}{41}$

76. a. 125 to 33, 125:33, $\frac{125}{33}$ **b.** 158 to 125, 158:125, $\frac{158}{125}$

77. a. $\frac{65}{25} = \frac{13}{5}$ **b.** $\frac{40}{50} = \frac{4}{5}$ **c.** $\frac{65}{180} = \frac{13}{36}$

78. a. $\frac{225}{60} = \frac{15}{4}$ **b.** $\frac{150}{225} = \frac{2}{3}$ **c.** $\frac{60}{435} = \frac{4}{29}$

79. a. $\frac{4 \text{ cups of coffee}}{3 \text{ minutes}}$ **b.** $1\frac{1}{3}$ cups per minute **c.** $0.45 per cup

80. a. $\frac{27 \text{ oranges}}{5 \text{ pints}}$ **b.** $5\frac{2}{5}$ oranges per pints **c.** $2.30 per pint

81. 10-ounce bag of popcorn for $1.20 at $0.12 per ounce
82. 12 ferry rides for $34.80 at $2.90 per ferry ride
83. 3 dozen bagels for $8.75 at $2.92 per dozen bagels
84. 12 yoga classes for $64.20 at $5.35 per yoga class   **85.** yes,

$\frac{\$152,000}{1600 \text{ ft}^2} = \frac{\$185,250}{1950 \text{ ft}^2}$ **86.** no   **87.** no   **88.** yes,

$\frac{\$52}{8 \text{ days}} = \frac{\$32.50}{5 \text{days}}$ **89.** 15 puppies   **90.** 3600 square feet

91. 135 notebooks   **92.** $3.25   **93.** 5 hours   **94.** 40 classes
95. 867 nails   **96.** 8 pounds of peaches   **97.** 12 pairs   **98.** 53.5
gallons of gasoline   **99.** 5,250,000 viewers   **100.** 240 gallons
101. $x = 8$ inches   **102.** $z = 50$ feet   **103.** 40 feet   **104.** 192 feet

105. 31 to 33, 31:33, $\frac{31}{33}$ **106.** 91 to 90, 91:90, $\frac{91}{90}$ **107.** 127

miles per hour of the Airbus A330 for every 106 miles per hour of
the Boeing 767   **108.** 100 passengers on the Boeing 787 for every
109 passengers on the Boeing 767   **109. a.** $\frac{186}{182} = \frac{93}{91}$ **b.** 202 feet

110. a. $\frac{198}{194} = \frac{99}{97}$ **b.** 176 feet

Assessment Test

1. 28 to 65   28:65 $\frac{28}{65}$ **2.** 5.8 to 2.1   5.8:2.1 $\frac{5.8}{2.1}$ **3.** $\frac{2}{3}$

4. $\frac{5}{2}$ **5.** $\frac{17}{9}$ **6.** $\frac{1}{30}$ **7.** $\frac{16}{5}$ **8.** $\frac{10}{3}$ **9.** $\frac{28 \text{ apples}}{5 \text{ baskets}}$ 28 apples for

every 5 baskets   **10.** $\frac{3 \text{ cabinets}}{22 \text{ files}}$ 3 cabinets for every 22 files

11. 32.1 miles per gallon   **12.** 3 birds per cage   **13.** $168.75 per
dining room chair   **14.** $0.48 per fish   **15.** $\frac{3}{45} = \frac{18}{270}$

16. $\frac{9 \text{ labels}}{4 \text{ folders}} = \frac{45 \text{ labels}}{20 \text{ folders}}$ **17.** 2 is to 17 as 6 is to 51.

18. 12 photos is to 5 hours as 24 photos is to 10 hours.

19. yes, $\frac{7}{16} = \frac{35}{80}$ **20.** no   **21.** $p = 6$ **22.** $c = 32$ **23.** $m = 47.5$

24. $t = 9$ **25. a.** 40 to 3, 40:3, $\frac{40}{3}$ **b.** 13.3 yards per carry

26. 3 pounds for $4.20 at $1.40 per pound   **27.** 24 ounces of sugar
for $4.08 at $0.17 per ounce   **28.** no   **29.** 22.75 miles   **30.** 78 feet

CHAPTER 5

Section 5.1 Review Exercises

1. percent **3.** 100 **5.** 100%, right **7. a.** 21% **b.** 79%
9. a. 32 **b.** $32\frac{8}{25}$ **11.** 0.29 **13.** $\frac{3}{5}$ **15.** $\frac{1}{10}$ **17.** $\frac{1}{4}$ **19.** $\frac{21}{50}$
21. $\frac{59}{400}$ **23.** $\frac{27}{200}$ **25.** $\frac{17}{400}$ **27.** $\frac{29}{200}$ **29.** $\frac{21}{200}$ **31.** $\frac{37}{200}$
33. $\frac{3}{80}$ **35.** $1\frac{1}{10}$ **37.** $1\frac{13}{20}$ **39.** $2\frac{3}{5}$ **41.** 0.45 **43.** 0.98 **45.** 1.5
47. 1.15 **49.** 0.982 **51.** 0.762 **53.** 0.574 **55.** 0.648 **57.** 0.878
59. 0.3574 **61.** 0.042 **63.** 0.0037 **65.** 0.0072 **67.** 0.00883
69. 81% **71. a.** 0.4375 **b.** 0.4375, 43.75% **73.** 45% **75.** 30%
77. 1% **79.** 76.9% **81.** 66.75% **83.** 7.2% **85.** 0.048%
87. 1000% **89.** 1600% **91.** 376% **93.** 226.8% **95.** 692%
97. 199% **99.** 235% **101.** 10% **103.** 20% **105.** 23%
107. 21% **109.** 12% **111.** 65% **113.** 112.5% **115.** 237.5%
117. 206.25% **119.** 281.25% **121.** 180% **123.** 188%
125. 260% **127.** 275% **129.** 46% **131.** 0.89 **133.** 0.384
135. 0.375 **137.** 122% **139.** 2.314

Cumulative Skills Review

1. 9^4, nine to the fourth power **3.** yes, $\frac{12}{39} = \frac{4}{13}$ **5.** $\frac{193}{500}$ **7.** 1
9. $\frac{22}{17}$ 22:17 22 to 17

Section 5.2 Review Exercises

1. equations, proportions **3.** multiplication, equality **5.** amount
7. base **9.** Base $= \frac{\text{Amount}}{\text{Percent}}$ **11.** decimal **13.** $75 = p \cdot 80$
15. $195.3 = 30\% \cdot s$ **17.** $10 = 3\% \cdot k$ **19.** $736 = 86\% \cdot f$
21. $38\% \cdot z = 406$ **23.** $v = 25\% \cdot 500$ **25.** $87\% \cdot 4350 = d$
27. a. amount: unknown, a, percent: 20%, base: 70
b. $a = 20\% \cdot 70$ **c.** $a = 0.2 \cdot 70$ **d.** $a = 14$ **29. a.** amount: 25,
percent: unknown, p, base: 500 **b.** $500 \cdot p = 25$ **c.** $\frac{500p}{500} = \frac{25}{500}$,
$p = \frac{25}{500} = 0.05$ **d.** $p = 5\%$ **31.** $1050 = 10\% \cdot b, b = 10,500$
33. $2350 = 25\% \cdot b, b = 9400$ **35.** $a = 2\% \cdot 1500, a = 30$
37. $2088 = 36\% \cdot b, b = 5800$ **39.** $a = 32\% \cdot 4900, a = 1568$
41. $6120 = p \cdot 12,000, p = 51\%$ **43.** $2700 = b \cdot 30\%, b = 9000$
45. $a = 3\% \cdot 3900, a = 117$ **47.** $13,248 = 69\% \cdot b, b = 19,200$
49. $p \cdot 13,000 = 2210, p = 17\%$ **51.** $a = 82\% \cdot 122, a = 100.04$
53. $a = 12\% \cdot 365, a = 43.8$ **55.** $a = 44\% \cdot 699, a = 307.56$
57. $p \cdot 751 = 518.19, p = 69\%$ **59.** $326.65 = 47\% \cdot b, b = 695$
61. 80% **63.** $275 in contributions **65.** 15 states **67. a.** 150
songs **b.** 350 songs **c.** 39% **69.** 1150 air conditioners were made
71. $162.50 spent on entertainment **73.** 15%
75. a. 24% **b.** 42 wax jobs **77.** 55 customers **79.** 365 papers
81. $700 profit **83.** 280 million people **85.** 9.43%
87. 345,500 bowlers

Cumulative Skills Review

1. 9 **3.** $\frac{3}{5}$ **5.** 6131 **7.** $\frac{13}{15}$ **9.** $y = 12$

Section 5.3 Review Exercises

1. $\frac{\text{Amount}}{\text{Base}} = \frac{\text{Part}}{100}$ **3. a.** amount: unknown, a, part: 85,
base: 358 **b.** $\frac{\text{Amount}}{\text{Base}} = \frac{\text{Part}}{100}$ **c.** $\frac{a}{358} = \frac{85}{100}$ **5. a.** amount: 16,
part: 28, base: unknown, b **b.** $\frac{\text{Amount}}{\text{Base}} = \frac{\text{Part}}{100}$ **c.** $\frac{16}{b} = \frac{28}{100}$
7. $\frac{a}{279} = \frac{12}{100}$ **9.** $\frac{a}{190} = \frac{88.5}{100}$ **11.** $\frac{200}{1,000} = \frac{p}{100}$
13. a. amount: 96, part: unknown, p base: 128 **b.** $\frac{96}{128} = \frac{p}{100}$
c. $\frac{3}{4} = \frac{p}{100}$ **d.** $4 \cdot p = 3 \cdot 100, 4p = 300$ **e.** $\frac{4p}{4} = \frac{300}{4}$,
$p = 75$; 75% of 128 is 96. **15.** $\frac{a}{700} = \frac{25}{100}, a = 175$
17. $\frac{330}{1100} = \frac{p}{100}, p = 30$ **19.** $\frac{1440}{900} = \frac{p}{100}, p = 160$
21. $\frac{a}{622} = \frac{150}{100}, a = 933$ **23.** $\frac{6975}{b} = \frac{31}{100}, b = 22,500$
25. $\frac{270}{b} = \frac{60}{100}, b = 450$ **27.** $\frac{a}{2000} = \frac{2.5}{100}, a = 50$
29. $\frac{288}{1200} = \frac{p}{100}, p = 24$ **31.** $\frac{300}{b} = \frac{16}{100}, b = 1875$
33. $\frac{a}{528} = \frac{25}{100}, a = 132$ **35.** $\frac{390}{300} = \frac{p}{100}, p = 130$
37. $\frac{a}{3525} = \frac{10}{100}, a = 352.5$ **39.** $\frac{1950}{6000} = \frac{p}{100}, p = 32.5$
41. $\frac{a}{263} = \frac{2}{100}, a = 5.26$ **43.** 6750 students
45. a. 50 grams of protein **b.** 25 grams of dietary fiber
47. $23,200 **49.** 9.4% **51.** 3350 deliveries **53.** 83%
55. a. 17.5% **b.** 82.5% **57.** 6.1% **59.** 16.7%
61. 14 vacation days **63.** 71% **65.** 9 million albums

Cumulative Skills Review

1. $\frac{17}{20}, 0.85$ **3.** < **5.** 0.225 **7.** No, the ratios are not
proportional. **9.** 1 cup

Section 5.4 Review Exercises

1. changed **3.** decrease **5.** Sales tax **7.** Tip = Tip rate · Bill
amount **9.** Commission = Commission rate · Sales amount
11. a. $123 - 100 = 23$
b. Percent change $= \frac{\text{Change amount}}{\text{Original amount}} = \frac{23}{100}$ **c.** 23% increase

	Amount of Change	Percent Change
13.	15	30% increase
15.	4	22% increase
17.	260	26% increase
19.	$80	53% decrease
21.	56	82% decrease

23. a. Sales tax = Sales tax rate · Item cost **b.** $t = 5\% \cdot \$55$
c. $t = 0.05 \cdot \$55 = \$2.75$ **d.** Item cost + Sales tax = Total purchase
price, $55.00 + 2.75 = \$57.75$ **25. a.** Commission = Commission
rate · Sales amount **b.** $c = 20\% \cdot \$600$ **c.** $c = 0.2 \cdot \$600 = \$120$
27. $3.92 sales tax **29. a.** $14.07 sales tax **b.** $341.26 **31.** $1.95;
$14.95 **33.** $30; 25% **35.** $12,500 **37.** 15.5%
39. a. $27 discount **b.** $63 sale price **41.** 12.6% discount rate

43. 40% discount rate   **45. a.** 20% + 100% = 120%
b. $a = 120\% \cdot 400$ pounds **d.** $a = 1.2 \cdot 400$ pounds = 480 pounds

Original Amount	New Amount
47. $290	$455
49. 6154	4000
51. $13,882	$11,800
53. $20,000	$23,800
55. 90	82
57. $100	$96
59. 16	15

61. The original price of the motor home was $54,375.
63. a. 15% decrease in customers **b.** 9350 customers are expected
next month.   **65.** 7 weddings   **67.** 27% of the trip was completed
the first day.   **69.** In 2004, 767 million rolls of film were sold.
71. a. 200% increase in size **b.** 24 inches   **73.** 27.7% increase in
GDP   **75.** 25.87% increase in spending for NASA   **77.** 32
pounds per square inch   **79.** 58% water saved per flush
81. 53.1% increase in cats   **83.** 4.5% increase   **85.** 136.7 million

Cumulative Skills Review

1. $\dfrac{25}{500} = \dfrac{r}{100}$ **3.** 59.38095   **5.** Yes.   **7.** 0.28819   **9.** $\dfrac{23}{25}, 0.92$

Numerical Facts of Life

a. Housing expense ratio = $\dfrac{\text{Monthly housing expense}}{\text{Monthly gross income}}$

$= \dfrac{1230.00}{4650.00} = 0.2645 = 26.5\%$

b. Total obligations ratio = $\dfrac{\text{Total monthly financial obligations}}{\text{Monthly gross income}}$

$= \dfrac{1230.00 + 615.00}{4650.00} = \dfrac{1845.00}{4650.00}$

$= 0.3967 = 39.7\%$

c. FHA

Chapter Review Exercises

1. $\dfrac{9}{200}$ **2.** $\dfrac{71}{25}$ or $2\dfrac{21}{25}$ **3.** $\dfrac{2}{25}$ **4.** $\dfrac{3}{4}$ **5.** $\dfrac{13}{40}$ **6.** $\dfrac{1}{400}$ **7.** 0.375
8. 0.568   **9.** 0.95   **10.** 0.4001   **11.** 0.88   **12.** 0.775   **13.** 165%
14. 20%   **15.** 900%   **16.** 45%   **17.** 0.28%   **18.** 31%
19. 220%   **20.** 150%   **21.** 84%   **22.** 34%   **23.** 87.5%
24. 340%

	Fraction	Decimal	Percent
25.	$\dfrac{3}{5}$	0.60	60%
26.	$1\dfrac{5}{8}$	1.625	162.5%
27.	$\dfrac{81}{100}$	0.81	81%
28.	$\dfrac{2}{5}$	0.40	40%
29.	$\dfrac{17}{25}$	0.68	68%
30.	$\dfrac{7}{50}$	0.14	14%
31.	$\dfrac{17}{400}$	0.0425	4.25%
32.	$\dfrac{79}{100}$	0.79	79%

33. $p = 0.22 \cdot 1980, p = 435.6$ **34.** $120 = 0.8 \cdot b, b = 150$
35. $p \cdot 50 = 7.5, p = 15\%$ **36.** $245 = 0.49 \cdot b, b = 500$
37. $2200 = p \cdot 4400, p = 50\%$ **38.** $0.7 \cdot 690 = a, a = 483$
39. $392 = 0.28 \cdot b, b = 1400$ **40.** $a = 0.60 \cdot 300, a = 180$
41. $p \cdot 400 = 64, p = 16\%$ **42.** $a = 0.3 \cdot 802, a = 240.6$
43. $13 = p \cdot 65, p = 20\%$ **44.** $64.08 = 0.72 \cdot b, b = 89$

45. $\dfrac{a}{2000} = \dfrac{7}{100}, a = 140$ **46.** $\dfrac{261}{450} = \dfrac{p}{100}, p = 58$

47. $\dfrac{30}{b} = \dfrac{20}{100}, b = 150$ **48.** $\dfrac{50}{50} = \dfrac{p}{100}, p = 100$

49. $\dfrac{a}{8000} = \dfrac{15}{100}, a = 1200$ **50.** $\dfrac{136}{b} = \dfrac{34}{100}, b = 400$

51. $\dfrac{a}{540} = \dfrac{9}{100}, a = 48.6$ **52.** $\dfrac{136}{b} = \dfrac{40}{100}, b = 340$

53. $\dfrac{516}{645} = \dfrac{p}{100}, p = 80$ **54.** $\dfrac{210}{b} = \dfrac{56}{100}, b = 375$

55. $\dfrac{245}{100} = \dfrac{p}{100}, p = 245$ **56.** $\dfrac{a}{833} = \dfrac{70}{100}, a = 583.1$

57. 20% increase in sales   **58.** 23.3% decrease in long distance
charges   **59.** 8% decrease in employees   **60.** 200% increase in
sales during the summer months   **61. a.** $15.90   **b.** $95.40
62. a. $2175.00   **b.** $39,675.00   **63.** $112,500
64. a. $1.60 discount   **b.** $14.50 sale price   **65.** 126,000 jobs
66. $50   **67.** $702 per month   **68.** 28% decrease in gasoline cost
69. 3.2%   **70.** $24.8 billion   **71.** $1,738,800,000 in nut sales
72. $4,338,200,000 in tortilla chip sales

Assessment Test

1. $\dfrac{19}{25}$ **2.** $\dfrac{3}{100}$ **3.** 0.135   **4.** 0.688   **5.** 57%   **6.** 645%
7. 137.5%   **8.** 1050%   **9.** $p \cdot 610 = 106.75, p = 17.5$
10. $186 = 0.62 \cdot b, b = 300$ **11.** $a = 0.47 \cdot 450, a = 211.5$
12. $367 = 0.2 \cdot b, b = 1835$ **13.** $a = 0.8 \cdot 4560, a = 3648$
14. $77 = p \cdot 280, p = 27.5$ **15.** $\dfrac{560}{b} = \dfrac{14}{100}, b = 4000$

16. $\dfrac{95}{380} = \dfrac{p}{100}, p = 25$ **17.** $\dfrac{a}{180} = \dfrac{83}{100}, a = 149.4$

18. $\dfrac{196}{490} = \dfrac{p}{100}, p = 40$ **19.** $\dfrac{a}{158} = \dfrac{29}{100}, a = 45.82$

20. $\dfrac{245}{b} = \dfrac{35}{100}, b = 700$ **21.** 37.5% decrease in small pizzas

22. 15% increase in price   **23.** 19% decrease in tax payment
amount   **24.** 88% increase in rent   **25.** $21.40   **26.** 5.9%
27. 175 pounds after the diet   **28.** 70 packages today
29. 280 pounds per square inch   **30.** 74°F

CHAPTER 6

Section 6.1 Review Exercises

1. measure   **3.** inch, foot, yard, mile   **5.** numerator, denominator
7. Weight   **9. a.** 1 mi, 1760 yd   **b.** 1 mi, 1760 yd, 1.5 mi   **11.** 75 feet
13. 2000 yards   **15.** 180 inches   **17.** 2.5 miles   **19.** 10 yards
21. 24 inches   **23. a.** 16 oz, 1 lb   **b.** 16 oz, 1 lb, 2432 oz
25. 192 ounces   **27.** 320 ounces   **29.** 768 ounces   **31.** 31.25 pounds
33. 110,000 pounds   **35.** 0.5 tons   **37. a.** 8 fl oz, 1 c

b. 8 fl oz, 1 c, 96 fl oz   **39.** 8 quarts   **41.** 7 pints   **43.** $\dfrac{1}{8}$ pint

45. 336 fluid ounces   **47.** 16 fluid ounces   **49.** 320 fluid ounces

51. 15,840 feet   **53.** 96,800 yards   **55. a.** 40 ounces **b.** 5.5 pounds
57. 240 ounces   **59.** 24 ounces   **61.** 6 teaspoons   **63.** 120 pints

Cumulative Skills Review

1. 3264   **3.** 2 trainers for every 5 dogs   **5.** 152.58   **7.** 1350
9. $\dfrac{44}{11} = \dfrac{4}{1}$

Section 6.2 Review Exercises

1. denominate   **3.** compound   **5. a.** 3   **b.** 8 R 2, 3   **c.** 8, 2
7. 5 yards 1 foot   **9.** 3 gallons 1 quart   **11.** 2 tons 1800 pounds
13. a. 16   **b.** 1, 4, 1, 4, 4, 4   **15.** 13 yards 1 foot   **17.** 10 pounds
11 ounces   **19.** 7 quarts 1 pint   **21.** 16, 4, 16, 1, 1, 17, 1   **23.** 7 ft 8 in.
25. 13 c 1 fl oz   **27.** 19 ft 4 in.   **29.** 5 gal 1 qt   **31.** 5 c 5 fl oz
33. 4 lb 14 oz   **35.** 40, 20, 40, 1, 8, 41, 8   **37.** 11c 4 fl oz
39. 46 lb 4 oz   **41.** 32 yd 2 ft   **43.** 27 ft 3 in.   **45.** 13 ft 4 in.
47. 2 lb 5 oz   **49.** 26 yards 2 feet   **51.** 143 pounds 12 ounces
53. a. 62 teaspoons   **b.** 20 tablespoons 2 teaspoons
55. a. 9 yards 9 inches   **b.** 5 yards 30 inches   **57.** 5 c 4 fl oz
59. a. 2 pounds 10 ounces   **b.** 3 pounds 1 ounce   **61.** 2 lb 15 oz

Cumulative Skills Review

1. 5 feet   **3.** 5495.8948   **5.** $\dfrac{21}{50}$ **7.** >   **9.** $3116.07

Section 6.3 Review Exercises

1. meter   **3.** liter   **5.** larger   **7.** gram   **9. a.** $\dfrac{1\ km}{1000\ m}$

b. $\dfrac{1\ km}{1000\ m}$, 0.0089 m, 3, left, 0.0089   **11.** 100 dekameters

13. 72.5 meters   **15.** 6.33 kilometers   **17.** 990 centimeters
19. 93,800 decimeters   **21.** 3, left, 5   **23.** 330 milligrams
25. 6.226 kilograms   **27.** 775,300 decigrams   **29.** 420 kilograms

31. a. $\dfrac{1000\ L}{1\ kL}$ **b.** $\dfrac{1000\ L}{1\ kL}$, 2,500,000 L, 3, right, 2,500,000

33. 23 liters   **35.** 0.626 liters   **37.** 180,000 dekaliters
39. 390,000 centiliters   **41.** 0.002 kiloliters   **43.** 3 millimeters
45. 40 liters   **47. a.** 562.5 milligrams   **b.** 0.5625 grams
49. 0.3 grams

Cumulative Skills Review

1. $\dfrac{41}{45}$ **3.** 12 ft 9 in.   **5.** 173 hours   **7.** 11 tons   **9.** $h = 55$

Section 6.4 Review Exercises

1. inches, centimeters   **3. a.** $\dfrac{0.31\ m}{1\ ft}$ **b.** $\dfrac{0.31\ m}{1\ ft}$, 1.55 m, 1.55
5. 186 meters   **7.** 83.82 centimeters   **9.** 37.2 miles
11. 60.75 kilograms   **13.** 239.8 pounds   **15.** 425.25 grams
17. 27.26 liters   **19.** 170.1 liters   **21.** 13.78 quarts
23. 120.75 kilometers per hour   **25.** 11 pounds
27. 67.5 kilograms   **29.** 5 mg   **31.** 0.000001 grams
33. 100,00 micrograms

Cumulative Skills Review

1. 1100.75   **3.** 237,600 feet   **5.** $\dfrac{17}{20}$ **7.** 68 ft 6 in.   **9.** $\dfrac{3\ swings}{7\ children}$

Section 6.5 Review Exercises

1. 60   **3.** 24   **5.** Temperature   **7.** Celsius   **9. a.** $\dfrac{7\ days}{1\ wk}$

b. $\dfrac{7\ days}{1\ wk}$, 84 days, 84   **11.** 720 minutes   **13.** 1095 days

15. 384 months   **17.** 920 centuries   **19.** 86,400 seconds

21. 36 days   **23.** 10,800 seconds   **25. a.** $C = \dfrac{5}{9}(F - 32)$

b. $C = \dfrac{5}{9}(77 - 32) = \dfrac{5}{9}(45) = 25, 25$ **27.** 29° Celsius

29. 52° Celsius   **31.** 194° Fahrenheit   **33.** 37° Fahrenheit
35. 167° Fahrenheit   **37.** 109° Fahrenheit   **39.** 1076° Fahrenheit
41. 34° Fahrenheit

Cumulative Skills Review

1. 52.5%   **3.** 6000 + 300 + 1 or 6 thousands + 3 hundreds + 1 one
5. 314.40   **7.** $6\dfrac{9}{10}$ **9.** 3 is to 42 as 5 is to 70

Numerical Facts of Life

a. Unit fraction $= \dfrac{\text{New units}}{\text{Original units}} = \dfrac{1\ dollar}{100\ cents}$

$0.002\ \cancel{cents} \cdot \dfrac{1\ dollar}{100\ \cancel{cents}} = \dfrac{0.002 \cdot 1\ dollar}{100} = 0.00002$ dollars

b. $35,893\ \cancel{kilobytes} \cdot \dfrac{0.002\ dollars}{1\ \cancel{kilobyte}} = 71.786$ dollars $= \$71.786$

c. $35,893\ \cancel{kilobytes} \cdot \dfrac{0.002\ cents}{1\ \cancel{kilobyte}} = 71.786$ cents $= 71.786¢$

Chapter Review Exercises

1. 3 feet   **2.** 3520 yards   **3.** 16 yards   **4.** 184 yards   **5.** 9.5 miles
6. 160,000 ounces   **7.** 6000 pounds   **8.** 124 gallons
9. 336 fluid ounces   **10.** 133 tablespoons   **11.** 8 cups
12. 26 quarts   **13.** 5 ft 7 in.   **14.** 17 yd 1 ft   **15.** 4 pt 3 fl oz
16. 19 ft 7 in.   **17.** 24 gal 2 qt   **18.** 3 lb 4 oz   **19.** 21 ft 5 in.
20. 34 c 2 fl oz   **21.** 45 lb 11 oz   **22.** 2 t 16 lb   **23.** 7 in.
24. 3 c 7 oz   **25.** 11 yd   **26.** 29 yd 1 ft   **27.** 17 qt 1 pt
28. 2 tbs 1 tsp   **29.** 2 ft 11 in.   **30.** 3 lb 6 oz
31. 6500 centimeters   **32.** 0.26 meters   **33.** 3.7498 dekameters
34. 1,477,400 meters   **35.** 187 centigrams   **36.** 8.575 grams
37. 199.836 kilograms   **38.** 550,000 milligrams
39. 0.037345 kilograms   **40.** 7 kiloliters   **41.** 580 deciliters
42. 12.8 liters   **43.** 8800 dekameters   **44.** 1000 milliliters
45. 469.7 hectoliters   **46.** 13.2 feet   **47.** 19.32 kilometers
48. 35.56 centimeters   **49.** 81.9 meters   **50.** 132 pounds
51. 112.5 kilograms   **52.** 453.6 grams   **53.** 15 liters   **54.** 30.4 liters
55. 27.3 gallons   **56.** 16.88 pints   **57.** 68.04 liters   **58.** 720 seconds
59. 364 days   **60.** 300 years   **61.** 31°C   **62.** 122°F   **63.** 38°C
64. 5 feet 4 inches   **65.** 6 months   **66. a.** 1860 meters
b. 7.44 kilometers   **c.** 4.6 miles using kilometers; 4.5 miles using feet
67. 59° Fahrenheit   **68.** 39 days   **69. a.** 3 decades   **b.** 120 months

c. 80 quarters   **70.** 2 grams   **71.** 11,340 liters   **72.** 20 centigrams
73. 4.5 teaspoons   **74.** 0.72 liters   **75. a.** 115° Celsius
b. 270 seconds   **76.** 23 minutes 37 seconds
77. 9 minutes 29 seconds   **78.** 1 hour 2 minutes 27 seconds
79. 2 minutes 5 seconds

Assessment Test

1. 2814 feet   **2.** 68 gallons   **3.** 48 ounces   **4.** 20 cups   **5.** 3 gal 3 qt
6. 24 yd 2 ft   **7.** 16 pt 1 c   **8.** 4 mi 1420 ft   **9.** 37 ft 8 in.
10. 53 t 1600 lb   **11.** 49 ft 8 in.   **12.** 1 lb 12 oz   **13.** 9870 milliliters
14. 840 decigrams   **15.** 320,000 centimeters
16. 3.155 dekagrams   **17.** 19.84 meters   **18.** 1.86 miles
19. 130.5 kilograms   **20.** 2.55 liters   **21.** 3000 years
22. 525,600 minutes   **23.** 149° Celsius   **24.** 46° Fahrenheit
25. 76 feet 6 inches   **26.** 6.75 kilograms   **27.** 6 teaspoons
28. 0.705 liters   **29.** 5 hours 15 minutes   **30.** 38.9° C

CHAPTER 7

Section 7.1 Review Exercises

1. Geometry   **3.** plane figure   **5.** solid   **7.** line
9. intersecting   **11.** endpoint   **13.** angle   **15.** degree
17. acute, right, obtuse, straight   **19.** point C, point T, point W
21. a. 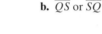   **b.** $\overline{QS}$ or $\overline{SQ}$

23. line segment, $\overline{PD}$ or $\overline{DP}$ **25.** ray, $\overrightarrow{AI}$ **27.** line segment,
$\overline{ZT}$ or $\overline{TZ}$ **29.** ray, $\overrightarrow{EK}$ **31.** line segment, $\overline{XM}$ or $\overline{MX}$
33. right, straight, obtuse, acute   **35.** $\angle N$, $\angle MNP$, $\angle MPN$; right
37. $\angle V$; straight   **39.** $\angle C$, $\angle JCH$, $\angle HCJ$; right
41. $\angle F$; straight   **43.** 65°   **45.** 56°   **47.** 137°   **49.** 140°
51. $m\angle N = 18°$ **53.** $m\angle DXW = 26°$ **55.** $m\angle H = 50°$

Cumulative Skills Review

1. 2500   **3.** $\frac{3}{5}$ **5.** $3 \cdot 5 \cdot 5; 3 \cdot 5^2$

7. The circle with diameter of $3\frac{2}{3}$ is larger.   **9.** 500

Section 7.2 Review Exercises

1. polygon   **3.** equilateral   **5.** scalene   **7.** right
9. quadrilateral   **11.** rectangle   **13.** square   **15.** circle
17. radius   **19.** half   **21.** rectangular   **23.** pyramid
25. cylinder   **27.** scalene, equilateral isosceles, isosceles
29. equilateral or isosceles, acute   **31.** isosceles, acute
33. isosceles, obtuse   **35.** isosceles, obtuse   **37.** scalene, obtuse
39. a. $50° + 30° = 80°$ **b.** $180° - 80° = 100°$ **41.** 54°
43. 80°   **45.** 52°   **47.** 58°   **49.** square, rectangle, or rhombus,
trapezoid; rectangle, rhombus   **51.** trapezoid   **53.** rectangle
55. trapezoid   **57.** square, rectangle, or rhombus   **59.** rhombus
61. triangle   **63.** hexagon   **65.** triangle   **67.** pentagon
69. triangle   **71.** octagon   **73.** 4 cm $\cdot$ 2 = 8 cm   **75.** 100 mi
77. 14 m   **79.** 22 yds   **81.** cylinder, cone, sphere   **83.** cylinder
85. cone   **87.** cube   **89.** rectangular solid   **91.** sphere
93. pyramid

Cumulative Skills Review

1. $\angle B = 123°$ **3.** $t = 39$ **5.** $3\frac{4}{15}$ **7.** 0.37   **9.** $120.55 per day

Section 7.3 Review Exercises

1. perimeter   **3.** $2l + 2w$ **5.** circumference   **7.** πd **9.** 13 ft
11. $(2 \cdot 2 \text{ in.}) + (2 \cdot 5 \text{ in.}) = 14 \text{ in.}$ **13.** 20 mi   **15.** 35 yd
17. 38 cm   **19.** 38 m   **21.** 16 cm   **23.** 37.7 miles   **25.** 15.7 cm
27. 21.98 cm   **29.** 40.82 cm   **31.** 62.8 mi   **33. a.** 96 ft   **b.** $2208
35. $P = 10$ mi

Cumulative Skills Review

1. 1019.8   **3.** $\frac{2}{5}$ **5.** 11.229   **7.** 64°   **9.** trapezoid

Section 7.4 Review Exercises

1. Area   **3.** $A = lw$ **5.** $A = bh$ **7.** $A = \frac{1}{2}(a + b)h$

9. 6.5 in.; 22.75 in.^{2} **11.** $A = 95.2$ yd^2 **13.** $A = 36$ cm^2
15. $A = 478.67$ in.^{2} **17.** $A = 196$ m^2 **19.** $A = 738$ mi^2
21. $A = 400$ ft^2 **23.** $A = 15,000$ mm^2 **25.** $A = 400$ ft^2
27. $A = 100$ m^2 **29.** 8 m; 96 m^2 **31.** 9 m, 17 cm; 272 cm^2
33. $A = 345$ mm^2 **35.** $A = 17$ mi^2 **37.** $A = 2250$ in.^{2}
39. $A = 172.5$ ft^2 **41.** $A = 42.5$ m^2 **43.** $A = 60$ yd^2
45. $A \approx 6079.04$ cm^2 **47.** $A \approx 12.56$ ft^2 **49.** $A = 56.25$ ft^2
51. $A = 4900$ mm^2 **53.** 236.3 mm^2 **55.** $A = 15,625$ yd^2
57. 62.5 ft^2

Cumulative Skills Review

1. equilateral or isosceles, acute   **3.** 164   **5.** 53% increase
7. 74°   **9.** 39 yd

Section 7.5 Review Exercises

1. square   **3.** radical sign   **5.** perfect square   **7.** legs   **9.** 9; 9
11. 1   **13.** 11   **15.** 21   **17.** 19   **19.** 9   **21.** 23   **23.** 17   **25.** 15
27. 13   **29.** 7   **31.** 5   **33.** 3   **35.** 4.12   **37.** 7.81   **39.** 17.64
41. 14.28   **43.** 8.12   **45.** 30.98   **47.** 12.04   **49.** 21.61   **51.** 15.87
53. 8ft, 64 ft^2, 76.25 ft^2, 8.73 ft   **55.** 44.40 m   **57.** 30.02 cm
59. 7.48 yd   **61.** 17.03 in.   **63.** 18.44 mi   **65.** 20.77 mm
67. 16.77 ft   **69.** 15.49 yd   **71.** 37.22 in.   **73.** $x = 57.15$ ft
75. 127.3 feet

Cumulative Skills Review

1. $A \approx 17$ mi^2 **3.** 106 tons   **5.** $\dfrac{595}{b} = \dfrac{17}{100}, b = 3500$

7. 28.5 in.   **9.** $v = 10$

Section 7.6 Review Exercises

1. volume   **3.** $V = lwh$ **5.** $V = \pi r^2 h$ **7.** $V = \frac{1}{3}Bh$

9. 7 ft, 11 ft; 924 ft^2 **11.** 135 m^3 **13.** 875 mm^3 **15.** 7800 cm^3
17. 5115 in.^{3} **19.** 148.5 m^3 **21.** 455 mi^3 **23.** 14.288 m^3
25. 6m, 19 m; 2147.76 m^2 **27.** 7 ft, 19 ft; 974.45 ft^2
29. $V = 4710$ cm^3 **31.** $V \approx 1128.31$ m^3 **33.** $V = 264$ m^3
35. $V \approx 3052.08$ m^3 **37.** $V \approx 339.12$ yd^3 **39.** $V \approx 1441.26$ cm^3
41. $V = 357$ yd^3 **43.** $V \approx 267,946.67$ cm^3 **45.** $V \approx 100.48$ in.^{3}
47. $V \approx 392.5$ yd^3 **49.** $V = 226.67$ in.^{3} **51.** $V \approx 523.33$ yd^3
53. $V \approx 141.3$ m^3 **55.** $V \approx 803.84$ in.^{3} **57.** $V = 308.75$ ft^3

59. $V \approx 1149.76 \text{ ft}^3$ **61. a.** 1077 ft^3 **b.** 8078 gallons
63. 208,333 ft³

Cumulative Skills Review

1. $\frac{83}{150}$ **3.** 39 mi   **5.** line, $\overleftrightarrow{WY}$ or $\overleftrightarrow{YW}$ **7.** 13.27 in.   **9.** 81°

Numerical Facts of Life

1. $\frac{1}{2}(45 \text{ ft})(54 \text{ ft}) = 1215 \text{ ft}^2$

3. $(1,000,000 \text{ BTUs})(0.78) = 780,000 \text{ BTUs per hour}$

5. $(1884 \text{ ft}^3)\left(\dfrac{7.481 \text{ gallons}}{1 \text{ ft}^3}\right) \approx 14,000 \text{ gallons}$

Chapter Review Exercises

1. point C, point B, point S   **2.** line, $\overleftrightarrow{BD}$ or $\overleftrightarrow{DB}$ **3.** segment, $\overline{GK}$ or $\overline{KG}$ **4.** ray, $\overrightarrow{CN}$ **5.** $\angle K$ or $\angle DKX$ or $\angle XKD$; right
6. $\angle W$; straight   **7.** $\angle L$ or $\angle SLE$ or $\angle ELS$; obtuse
8. $\angle H$ or $\angle OHM$ or $\angle MHO$; acute   **9.** 65°   **10.** 50°   **11.** 162°
12. 43°   **13.** $\angle LMO = 60°$ **14.** $\angle PDC = 62°$
15. $\angle OKH = 73°$ **16.** $\angle AXZ = 155°$ **17.** isosceles, acute; scalene, obtuse; scalene, obtuse; equilateral or isosceles, acute
18. scalene, obtuse; isosceles, acute; equilateral or isosceles, acute; isosceles; acute   **19.** scalene, right; scalene, obtuse; equilateral or isosceles, acute; equilateral or isosceles, acute   **20.** isosceles, acute; scalene, right; isosceles, obtuse; scalene, right   **21.** 32°
22. 58°   **23.** 47°   **24.** 62°   **25.** square, trapezoid, rectangle, rhombus   **26.** trapezoid, rectangle, rhombus, square
27. hexagon, octagon, quadrilateral, pentagon   **28.** octagon, hexagon, quadrilateral, pentagon   **29.** 28 meters   **30.** 7.5 inches
31. 50 feet   **32.** 98 yards   **33.** 4.5 miles   **34.** 60 centimeters
35. cube, rectangular solid, pyramid   **36.** cone, sphere, cylinder
37. 37.5 cm   **38.** 60.5 in.   **39.** 15 m   **40.** 12 mi   **41.** $C \approx 314 \text{ ft}$
42. $C \approx 94.2 \text{ m}$ **43.** $C \approx 56.52 \text{ mm}$ **44.** $C \approx 50.24 \text{ ft}$
45. $C \approx 6782.4 \text{ mi}$ **46.** 680 feet   **47.** $A = 4 \text{ ft}^2$
48. $A = 345 \text{ mm}^2$ **49.** $A = 71.5 \text{ yd}^2$ **50.** $A = 738 \text{ mi}^2$
51. $A \approx 314 \text{ m}^2$ **52.** $A \approx 6079.04 \text{ cm}^2$ **53.** $A = 1856 \text{ cm}^2$
54. $A = 28 \text{ yd}^2$ **55.** $A \approx 28.26 \text{ ft}^2$ **56.** $A \approx 1256 \text{ m}^2$
57. 6   **58.** 8   **59.** 4.12   **60.** 7.62   **61.** 5 m   **62.** 13.65 ft
63. 16 in.   **64.** 3.12 cm   **65.** Yes, Pete can use his ladder because the hypotenuse of the right triangle, which corresponds to the length of the ladder, is 3.6 m.   **66.** 30 ft   **67.** $V = 1404 \text{ in.}^3$
68. $V = 29,700 \text{ cm}^3$ **69.** $V \approx 83,053 \text{ cm}^3$ **70.** $V \approx 282.6 \text{ ft}^3$
71. $V \approx 1128.31 \text{ m}^3$ **72.** $V \approx 167.47 \text{ mi}^3$ **73.** $V \approx 2143.57 \text{ ft}^3$
74. $V \approx 1436.03 \text{ in.}^3$ **75.** $V = 110 \text{ in.}^3$ **76.** $V \approx 113.04 \text{ in.}^3$
77. $V \approx 369.867 \text{ m}^3$

Assessment Test

1. line, $\overleftrightarrow{LR}$ or $\overleftrightarrow{RL}$ **2.** segment, $\overline{PD}$ or $\overline{DP}$ **3.** $\angle Y$ or $\angle PYH$ or $\angle HYP$; right   **4.** $\angle X$; straight   **5.** $\angle R$ or $\angle ARJ$ or $\angle JRA$; acute   **6.** $\angle X$ or $\angle VXF$ or $\angle FXV$; obtuse   **7.** 52°   **8.** 128°
9. $\angle RPO = 50°$ **10.** $\angle TMK = 60°$ **11.** isosceles   **12.** acute
13. 18°   **14.** 81°   **15.** trapezoid, square, rhombus, rectangle
16. hexagon, pentagon, quadrilateral, octagon   **17.** 10 inches
18. 16 meters   **19.** cube, rectangular solid, pyramid
20. cone, sphere, cylinder   **21.** $P = 34 \text{ yd}$, $A = 63 \text{ yd}^2$
22. $P = 20 \text{ in.}$, $A = 22.75 \text{ in.}^2$ **23.** $P = 53.4 \text{ ft}$, $A = 172.5 \text{ ft}^2$
24. $P = 36.7 \text{ cm}$, $A = 77 \text{ cm}^2$ **25.** $C \approx 157 \text{ ft}$, $A \approx 1962.5 \text{ ft}^2$
26. $C \approx 56.52 \text{ m}$, $A \approx 254.34 \text{ m}^2$ **27.** $A \approx 3846.5 \text{ mi}^2$

28. $A = 2645 \text{ cm}^2$ **29.** 12   **30.** 7.42   **31.** 10.30 yd   **32.** 42.65 m
33. $V = 288 \text{ mi}^3$ **34.** $V \approx 75,360 \text{ cm}^3$ **35.** $V = 264 \text{ m}^3$
36. $V \approx 113.04 \text{ ft}^3$ **37.** $V \approx 38,772.72 \text{ mi}^3$ **38.** $V \approx 3589.54 \text{ in.}^3$
39. $V \approx 226.67 \text{ in.}^3$ **40.** $V = 184.4 \text{ km}^3$

CHAPTER 8

Section 8.1 Review Exercises

1. statistics   **3.** line   **5.** time, numerical value   **7.** circle, pie
9. a. Occupation, Percentage Increase in Jobs from 2006, Median Salary   **b.** The various occupations   **c.** U.S. Department of Labor, Bureau of Labor Statistics   **11.** *Queen Mary 2*
13. 22,000 tons   **15.** Royal Caribbean and Princess   **17.** Honda and Toyota   **19.** Honda Civic   **21.** Lexus GS450H, 25 miles per gallon   **23 a.** Widget sales from 2000 to 2007   **b.** Sales, in billions of dollars   **c.** Time, from 2000 to 2007   **d.** $1.0 billion
e. 2005   **f.** $0.4 billion

25.
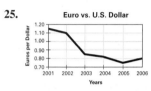

27. 3 million   **29.** 2.8 million   **31.** 30%   **33.** 2003   **35.** 2003 and 2004

37.

39. a. Salaries of U.S. senators, 2000–2006   **b.** Time, 2000–2006
c. Numerical values, salaries   **d.** $158,100   **e.** $4000   **f.** 2003
g. 2002, $4900

41.
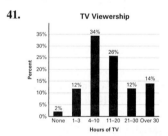

43. 19.9 million   **45.** 3.1 million   **47.** 38 grams   **49.** 34 grams
51. 8100 calories

53.

55. a. Proved oil reserves   **b.** BP Statistical Review of World Energy 2006   **c.** Middle East, 61.8%   **d.** 9.5%   **e.** Asia Pacific, 3.4%   **f.** 6.8%   **57.** 24%   **59.** 8%   **61.** Identity theft
63. Shop-at-home/catalog sales and foreign money offers

65.

PERCENT	DEGREES
35	126
20	72
25	90
15	54
5	18

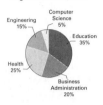

Penta College —
Degrees Granted, 2008

Cumulative Skills Review

1. 30   **3.** 45°   **5.** 400, 419.743   **7.** $h = 45$ **9.** 125 yards

Section 8.2 Review Exercises

1. statistic   **3.** set   **5.** arithmetic mean   **7.** weighted   **9.** larger, smaller   **11.** mode   **13.** range   **15. a.** 8   **b.** 224   **c.** 28   **d.** mean   **17.** 8   **19.** 45.6 lbs   **21.** 46.3 ft   **23.** 54.4 in.

25.

CREDITS	GRADE VALUE	QUALITY POINTS
	2	6
	3	9
	2	10
	4	12
14		37

GPA ≈ 2.64

27.

CREDITS	GRADE VALUE	QUALITY POINTS
	3	9
	3	15
	2	2
	4	16
	2	6
16		48

GPA ≈ 3.0

29. a. 11, 24, 27, 36, 45, 54, 75   **b.** 36   **c.** median   **31.** 62
33. $33   **35.** 632 mi   **37.** 49.5 acres   **39. a.** 4   **b.** mode   **41.** 70
43. No mode   **45.** 53 cats   **47.** $860, $267   **49. a.** 5   **b.** 61
c. 56   **d.** range   **51.** 71   **53.** 51 pens   **55.** 86 lbs   **57.** 62%
59. Mean: $251,750, Median: $260,000, Range: $157,000
61. GPA: 3.69   **63.** Mean: $12,040, Median: $12,100, Mode: $7300,
Range: $10,700   **65.** Mean: 34.2, Median: 30, Mode: 25, 30,
Range: 33   **67.** Mean: 9.6 inches, Median: 9 inches, Mode: 9 inches,
Range: 13 inches

Cumulative Skills Review

1. 20%   **3.** 37.68   **5.** 0.89   **7.** 85% remains on the roll
9. 82,312

Numerical Facts of Life

1. $180.00 + $180.00(289.5%) = $180.00 + $521.10 = $701.10
3. $40.00 + $40.00(137.3%) = $40.00 + $54.92 = $94.92

Chapter Review Exercises

1. 190 mg   **2.** 130 calories   **3.** 8%   **4.** 10%   **5.** 0 mg
6. 90 grams   **7.** 336 million   **8.** 186 million   **9.** India

10. Brazil   **11.** 124 million   **12.** 2635 million   **13.** 2003
14. $956,500   **15.** 2002   **16.** Advertising rates have generally
increased over the years, while viewership has declined.
17. 2010   **18.** $392 billion   **19.** $900 billion   **20.** Medicare
21.

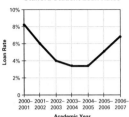

Stafford Student Loan Rates

22.

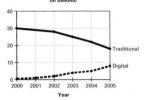

Photo Prints Made at Labs
(in billions)

23. 1996   **24.** 2003   **25.** 2001 and 2002   **26.** 5%
27. 714 million   **28.** France   **29.** 16 million gallons
30. United States
31.

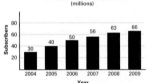

Estimated U.S. Residential
Broadband Subscribers
(millions)

32.

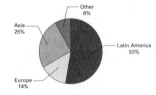

NFL Average Salaries
(in millions of dollars)

33. SBC/AT&T   **34.** 15%   **35.** MCI   **36.** No   **37.** 3%
38. Benefits   **39.** It will decrease 27%, from 43% to 16%.
40. All else
41.

U.S. Foreign-Born Population

42.

PERCENT
22
19
43
16

Back-to-School Spending

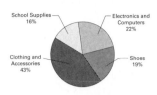

School Supplies 16%
Electronics and Computers 22%
Clothing and Accessories 43%
Shoes 19%

43. mean: 37.6; median: 35   **44.** mean: 75; median: 78
45. mean: 64.5; median: 70.5   **46.** mean: 50; median: 52
47. mean: 27.6; median: 20   **48.** mean: 34; median: 21
49. mode: 48; range: 37   **50.** mode: 68; range: 50
51. mode: none; range: 53   **52.** modes: 35 and 51;
range: 44   **53.** mode: 43; range: 43   **54.** mode: 14;
range: 59   **55.** modes: 24 and 16; range: 35   **56.** mode:
none; range: 105

Assessment Test

1. $22,240   **2.** $6743   **3.** $16,899   **4.** 50   **5.** 70   **6.** July   **7.** 81%
8. 41%   **9.** 2004   **10.** 2006   **11.** Highest: Phillips; lowest:
Samsung   **12.** 48%   **13.** 18%   **14.** $2000 \cdot 0.40 = 800$ units
15.

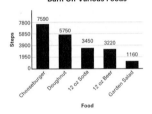

Approximate Number of Steps to Burn Off Various Foods

Steps
7800, 5850, 3900, 1950, 0

7590 Cheeseburger
5750 Doughnut
3450 12 oz Soda
3220 12 oz Beer
1160 Garden Salad

Food

16.

PERCENT	DEGREES
20	72
40	144
30	108
10	36

Apex Entertainment, Inc. 2007 Revenue
(by Division)

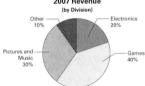

Other 10%
Electronics 20%
Pictures and Music 30%
Games 40%

17. 40   **18.** 38   **19.** 60 and 69   **20.** 218

CHAPTER 9

Section 9.1 Review Exercises

1. positive   **3.** origin   **5.** opposites   **7.** rational
9. -8 **11.** -14 **13.** 23.5   **15.** $-\dfrac{2}{9}$ **17.** $\dfrac{5}{2}$

19.

21.

23.

25. 15   **27.** 43   **29.** 31   **31.** 2.7   **33.** $7\dfrac{2}{9}$ **35.** $<,>$
37. $2 < 7, 7 > 2$ **39.** $-24.8 < -24.0, -24.0 > -24.8$

41. $-15 < 21, 21 > -15$ **43.** $-11.0 > -11.5$,
$-11.5 < -11.0$ **45.** $-\dfrac{7}{9} < -\dfrac{2}{3}, -\dfrac{2}{3} > -\dfrac{7}{9}$ **47.** $-\dfrac{6}{5} < -\dfrac{13}{12}$,
$-\dfrac{13}{12} > -\dfrac{6}{5}$ **49.** 2 points   **51.** -6.5 sec, 2.4 sec, -4.1 sec
53. 6000K°

Cumulative Skills Review

1. $5\dfrac{11}{15}$ **3.** 1822.4   **5.** $\dfrac{3}{1}$ **7.** 1200 g   **9.** 15

Section 9.2 Review Exercises

1. positive   **3.** Subtract   **5. a.** 12.3, 31.5   **b.** 31.5, 43.8   **c.** -43.8
7. 9   **9.** -10 **11.** -15 **13.** -68 **15.** -145 **17.** -618
19. -549 **21.** -465 **23.** 6.05   **25.** -37.3 **27.** -17.71
29. -97.341 **31.** $-\dfrac{4}{4}$ or -1 **33.** $-\dfrac{16}{21}$ **35.** $-\dfrac{23}{24}$
37. $-\dfrac{11}{10} = -1\dfrac{1}{10}$ **39.** $-5\dfrac{3}{4}$ **41.** $-54\dfrac{35}{36}$ **43.** $-30\dfrac{1}{2}$
45. $-69\dfrac{17}{36}$ **47. a.** 15.2, 42.9,   **b.** 15.2, 27.7   **c.** -27.7
49. 3   **51.** 7   **53.** 4   **55.** 0   **57.** -11 **59.** 36   **61.** -63
63. -360 **65.** 1889   **67.** $-11,067$ **69.** 1.1   **71.** 0.33
73. 7.6   **75.** 5.07   **77.** -15.3 **79.** 64.67   **81.** $-\dfrac{1}{5}$ **83.** $\dfrac{1}{6}$
85. $-\dfrac{17}{24}$ **87.** $\dfrac{7}{18}$ **89.** $-5\dfrac{5}{24}$ **91.** $-7\dfrac{1}{4}$ **93.** $-7\dfrac{2}{5}$
95. $-11\dfrac{5}{18}$ **97.** 44 BC   **99.** 14,495 feet

Cumulative Skills Review

1. $\dfrac{11}{24}$ **3.** 959.82   **5.** $-128.5°F$ **7.** 507
9.

Section 9.3 Review Exercises

1. $(-b)$ **3. a.** (-15) **b.** $8, -15, 15$ **c.** $15, 8, 7$
d. $(-15), -7$ **5.** 7   **7.** 16   **9.** -6 **11.** -17 **13.** 27   **15.** 81
17. 307   **19.** -17 **21.** -3623 **23.** 131   **25.** 262   **27.** -789
29. $-\dfrac{4}{5}$ **31.** $-\dfrac{5}{24}$ **33.** $-\dfrac{1}{2}$ **35.** $\dfrac{29}{36}$ **37.** $-4\dfrac{8}{35}$ **39.** $26\dfrac{2}{9}$
41. $-2\dfrac{1}{8}$ **43.** $-3\dfrac{1}{36}$ **45.** 5.53   **47.** -2.55 **49.** -8.96 **51.** 4.78
53 -33.05 **55.** 16.06   **57.** -156.1 **59.** 231.1   **61.** 1989 years
63. 355.6 °F

Cumulative Skills Review

1. 31%   **3.** line, $\overleftrightarrow{FB}$ or $\overleftrightarrow{BF}$ **5.** 216 square feet   **7.** $7 > -12$ and
$-12 < 7$ **9.** 202.5

Section 9.4 Review Exercises

1. negative   **3. a.** 7, 12   **b.** 12, 84   **c.** -84
5. a. $\dfrac{12}{25}, \dfrac{5}{32}$ **b.** $\dfrac{5}{32}, \dfrac{3}{40}$ **c.** $-\dfrac{3}{40}$ **7.** 24   **9.** -27 **11.** -100
13. 132   **15.** -512 **17.** 721   **19.** -3432 **21.** 6682   **23.** $-\dfrac{2}{11}$
25. $\dfrac{5}{14}$ **27.** $-\dfrac{5}{27}$ **29.** $\dfrac{1}{4}$ **31.** $\dfrac{3}{8}$ **33.** $-\dfrac{2}{15}$ **35.** -24 **37.** $14\dfrac{1}{4}$

39. $\frac{2}{7}$ **41.** $-2\frac{1}{2}$ **43.** 207.4 **45.** -18.36 **47.** -0.00234

49. -1.377 **51.** -588 **53.** $-15,696$ **55.** -220 **57.** 144

59. -1620 **61.** $-\frac{3}{49}$ **63.** $-2\frac{5}{8}$ **65.** 1.426 **67. a.** 56, 8

b. 8, 7 **c.** -7 **69. a.** $\frac{3}{8}, \frac{9}{4}$ **b.** $\frac{9}{4}, \frac{4}{9}, \frac{1}{6}$ **c.** $\frac{1}{6}$ **71.** 3 **73.** 7

75. -7 **77.** 9 **79.** -33 **81.** -15 **83.** -19 **85.** -13

87. $-2\frac{1}{3}$ **89.** $-3\frac{1}{2}$ **91.** -6 **93.** $-\frac{11}{60}$ **95.** $-\frac{2}{7}$ **97.** $3\frac{5}{6}$

99. $-\frac{16}{21}$ **101.** -34 **103.** 0.044 **105.** 0.07

107. -8.9 **109.** -0.02 **111.** 45.3 **113.** -14.3
115. $31.8 billion **117.** $225

Cumulative Skills Review

1. 12 students for every pie **3.** 150 months
5. $V = 828,868 \text{ mm}^3$ **7.** -58 **9.** -62

Section 9.5 Review Exercises

1. grouping symbols **3.** multiplications, divisions **5.** 16, 80, 87
7. 7 **9.** 10 **11.** 17 **13.** -32 **15.** -180 **17.** 57
19. 118 **21.** -8 **23.** -11 **25.** 8 **27.** -2 **29.** 134

31. 4 **33.** 50 **35.** $-\frac{7}{24}$ **37.** $-\frac{17}{27}$ **39.** 2 **41.** -1.503

43. -2.15 **45.** -2.4401 **47.** -18 **49.** 5 **51.** 54
53. a. $3(-1) + 3(-2) + 2(0) + 1(1)$ **b.** -8 **55.** 64 feet
above the point

Cumulative Skills Review

1. -6 **3.** $78.322 > 78.32$ and $78.32 < 78.322$ **5.** $\frac{6 \text{ bottles}}{1 \text{ case}}$

7. 15 **9.** $V = 168 \text{ yd}^3$

Numerical Facts of Life

1. $-33\,°F$ **3.** $-48\,°F$

Chapter Review Exercises

1. -15 **2.** -2.34 **3.** 47 **4.** 8.094
5.
6.
7. 12 **8.** 52 **9.** 2.314 **10.** 7436 **11.** $2 < 7, 7 > 2$
12. $-3 > -8, -8 < -3$ **13.** $-2.05 < -2, -2 > -2.05$
14. $7 < 7.4, 7.4 > 7$ **15.** $-210\,°F$ **16.** $1,000,000\,°K$ **17.** $-$$45.00
18. 3500 feet **19.** 110 **20.** -154 **21.** $\frac{19}{30}$ **22.** $-\frac{17}{36}$ **23.** $-1\frac{1}{14}$

24. $3\frac{17}{24}$ **25.** 1.56 **26.** -16.9 **27.** -28 **28.** 7.71 **29.** $-\frac{3}{8}$

30. $-2\frac{1}{9}$ **31.** -15 **32.** 0.9 **33.** $-\frac{7}{12}$ **34.** 4 **35.** -9 **36.** 11

37. $-\frac{2}{3}$ **38.** $-\frac{23}{30}$ **39.** 7 **40.** 1032 **41.** 15 **42.** -4

43. a. $250 + $105 + $215 + (-$55) **b.** $515
44. a. $46 - (-323)$ **b.** 369 years **45.** 38 feet below ground
level **46. a.** $500(-$2.40) **b.** $-$1200, a loss of $1200
47. $86

Assessment Test

1. -457 **2.** 5713
3.
4.
5. 350 **6.** 453 **7.** $7 > 4, 4 < 7$ **8.** $-19.5 < -19.0$,
$-19.0 > -19.5$ **9.** $-39\,°C$ **10.** $-$$3.24 **11.** -103 **12.** 27
13. -12.06 **14.** 5.85 **15.** $-\frac{19}{48}$ **16.** $-2\frac{7}{10}$ **17.** 27 **18.** -9.37

19. $\frac{7}{18}$ **20.** $-5\frac{1}{24}$ **21.** -0.6 **22.** $\frac{4}{45}$ **23.** 80 **24.** $-\frac{2}{5}$ **25.** 8

26. 40 **27.** 30,300 feet **28.** $52.79 **29.** -285 students **30.** $63

CHAPTER 10

Section 10.1 Review Exercises

1. variable **3.** evaluate **5.** variable, constant **7.** like
9. a. 7, 21 **b.** 7, -5 **c.** 7, 8, 32 **11.** 29 **13.** 63 **15.** 72 **17.** 17
19. -52 **21.** -13 **23.** 12 **25.** -10 **27.** -30 **29.** 9
31. a. $3x^4, -2x^3, -9x^2, x$ **b.** -1 **c.** $3, -2, -9, 1$
33. Variable: $4a^3, 3a^2, -9a$, Constant: -5, Coefficient in $4a^3$: 4,
Coefficient in $3a^2$: 3, Coefficient in $-9a$: -9
35. Variable: $-y^4, -y^2, -3y$, Constant: -9, Coefficient in $-y^4$: -1,
Coefficient in $-y^2$: -1 Coefficient in $-3y$: -3

37. $8s + 7t$ **39.** $\frac{11}{4}x + \frac{5}{4}y$ **41.** $x^2 - 2xy + y^2$

43. $8u^2v - 5uv^2$ **45.** $-9r^2s + 4rs + 7rst$ **47.** $2x^2 + 4xy + 2y^2$

49. $\frac{1}{15}m^4 + 2m^2 + \frac{3}{10}$ **51. a.** 5, 15 **b.** 5, -2 **c.** $-\frac{3}{5}, -\frac{2}{15}$

53. $21x$ **55.** $-35b$ **57.** $-8n$ **59.** $2.4d$ **61.** $0.2n$ **63.** $\frac{5}{14}x$

65. $5x + 10$ **67.** $4a - 4$ **69.** $-2n + 4$ **71.** $27x - 72$

73. $9n + 21$ **75.** $48x + 56y$ **77.** $-2t + 3$ **79.** $\frac{15}{28}x - \frac{30}{7}$

81. $0.04y + 0.3$ **83.** $0.72d - 2.7$ **85.** $3y^2 - 6y + 18$
87. $-2k^2 - 4k + 6$ **89.** $17x + 3$ **91. a.** $x - 421$ **b.** 1250 feet

Cumulative Skills Review

1. 2880 minutes **3.** 18.4 km **5.** $\frac{17}{100}$ 17 to 100 17:100
7. 9912.444
9.

Section 10.2 Review Exercises

1. equation **3.** addition **5.** solving **7.** 3, 9, 18, 3 is a solution
to the equation $3x + 9 = 18$. **9.** solution **11.** not a solution
13. not a solution **15.** solution **17.** solution **19.** not a solution
21. solution **23.** solution **25.** solution **27.** not a solution
29. not a solution **31.** solution **33.** not a solution
35. solution **37.** 8, 8, 13, 13, 13 **39.** 8 **41.** 12 **43.** -2 **45.** 4
47. -5 **49.** -6 **51.** 20 **53.** 48 **55.** 67 **57.** 55 **59.** 56

61. 13 **63.** 0 **65.** 10 **67.** 3.5 **69.** 1.47 **71.** 15.8 **73.** $-\frac{1}{6}$

75. $\frac{5}{8}$ **77.** $4\frac{1}{2}$ **79.** $22,584,000,000 **81.** $5,260,000,000

Cumulative Skills Review

1. $20,746.14   **3.** 224 days   **5.** $\dfrac{14}{98} = \dfrac{p}{100}$ **7.** $-8q - 120$

9. diameter = 26 units

Section 10.3 Review Exercises

1. multiplication   **3.** 9, 9, 5   **5.** $\dfrac{7}{2}, \dfrac{7}{2}, \dfrac{7}{6}$ **7.** 4   **9.** -5

11. 3   **13.** -5 **15.** 12   **17.** -25 **19.** 6   **21.** -14 **23.** 46

25. $\dfrac{3}{5}$ **27.** $-\dfrac{1}{20}$ **29.** $19\dfrac{1}{5}$ **31.** -24 **33.** $\dfrac{7}{18}$ **35.** -4

37. -7.5 **39.** 14   **41.** 3.4   **43.** 4 hours 30 minutes

45. $533\dfrac{1}{3}$ mph

Cumulative Skills Review

1. 0.899   **3.** segment, $\overline{PD}$ or $\overline{DP}$ **5.** 11,750 m

7. 34   **9.** yes

Section 10.4 Review Exercises

1. subtract, divide   **3. a.** 14, 14, 21, 21   **b.** 3, 3, 7   **c.** 7, 21, 35
5. a. $2x, 2x, 2x, 2x$ **b.** 2, 2, 18   **c.** 18, 18, 72, 36   **7.** 3   **9.** 6   **11.** 0
13. 9   **15.** -6 **17.** -3 **19.** -9 **21.** 18   **23.** -114 **25.** 2

27. 33   **29.** $-\dfrac{3}{2}$ **31.** 2   **33.** $\dfrac{1}{4}$ **35.** $-\dfrac{18}{5}$ **37.** 3   **39.** 6   **41.** 8

43. $\dfrac{1}{2}$ **45.** $\dfrac{2}{3}$ **47.** -2 **49.** 18   **51.** -5 **53.** -14 **55.** -2

57. -45 **59.** $\dfrac{1}{2}$ **61.** $\dfrac{7}{3}$ **63.** -4 **65.** $\dfrac{3}{4}$ **67. a.** $2x, 12$ **b.** $2x, 12,$

$2x, x, 12, x, 12$ **c.** $x, 12, 6, 6, x, 6, 6$ **d.** 6, 6, 8, 12   **69.** 6   **71.** $\dfrac{4}{5}$

73. -5 **75.** -3 **77.** 34   **79.** 0   **81.** -15 **83.** $\dfrac{3}{2}$ **85.** 9 inches

87. 10 hors d' oeuvres

Cumulative Skills Review

1. $\dfrac{3 \text{ course credits}}{\$750} = \dfrac{12 \text{ course credits}}{\$3000}$ **3.** 5   **5.** 47
7. 5.78 years, 2110 days   **9.** $s = 32$

Section 10.5 Review Exercises

1. read   **3.** equation   **5.** check   **7.** $x - 15 = 23$ **9.** $x + 7 = 15$

11. $3x = 5$ **13.** $-8x = \dfrac{1}{2}$ **15.** $8 + 2x = 38$

17. $18 - \dfrac{2}{3}x = 10$ **19.** $3(x + 10) = 36$ **21.** $x + 8 = 15; 7$

23. $3x = \dfrac{1}{4}; \dfrac{1}{12}$ **25.** $2x - 5 = 3; 4$ **27.** $x + 4 = 2x; 4$

29. $x - 6 = 3(4 + x); -9$ **31.** $x + 55 = 505; 450$ mph
33. $w + 21.5 = 78; 56.5$ feet   **35.** $1671 = x - 979; 2650$ feet
37. $0.45C = 12.6; 28$ days   **39.** $8s = 14; \$1.75$
41. $3.00 + 1.50(h - 1) = 15.00; 9$ hours
43. $7.50(3s) + 4.00s = 795.00;$ 90 adult tickets, 30 student tickets
45. $4b + b + (4b - 5) = 40; a = 20$ inches, $b = 5$ inches,
$c = 15$ inches   **47.** $2c + (3c + 4) + c = 250;$ first piece: 82 feet,
second piece: 127 feet, third piece: 41 feet

Cumulative Skills Review

1. 12   **3.** 5.78   **5.** 90   **7.** 5   **9.** $56l - 48$

Numerical Facts of Life

1. $T = P + \dfrac{1}{7}t - \dfrac{1}{14}t + \dfrac{1}{26}t$ or $T = P + \dfrac{10}{91}t$

3. Since it takes 9.1 seconds to add 1 person, it takes 9,100,000 seconds to add 1,000,000 people. Consequently, it took approximately 105 days to add an additional 1,000,000 people to the population.

$9{,}100{,}000 \text{ seconds} \cdot \dfrac{1 \text{ minute}}{60 \text{ seconds}} \cdot \dfrac{1 \text{ hour}}{60 \text{ minutes}} \cdot \dfrac{1 \text{ day}}{24 \text{ hours}}$

$= 105.3241 \text{ days} \approx 105 \text{ days}$

Alternatively, we can solve the equation with $T = 301{,}000{,}000$ and $P = 300{,}000{,}000$ to find t.

$301{,}000{,}000 = 300{,}000{,}000 + \dfrac{10}{91}t \Rightarrow 1{,}000{,}000 = \dfrac{10}{91}t$

$\Rightarrow 9{,}100{,}000 = t$

Chapter Review Exercises

1. -5 **2.** 1   **3.** 0   **4.** 22   **5.** $11a + 4b$ **6.** $16x + 2y$
7. $-3v + 10z$ **8.** $-2r - 5rt + 5t$ **9.** $-7a^2 + a$
10. $-3m^3 + m^2n + 8mn^2$ **11.** $g^2 + h^2$,   **12.** $-29x^3y + 8x^2y$,
13. $6x$ **14.** $-25y$ **15.** $6.3a$ **16.** $4d$ **17.** $3x - 45$
18. $16k^2 + 8$ **19.** $-b + 7$ **20.** $-4z - 8 + y$ **21.** $-24p - 21$
22. $-20t^2 + 8$ **23.** $6m^2 - 4mn + 18n^2$
24. $-35y^2 + 15yz - 10z^2$ **25.** solution   **26.** not a solution
27. not a solution   **28.** solution   **29.** not a solution   **30.** solution
31. not a solution   **32.** solution   **33.** 19   **34.** -13 **35.** 7.7

36. 14.1   **37.** -8 **38.** -13 **39.** $\dfrac{1}{6}$ **40.** $\dfrac{1}{10}$ **41.** 12

42. 8   **43.** $\dfrac{25}{2}$ or $12\dfrac{1}{2}$ **44.** $\dfrac{47}{3}$ or $15\dfrac{2}{3}$ **45.** -30 **46.** -56

47. 13   **48.** 9   **49.** 3   **50.** 5   **51.** 10   **52.** 13   **53.** 0   **54.** -9
55. 20   **56.** -3 **57.** $2(10 - x) - 12$ **58.** 2,500 feet
59. $41.31   **60.** $7.75 per hour   **61.** 13 female, 19 males

Assessment Test

1. 37   **2.** 48   **3.** $8m^4n^3 + 20m^4n$ **4.** $-7a^2 + 7ab + 2b^2$

5. $-27d + 24$ **6.** $40m - 35$ **7.** not a solution   **8.** solution

9. -7 **10.** -3 **11.** 12   **12.** $\dfrac{10}{3}$ **13.** 41   **14.** -3 **15.** $\dfrac{3}{4}$ **16.** $\dfrac{8}{7}$

17. $3x - 24$ **18.** $3(x^2 + 15)$ **19.** 41 degrees   **20.** 550 miles
per hour   **21.** 40 words

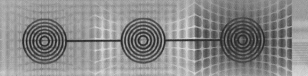

Math Study Skills

Your overall success in mastering the material this textbook covers depends on you. You must be *committed* to doing your best in this course. This commitment means dedicating the time needed to study math and to do your homework.

In order to succeed in math, you must know how to study it. The goal is to study math so that you understand and not just memorize it. The following tips and strategies will help you develop good study habits.

GENERAL TIPS

Attend every class. Be on time. If you must miss class, be sure to get a copy of the notes and any handouts. (Get notes from someone in your class who takes good, neat notes.)

Manage your time. School, work, family, and other commitments place a lot of demand on your time. To be successful, you must be able to devote time to study math every day. Writing out a weekly schedule that lists your class schedule, work schedule, and all other commitments with times that are not flexible will help you determine when you can study.

Do not wait to get help. If you are having difficulty, get help immediately. Since the material presented in class usually builds on previous material, it is very easy to fall behind. Ask your instructor if he or she is available during office hours or get help at the math lab/tutoring center on campus.

INSTRUCTOR CONTACT INFORMATION
Name:
Office Hours:
Office Location:
Phone Number:
E-mail Address:

CAMPUS MATH LAB/TUTORING CENTER
Location:
Hours:

Form a study group. A study group provides an opportunity to discuss class material and homework problems. Find at least two other people in your class who are committed to being successful. Exchange contact information and plan to meet or work together regularly throughout the semester either in person or via email or phone.

Use your book's study resources. Additional resources and support materials to help you succeed are available with this book.

NOTEBOOK AND NOTE TAKING

Taking good notes and keeping a neat, well-organized notebook are important factors in being successful.

YOUR NOTEBOOK

Use a loose-leaf binder divided into four sections

1. notes
2. homework
3. graded tests (and quizzes)
4. handouts

TAKING NOTES

- Copy all important information written on the board. Also, write all points that are not clear to you so you can discuss them with your instructor, a tutor, or your study group.

- Write explanations of what you are doing in your own words next to each step of a practice problem.

- Listen carefully to what your instructor emphasizes and make note of it.

CLASS TIME

BEFORE CLASS

- Review your notes from the previous class session.

- Read the section(s) of your textbook that will be covered in class to get familiar with the material. Read these sections carefully. Skimming may result in your not understanding some of the material and your inability to do the homework. If you do not understand something in the text, re-read it more thoroughly or seek assistance.

DURING CLASS

- Pay attention and try to understand every question your instructor asks.

- Take good notes.

- Ask questions if you do not understand something. It is best to ask questions during class. Chances are that someone else has the same question, but is not comfortable asking it. If you feel that way also, then write your question in your notebook and ask your instructor after class or see the instructor during office hours.

AFTER CLASS

- Review your notes as soon as possible after class. Insert additional steps and comments to help clarify the material.

- Re-read the section(s) of your textbook. After reading through an example, cover it up and try to do it on your own. Do the practice problem that is paired with the example. (The answers to the practice problems are given in the back of the textbook.)

HOMEWORK

The best way to learn math is by *doing* it. Homework is designed to help you learn and apply concepts and master certain skills. Some tips for doing homework are as follows.

- Do your homework the same day that you have class. Keeping up with the class requires you to do homework regularly rather than "cramming" right before tests.

- Review the section of the textbook that corresponds to the homework.

- Review your notes.

- If you get stuck on a problem, look for a similar example in your textbook or notes.

- Write a question mark next to any problems that you just cannot figure out. Get help from your instructor or the tutoring center or call someone from your study group.

- Check your answer after each problem. The answers to the odd-numbered problems are in the back of the textbook. If you are assigned even-numbered problems, try the odd-numbered problem first and check the answer. If your answer is correct, then you should be able to do the even-numbered problem correctly.

TESTS

Tests are a source of anxiety for many students. Being well prepared to take a test can help ease anxiety.

BEFORE A TEST

- Review your notes and the sections of the textbook that will be covered on the test.

- Read through the *10-Minute Chapter Review* in the textbook and your own summary from your notes.

- Do additional practice problems. Select problems from your homework to work again. In addition, your textbook contains at the end of every chapter a set of *Chapter Review Exercises* that provides practice problems for each chapter section.

- Use the *Assessment Test* at the end of the chapter as your practice test. While taking the practice test, do not refer to your notes or the textbook for help. Keep track of how long it takes to complete the test. Check your answers. If you cannot complete the practice test within the time you are allotted for the real test, you may need additional practice in the tutoring center to speed up.

DURING A TEST

- Read through the test before starting.

- If you find yourself panicking, relax, take a few slow breaths, and try to do some of the problems that seem easy.

- Do the problems you know how to do first, and then go back to the ones that are more difficult.

- Watch your time. Do not spend too much time on any one problem. If you get stuck while working on a problem, skip it and move on to the next problem.

- Check your work, if there is time. Correct any errors you find.

AFTER A TEST

- When you get your test back, look through all the problems.

- On a separate sheet of paper, do any problems that you missed. Use your notes and textbook, if necessary.

- Get help from your instructor or a tutor if you cannot figure out how to do a problem. Or set up a meeting with your study group to go over the test together. Make sure you understand your errors.

- Attach the corrections to the test and place it in your notebook.

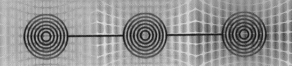

Table of Squares and Square Roots

n	n^2	$\sqrt{n}$	n	n^2	$\sqrt{n}$
1	1	1.000	51	2601	7.141
2	4	1.414	52	2704	7.211
3	9	1.732	53	2809	7.280
4	16	2.000	54	2916	7.348
5	25	2.236	55	3025	7.416
6	36	2.449	56	3136	7.483
7	49	2.646	57	3249	7.550
8	64	2.828	58	3364	7.616
9	81	3.000	59	3481	7.681
10	100	3.162	60	3600	7.746
11	121	3.317	61	3721	7.810
12	144	3.464	62	3844	7.874
13	169	3.606	63	3969	7.937
14	196	3.742	64	4096	8.000
15	225	3.873	65	4225	8.062
16	256	4.000	66	4356	8.124
17	289	4.123	67	4489	8.185
18	324	4.243	68	4624	8.246
19	361	4.359	69	4761	8.307
20	400	4.472	70	4900	8.367
21	441	4.583	71	5041	8.426
22	484	4.690	72	5184	8.485
23	529	4.796	73	5329	8.544
24	576	4.899	74	5476	8.602
25	625	5.000	75	5625	8.660
26	676	5.099	76	5776	8.718
27	729	5.196	77	5929	8.775
28	784	5.292	78	6084	8.832
29	841	5.385	79	6241	8.888
30	900	5.477	80	6400	8.944
31	961	5.568	81	6561	9.000
32	1024	5.657	82	6724	9.055
33	1089	5.745	83	6889	9.110
34	1156	5.831	84	7056	9.165
35	1225	5.916	85	7225	9.220
36	1296	6.000	86	7396	9.274
37	1369	6.083	87	7569	9.327
38	1444	6.164	88	7744	9.381
39	1521	6.245	89	7921	9.434
40	1600	6.325	90	8100	9.487
41	1681	6.403	91	8281	9.539
42	1764	6.481	92	8464	9.592
43	1849	6.557	93	8649	9.644
44	1936	6.633	94	8836	9.695
45	2025	6.708	95	9025	9.747
46	2116	6.782	96	9216	9.798
47	2209	6.856	97	9409	9.849
48	2304	6.928	98	9604	9.899
49	2401	7.000	99	9801	9.950
50	2500	7.071	100	10,000	10.000

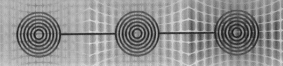

Index